A MEANS TO FREEDOM

A Means to Freedom

The Letters of H. P. Lovecraft and Robert E. Howard: 1933–1936

Edited by S. T. Joshi, David E. Schultz,
and Rusty Burke

Hippocampus Press

New York

A Means to Freedom:
The Letters of H. P. Lovecraft and Robert E. Howard: 1933–1936

H. P. Lovecraft's letters published with the permission of the Estate of H. P. Lovecraft, Robert C. Harrall, Administrator. Robert E. Howard's letters published by permission of Robert E. Howard Properties Inc.

"With a Set of Rattlesnake Rattles": *Leaves*, Summer 1937; reprinted in *The Howard Collector*, vol. 1, no. 1, Summer 1961; reprinted in *The Howard Collector*, Ace Books, 1979

"The Beast from the Abyss": *The Howard Collector*, vol. 3, no. 3, whole no. 15, Autumn 1971; reprinted in *The Howard Collector*, Ace Books, 1979; an abridged version, with illustrations, was published as *The Last Cat Book*, Dodd, Mead & Co., 1984

Cover art by David C. Verba depicting Cathedral of St. John (1810), Providence, RI.
Cover design by Barbara Briggs Silbert.
Hippocampus Press logo designed by Anastasia Damianakos.

Hippocampus Press, PO Box 641, New York, NY 10156
www.hippocampuspress.com

Second Softcover Edition, 2017
ISBN 978-1-61498-187-9 (Volume 2)
ISBN 978-1-61498-188-6 (2 Volume Set)

Contents

1933

[76]   [non-extant letter from REH to HPL]

[77]   [AH 18.15; *SL* 595]

10 Barnes St.,
Providence, R.I.,
Jany. 21, 1933.

Dear R E H:—

I duly received your ample and interesting letter plus the subsequent note, and have read both text and enclosures with the keenest pleasure. Yes, indeed, I have often heard of the cat phobia—which is possessed to some extent by the wife of my friend Wilfred B. Talman. This type of phobia also exists in connexion with other animals—for example, the celebrated Renaissance astronomer Tycho Brahe was mortally afraid of a fox. Mrs. Talman isn't as bad a case as the one described in the cutting, but cats make her very nervous—so that Talman can't keep one despite his own fondness for them. I myself am an inveterate cat-lover—I'd have a dozen if there were any place to put them and any way to take convenient care of them. The acuter phobias aren't very common anywhere, I imagine. I hear of them constantly, but don't recall any case personally. They are probably most frequent among persons of a high degree of nervous organisation, and least frequent among those whose energies all go into a desperate struggle for survival.

Glad your local gaol is empty for once! As to crime and police in general—I certainly think that a temperate, scientific, and unsentimental report on the situation would do good in many quarters. Nothing convinces persons of sense like dispassionately marshalled and accurately documented data, and you have surely cited material enough for an impressive array. The cases of arrogance, unscrupulousness, and irrational brutality are so numerous and so evidently typical, that no one could read a massed account of them without feeling the need of a thorough investigation and remedial programme. That bullying of the unoffending boy was especially significant of the psychological side of the situation. I have seen some cases of impatience and apparent overbearingness by traffic policemen, but have always had an inclination to pardon most of these in view of the constant irritation and nervous strain under which the guardians of heavy and complex traffic must labour. That kind of work and responsibility must wear down the nerves even worse than the more seemingly arduous duties of the men on beats. Traffic rules—and the men who enforce them—tend to be stricter in the west, and in the larger Southern cities, than in the northeast. Cleveland and New Orleans have the most ironclad systems of regulating pedestrians that I have encountered anywhere. Of northeastern traffic policemen, those of New York city are held to be the most inclined to discourtesy. New England is very free and easy regarding pedestrian traffic. Regulative laws are on the statute-books of most cities, but they are seldom enforced—so that in practice the pedestrian can go virtually where he likes when he feels like it. If he doesn't succeed in dodging the vehicles, that's his fault. I hope that the Ferguson administration can do something to mitigate the Texas situation. They of course have jurisdiction over the state forces, and I presume that there are ways (even if requiring legislative enactment) in which the state government can bring pressure on its maladministered smaller units. Probably the Gladewater Journal does considerable good in exposing conditions to the population at large, though a more scientific and businesslike type of report would tend to have more weight in official quarters. However—as you say, reform is always a slow process, and even when achieved in full or in part tends to be neutralised by relapses. It is, though, distinctly possible for the administrative standards of a region to undergo certain very gradual and deeply-seated changes as changed ideas work slowly into the daily lives and thoughts of the people—so that I imagine the present state of things will not last forever. But that, of course, doesn't make matters any the less painful for those who have to endure bad conditions now! I certainly hope you will prepare that treatise on the social and historical factors behind the existing state of affairs in Texas, for no one is better fitted than you to perform that much-needed task. I shall read it with the greatest interest whenever you do write and send it. Incidentally, you could make of Texas life a magnificent background for fiction if you chose to turn from phantasy to the realistic type of literature which is rooted in the soil. A record of 377 homicides in a year assuredly bespeaks a very singular condition as judged by the general standard of Western civilisation—and such a condition deserves ample chronicling and portrayal in national literature before it disappears in the course of social evolution.

That Iowa cutting seems to me symptomatic of the kind of blind popular revolt against wholesale and relentless impoverishment which is going to scare some concessions out of the holders of wealth and power during the next two or three decades. I can't agree that anything resembling wholesale slavery is likely to result from the present confusion, since (as I said before) such a course would demand a greater concentration of obedient man-power than the controlling elements are ever likely to command again during the life of this civilisation. Theoretically, a relatively few men with the latest technical appliances could hold the balance of the race in subjection. Practically, they could never secure an absolute "corner" on the necessary appliances. Men are not as unanimous as all that, and it is a virtual certainty that those able to make and use highly developed armaments would not all be on the plutocratic side. Armies of resistance would be able to seize and operate munitions works, and would undoubtedly secure aid from certain foreign countries. There would be no such one-sided struggle as you envisage—things simply don't work out that way. Even in Russia, if the majority were really anxious to have a different government they would have it. The army would revolt, and the peasants would unite and drill. Of course, there *is* a way in which the plutocratic element could preserve absolute power—by spreading work, pensioning the unemployable, and in general producing a set of endurable conditions from which the majority would not tend to revolt. But that would hardly form a true slavery—and what is more, it is doubtful if the plutocrats would ever consent voluntarily to such an arrangement. Of course, no possible system can ever give the individual that almost wholly unrestricted choice of action and enterprise which he had in the agricultural-handicraft past, but that is nobody's fault. It is merely the inevitable result of an increasing population—which causes people to get in one another's way more and more—and of a mechanised industrial system which makes production impossible to the average unaided individual, yet makes it virtually unlimited in quantity for the individual or group in possession of the elaborate machinery and resources of production. These two factors are wholly natural and inevitable, and can never be banished. It is useless to sit back and regret the passing of the Golden Age of individualism. Dense population and machinery are upon us, and the only thing to do is to adapt our lives and standards to fit the existing realities. Our fight cannot logically be against these basic realities, but must be merely against their abuses. We can legitimately demand that the new crowding and quantity production be not used as a basis for *one-sided* change. If the majority have to alter their ways because of new conditions, so must the processes of industry and business alter their ways. Untrammelled individual freedom of action is nothing sacred or necessarily inviolate. All civilisation—with its infinite enrichment of life—involves more or less of it. But likewise, untrammelled individual industry and profit-getting are nothing sacred or necessarily inviolate. If modern conditions give to laissez-faire individual profit-getting a deleterious social effect—i.e., a narrow concentration of resources, and a complete impoverishment of the majority—then that form of industry and profit-getting, like unrestricted individual liberty, must go. The object of good government is not to fulfill catch slogans like "liberty" or "sound business", but simply to provide a decent distribution of existing resources and to make the course of life conform to the normal needs and instincts of the population as best it can without wrecking the system and plunging everyone into greater misery than they could possibly suffer under any conceivable future order of things—but on the other hand, a policy of sane conservatism can retain a great many things which rash radicalism would discard. Perfect liberty of thought, opinion, scientific research, and artistic endeavour can certainly be salvaged in a truly civilised modern state, though Russia has repudiated them. Likewise, all amenities of living need not be destroyed merely because all types of people are not able to share in them. As for your ideal of complete barbaric freedom—surely you realise that it is one of those theoretical, unattainable things like "justice" or "heaven", which can hardly figure usefully in the planning of a course for a social fabric which has automatically (*not* as a result of the efforts of any class or group of individuals) and inevitably outgrown the possibility of its maintenance. It is noble enough as a poetic conception, and as a fact of chapters of history now closed; but you cannot fail to see that emotion is merely wasted in lamenting its absence from the mechanised present and future. No emotion or principle is really "sacred"—for each of our instinctively cherished values is merely an outgrowth of some former stage of anthropological experience wherein the given quality actually possessed a strong survival-value. We are fortunate when our later stages of social evolution enable us to retain such emotional imprints without conflicts with reality—but now and then there comes a change in basic conditions which turns the former asset to a decided hindrance and liability. We must then adjust ourselves to the new age, not allowing our romantic and sentimental attachment to the now impracticable ideal to hamper us in our job of making the most of what we have. Naturally, the relinquishment of traditional standards and conditions (which lend so many illusions of significance and purpose to the empty process of life) is a woefully painful process for members of the two or three transitional generations—but sometimes it has to be accomplished. It is, however, foolish, anticultural, and inadvisable to try to root out such ancient standards and perspectives as do not *need* rooting out—for if all our inherited background be taken away, then what is there left to live for? That is my great quarrel with Soviet Russia. To my mind, the one irreducible minimum of personal independence worth fighting for till the last is *freedom of thought, opinion, research and art.* These are the things which really constitute human personality in its finest sense, and without them all the boasted physical freedom of the savage means nothing. Grant them, and slavery cannot exist. But of course, there are *degrees* of personal freedom on which it is still necessary and desirable to insist. When we say that the utter liberty of the individual must be curtailed, we do not mean that his daily motions must be constantly restricted, or that during his entire life he must be liable to governmental drafting and transference to distant fields of industry, as under the Soviet programme. *These* extremes are indeed unnecessary and intolerable, for they make impossible a reasonable satisfaction of normal instincts, while it cannot be said that they are demanded by the existing and probable future conditions of industry. There must be moderation in all things, and we cannot interpret the necessary decrease in individual latitude as an excuse for the arbitrary and capricious restrictions of tyranny.

I read with great interest what you said of a certain physically overcharged and restless type of individual whose assimilation to an orderly state will always be difficult, and agree that the problem is no imaginary one. At the same time, I hardly think it is altogether beyond solution. Strenuous games and physical exercises are fostered by all nations, including Soviet Russia, and there is no reason why such a practice should not indefinitely continue. Although continual hard *work* can hardly be provided for persons of this type, there is every likelihood that they can always be provided with plenty of hard *play*—boxing, football, and anything else of the sort that they may desire. Nothing will hinder them from indulging in feats of adventure and daring—indeed, such feats may be especially encouraged. In Russia a tremendous amount of exploration and other forms of hazardous pioneering can be constantly met with. With such a continual normal outlet, it does not seem likely to me that the energies of this supervitalised type would ever become an unmanageable problem, or that they would burst forth in unconquerable crime or destructive revolt. Of course, some members of this type would loose their energies anti-socially, just as some members of the calculative type will always loose their energies anti-socially in the form of cheating and corruption; but I fancy that the physically regulative powers of the state will be as able as in the past to preserve a fair degree of balance and order. It is never possible to assimilate every single individual to the social pattern—hence the need of police, prisons, and madhouses. Incidentally, though, it is virtually certain that this physically overcharged element will tend to decrease under the more stabilised conditions of a socialistic future. You can see how much less numerous it is even now in the more settled and urbanised parts of the world, and it is likely that the decrease will continue at an accelerated rate. The conditions which called forth this type have largely disappeared, and future generations will tend to produce types more adapted to the existing conditions. That is the way the slow, gradual processes of evolution always work. If anything, the ultimate danger will probably be that the race will have too little rather than too much physical energy and stamina . . . although the need of military defence against other groups will always call forth a certain amount of bodily resourcefulness. However—all prediction is really futile, since unexpected developments and overlooked factors so frequently turn out to be the actually decisive elements.

I certainly don't think that the existing civilisation will last indefinitely, and am rather inclined toward Spengler's view that all cultures must necessarily perish of old age.[1] Any full-sized war might reduce us at once to barbaric chaos; and if we escape this, the debilitating effects of sheer ennui are almost certain to set in ultimately. People will take their civilisation so implicitly for granted that it will cease to mean much to them. They will become lax in its defence, and apathetic in maintaining the conditions on which it is founded. Decadent cults will arise, in which weary worldlings will preach that the complex industrial order is not worth the labour and self-sacrifice necessary for its maintenance, and this feeling will subconsciously penetrate even those who do not consciously cherish it. There will be a steady letdown and return to the primitive—with the social disorders naturally accompanying such a readjustment. Finally some hostile civilisation will conquer the decaying culture, and the Western world as we know it will be ended. Just what the *race* of the next major civilisation will be, I don't know—but I have a suspicion that it will be a mixture of Slav and Mongol.

As for the "physical-mental" argument—it ought to be clear at the outset that no modern thinker wishes for even a moment to represent the mind as other than a very delicate and infinitely complex branch of physical activity. Thus to use a pedantic degree of accuracy, the controversy is between those who exalt the simpler and more primitive bodily processes, and those who exalt the most specialised and highly evolved of the bodily processes—i.e., the neuro-cerebral processes as expressed in consciousness and its fruits. You will no longer find in Western civilisation any reputable thinkers who advocate asceticism of the Yogi sort—that is, the actual mortification of the flesh for the sake of some supposed separate mental or "spiritual" essence. No one advocates the deliberate neglect or injury of the body; and even the most fanatical anti-physicalist presupposes the ample care of health, to such a degree that the mental processes will be adequately nourished. The real argument is between those physicalists who glorify the athletic development of the body beyond the actual needs of civilised life, and those anti-physicalists who consider such extra development a rather childish waste of time and energy. Incidentally, no rational anti-physicalist objects to the continued athletic training of those whose actual occupation demands physical strength. It is *unnecessary* athleticism which they consider essentially trivial. They point out that under a mechanised regime there is little need for marked physical strength on the part of the majority—which of course is urban. They do not see why the whole race should try to meet standards which are now necessary only to a minority of it—the implied waste of time and energy offending their sense of logic. Their distinct shading of actual *contempt* for physical strength is due to their belief that, under the existing social-economic order, only inferior individuals need to use physical strength in the struggle for survival. They argue that a superior man is able to raise himself to a directive, executive, clerical, or other post not demanding manual toil, so that such manual toil is necessarily the work of an inferior mind and stamina—although of course they do not deny that many non-manual tasks (those of store clerks, doormen, errand boys, elevator boys, etc.) are equally characteristic of inferior types. All this reasoning, whether or not true as a whole or in part, of course applies to the relatively stable social order preceding the present increasing chaos. The ideology may or may not be a basically false one, but the fact remains that (except when the recommended standard of physical development falls so low as to coddle weaklings unable to walk a block or stay up all day without a nap) it is not inherently illogical, inconsistent, or ridiculous. Carried to extremes, it contains its own paradoxes; but it is at least worthy of being reckoned with as an antidote to the romantic super-physicalism of the opposite type of sentimental extremist.

Coming now to your specific argument (concerning which it must be noted that I am not on the side of your extreme opponents, but on a conservative middle ground), you say that you do not see why you should despise, neglect, or ignore your body (i.e., its simpler, non-mental aspects) because it is not as strong as a bull, elephant, or dynamo. Well—in sober fact, no one would ask you to despise, neglect, or ignore it. One would merely suggest that its position in your personality is necessarily less than its position in the personality of a bull, elephant, or dynamo; because you have a specialised development which the bull, elephant, and dynamo lack, and which is so utterly beyond competition from non-human sources that it would be foolish if you placed your chief pride in something held in common (and inferiorly) with the bull, elephant, and dynamo, instead of in it. That covers the whole ground. The objection is against your placing chief pride in a quality belonging definitely to the lower stages of evolution and not forming a markedly developed attribute of the higher species, when you have a radically higher endowment peculiar to your intensively developed species and forming an absolute and definite advance in your progression from the primal protozoan slime. To look at it concretely, it is *no distinction at all* for you to be able to lift a certain weight, knock down a certain man, or carry a bale of hay. A bull gorilla could do more. But it *is* a rare distinction for you to be able to write a story like "Worms of the Earth", dream a character like *Kathulos*, or create an exquisite poem like "Cimmeria". The one type of accomplishment—the physical—means nothing whatever in relation to your excellence as a person—as a specimen of highly and complexly evolved life. Thousands of brainless clods and lower animals can do as well or better—so that when you put chief pride in that sort of endeavour you are exalting a very minor and incidental side of yourself. But the other type of accomplishment—the mental—means everything. It is what distinguishes Robert E. Howard from all the rest of creation, proves that he is a highly organised specimen of life infinitely remote from the amoebal stage, and asserts his individual superiority over vast numbers of his own evolved species. When you have so much to be proud of in a high field peculiar to superior men, it is *incongruous* that you should reserve your chief pride for some minor attribute like great strength, which is in no way individual or a mark of superior personality. It seems to me that, upon reflection, you cannot fail to see the force of this point. Naturally I'm not urging you to let your body run down below the requirements of the duties you choose to perform, or to refrain from having a legitimate and well-proportioned pride in its points of excellence (as a man may be moderately proud of a minor possession like a fine horse, while reserving supreme pride for such major possessions as books, wife and children). I am simply urging that you think of these things *in their true proportion*, and that you realise how much more of a real honour it is to be the author of "The Black Stone" and "The Cairn on the Headland" than it is to be able to load a wagon or flatten a drunk. Of course, it is better to be able to do *both* sets of things than to be able to do only the first set. No one claims that physical strength is other than an advantage. But when it comes to feeling pride in your own personality you can't escape the fact that the first set of accomplishments means a lot more—in relation to your status as a superior human being—than the latter set.

If anything is close to an axiom, it is that *superiority* in the organic field means *degree of evolutionary removal from* the unicellular stage. Of course, we have our proximate standards of excellence based on the possession of certain emotional attitudes which racial experience has fixed upon us because of former or present value in the survival struggle (thus the Nordic exalts courage and unbrokenness; the Hindoo, self-abnegation; the Jew, sharpness and passivity; etc., etc.), but the fact remains that underneath them all the one real criterion of cosmic value is *degree of evolution*—advance from the gorilla, the Piltdown skull,[2] the Neanderthaloid, the Australian blackfellow, or the nigger. *This advance of evolutionary degree, marking absolute superiority, is not in any way measured by physical strength, but is directly measured by the development of the intellect, the imagination, and the more complex and delicate emotions.* To me, at least, that argument seems unanswerable; and I cannot see how you can fail to concur in its essence. It does not mean that physical strength is contemptible or other than desirable, but is simply a reminder *to put first things first.* Popular recognition of the principle is well expressed in the different degrees of derogation implied in the statement that a man has a weak ankle, and the statement that he has a weak brain. And so what the anti-physicalist is really driving at is merely that the cultivation of excess strength is not worth the trouble if the process involves inconvenience or takes time and energy from the cultivation of the mind—and also, that the placement of too much pride and interest in purely physical matters is a waste of attention on a side of life which is, however intrinsically desirable and worthy of *properly proportioned* attention, an essentially minor one.

Probably you see the gist of this position so well by this time that further elaboration is unnecessary. You will realise that no thinker despises the cultivation of whatever amount of strength is needed for a given manner of life—but will also realise that the bulk of mankind in western civilisation lives an urban life in which the normal physical demands are vastly below anything which you have been accustomed to regard as normal. As for *the aesthetic pride of carrying to perfection any thing or process connected with oneself*—I can well understand that feeling, and appreciate its application to the development of the body. Amidst a multiplicity of interests and duties not everyone can exercise this aestheticism in every field; so that some must be content to remain outside the Hercules-Apollo class—but the principle at least is sound, and I have no sympathy with the extremists who consider the body too trivial a thing to occupy their aesthetic attention. Besides—these extremists often show their inconsistency (as Long does) by bestowing a dandified amount of grooming and dressing upon the very body which they profess to consider unworthy of organic development! The Greeks always insisted on a fine physical development to parallel the mental, and Horace was not the only Roman to value a *mens sana in corpore sano*.[3]

What you say of the need of strong hands in building civilisation is true, but these hands are generally those of inferior personalities whose function is only a step removed from that of the pack-animals who also uphold civilisation. The anti-physicalist understands all this—pointing out that brains and superiority direct, while brawn and inferiority obey. Therefore, he argues, men of superior capacity ought to cultivate their brains in order that they may fulfil the superior functions to which they are adapted. On the other hand, I realise the force of your argument that in uncertain times (though of course it would be rather extreme if everybody through all the ages felt obliged to prepare for upheavals which come only at virtually millennial intervals) men are liable to be thrust into occupations wholly unrelated to their capacities, so that it does not pay to lack the basic requirements of any widely demanded sort of labour.

As to the *joy* which some times of person find in muscular exertion (although these types are less numerous than you think)—no one begrudges this boon to those able to enjoy it. When physical exercise really brings intrinsic pleasure, it certainly cannot be held to be more trivial than any other ephemeral and non-intellectual pleasure. And in cases where mental vigour depends on physical exercise, I fancy that even the most acute anti-physicalist would approve of the exercise in question—as a stimulus allied to the alcohol, tobacco, or other drugs which many physicalists (though with far less justification) seem to regard with surprising tolerance.

As for the *geometrical* beauty of the finely-developed body (as distinguished from the aestheticism of functional perfection)—no anti-physicalists attempt to deny that. They merely point out that it is greater to be an artist than a mere model. And regarding the element of *drama* in physical struggle (which is unquestioned, though of course all agree that it is inferior to the drama of mental or emotional struggle)—I presume that anti-physicalists would rather be appreciators than actors.

I am not, myself, by any means what I have described as an "anti-physicalist". It is my opinion that any superior man should keep his bodily strength at a considerable pitch above the urban necessity-level, in order that he may confront with dignity the numberless irregular situations and menaces—accidents, assailants, etc.—which inevitably occur in even the best-ordered mechanical civilisations, and that he may make the most of life by being equal to the demands of all forms of enjoyment. When one is below a certain physical level he is often—unless supported by a tremendous mental courage, recklessness, and magnetism—placed in situations which to any traditional taste are distinctly ignominious, while he loses a vast amount of pleasure by being unequal to the physical demands connected with it. (i.e., long-distance walking, mountain-climbing, camping, etc.) And as regards the psychological attitude—I think too great an indifference to physical conquest and prowess marks a certain decadence of fibre speaking ill for the future of the race and civilisation among its competitors. The complete modern, with his submerged sense of a physically defended personal honour and his active opposition to all military feeling, is not the best possible material for a nation which must fight for its place among greedy competitors. So I stand half-way betwixt Long and yourself—insisting on the one hand that the glorification of the physical ought to be subordinated to the glorification of the mental, but on the other and insisting that the loss of a certain standard of physical prowess and combative interest means effeminacy and decadence.

Too bad the detail in "The Cairn on the Headland" was changed—and the change was so pointless and unnecessary, too. I simply will not endure the mutilation of my yarns, and prefer not to have them appear if they can't be printed just as written. As for the Latin name of York—the Celtic was *Caer-Ebroc,* but I never met with any Latin form save *Eboracum*—except in "Worms of the Earth". I shall be on the lookout to see if I can find your form anywhere. So you didn't know "The Black Stone" had landed in the "Not at Night" anthology? That's odd, for you ought to have received a small cheque from Charles Lovell (W.T.'s London agent) for the reprint rights. Better ask Wright about it. The address of the "Not at Night" firm is as follows: *Selwyn & Blount, Paternoster House, Paternoster Row, London, E.C.4., Eng.* About your poetry—I sincerely envy you the ability which produced the three magnificent specimens enclosed in your letters. I'm not flattering when I say that "Cimmeria" is one of the most haunting, vision-evoking things I've read in ages, that "The Man in the Myth" is a splendidly musical lyrical ballad, and that "Saul Falls on his Sword" is a magically potent crystallisation of the mood behind it. You are a real poet if there ever was one, and I certainly hope these specimens will be published if they haven't been already. Wright ought to be enthusiastic about "Cimmeria" if he has even the rudiments of a real poetic appreciation. Some of these things ought to be set to appropriately macabre music some day—and that ought, also, to be collected in book form. Again, let me congratulate you upon your genuine poetic gifts.

I certainly appreciated the rattles—but please don't run into needless danger for the purpose of securing a larger set! As I said, this set is much larger than the set my grandfather got in Idaho, and which my surviving aunt now has. What you say of hibernation-dens makes my hide creep . . . . I surely wouldn't care to be the fellow who had that animated collar blown around his neck . . . . . ugh! An increase in snakes and wild life at the present period is not peculiar to Texas. In New England the rattlers seem to be coming back, while deer are more plentiful. Wolves have been seen again in northern New York State, and there are persistent reports of bear tracks in western Rhode Island. The primary reason for this return of the wilderness is the desertion of the countryside in favour of cities. As agriculture passes more and more to the large-scale mechanised farms of the west, the rural parts of New England become more and more deserted. Farm after farm is abandoned and reverts to the primitive state, while fewer and fewer hunters comb the woods and kill off the woodland denizens. One of the paradoxes of the machine age is that it increases the loveliness of the countryside while it swells the cities with greater and greater gregariousness.

As for fish—ugh! Corpus Christi is one of the places in Texas which I certainly *shan't* visit when I get around your way! Some years ago Long and I attempted to explore the Fulton Fish Market section of New York—which is full of quaint scenes and buildings. Ordinarily I have about 50 times the vigour and endurance of young Belknap—but for once he had grandpa at a disadvantage! I don't know where I left the lunch I had eaten an hour previously—for I was too dizzy to read the street signs! In the end I managed to stagger out of the stench without actually losing consciousness—but when I regained the power of speech I fervently repeated the closing line of Hoyt's old Bowery song—"I'll never go there any more!"[4] There are parts of the doomed French Market in New Orleans which remind one ever so faintly of this olfactory inferno—but no description or parallel could convey the utter loathsomeness of Fulton Market. That is the district where Alfred E. Smith grew up—probably he needed such hardening in order to be able to face Tammany politics. There must be a stamina in a man who could survive long residence in a region like that! Actual fishing ports like Gloucester, Mass. (a marvellously quaint old town) are by no means as bad as Fulton market. I can even retain the contents of my stomach in Gloucester. But somehow I'm afraid I wouldn't care to try my endurance on Corpus Christi!

Your account of your dietary tastes is indeed interesting. On some points you coincide with me, while on others you differ. I *can't* get enough of ice cream, and frequently make a full meal of it (and nothing else) in summer. I like large doses of almost all sweets, though I *don't* like custards and am rather lukewarm toward puddings. Ice cream or pie—blueberry, mince or apple (with ice cream on it) forms my favourite dessert. I don't care for tea but like coffee . . . . . . and oddly, I think I like fried sausage about as well as any part of a hog. We could divide a porker between us with great justice and satisfaction—although I do like good boiled (never fried) ham. I notice that ham tends to be both better, and more frequently served, in the south than in the north. Whitehead *always* had some on hand as a staple—just as one ordinarily keeps stocked with butter, cheese, or bread. And as for turkey dinners—we are unanimous! Fortunately, I have been [able] to surround several of these feasts during the present autumn and winter.

Glad to hear of your pleasant Thanksgiving and Christmas. It makes the old planet seem small to reflect that you listened to a radio broadcast from the Brown stadium—less than a mile from this house, and also less than a mile (in another direction) from the house in which I was born and dwelt for the first 14 years of my life. I didn't attend the game, but my surviving aunt (with whom I dined later in the day) heard it over her radio. Which reminds me that her radio easily picks up San Antonio in your state, although it fails to get many nearer stations. Just for the fun of it, I have listened to many a speech and musical programme from the shadow of the old Alamo! Your account of the game you witnessed—and especially of the Indian fullback—is a veritable Iliad in miniature—a genuine poem of conflict and emotion. Alien though sport is to me, I read the account with the keenest admiration and without a moment's lapse of interest. Glad to hear, by the way, that the Nordic blonds won in their contest with the swart southrons!

I spent Thanksgiving with my aunt, and also Christmas—but at 2:10 a.m. following the Yuletide celebration I took the coach for New York, whither Long's parents had invited me, to pay the kid a surprise visit. The route into Manhattan has been lately changed, so that it extends down upper Broadway past the Long domicile at the corner of 97th St.—hence I was able to alight at my destination direct from Providence without going downtown. It was 8:30 a.m. when I reached there, and Belknap was not up. When he finally came out to breakfast and found the Old Gentleman in the dining-room nodding over the morning Tribune he was very properly astonished! I later gave others of the local group the same sort of surprise, and on Dec. 30 the whole crowd assembled at Belknap's for one of our old-time discussion meetings. Among those whom I saw was Wandrei, who still lingers in the east finishing a rather unusual psychological novel.[5] During my stay I saw everything new that the museums had to offer—including the archaic Greek Apollo at the Metropolitan, the modernistic atrocities and shrieking attic murals at the Whitney, the two Dutch rooms at the Brooklyn, and the American primitives and famous Whistler portrait of his mother (lent by the Louvre) at the now adequately housed Museum of Modern Art. I also saw the fine Gothic interior of the new Riverside church (which the senior Longs attend) for the first time. Here are a couple of cards illustrating the Gothic attractions which Manhattan has to offer. I saw the old year out at the new Brooklyn apartment of my friend Samuel Loveman—whose many curiosities and art treasures are now adequately displayed for the first time. Very generously, he presented me with two highly interesting objects—a prehistoric and very primitive stone idol from Mexico, and a primitive African cutting implement of flint, with carved ivory handle. I shall have quite a museum myself before long! When I returned home I found 22 letters, 2 revision jobs, and a mountainous pile of newspapers and periodicals awaiting me—a maelstrom in which I am still writhing! One very welcome item was a gift from W. Paul Cook—a fragment of the once marvellous library which he dispersed in 1930 . . . . nothing less than a 3-volume copy of Maturin's famous "Melmoth, the Wanderer", which I had long been anxious to own. Another accession to my library is something which I picked up for 79¢ as a remainder—E. R. Eddison's marvellously fantastic tale, "The Worm Ouroboros". A third accession—a gift—is fairly interesting but not so remarkable—S. Fowler Wright's scientific novel "The World Below",[6] in which a man of today is transplanted to an age 500,000 years in the future. It has some vivid moments, but is a bit diluted with sociological satire like most books of this kind. I had never read this item before.

Regarding the relative happiness of barbarians and civilised men—of course, many complex and unfathomable factors make judgment difficult, just as it is difficult to decide on the relative happiness of human beings and other forms of organic life. The happiness of primitively organised or undeveloped forms of life is to some extent—or in certain directions—more like the painlessness of oblivion, non-existence, or inorganic existence than like the active, varied, and poignant pleasure of a fully utilised consciousness, for even its most violent physical and crudely emotional forms are strongly localised in an extremely small part of the potential experience-field of the human species. The barbarian is really only a quarter or a sixteenth alive, since the most human and finely organised parts of his fabric are left inactive and dormant. For him the complex rhythms of energy-transformation which give consciousness its most intense vitality and pleasure-reactions do not exist. The real question is as to whether the amount of pleasurable energy-conversion in the pitifully restricted consciousness of the barbarian can give him as keen a psychological satisfaction—as measured by any conceivable unit—as the stupendously vaster amount of pleasurable energy-conversion in the enormously greater consciousness-area of the civilised man. It is understood, of course, that the barbarian knows of no pleasures beyond his own, and therefore cannot consciously *miss* anything which civilisation might give him. All sense of *deprivation* may thus be ruled out. But at this point the thoughtful investigator, mindful that all sensation is really chemical or physical action and therefore theoretically measurable in energy-units, will pause to enquire *whether a small amount of sensation can ever be actually as poignant as a large amount of sensation*, even when it forms the maximum of which the experiencer has any conception. This is a highly important and significant point which deserves careful reflection. A stick of wood, a starfish, a dog, a savage, and a civilised man may all be equally *contented* at a given moment. Each will have, at that moment, as great an amount of pleasurable nervous activity as it believes any object to be capable of having. Yet the amount of pleasurable energy-conversion in the nervous systems of the respective objects will be enormously different. In the stick it will be 0; in the starfish it will be (let us say) 5; in the dog, 100; in the savage, 1000; and in the civilised man 100,000. To fancy that the equal balance betwixt desire and fulfilment manifest in each of these objects means an equal amount of positive pleasure-experience for each is a very bold assumption indeed. The prodigiously different amount of in-

trinsic energy-conversion stand out as highly challenging facts, and from what
we know of nervous organism it does not seem likely that the different sorts
of equilibria can mean anything like identical emotional states. The lower organisms do not feel the lack of anything which the higher possess, hence have
just as little positive pain; but their difference from non-existence is far less,
hence they cannot experience any such intensity of pleasure as is possessed by
the finely evolved and more or less fully developed forms. The difference
between the content of a barbarian and the pleasure of a civilised man is that
between numbness and agreeable sensation—between the taste of an inoffensive and faintly palatable food and that of a keenly delightful and well-
seasoned food. You will probably admit that, although a blubber-eating Es-
quimau does not know or long for the taste of fruit or honey, he can undoubtedly experience a quantitatively greater total of pleasure-sensation when
fruit or honey is added to his diet. There is room, of course, for metaphysical
debate on this point; but to my mind the evidence all points to the superior
pleasure of large-area'd energy-conversions. I do not think it even conceivable that the civilised man does not obtain a titanically greater amount of satisfaction and positive pleasure from life than does the barbarian. However—
if we estimate the possible pleasure-advantage of the civilised man as 100 to 1,
we must of course realise that certain contrary factors cut down this margin
considerably—though by no means to the point or even to the vicinity of
nullification. In the first place, civilisation increases pain-capacity as well as
pleasure-capacity. Secondly, certain crude sources of pleayure are eliminated
as finer and richer ones are opened up. Lovers of barbarism like yourself—
and like Lord Monboddo in the 18th century—make the most of these
points; yet I really cannot see that they have any real determinant force.[7] To
take the first one—while of course civilisation *does* increase pain-capacity, it is
obvious that the vast bulk of mankind's pain comes from primitive sources
felt in common by barbarian and civilised man. The increase in man's already
tremendous store of pain can hardly be held comparable to the *overwhelming*
increase in his pleasure—an increase which includes what is probably the
most powerful single source of pleasure possible to the high-grade human
being—i.e., the systematic gratification of intellectual curiosity. As for the
second point—the pleasures lost by the increasingly civilised man are mainly
those of a rather low order psychologically—pleasures connected with the
simpler bodily instincts and directly derivative emotions, and not linked even
nearly as closely to the sensation-registering consciousness as are the flood of
new and psychologically higher pleasures which the civilising process brings.
After all the discounts are deducted, it seems to me that the balance stands so
high in favour of the civilised man that we may say his net pleasure-capacity is
perhaps 50 to 75 times that of the barbarian. This applies, of course, to human types representing the most advanced degree of biological evolution—
the types which any absolute standard must necessarily adjudge superior, and

which it is only logical to select as representative of the race at its best—as representing the goal toward which the development of all deserves to be encouraged. Naturally, there are primitive, retarded, and atavistic types to whom barbarism would be better suited than civilisation—types biologically incapable of extracting pleasure from the more evolved intellectual-aesthetic sources, and therefore sadly missing the lost, cruder pleasures of barbarism. But it is certainly not fair to try to hold back the superior for the benefit of the inferior, when the former so clearly represent nature's deepest intention in the unfolding of the racial pattern. Man and mosquitos have different environmental desiderata—but we continue to organise the world for men instead of for mosquitos. So, on the same principle, it is best that the social pattern be that suited to superior rather than to inferior man. The irony of your own position lies in the fact that you undoubtedly belong most emphatically to the superior type which would lose most through a relapse of the world into barbarism. In spite of the residual delight which you still take in primitive things (a large part of whose attractiveness to you, by the way, is purely the result of your highly civilised dramatic imagination, hence would not exist if you had the things without the perspective-giving civilisation), it remains a fact that your natural imaginative processes are of a powerful, delicate, and highly evolved kind which could never find satisfaction in the primitive world you idealise. You claim—as a result of your civilised knowledge of the structure of barbaric society and your civilised sense of the dramatic functions of its several elements—that in a primitive community you would wish to be a wholehearted animal guzzler and fighter than a minstrel or shaman. Now as a matter of fact you could not, in such a community, possibly be anything else than a minstrel or shaman—for your imagination would not let you. You would doubtless be a *fighting* bard or priest—but with your endowments you could not conceivably stay on the undeveloped plane of the dulled, callous flesh-hackers whose qualities and personality all stem from a lack of imaginative sensitiveness and development. Your alert and image-building mind would be constantly troubled with visions of things which never were, and speculations as to the sources, value, and true functions of the things and ways around you. Even the most engrossing and exhausting physical activities could not quite stifle the restless questing of a mind as finely organised and alert as yours. That is why barbarism always perishes in the long run—because it is essentially a system suited to mentally undeveloped types, which fails to satisfy its members as soon as any lull in the deadly struggle for physical survival permits their personalities to expand from a narrowly fragmentary to a somewhat ampler stage. If barbarism were suited to superior men it would have remained the dominant system. Only the sheerest academic quibbling can dispute the absolute and intrinsic improvement inherent in the transition to civilisation. Absurdity and ineptitude are written all over a system which (like an eight-cylinder motor car with only one cylinder hitting) employs only a minute fraction of the total capacities of the race—rejecting, incidentally, the very finest part (as measured by the absolute standard of evolutionary status) of those capacities. It is ironic and illogical to call such a fragmentary type of life a *full* one—for what barbarism ignores and rejects is infinitely more both qualitatively and quantitatively than what civilisation rejects. Those sides of life which barbarism develops and civilisation eliminates are almost without exception very crude and trivial sides as judged by a sensible evolutionary standard—sides which are related only to the least important and most obsolescent parts of the advancing species. What is more, barbarism contains gross uglinesses (such as the ready willingness to disturb the most complex harmonies of nature by lightly and indifferently slashing and mangling the human organism) which cannot be regarded as other than revelations of a disgustingly low-grade emotional organisation—a callousness and imaginative deadness indicative of the paralysis or unawakenedness of all the higher fruits of human evolution. Altogether, when we compare the things gained and the things lost in the process of dawning civilisation, we cannot justly deem ourselves anything but prodigious gainers. Behind every argument in favour of barbarism, it seems to me, there lurks a fatally fallacious romanticism and sentimentality, and a fatally reckless disregard of the actual facts and values involved. Indeed, it is clear to the careful thinker that most of the defects of our imperfect civilisation are of the nature of leanings backward toward barbarism—a result of the ascendancy of brutish and greedy primitive minds—rather than departures from barbarism. Really, it is quite impossible to make out a soundly convincing case for barbarism. All the facts are against it. For once, the common opinion of the "man in the street" happens to be the right one so far as rational and impartial research can determine. Civilisation is *not* something to be rejected.

Concerning Indian cultures—I think you are right in assuming the superiority of the southeastern or "Mobilian" and Iroquois groups to others north of Mexico. I think also that, within the southeastern group, the superiority of the Cherokee is clear. Recent ethnologists have come to regard the Cherokee as a detached kinsman of the Iroquois. As to the Iroquois—you may possibly have read of the very recent theory of Dr. William D. Lighthall that they have an origin different from that of the bulk of aboriginals.[8] It has, of course, long been recognised that *some* elements alien to the Mongoloid Behring-Strait invaders must have existed in pre-Caucasian America. The vast observed physical differences between different groups in both North and South America suggests as much, as do also the physiognomies represented in Mayan sculpture. Also—the culture and art of Central America suggest Asian influences not likely to have been retained through an Alaskan migration. Aside from any possible accessions through Atlantic migration, it is thought that the aboriginal population received certain elements from the Pacific islands—brought by canoe migrations, and perhaps involving the transfer to the Maya culture of some phases of Indo-Chinese art and lore. Now what Dr. Lighthall has to say is quite specific. He finds in the Iroquois not only the general superiority to the surrounding Algonquins which all have noticed from the earliest times, but a profound and significant culture-cleavage as well. While many of their customs are of course like those of the other Indian tribes with which they have been long in contact, Dr. Lighthall believes that there is a certain nucleus of Iroquian folkways not reconcilable in any way with a Mongoloid-Indian origin. He points to their custom of sleeping in hammocks and on raised platforms (a *tropical* tendency), their type of "long house", their mode of reckoning family descent, and other traditional habits, and to the measurements of their skulls as exhumed from burying-grounds. His final conclusion is that the Iroquois are *Polynesians*—like the Tahitians and Hawaiians—who reached northeastern America by a very devious course including South America. Of course, he recognises that they have picked up an enormous amount of blood and lore from the surrounding tribes of true Indians. Just how the Lighthall theory will be received by conservative ethnologists remains to be seen. At any rate, it opens up a highly interesting set of speculations. Incidentally—I am enclosing a cutting which describes some important Indian finds near the junction of the Mississippi and Ohio rivers. It is clear that at one time there was a great deal more settled life in prehistoric America than is commonly assumed, and it seems to me probable beyond any reasonable doubt that a distinctive North-American civilisation would have developed but for the coming of the white man. How different would the modern world have been if the Indian had occupied America 2000 years earlier than he did!

I think I agree with you about the Philippine Islands. As for Ulster—the point I wanted to bring out is that the *present* generation of inhabitants is in no way responsible for the wrongs of three centuries ago. We have to think in terms of individuals as well as of groups. These people—as individuals—have merely been born in a region which they know as their own, and to which they are adjusted by ten generations of continuous life. Whatever the crimes of their ancestors, they themselves form a present reality which cannot be ignored. They live in a certain place through no fault of their own, personally, and have a certain language and set of folkways. It is perfectly right and natural for them to defend what they have been born to—and I surely applaud their efforts to do so. To try to go back and theoretically right all the wrongs of history is simply fantastic. On that basis the Aryan race has no business in Europe at all, since it probably took it by force from Neanderthalers and Mongoloids. When a region is inhabited by its own race and unwillingly held in subjection, there is legitimate ground for revolt; but the idea of dispossessing long-adjusted present populations in favour of remote historical claims—however just in theory—is chimerical to the point of downright criminality. The fact that Alsace-Lorraine was originally German, and seized high-handedly by Louis XIV in 1796, did not make any the less brutal the German reconquest and Prussianisation of 1870–71, after the inhabitants had become naturally and instinctively Gallic. So far as Ulster is concerned—an ultimate sensible solution would be its union (for political and economic purposes) with the Free State, with special provisions (like those whereby the French in Quebec secured the preservation of their language and institutions after British conquest) for the retention of Anglo-Saxon speech and institutions in a position of dominance, and for a complete freedom from the romantic antiquarian experimentation of the Free State. Some such plan may eventually be worked out if the moderate elements of all the governments concerned ever remain in simultaneous control over a long period. Incidentally, it can hardly be said the Ulstermen are wholly alien to the South Irish, since they are largely Scottish and descended from Irish Gaels who forcibly invaded and possessed Scotland at the end of the Britanno-Roman period. When one tries to invoke long bygone history, one can find fantastic evidence for almost every side of any national question.

As for literature—it does not pay to be narrow, or to let one's own accidental preferences affect one's judgment of the intrinsic merit of various authors, schools, and national traditions. We all have specialised tastes—like mine for weirdness and phantasy and yours for romantic combat and physical adventure—which make our lists of favourites rather one-sided and prone to include mediocrities along with the first-raters. Enclosed is a cutting by a very sensible and well-rounded commentator (Bertrand K. Hart, Literary Editor of the Providence Journal) in which some of Jack London's limitations are suggested. My friend James F. Morton—now curator of the Municipal Museum in Paterson, N.J.—knew Jack London in San Francisco 30 years ago, when a joint interest in Socialism (now repudiated by Morton) drew them together. London put Morton into one of his books—"Martin Eden"—under the slightly altered name of "Norton".[9] At that time Morton was very hard pressed financially, and London helped him considerably. When he returned East he was very proud to be wearing London's old clothes—to which he clung admiringly until they virtually fell to pieces! You are certainly a bit hasty and unjust in giving a blanket condemnation to thoughtful writers like Dreiser, Lewis, Hecht, Bromfield, O'Neill, Anderson, etc. These are really the greatest writers—despite all limitations—whom we have in America, for they are the only ones who actually try to understand people and present them as acting from the deep hidden motives which truly animate them. The superficial writers—like Zane Grey—merely reproduce conventional situations and tickle the facile emotions of those who like to see certain external tricks of glamour, appearance, and dramatic contrast mechanically and thoughtlessly repeated. They represent people as acting from fictitious motives which do not exist, and distort the whole pattern of life and human nature in the direction of artificial convention and childish oversimplification. So far as people, life, and reality—the bases of art—are concerned, these scribblings are essentially frivolous and irrelevant. Mencken—despite his sometimes wearying tendency to keep on shouting after the battle is over—actually performed a tremendously valuable service in helping to break up the empty, sterile, and infantile genteel-romantic tradition in American literature, and to establish an appreciative public for civilised and adult-minded authors. Of course, one may not take as much light personal enjoyment in the genuine literature which stems from life as from something more allied to the processes of imaginative escape. I don't myself, since phantasy best suits my particular set of emotions. But that's no excuse for failing to give real literature objective credit for its function and stature.

You might not care for Shaw, but you've missed something big if you don't know Conrad. He is one of the most powerful novelists of the 20th century, with a splendidly vivid conception both of human motives and of the relentless power of nature—especially as manifest in the *sea*. Nor is he indifferent to the violent action which you value so highly—for struggle, man against man and man against nature, is always a prominent element in his work. No more thoroughly and basically virile author ever wielded a pen—and his virility is no mere matter of surface gesture and stock situation as it is with the second-raters. Begin with "Lord Jim" and see if you don't want to read all the rest! I can't get enthusiastic about Kipling, for to me to glib *mechanism* of his products is always visible. His stories have a certain meaningless jauntiness and affectation which prevents me from enjoying them, while his verses never get very deeply beneath the surface of things. I never read anything by Jim Tully, but fear his work (which I have seen reviewed) is a trifle too narrow in scope to make him a major figure. Sinclair is a political propagandist—not an artist or literary creator. As for my own junk—let me warn you that it does not merit classification as literature at all. I try to keep it above the pulp-magazine average—but it is not even within striking distance of the solid and permanent merit represented by Poe, Machen, Blackwood, Dunsany, James, and de la Mare. The more I analyse the stuff, the less I think of it—out of the whole batch I doubt if anything except "The Colour out of Space" and "The Music of Erich Zann" is worth publication between cloth covers. Whether I'll ever do any better, I can't yet say—but I am none too optimistic. I hope to get time for some more fictional experimentation before 1933 is over. By the way—I can agree with the majority of your poetic judgments.

Whitehead's death has proved a shock to everybody—for his brilliant accomplishments and admirable personality made him an unique figure. There will be an obituary note in next month's Eyrie, but a whole book couldn't do him real justice.[10]

Well—I hope these 22 pages haven't reduced you to a coma! I'm sure that you'll pardon the many arguments and differences of opinion—being aware that my sole object is the recognition of abstract truth and of sound values. The winter has been commendably warm so far—today is rainy. Hope Cross Plains is similarly free from extreme weather.

With best wishes, and renewed appreciation of your splendid poems, I remain

Yrs most cordially and sincerely—

H P L

P.S. Enclosed is a cutting from the Literary Digest illustrating an interesting angle of the Saga of the Southwest.[11]

Notes

1. HPL read the first volume of Oswald Spengler's *The Decline of the West* (1926)—a translation of *Der Untergang des Abendlandes* (1918–22)—in 1927 (see *SLL* 2.120–21). He does not appear to have read the second volume (1928). HPL was much influenced by Spengler's theories of the successive rise and fall of civilizations, and by his likening of societies to organisms that progress from youth to adulthood to old age.

2. HPL could not have known that the Piltdown man—remains of which were found in England in 1912—was a hoax, as the hoax was not exposed until 1953. He cites the Piltdown man in several tales, including "Dagon" (1917) and "The Rats in the Walls" (1923).

3. The quotation is not from Horace but from Juvenal, *Satires* 10.356 ("a sound mind in a sound body"). In the juvenile poem "On the Vanity of Human Ambition" (1902) he provides a loose paraphrase: "True bliss, methinks, a man can only find / In virtuous life, & cultivated mind" (*AT* 13).

4. Charles Hale Hoyt (1860–1900), American songwriter and playwright. "The Bowery Song" (music by Percy Gaunt) appears in the musical *A Trip to Chinatown* (1892).

5. The work in question is *Invisible Sun*, an autobiographical mainstream novel about college life. It is forthcoming in Wandrei's *Dead Titans, Waken! and Invisible Sun* (Fedogan & Bremer).

6. *The World Below* was given to HPL by Ernest A. Edkins.

7. James Burnett, Lord Monboddo (1714–1799) was a Scottish judge and anthropologist who, in *Of the Origin and Progress of Language* (1773–92) and *Antient Metaphysics* (1779–99), championed primitive societies over civilized ones, as he believed the latter subject to corruption and degeneracy.

8. See William Douw Lighthall (1857–1954), "The Remoter Origins of the Iroquoian Stock," *Transactions of the Royal Society of Canada,* Third Series, 25 (1931). HPL no doubt learned of Lighthall's findings in a newspaper or magazine article.

9. The character Norton has no first name. London based another character in the novel, Russ Brissenden, on his friend George Sterling (1869–1926).

10. The unsigned obituary that appeared—"In Memoriam: Henry St. Clair Whitehead" (*WT*, March 1933)—was by HPL and substantially truncated from the original version, which is non-extant. That version, however, was probably similar to the letter that HPL wrote to E. Hoffmann Price on the subject (7 December 1932; partially printed in *SLL* 4.116–17).

11. Probably an unsigned article, "Fabulous Southwest," *Literary Digest* 114 (17 December 1932): 35–37, a survey of interesting sites in Texas, Arizona, and New Mexico.

[78]   [TLS]

[March 6, 1933]

[Note by HPL:] Fra Bernardus to Francis, Lord Belknap. Comrade Belnapovitch to Grandpa—or incur the direst consequences!!

Dear Mr. Lovecraft:

I have just read your recent letter with the usual appreciation. Thank you very much for the clippings, as well as the post-cards. Both proved of much interest. Later in this letter I will comment on the former.

But before I take up any other matter, I think it's time we reached a true understanding concerning the "mental-physical" argument. This continual debating is as unnecessary as it is fruitless. My position on the matter is much the same as yours, modified on my part only by a greater interest in physical things than you possess. You mention my position as being at the other extreme from—I believe it was Long you mentioned. In other words, you assume that I worship brawn to the exclusion of all else. To put it bluntly, this assumption is absolutely unwarranted. Throughout our discussion of the matter, I have tried to emphasize the fact that *I did not glorify the physical above the mental.* If I had, or did, I would never have bothered to learn to read or write; I would have devoted all my time to muscle-building, to developing myself into a gigantic statue of mindless beef. I am quite aware of the fact that the Mind is the real measure of Mankind. I am aware that a finely developed mentality is infinitely more important in the daily struggle of Life than any amount of muscle. I am aware that the average civilized man does not need unusual strength. The fact that I, for my own amusement, had rather watch a battle of brawn than a battle of wits, does not, as I seem to have said before, mean that I underrate a keen wit. The fact that I enjoy watching athletic sports, and have in the past enjoyed in participating in them, does not mean that I accord sheer muscle the undivided worship you appear to think I accord it. Each man has his hobby; because Frank Buck[1] studies and captures animals and makes his living by it, nobody supposes he places lions and tigers above human beings, or desires to divest himself of his garments and live in the jungle with them. Because I love to watch, discuss, write about and occasionally participate in physical contests, does not necessarily mean that I despise everything else in the universe, and would like to be a mass of mindless brawn. Nor have I ever advocated over-athleticism, whatever that may be.

You are certainly wrong in thinking I possess an inordinate pride in my physical development. I have no reason under the sun for feeling any pride in my muscles, which are very ordinary indeed. When I meet every day scores of men who are my physical superiors in every way, is it likely that I would retain any vanity in regard to my inferior muscles? In fact, in my last letter I tried to emphasize the fact that it was foolish for a man—even a really powerful man—to feel any particular vanity because of his strength. Apparently you got the idea that I was proud of my ability to unload a wagon of feed. If I were proud of so trivial a thing, I would be the biggest fool that ever went down the pike. I mentioned that fact, not because I was proud of it, God knows, but simply as a way of pointing out that a goodly proportion of life, in this country at least, was physical, requiring physical exertion. And that statement is true. Unloading that wagon wasn't a matter of pride, but necessity. As I said before, the fact that a gorilla could have done it easier than I, didn't help me a damned bit. If I'd had a trained gorilla there, I'd have made him do it, while I sat in the shade and rested. But please don't get the idea that I felt any *pride* about doing the work, outside the natural pleasure any man feels in knowing that his body is sound and normal, and all his legs and arms are in place.

Frankly, I was utterly astounded to realize that you considered me to be *boasting* about the work I have to do with my hands. I said nothing at all that could be taken to mean I was inordinately proud of my ability to unload a wagon of feed, or anything else. You say it is no distinction for me to be able to carry a bale of hay, and that a gorilla could do more. That isn't much different from what I said. I never said it was any distinction; what I said was this: that the fact a bull-ape could do the work better, didn't make it any easier on me. You say you do not urge me to let my body run down below the requirements of duties I *choose* to perform. I am forced to the conclusion that you suppose I milk cows, load steers, and unload wagons from choice, and as a sort of self-expression. You should realize that I live in a sphere entirely different from that in which you live. The fact that I make my living with my typewriter certainly doesn't mean I have no other work to do. I don't live on a farm, but it's almost like one. Specifically, I milk cows, clean out pig-pens and stalls, dig ditches, behead chickens, and unload feed wagons when necessary, just as I help butcher hogs and load calves. Nor is it a matter of pride or choice, but necessity. If I didn't do it, somebody'd have to be hired to do it, and money is not so damned plentiful nowadays that I can afford to keep my hands clean at the expense of my pocket-book. This morning I helped load a steer into a truck, for butchering. It was a dirty, back-breaking job. Just awhile ago I got through storing a wagon-load of peanut hay in the barn. I don't know anything as mean as peanut-hay. It's infinitely heavier than any other kind of hay, it's stiff, full of bristles and dried briar-like points. It was lousy work. Every time I picked up a bale, the wind filled my face and eyes with chaff. The stuff got inside my shirt and down my neck, and nearly ran me crazy with irritation. My hands and arms are covered with scratches and lacerations. You surely can't believe that I worked with that infernal stuff in the muck and manure of a cow-lot, with a biting wind blowing, because I *chose* to, or because it tickled my vanity? Or that I felt any particular pride in what I was doing? Why, God knows, I'm not ashamed of any work I ever did, but if I felt any emotion regarding it, it was simply gratification that I was healthy and strong enough to do it, and didn't have to be out money hiring it done. I hardly think that feeling justifies your assumption that I place my chief pride in the work I do in the cow-stalls and pig-pens. If I had had any idea you thought I was bragging about so trivial a thing as storing a load of feed, I would not have mentioned it. Why, good God, it would put me on a level with a ten-year old child, to be vain about that.

The point I was trying to make, was the same I am trying to make now:—that not all men can for ever avoid physical exertion, and that the stronger and more fit such men are, the easier their work is. That was—and is—the whole gist of my argument, and it goes without saying that anyone will agree to that. I am one of those men. I know my needs and necessities. I know that one of my necessities is a strong physique—much stronger than I possess at present. That there are millions of men in the world who do not need strength and endurance is immaterial. That's their business. I do not expect them to go through needless exertions to attain an estate that would be worthless to them. On the other hand they can not expect me to try to mold from their standpoint a life so radically different from theirs in actual reality. So, even if the whole world *were* urging me to let my body run down, because only my mind was important, I couldn't oblige them—not unless the world offered to pay somebody to do what I have them do now, and I have a shadowy doubt that the world would make any such offer.

You say it is incongruous for me to reserve my chief pride for a minor attribute like great strength. I can only reply that I have never said that I did. I do not possess great strength, anyway. I merely said that I had work to do of a physical nature, and the knowledge that it could be done better by an animal did not lighten my load, when I had no animal to do it for me.

You remark that it is more honor to be able to write "The Black Stone" than to have unloaded a wagon of feed. The question of honor is entirely beside the point. I wrote the story because I needed the money; I unloaded the wagon because it was necessary to do it in order to save money. Exactly the same motive was behind both endeavors.

As for pride—I am proud of my family, I am proud of my State, my country and my race. As an individual I scarcely think I've ever done anything to strut about, physical or mental. Nobody ever heard me say that I considered myself superior to the masses of humanity.

I see no reason for our argument on this matter, since it is evident we hold practically the same opinion. As I understand it, you believe in the idea of a sound mind in a sound body, with the body subordinated to the mind. That is exactly what I believe. Simmered down, the real difference between our opinions is: you are interested wholly in the fruits of the mind, and I divide my interest between the fruits of the mind, and the exertions of the body. (As for subordinating the mental to the physical, I never heard of anyone advocating such a fantastic thing.)

When you thought I was exalting the body above the mind, I was merely remarking on the advantage—and occasionally the absolute necessity of a strong body. That the body should be guided by a mind developed as highly as possible, goes without saying. The fact that the greatest instinctive thrill I ever got in my life was obtained in a slugging-match rather than through some purely mental process, does not in the least affect what I have just said. That was purely personal, natural, and instinctive, with no question of the relative merits of physical or mental pride, or intrinsic values. When I box, wrestle or lift weights, it is again an entirely personal matter, and it should not be taken that I despise people who don't do these things. At the same time I deny the right of these people to despise me, because I do. But that again, is beside the point. The point is: I recognize the superiority of the mentality, but I can not afford to neglect my physical side. As you do not ask me to neglect it, there is no cause for debate.

Leaving my own feelings and experiences aside, I see no reason why a fine athlete shouldn't feel a real pride in his athletic ability, when it brings him wealth, fame, and happiness that would not have been his had he depended on his mind. If Jack Dempsey's muscles pulled him up out of the gutter and the hobo-jungle into the ranks of the millionaires, while many a man infinitely his mental superior is still drudging away at a one-horse job, why shouldn't Jack be proud of his tigerish thews? I'd rather be an athlete with my pockets full of gold, than a university professor or a scientist with patches in the seat of my breeches.

If we must consider the question of *pride*—if I remember rightly, what I said was, in substance: that it was not particularly vain for a man—any man— to wish to feel himself able to hold his own with other men of the world, physically as well as mentally. It is not to be assumed that I am advising every one to slave night and day and neglect everything else in order to be as strong as a wrestler or a weight-lifter. I was merely trying to point out that a man wasn't necessarily a fool because he chanced to value strength and endurance a little more highly than the average mental worker values it.

In an attempt to further make my position understood, let me quote from a letter written to Mr. Hoffmann, editor of Adventure, by your friend Whitehead (1923). He said in part:

"My chief interests—the things I like to do—include certainly the follow-ing: Being at sea. Hunting small game with a good setter-dog. *All kinds of ath-letic exercises*. The good Lord gave me a lot of health and I've always thought it worth while to keep hold of it and use it. Amusing a lot of kids (as at a boys' camp, for instance) with stories and faking on a guitar while I sing a lot of junk to them. Having a couple of nice little girls cuddle up to me one on each side on a big sofa and carrying on a conversation with them, letting them do most of the talking.

"Of course I like to write. * * * * * * * * * *

"—I am appending extracts from a letter written by a Santa Cruz (Virgin Islands) official to a friend of his in the United States about me. This friend was a mutual friend, and handed me on the letter. He thought it would please me.

"'He is the strongest man, physically, I ever saw. Soon after he came here to Santa Cruz, it was discovered that he took a great deal of exercise. One evening he was asked to do a 'stunt' for a large group of people who were having an old-fashioned Crucian jollification, and he called for a pack of cards. He tore them squarely in half, and then quartered them. I had heard of cards being torn in two, but never quartered. Incredulity was expressed. The people present thought it was a trick, and said so, though pleasantly and in a bantering way. Father Whitehead asked for another pack to destroy, and for two wire nails. He nailed the pack through at both ends, so that the cards could not be "beveled", and then quartered that pack. He had to do this everywhere he went after that. Everybody wanted to see it done. One night Mrs. Scholten, the wife of our Danish Bank manager, gave him a small pack of brand new Danish cards. They were made of linen! He tore those in two.
* * * * * * * * * *

"'I don't see how he does the things he does. His physical strength is incredible. I was in his house one day when they were moving one of his big mahogany beds. This * * * * * must have weighed a ton by the looks of it. He picked up the heavy end, the head, with one hand and carried it across the room and set it down, like me lifting a waste basket. It took four able-bodied men to lug the other end along.'

"This letter interested me very much. As usual the people of Santa Cruz were most interest [*sic*] in what I didn't go there to do—strongman stunts. The card thing I have practised since I was about seventeen."[2]

If Mr. Whitehead had not felt a certain pride in his muscles, it's not likely he'd have included the above remarks in a letter intended for publication in a magazine. It is not to be supposed that he was unduly conceited about his strength, or that he "glorified the physical above the mental", or that his whole life was wrapped up in tearing cards. Neither is my whole life wrapped up in boxing or lifting weights. Lord Byron was fond of boxing; Poe was a runner and a swimmer in his youth; Rupert Brooke was fond of diving and hiking; de Castro tells us Bierce was very proud of his skill at knife-throwing; de Castro himself found it necessary to put in a year at muscle-building; Jack London loved to box, fence and wrestle; Frank Harris was once a prizefighter, and so was Jim Tully; even the superior Mr. Shaw was once a clever boxer. I don't suppose anybody ever accused these men of glorifying the physical at the expense of the mental. My attitude is much like theirs, and it strikes me it's just a damned sight broader and more reasonable than that of the "anti-physicalist".

With the world full of stronger men than I, and smarter men than I, I have no cause for vanity concerning either my ordinary muscles or mediocre mental power.

Concerning those people who derive pleasure out of athletics, I think, instead of being less numerous than I suppose, they are rather more numerous than you suppose. There are about three hundred and thirty colleges and universities listed in my encyclopedia. How many more there are, I have no idea, since this does not include most of the technological schools. But I know there are several in Texas not included, and have no doubt there are hundreds of more or less importance left out of the list. We may assume that at least ninety per-cent of these schools play football. Anywhere from eleven to a hundred or many more men come out annually at each of these institutions. That alone mounts up to a goodly figure. Then consider the thousands of high schools all over the country. Consider not only football, but the thousands of college students that each year take part in basket-ball, baseball, wrestling, boxing, field and track events. That takes into consideration only the amateur sports. Consider the professional baseball teams, the pro. hockey teams, basket-ball teams, lacrosse-teams, the thousands of pro. boxers and wrestlers. Amateur athletes compete for various reasons, and pros. are out for the money, of course. But every man, amateur or pro. loves the game he plays, or he wouldn't be doing it. Nobody makes him. No, athletics, over-emphasized or not, play an important part in modern civilization. Nobody tries to maintain that the physical side of a man is superior to his mental side, but if he can make a good living with his muscles and enjoy himself at the same time, is that privilege to be denied him, simply because our intellectual class doesn't care for sports? I never heard of a couple of intellectuals giving a debate and handing over the money the charity, but every year in New York a big boxing show is given in Madison Square Garden, and the bulk of the proceeds goes to the milk fund for the starving kids in the slums. Every year the revenues of the states and big cities are swelled with receipts from sporting events. Athletics may be a minor part in the life of man; in the life of the average man it is. But many a man is making his living today by athletics. Each football team must have a coach; the coach must have assistants, naturally. Schools like Notre Dame employ a veritable army of coaches. Each prize-fight, wrestling-match, or game of any kind must have referees or umpires. Then there are the trainers, the cooks and waiters who attend to the training-tables, the seconds, the handlers—why, the hangers-on of sport alone constitute a regular army. There is much howling and caterwauling—especially on the part of various intellectuals—about the over-emphasis of sports. Sports are no more over-emphasized than any other phase of this enormous and complex civilization. Would they add to the great army of the unemployed by booting out the thousands of men whose lives are wrapped up in sports, and many of whom would be unable to make a living at anything else? What if the average coach is paid more than the average professor. Usually he knows his job better, and does his work more thoroughly than the professor. He touches more human beings in his career, and has more effect, for good or bad, on the boys that come under his hands, than a whole squad of professors would have.

Let me again remind you that all this is not exalting the physical above the mental. But there are various sides of every question to be considered. What I'm trying to show is that the physical side of man—*admittedly inferior to the mental side*—is nevertheless a living vital factor in the development of society. And sports, artificial in their nature as they may be, are no more so than nine-tenths of the muck glorified by the intellectuals.

(Concerning your example of the relative pride a man should take in horses and in books, if I, by careful and intelligent selection, mating and breeding, produced a fine race horse, I should most certainly feel more pride in him than in the possession of books, things any man can own if he has money enough to buy them. To be vain of one's books is as childish as to be vain of one's food, clothes, house, automobile or theater ticket.)

To sum it up: you advocate a sound mind in a sound body, but your personal interests lean toward the mental. I advocate a sound mind in a sound body, but some of my personal interests lean toward the physical. I do not deny a keen—perhaps passionate—interest in sports and athletics. This needs no apology. There are a few other things in which I'm as passionately interested as athletics. I do not deny that I had rather been an athlete than a writer; if things had run right, I'd have probably been both, I do not deny that I would like to have the physique of a wrestler or a prize-fighter. I do deny that I glorify the physical to despise the mental. I simply do not subordinate the physical to the mental as much as you do. I do deny—and flatly deny—that I take, or have any reason for taking, any such childish pride and vanity in my mediocre muscular powers as you would seem to think. Putting Long at one end of the rope, and me at the other, of course, you know Long, but in justice to myself, I must assure you that you are wrong about my position at the other extremity. In fact, I strongly doubt if there is any man in the world who accords the purely physical as much worship as that. If there is, it is certainly not me. So with my usual rambling way, I have taken up a lot of paper in order to show that the different between our opinions on the matter is too trivial to argue about, consisting entirely in the fact that I have to do more physical work than the average writer does, and that I am more interested in athletics than the average writer is.

A last word concerning the "anti-physicalists". I remember one of those persons particularly. He said he was a singer of some note; he was well-dressed, well-fed, and had an abiding scorn for anything resembling physical combat. He said only dogs fought. They brought him into my father's office to be patched up after he had encountered a man who held different ideas— and not a hoodlum or bully, either, but a prominent business man of the town. I wish all who think as he thought, could have seen the songster. His face looked like a chunk of raw beef; clotted blood oozed from his smashed-in nose and his pulped ears; his lips hung in bloody shreds through which could be seen the broken remnants of teeth, and gaping sockets where teeth had been; his eyes were glazed, his head rocked drunkenly on his shoulders, and he could barely weave along, held by a man on each side. His intellect hadn't kept him from getting the devil beaten out of him by a man smaller and older than himself; and I'll bet that, while his teeth were being spattered out by his opponent's fists, he'd have traded some of his artistic talents for a little skill at boxing and wrestling. As soon as he could, he hastily took his departure for the cities in the eastern part of the state (on the streets of which his Nemesis later met him and gave him a round cursing for good measure). Little sympathy was wasted on him, this is no country for a person with a supercilious nature combined with an inability or unwillingness to defend himself with his hands. The people are democratic; they are not fond of superior persons; and many of them are so little awed by intellectual accomplishments, that they'll kick the ears off an artiste as quickly as anybody else.

I was much interested in what you said about the cat-phobia. A most peculiar phenomenon, and one that seems absolutely inexplicable to me. I suppose it is in some way allied to the repulsion most people have at touching a reptile—but the difference between a feline and a reptile is so great, I still don't understand. I reckon it's a phobia of long standing. Seems like I remember Shakespeare making some sort of a crack about.[3] When I was five a horse ran away with me, and threw me out of the buggy, giving me a most infernal jolting and bruising; I was afraid of horses for a few years afterwards, but soon got over it after moving back to West Texas again. My distrust of horses never amounted to an actual phobia. If you like cats, you'd enjoy being here now. A regular mob of them hang around the feed-barns, chasing mice—also a goodly gang hang around the back door, looking for hand-outs.

I'll try to prepare that treatise on Texas political and historical background for you—and for you alone. Though I don't know when I'll get to it. When I approach it, the thought of the comparison of early days with conditions now rather turns my stomach. Yes, we are swiftly being incorporated into the dung-heap called civilization.

Slavery? If three-quarters of the world isn't enslaved now I'm much mistaken. What's the Fascist regime in Italy if it isn't rank enslavement? Of course the bulk of the people desire it. The bulk of the people always desire what their leaders say is good for them—for a while.

I don't know as I said it was anybody's fault that there's no such thing as individual freedom any more. Unless I'm much mistaken I said it is a dream which is outworn. I think you'll find I said that, if you'll look at my letter again. I realize that such a state is impossible in a highly developed civilization; which is one thing I have against such civilizations. True, it is useless to regret the passing of the age of individualism. But I can't help it. I was born about a hundred years too late; that's not my fault; it's my misfortune. Let it not be assumed that I spend my time lying under a tree and bewailing my case. I do my share of the world's work, and perform my duties as a citizen and a member of society. Nor have I ever said that individual freedom was sacred. My favorite food is fried liver and onions, but I don't look on that dish as sacred; but I'd rather eat it than to eat spinach; I'd rather have lived under the comparative freedom of the old frontier than under present conditions. I'd gladly trade all the "enrichment" of modern civilization for that existence. I realize the object of "good government" is not to fulfill what you call the catch slogan of liberty. No; its object is to emasculate all men, and make good little rabbits and guinea pigs out of them that will fit into the nooks designed for them, and stay there contentedly nibbling their fodder until they die of inanition. Liberty of action, is of course, impossible under these ideal conditions. Oh, no doubt we will have freedom of thought; a man sitting in a dungeon with his legs in iron stocks can think as he wishes. And no doubt our artists will be allowed to smudge their canvas and scribble their sheets just about as they desire. And our scientists will be allowed to pry into the secrets of the cosmos, no doubt. But what about the people who are neither artists, intellectuals, or scientists? They do exist, in large numbers.

I do not realize that my ideal of freedom is theoretical, or has always been unattainable. My grandfathers had it, and they were not theories. They were solid men of material flesh who lived, lusted, wandered, fought, loved and transmitted their restlessness to me. Because I happen to live in a cage myself does not mean that all humanity have dwelt in cages since the beginning of time. I repeat that I do not expect to possess the freedom they possessed. But I think any emotion that I waste in looking back and wishing I had lived then instead of now, will hardly upset the social balance of the civilization in which I live. As for as that goes, I can remember when life was freer than it is today, and the fact was not, as you call it, a noble poetic conception. I think I've managed to adapt myself fairly well to the conditions under which I am forced to live. At least, I've managed to keep out of prison and the poorhouse for more than a quarter of a century. Because I chance to voice my inner feelings in the matter to one I consider as a friend doesn't necessarily imply that I go around in the buckskins and coonskin cap of a former age, or waste my strength in vain striving against conditions beyond my control.

I agree with you that the restless, super-vital type is vanishing. That is a natural result of civilization. Generation by generation men will grow more flabby, slothful and effeminate, until at last the very crest, pinnacle and epitome of civilization will be reached in a blind, helpless, crawling human worm, at which civilization's builders can point with excusable pride, and say: "Behold what we have wrought!"

Well, I recently reached the ripe age of twenty-seven. When I was a child I used to wish that I had not been born until several years later than I was, so that I might watch all the "improvements" of the machine age unfold. I was a fool. I thank what gods there are that I was not born a single hour later than I was. I only wish I had been born earlier—thirty years earlier, anyway. As it was I only caught the tag-end of a robust era, when I was too young to realize its meaning. When I look down the vista of the years, with all the "improvements", "inventions" and "progress" that they hold, I am infinitely thankful that I am no younger. I could wish to be older, much older. Every man wants to live out his life's span. But I hardly think life in this age is worth the effort of living. I'd like to round out my youth; and perhaps the natural vitality and animal exuberance of youth will carry me to middle age. But good God, to think of living the full three score years and ten!

I am glad you had such an enjoyable Christmas. I'd like to have looked in on that conclave at Long's place. The sight of a number of literary men gathered in one place would have been most interesting. You know, I've never even met one writer or author. Or editor either, for that matter, with one exception. I once met a noted poet, who had been kind enough to praise my verse most highly, and with whom I'd had an enjoyable correspondence. But I reckon I didn't come up to his idea of what a poet should be, because he didn't write me, after he returned East, or even answer the letter I wrote him.[4] I suppose he expected to meet some kind of an intellectual, and lost interest when he met only an ordinary man, thinking the thoughts and speaking in the dialect of the common people. I'll admit also that after a part-day's conversation with him, I found relief and pleasure in exchanging reminiscences with a bus driver who didn't know a sonnet from an axle-hub.

I envy you your access to the museums you mentioned. I've, naturally, never seen anything of the sort, though I remember some very good displays in the museums of New Orleans, especially Civil War relics. Weapons, especially edged weapons, axes, sword, and spears, hold my attention as nothing else can. Long ago I started collecting them, but found it a taste far too expensive for my means. I still have the things I did manage to get hold of—a few sabers, swords, bayonets and the like.

By the way, you've never said anything about your schooldays. Where did you attend college?—for I presume you are a college or university graduate. I think I've remarked that the nearest I came to college was the business department where I studied such non-literary things as shorthand, typing, business arithmetic, commercial law, and the like. A literary college education probably would have helped me immensely. That's neither here nor there; I didn't feel that I could afford it, and that's all there was to it.

I might have liked college, but I hated grammar and high school with a vindictiveness that has not softened in later years. I didn't spend too much time there, anyway; I didn't start to school until I was eight, and I graduated at seventeen. No record broken there, but no time lost, either. I hated school as I hate the memory of school. It wasn't the work I minded; I had no trouble learning the tripe they dished out in the way of lessons—except arithmetic, and I might have learned that if I'd gone to the trouble of studying it. I wasn't at the head of my classes—except in history—but I wasn't at the foot either. I generally did just enough work to keep from flunking the courses, and I don't regret the loafing I did. But what I hated was the confinement—the clock-like regularity of everything; the regulation of my speech and actions; most of all the idea that someone considered himself or herself in authority over me, with the right to question my actions and interfere with my thoughts. Some of my teachers I liked, and those liked me; most didn't. I complied with the rules of the school as well as I could, got up my lessons at least as well as most of the others, and was careful to cause the teachers no unnecessary trouble; beyond that I lived my own life, and fiercely resented any interference or regulation. I realized even then that the teachers had their troubles. Thunderation, teachers now don't have to put up with much that they did even when I was school-kid. I never attended a school like that in Coleman County, some forty years ago, where the kids brought their squirrel-rifles to school, and the teacher kept a sixshooter in his desk and a mirror on the wall behind him so the scholars wouldn't shoot him in the back when he turned towards the blackboard; (when he licked a kid he held a gun on him with one hand and lammed him with the other; this may sound like a lie, but I can prove it.) but I did know a schoolmaster who kept a blackjack in his desk. He called a kid up to give him a beating, and the kid promptly slugged him and broke his jawbone. After that the teacher kept the billy in his desk. My cousin once witnessed a free-for-all between a whole faculty and a bunch of boys—brothers—they were trying to chastise. Knives flashed freely, he said, and finally the scrap was brought to a bloody termination by one of the boys taking the biggest teacher on the side of the head with a hunk of lead. Sometimes parents took up school-quarrels. I remember one time in this country—it must have been about nineteen years ago—some women didn't like the way a young lady teacher was handling their kids, and they stripped her naked and whipped her with a wet rope, while their husbands sat on a rail-fence, and—doubtless—enjoyed the show. Not nearly so long ago a schoolmate of mine taught school down on the Bayou, and one of the kids gave him a Hell of a tussle. He finally knocked the youth senseless with a chunk of stove-wood. So you see that even in educational circles muscular exertion is sometimes necessary. Of course, generally, the victim didn't put up any scrap. Beatings and lammings were the order of the day; scholars were often whipped with no more mercy than if they had been mules; sometimes till their garments were wet with their blood. I never got a beating at school; once a teacher intended to lam me, but he changed his mind, which was a good thing for him, because I was all set to carve jingle-bobs and under-crops all over his carcass.

Our discussion concerning the relative merits of civilization and barbarism seems to have been precipitated by a remark of mine that *if* I were transferred to a former life, I should prefer having my lot cast among Celtic or

Germanic tribesmen rather than among the cultivated Grecians and Romans. I have no feeling of connection with the Greeks and Romans; I do feel a strong kinship with the Goths and Gaels. As a matter of fact, if I could choose my age and place, there is no country and no time I would choose except the American frontier, between 1795 and 1895. If I am to be blamed for this preference, one may with equal logic blame me for not instantly abandoning all my interests in Texas and rushing to live in New York—since no one denies that New York is infinitely more civilized than the hill country of Texas. I am happier in Texas than I could possibly be in New York; I would have been happier in the early Southwest than I am now. The matter of relative superiority is beside the point. I never heard of that Lord—whatever you call him, who idealized barbarism in the 18th Century. I don't idealize anything. I don't idealize the frontier days of Texas; I'm close enough to them to know the hardships they entailed. You could be accused of idealizing this age, as justly as I could be accused of idealizing that one. I simply feel that I would have fitted into the early 19th century better than I fit into this age. Because I have read a few more books than my grandfathers read, and can scribble things on paper they couldn't, I am not such a conceited jackass as to fancy that my life is fuller and richer than theirs, who helped to fight a war, open a frontier and build up a new nation. Of all snobberies, the assumption that intellectual endeavors, attainments and accomplishments are the only worth-while and important things in life, is the least justifiable.

You say it would not be fair to hold back the superior types on account of the inferiority of a portion of humanity. I never advocated that plan. I clearly remember having said in a previous letter that undoubtedly even a decaying civilization is preferable for humanity as a whole, than a state of barbarism. If I wished to become a barbarian, I would adopt the loin-cloth and thatched hut of an African savage without more ado. I have repeatedly emphasized the fact that in my present state I would be unfitted for a life of barbarism. If I could be reborn with no knowledge of civilized ways, that would be something else again. But in no case do I advocate the abandonment of the modes of life to which moderns are accustomed. I have never made any remark about wishing civilization to fall back into savagery. If I would wish personally to live life in a different sphere, that is quite another matter. That concerns only myself, and not the world at large. As for my civilized imagination, how can my imagination possibly be the result of any civilizing process, since I am myself am not civilized, according to the urban, Eastern standard? (Of this fact various intellectual acquaintances have assured me.) At any rate, if I were to retain this imagination, there would be no point in retracing my steps. If I could leave it somewhere on the road, the mere ridding myself of it would be ample repayment for any hardships I might suffer as "a whole hearted animal guzzler." There is nothing ironical or illogical in my position. I appreciate the kind things you said about my mind. But if I were to return to the wattle huts and the tribal fires, I would wish to leave on the road all attributes, mental and physical, except such as would fit me for the barbarian's struggle for existence. Granted that I would gain little; on the other hand I hardly think I'd lose much of value either. That barbarism contains features hideous to civilized minds, I would be the last to deny. But civilization is full of hideous things, too. As for the slashing and mangling of human organisms, it can not be denied that the true barbarian—of the original Aryan type at least—derived a keen pleasure from this very slashing when applied to others, and endured it with a stoicism unknown to moderns when applied to himself. That was part of his life, just as grinding men and women to dust and crushing their souls into ashes is part of the civilized system. He tortured, too; but I can not see why he is to be denied that sport, by a civilization which countenances and upholds the torture of its members in police-courts, prisons and madhouses. I see little difference in the torture inflicted by a heathen on his enemy and that inflicted by polite and civilized Europeans, who crush the testicles and tear out the pubic hair of persons who chance to disagree with them politically. Are our civilized wars any less brutal than the wars of the barbarians? Or any less disturbing to universal harmony?

We have talked much of "civilization" and "barbarism". Just what is civilization? Where does barbarism leave off and civilization begin? We can hardly conceive ourselves to be the sole possessors of the only true civilization that the world has ever known. Egypt, Babylon, Greece, Rome—in many ways each of these civilizations was superior to ours, just as ours in many ways is superior to them. What constitutes the barbarian? The Grecians called the Persians barbarians, yet the Persians were as highly developed as the Greeks, in their own particular way. The Romans called the Gallic and German tribes barbarians, yet these races were superior to the later Romans in courage, honor and honesty. The Saxons that destroyed the British-Roman civilization of Britain were called barbarians, yet they were better armed, better trained, and knew more about the arts of war and voyaging than the "civilized" people they dispossessed. These same Saxons, and the Franks, later called the Vikings barbarians; yet these Vikings built the best ships the world had ever known, knew more about navigation than any seamen before them, created poetic sagas that have never been surpassed for strength and beauty, and introduced into the world a spirit for exploration and adventure that has not yet faded out. You say the attractions of a barbaric life could not exist without the perspective of civilization. Yet (if we call the Vikings barbarians) do you not think that they found their life good without that perspective? The sagas hum with self-glorification, with praise of "the whale-path", and the glory of the foray. Dull, mindless clods, mere hulks of inert, dead matter? I can not agree there. Such men as Eric the Red, Leif the Lucky, Hrolf the Ganger, Hengist—they could not have been feeble jelly-like organisms groping blindly through the scum of primordial night. They were alive; they stung, burned, tingled with Life—life raw and crude and violent, doubtless; but Life, just the same, and worthy to be classed with the best efforts of the intellectual side of man. As well say David Crockett, Sam Houston, and Bigfoot Wallace were masses of dead tissue moving sluggishly through the slime. Because a man lives an active life rather than one of study and contemplation does not necessarily imply that he is dead from the neck up. If it wasn't for the workers, the scholars would be in a hell of a jamb.

I read your remarks concerning the Iroquois with much interest. I'd read that the Cherokees were a branch of that race, but hadn't read anything about the Polynesian theory. It's a pity the Indians didn't get a chance to show what they might have done in the way developing a culture of their own. Though I doubt if such tribes as the Comanches would ever have been anything but nomads and raiders. Doubtless they would have disappeared before the more highly-developed tribes just as all eventually vanished before the coming of the white men.

Discussions concerning the Irish question would be fruitless. We could twist words by the bushel, and cover pages with high-sounding reasons for our differences of opinion, but the naked core of the matter is: you're English, and I'm Irish.

Concerning literature, I don't pretend to be any judge of its merit. I'm perfectly indifferent as to whether my views are narrow, or broad. I read what gives me enjoyment, and I avoid what bores me. Its place in the world of literature, as decided by the critics, interests me not at all. If I like it, then as far as I'm concerned it's good, whether the author is Zane Grey or Voltaire; if I don't like it, then I'm not going to bother with it—regardless of the author. My attitude needs neither apology nor defense. In my earlier years I thought it was my duty to read stuff the critics praised; and I could kick myself when I think of some of the junk I waded through. Doubtless the critics were right when they gave it a place in the sun; but what of it? There are too many books in the world that I enjoy for me to slave through stuff I don't enjoy, just because some other man, or men, happen to like it. Understand, I speak from my true position in life, which is that of any man in the street. I am not an intellectual, a critic, nor an artist. My occupation does not color my view-point—or lack of view-point. I am simply a working-man who took up writing because it seemed to offer an escape from back-breaking drudgery. Unless this fact is fully realized, my attitude in regard to the arts will always seem incongruous and paradoxical. Literature is a business to me—a business at which I was making an ample living when the depression knocked the guts out of the markets. My sole desire in writing is to make a reasonable living. I may cling to many illusions, but I am not ridden by the illusion that I have anything wonderful or magical to say, or that it would amount to anything particularly if I did say it. I have no quarrel with art-for-art's-sakers. On the contrary, I admire their work. But my pet delusions tend in other directions. I took up writing simply because it seemed to promise an easier mode of work, more money, and more freedom than any other job I'd tried. I wouldn't write otherwise. If it was in my power to pen the grandest masterpiece the world has ever seen, I wouldn't hit the first key, or dip the pen in the ink, unless I knew there was a chance for me to get some money out of it, or publicity that would lead to money. That's why I gave up scribbling verse. I couldn't sell enough of it to justify me in dabbling with it. By the way, I wish to thank you very much for the kind things you said about that verse. Even if I can't afford to devote much time to rhyming, it always pleases me to learn that my efforts are not entirely without merit. Sometimes I dally with the idea of verse-writing, and even of bringing out a book, but the thought of devoting so much time, and money, to something that probably wouldn't bring me a cent, always takes the starch out of the idea.

You know, the finest poets the Southwest has ever produced are absolutely unknown, and are not even listed in the Texas Almanac. (Neither am I, for that matter, though it lists dozens of youngsters who never sold a line for cash in their life.) They are my very good friend Tevis Clyde Smith Jr., of Brownwood, and the sister of another friend, Lenore Preece of Austin. Clyde is the lad who collaborated with me on that yarn "Red Blades of Black Cathay" which appeared in the old Oriental Stories, and which Whitehead was kind enough to praise. Clyde is a fine upstanding young man, three years younger than myself, six feet one inch in height, a perfect blond type; athletic in appearance. (He broke my nose once with the most beautiful straight right I ever stopped with my face, and hit me the hardest body-blow I ever felt; it was a right hook to the kidney, and I distinctly felt the kidney close up like an inflated balloon, and then open up again.) He's a college graduate; had a fling at the writing game, during which time he wrote some of the finest poetry I ever read. None of it was ever published, but if I ever have the opportunity I intend to bring it all out in book form. I think his brief experience in the literary world rather sickened him of it. At present he's working in the warehouse of a wholesale grocery company; he is a man who'll climb high at anything to which he turns his hand, and I sometimes doubt if he ever returns to literary work again. But even if he doesn't, he's accomplished more in the way of real poetry, than many a widely-known scribbler ever does. He's of old American stock—Cornish-Irish—some of his ancestors having come to Connecticut—or maybe it was Vermont—back in the 17th Century, thence going to Kentucky, from which they came to Texas after the Civil War. The other branch of his family came to Texas from Tennessee about the same time. He had kin who rode with Morgan, and a more ardent Southerner is hard to imagine. The other poet—or poetess—I mentioned, Lenore Preece, I have never seen, but we used to correspond, and to my mind she is superior to any other woman-poet America has yet produced. As I said before, I do not consider myself an art critic; but I do believe that most critics would admit that Lenore and Clyde are real poets.

Speaking of verse reminds me of a couple of letters I got from readers of Weird Tales, one from Kansas and the other from Pennsylvania, who wished to know where they could procure the complete rhyme, "The Road of Kings", verses from which I occasionally use as chapter-headings for my yarns of Conan the Cimmerian. I was sorry to have to tell them that it didn't exist. I'm curious to know how the readers will like Gottfried von Kalmbach, one of the main characters in a long historical yarn I sold Wright, concerning Suleyman the Magnificent's attack on Vienna.[5] A more dissolute vagabond than Gottfried never weaved his drunken way across the pages of a popular magazine: wastrel, drunkard, gambler, whore-monger, renegade, mercenary, plunderer, thief, rogue, rascal—I never created a character whose creation I enjoyed more. They may not seem real to the readers; but Gottfried and his mistress Red Sonya seem more real to me than any other character I've ever drawn.

Getting back to literature, if I included O'Neill in my aversions, it was unintentional. I got a big whang out of his "The Hairy Ape". As for Mencken I esteem him no more than any other maggot spawned in buzzard's puke. I may read Conrad some day. I don't know. I don't have a great deal of time to spend on reading these days. I must disagree with your estimate of your work. As far as I am concerned, your stories and poems are superior to anything of the sort ever written by Dunsany, Machen, Poe, or any of the others. And there are several thousand readers who agree with me.

I read Mr. Hart's essay about Jack London, but found nothing new or original in it. Many of his remarks are merely repetitions of what Jack himself said not long before his death, set forth in different style. The reason Jack lost interest in literature and in life, was because he came at last to realize that the aims, pretenses and aspirations of Art and artists are basically and ultimately as empty, futile and meaningless as those of the wallowing masses. Mr. Hart takes in quite a bit of territory when he says nobody "in the world" reads Jack's books. I read them, continually, and several of my friends do. As far as I am concerned, he stands head and shoulders above all other American writers.

Thanks for the clippings regarding the cowpunch-buffalo hunter feud. That was a real factor in early days. The buffalo hunters were a hard lot. In fact, I feel confident in saying that the business produced the most ferocious tribe of barbarians that this continent has ever known, red or white. Of course, not all were like that, but a lot of them were. They dressed in buckskins, wore their hair long, lived in Indian country most of the time, mated with Indian women, and their continual butchering of animals by trade and red men by necessity, seemed to have instilled in them a blood-thirstiness that was nothing less than a throw-back to the days of stone axes and the tribal drift. They were knife-fighters and gun-fighters. Pat Garrett, who killed Billy the Kid was a hunter of a later day, and helped exterminate the remnants of the great herds in the Texas Panhandle. Bat Masterson, mentioned in the article you sent me, was another notable who got his start skinning bison. He was one of the few old-time bad-men who died without their boots on, and his end was fantastic, considering his career. He was found dead at his desk in the offices of a New York newspaper, where he was working as a sports editor. He had written a note which went something like this: "Everything is even in life, after all; the rich get their ice in the summer, and the poor get theirs in the winter." He'd been brought to New York to protect some wealthy magnate whose conscience had got him scared of his shadow, and somebody gave him the newspaper job. Bat was a good marshal. in Dodge City, except when Clay Allison and his Texas riders would sweep into the town, blazing right and left with their sawed-off shotguns. Then Bat and his deputies would take to the brush.

The Kansas towns hired the toughest, meanest gunmen they could find for the job of officers, figuring they'd need them, and these men committed so many outrages that pretty soon they did need their gun-skill. The first cowmen that came up the Chisholm were not looking for trouble. They had enough trouble on the trail, fighting their way through wildernesses swarming with outlaws and hostile Indians. All they wanted to do was to find a market for their longhorns. They did, and money flowed like water through the Kansas cowtowns, and thence all over the United States. But the boys wanted a little fun, after the long drive; who wouldn't? Down in Texas, when the cowpunchers came into town, they blew in their money on whiskey, women—if there were any handy—, and gambling, and did a good deal of harmless shooting in the air. Nobody paid any attention. They meant no harm when they tried the same forms of amusement in Kansas. But the people weren't used to such stuff, they got scared and summoned their buffalo-hunting laws to stop it. These gentlemen tried to enforce the law quite often by shooting down the punchers from behind without warning. They also stood in, in many cases, with the crooked gamblers and dance-hall owners. At first about the only victims were unsuspecting cowboys. But they were dealing with the wrong breed. Men began to come up the Trail with their guns strapped down, looking for trouble and ready for it: such men as Ben Thompson, King Fisher, John Wesley Hardin. The bosses of the cowtowns had started something they couldn't stop. Helpless in the teeth of conditions, for which they themselves were mainly responsible, they hired the Texans themselves for their officers.

Concerning weather conditions, this winter has been unusually mild, except for the blizzard which swept the nation several weeks ago, and hit nearly 18 below Zero in Texas. I was made to realize my physical limitations more fully by the rheumatism which tied me into knots, as a result of getting half frozen while doing my outdoor work. If my life for the last several years had been lived as vigorously as my boyhood, milking in an open shed in a subzero snow-storm, and the other things I did, wouldn't have hurt me. But the easy, sheltered life of a writer and would-be student has made me so damned soft and weak that I'm ashamed of myself.

Well, I've maundered on long enough. This letter can't be very interesting, being filled up with arguments. But it's inevitable that you and I should disagree on practically every subject under the sun. We are so utterly different in tem-

perament, racial stock, traditional and geographical background and environment; about the only thing we have in common is an interest in literature, and
even there most of our ideas and preferences are as far apart as the Poles.

Thanking you again for the clippings, and for the kind things you said about
my verse, and hoping to see some of your work in Weird Tales soon, I am,

Cordially,

R E H.

Notes

1. Frank Buck (1884–1950) was an American hunter and animal collector born in
Gainesville, Texas. He was coauthor (with Edward Anthony) of the best-selling book
Bring 'Em Back Alive (1930), and starred in and directed several jungle adventure films.

2. Arthur Sullivant Hoffman (1876–1966) was editor of *Adventure* from 1911 to 1927.
The quotation is excerpted from Whitehead's letter, published in "The Camp Fire"
(*Adventure*'s letters column), 10 November 1923, pp. 177–79.

3. REH probably refers to the line "Some, that are mad if they behold a cat" (*The
Merchant of Venice* 4.1.48). See also "I could endure any thing before but a cat, and now
he's a cat to me" (*All's Well That Ends Well* 4.3.266).

4. Probably Benjamin Francis Musser (1889–1951), whom REH met in the fall of 1929.
As editor of *Contemporary Verse* and *JAPM: The Poetry Monthly*, Musser accepted two of
REH's verses in 1929, and the two met at the home of poet Lexie Dean Robertson in
Rising Star, Texas, during Musser's lecture tour that year. Musser apparently rededicated
himself to his Catholicism shortly after that meeting: in December his magazines were
abruptly merged with Ernest Hartsock's *Bozart*, out of Atlanta. In a later autobiographical
piece Musser described "a period in which Bohemianism rivalled Catholicism for the field
and finally, I pray forever, fell before the Cross. That 'arty' interlude included the editor-
ship of several poetry magazines." As to whether Musser ignored REH after their meeting, note that in his letter to HPL in December 1930 (p. 97), REH refers to "my friend
Ben Musser" as a "shining example of tolerance and broad-mindedness among the moderns," and that Musser sent REH a copy of his *As the Poet Says*— inscribed "Greetings for
Christmas 1931 to my friend Bob Howard, from Ben Musser." (The chapbook is in the
possession of the Robert E Howard House and Museum.)

5. Gottfried von Kalmbach is the protagonist in "The Shadow of the Vulture."

[79]   [AH 18–19.17; *SL* 611]

10 Barnes St.,

Providence, R.I.,

March 25, 1933.

Dear R E H:—

I digested your extremely interesting letter of the 6th with
the usual attention and pleasure, and appreciate the Russell cutting enclosed.
Meanwhile—although I've not yet had time to go through the last 7 numbers
of W.T. with anything like thoroughness—I have read your "Scarlet Citadel",

"Tower of the Elephant", and "Autumn", and wish to congratulate you on the splendid effects obtained in each case. The stories are unutterably fascinating—full of vivid pictures and a haunting sense of unhallowed antiquity—while the poem forms a splendid capture of a mood. It is hard to believe, in view of the charm and vitality of these things, that your claim of writing for money alone really represents the full sum of unconscious impulses involved in the process of creation. You may think so, externally, yet I'd be willing to wager that something of the genuine artist's impulse is at work beneath—even if consciously disavowed by you. Such good products couldn't come from commercial calculativeness alone! It seems to me that—good as your earlier tales were—your work is very perceptibly improving and maturing. It is getting an added smoothness, mellowness, and evenness of tone which contribute to its ultimate impression. More and more you are getting Dunsany's power to make strange visions of palaeogean architecture spring alive—while your unique skill in suggesting the horror of infinitely ancient subterrene crypts remains unimpaired. Again, my profoundest congratulations!

Regarding our controversy—I am sorry if I seemed at any time to misinterpret your position. Possibly I did not make my estimate of your position as clear as I should have—for I really did not mean to imply that you represent the greatest possible extreme in the championship of the physical against the mental. In contrasting you and Long I meant only to convey that your respective positions represent extremes *within the very narrow circle of my active correspondents*. Of course, I realise very keenly that extremes exist in both directions, which far transcend your position on the one hand and Long's on the other.

Nor did I fancy that you have any undue pride in your physical development. My mention of the feed-wagon incident was purely incidental, and certainly involved no assumption of boasting on your part. If I remember rightly—amidst my disconcertingly large and unfortunately hasty correspondence—my only purpose was to contrast this incident, and the kind of activity concerned, with your other set of activities—the set that produces things like "The Scarlet Citadel". I didn't think you were over-proud of unloading the wagon—but I did think you were a bit *under*-proud, in proportion, of your intellectual and aesthetic work. That is, it seemed to me you were placing these things too much on a plane of equality, merely because under a given set of conditions (only one of many sets existing on the planet) they happen to be of equal value in giving you material security. I objected to what seemed to be your criterion—an empirical, fortuitous, and unsound one depending upon accidental circumstances and wholly ignoring the intrinsic qualities of the things compared—and wished to point out the vast and abysmal difference (a difference wholly in favour of your mental work) existing between the kind of qualities demanded by wagon-unloading on the one hand and by story-writing on the other hand. I knew that you knew a trained gorilla could unload a wagon as well as a man, but I wanted to emphasise very strongly the fact that no gorilla, and no inferior man, could possibly have written "The Black Stone". It did not seem to me that you sufficiently *appreciated* the enormous superiority of the story-writing process over the feed-pitching process. I knew you *knew* the difference, but I didn't think you gave it its full value in your *emotions*. You seemed to adopt, as your sole criterion of various human attributes, the superficial and accidental quality of material survival-value under a certain arbitrary set of conditions. It was merely against that that I protested. I was simply urging you to consider the *intrinsic qualitative difference* between the crudely primitive energy-process (a process widely distributed in nature, and involving none of the aeon-long refining action which builds up the qualities of consciousness, reflection, and experience-capacity we know as human) expressed in feed-pitching, and the prodigiously complex and delicately evolved energy-process (a process achieved only after millions of years of biological advancement, and connected with everything which removes man from the state of amorphous protoplasm) expressed in the writing of a really good story. Your tendency to judge things merely in relation to the fulfilment of certain immediate material needs seemed to me (whether erroneously or not) to be blinding you emotionally (though perhaps not intellectually) to the actual relative values concerned in the problem at issue. Not that you were especially proud of feed-pitching, but that you did not seem to *feel fully* the tremendous—actually incomparable—superiority of story-writing; that is, the incomparable superiority, as measured by the standard of biological removal from protoplasmic jelly (the only approach to an absolute standard which we have), of the kind of activity employed in good story-writing. Boiling it all down, my great objection was to the use of *mere material survival-value under certain conditions* as a standard of quality. I was urging you to examine each of the opposed sets of process intrinsically and independently—judging each by its actual place in the scheme of cosmic organisation so far as known to us.

Have I made it clear that my misconception of your position was not as great as my former clumsy presentation suggested? As to my assertion that one certainly ought not to let his body run down below the requirements of the duties he *chooses* to perform—I am indeed sorry that my careless phraseology gave rise to an erroneous impression! Of course, I meant 'duties he *chooses or is obliged* to perform'—but neglected to be sufficiently specific. My idea was, simply, *whatever duties fall to one*—whether from choice or necessity. I didn't think the *source* of the duties was of major significance in the argument—and I regret that my lack of explicitness brought up a needless point. Of course, in some cases an element of choice does exist. Broadly speaking, a man can usually decide for himself whether or not he will live and work in the country or in the city, whether he will live in a long-settled or pioneering region, and whether he will pursue a physically exacting or relatively sedentary occupation. But one realises that in actual daily life elements of opportunity, especial aptitude, responsibility, etc., do often restrict one's range of choice (especially in these abnormal times); hence I ought to have been specific in saying 'duties one *chooses or is obliged* to perform'. You can see, however, in the light of the foregoing observations, that this point was not truly germane to the main argument. My point was, that I freely acknowledge the need of maintaining a certain level of physical development determined by one's (voluntary or involuntary) environment. One might make a further concession in your direction by saying that the level ought to be determined not merely by one's *immediate* environment, but by whatever range of environments one may reasonably expect to encounter in the course of natural vicissitudes. This, I think, removes what looked like a very naive estimate of your tastes. And I hope you did not think I was questioning your own personal need of a strong physique. Obviously and logically, you do need just that as long as you continue in your present environment—an environment which probably has enough points in its favour to make it worth retaining at the cost of severe exertion. That much was understood from the first. All I criticised was the assumption of some that this special and local standard of physical development ought to be *universal*, even though only a minority actually require it. That was not a criticism of you. My point involving you was merely an inquiry as to whether you fully appreciated—emotionally—the intrinsic superiority of the processes involved in effective story-writing or mental achievement of any sort, over those involved in hauling logs or digging ditches or punching people's chins. As for *pride*—I was speaking only in a relative sense. I realise that you are very modest in your appraisal of yourself, but was simply urging you to apply a rational sense of intrinsic values in comparing the importance of the various sides of your personality—or of anyone's personality. In this connexion, by the way, I hope I did not seem to disparage a just pride in physical prowess. Certainly, there is reason to be proud of any possession or accomplishment, major or minor—and the pride is well justified provided it does not distort one's sense of proportion regarding the relative importance of the thing in question in the total personality. Whitehead has a right to take satisfaction in his original physical strength (thanks, by the way, for the transcript from his *Adventure* letter, which I had not seen before), and nobody I know of (except Long, who thought it just a bit juvenile for a man of his high development in superior lines) ever criticised him for that satisfaction. But of course it was a well-proportioned pride, and did not for a moment make him fancy that his physical strength and athletic skill were the really important things about him. When long illness took away his strength, he bore the deprivation with good-humour and equanimity . . . . but surely you realise that he would not have been equally complacent about a decline in his keen intellect and sensitively developed taste. The strength was an interesting, amusing, and potentially useful possession—but the intellect and taste were Henry St. Clair Whitehead himself.

When I spoke of the (in my opinion) limited number of persons deriving pleasure from athletics, I meant of course, *athletics actively participated in*. I am fully aware of the popularity of the pastime of sitting comfortably on a bench and watching other people exert themselves in trials of physical skill, but really doubt if this is any more an athletic pastime than any other form of spectatorship. To the spectator, an athletic contest is merely a source of vicarious thrills like a cinema show—and indeed, the majority of prize-fight followers are soft-bodied urban "sports" and poolroom loafers who never willingly walk a block if they can find a way to ride. However, all this (in which you doubtless agree) was not your point. You, in disputing my assumption, were calling attention to the probable number of persons *really active* athletically; and were basing your argument upon the probable percentage engaged in high-school, collegiate, and professional athletics. Regarding this point—I am no statistician, but I doubt if the whole array totals up into more than a substantial minority. Though each school and college has a small circle of athletes, it has likewise a large student body not active in this way, and with varying degrees of indifference toward athletics. All agree that collegiate athletics, now highly professionalised, forms less and less of an interest among the students. Young men are growing more adult-minded, so that college undergraduates pay more and more attention to the real problems of life— economic and social organisation, the arts and sciences, etc.—and less and less to the 'rah! 'rah! kind of thing. 'Dying for dear old Yale' and all that are getting a bit baroque. What is more—the small circle who do go in for school and college athletics do not necessarily retain that interest permanently. Some do, of course, but others drop it—thus further restricting the number of the actively interested. I don't say that the number of athletes and near-athletes is not considerable, taken as a group. I merely say that this group seems to me rather small in comparison with the whole population. As for those who censure this popular interest in sports—I don't imagine that they censure this any more than they censure the popular interest in other things which are essentially secondary, superficial, and trivial in varying degree . . . . . cheap novels, tabloid newspapers, dancing, cinema shows, Coney Island frivolities, and so on. Indeed—so far as *active* sports go, I feel sure that the wisest critics do not condemn them at all, or class them with the extremely trivial diversions. A certain amount of athletics, especially for boys and youths, is always highly encouraged and in most schools is now made compulsory. When people condemn the indiscriminate popular devotion to the sports page and the comfortable seats of the football stadium they are really not so much objecting to the sport itself as to the more solid interests which this rather aimless (and generally inactive) devotion crowds out. The real complaint is against the sterile and trivial mental and emotional life of the average citizen—who is not getting as much out of the experience of being alive as he could if society could find a way to develop his full personality. Today only a minority achieve a full opening to the limit of their evolutionary capacity—an undemocratic state of things which many deplore and would like to see replaced by a society in which the majority might reap the fruits of intellectual and aesthetic experience. In such a society the more superficial and primitive things would have their place, but it would not be as grotesquely and disproportionately dominant a place as in a society where the majority remain culturally undeveloped and childish.

To sum up—the only object in my argument is to keep the record straight regarding intrinsic qualititative standards; to make clear the fact that physical considerations (no matter how *necessary*) pertain to a primitive and undistinguished level of biological organisation not particularly human, whereas mental and imaginative considerations pertain to the most specialised, complex, and experience-giving form of biological organisation which this planet has yet witnessed, and which marks the specific difference between man and the other species of animal life. This fact is extremely important to keep in mind, because *upon it rests the only possible system of absolute or quasi-absolute criteria of human values which we can discover in the universe*. Aside from the single matter of *degree of biological advancement from amorphous protoplasm toward complex specialisation*, there is not a single criterion visible to us in all the expanse of the cosmos whereby we can justify the use of the conceptions "high" and "low", "superior" and "inferior", and so on, in anything like an absolute sense. If, then, we desire to form any sort of appraisal of the various elements in human life with a view to understanding, ordering, and perhaps improving the process of living, we must very obviously entertain a clear idea of the relative place of each of these elements in the evolutionary scale; acknowledging that what is most evolved and most particularly human is necessarily of greater importance (important in the sense that a man is more important than a tiger, a tree, or a boulder) than what is less evolved and less particularly human. Of course, it is perfectly possible for an academic theorist to deny even this quasi-definite system of criteria, and to claim that—in the limitless and impersonal cosmos—even evolutionary degree is a mere incident without *meaning*. This is *theoretically* so. *Theoretically* a man, a tiger, a tree, and a boulder are of merely equal *cosmic* "importance" or lack of importance. But all this theory has no real application. We know, as a practical thing, what the difference between being a man (with a maximum capacity for conscious knowledge of cosmic placement, maximum capacity for sensation, perception, correlation, etc., maximum susceptibility to continuous and highly diffused pleasure, and maximum power of achieving domination and a satisfying emotional catharsis) and being a tiger or tree or boulder is; and all normal thinkers are satisfied that the rich life of man (when all his latent powers are put to use) involves an intrinsically *higher* or *more important* adjustment to the cosmic flux—an intrinsically *superior place in nature*—than does any other form of existence known to us. Practically, then, *it ought not to be necessary to defend the specifically human or highly evolved as a standard of value.* Indeed, it seldom is necessary because most cases of *apparent* attack on this standard really involve no more than attacks on *applications and interpretations* of it. But the principle as a whole should be kept fresh in memory. Any discussion of human society, or of individual human qualities, demands frequent reference to an absolute standard of value; and unless we have the valid standard of evolutionary degree ready for reference and application, we are bound to be lost in confusion and cross-purposes. Don't think I'm overemphasising this matter. We shall have occasion to refer back to it later on.

But at the same time, don't fancy that my general estimate of human values causes me to decry an interest in athletics and physical development as a hobby. On the contrary, I think it forms one of the most wholesome of mental relaxations, and I really regret that my own natural interest in it is no keener than it is. Thus you see that I have no real quarrel at all with your range of personal interests. I am merely striving to define *general values* as regards life as a whole. All that brought me into argument with you was an impression (whether or not erroneous) that you were not giving the more evolved human values the emotional recognition and appreciation to which their intrinsic biological rank entitles them—that you were, in a word, inclined to sneer ever so subtly at intellectual and aesthetic achievement, and to belittle their fruits rather systematically through various disparaging references to human types and institutions which embody them. Having that impression, my arguments were really of the defensive rather than aggressive sort. I was not attacking the physical, but merely defending the more purely human values of life.

As to the truth or falsity of my impression that you tend unconsciously to belittle the more evolved and human side of life—I may say that I formed it from what appeared to be questionings of the higher values. You appeared to deny the supreme emotional value of intellectual and aesthetic experience for their own sakes—to regard as mythical or feigned the fact that for people of the highest type *the intrinsic acts of intellectual expansion or artistic creation are primary and satisfying ends in themselves,* forming the main and indispensable objects of life, and conducted without ulterior motives or hope of material gain. (A fact, of course, in no way contradicting the equally valid fact that many of these people may have keen athletic and other interests as hobbies or parallel activities.) Perhaps you did not specifically and consciously form this denial and repudiation, but you tended to show a certain ironic contempt in alluding to highly evolved experience—as in your recent letter, when you belittle rather bitterly the 'artists who smudge their canvas and scientists who pry into the secrets of the cosmos'; ignore the titanically increased opportunities for a full mental-aesthetic life which civilisation has brought; prefer gold-getting pugilists to idea-enjoying college professors; and (in asserting that you write for money alone) deny by implication the superlatively keen joy of literary creation—or any aesthetic craftsmanship for its own sake . . . . . a joy which for many forms the sole reason for remaining alive. In view of all these varied evidences of an anti-intellectual or anti-aesthetic emotional bias, I am sure that you can hardly blame me for forming an opinion which may be errone-ous so far as your soberly considered conscious opinions are concerned—and which indeed is contradicted from another angle by the great and increasing excellence of your own literary work—work which exhibits your gratifyingly ample possession of these very evolved qualities at which another side of your emotions seems to enjoy taking a subtly hostile fling now and then. Looking over the field objectively and analytically, and reviewing your own utterances regarding matters in which the various human values are at stake, you can hardly fail to agree that I had at least some ground for bewilderment as to the exact nature of your real attitude. But at any rate, I fancy that the matter of the valuation of the physical is cleared up on both sides. I certainly realise that you do not worship blind physical strength as a supreme value, and I trust that you realise that I do not in the least criticise a keen interest in athletics, physical development, and the like as a hobby. Indeed—I believe that we might argue much more extendedly on the subject of *material gain* as a human value (a subject not even touching on the brawn versus brain contro-versy) than on any other so far brought up. I am squarely against you here—for I do not regard financial advantageousness as any indication of an activ-ity's real merit or dignity, or financial prosperity as any indication of a man's real worth. You say you prefer a rich athlete to a poor professor—but I can't see any justification for this. The athlete (unless of course he has other quali-ties not brought out in the discussion) has merely profited by certain chance conditions which happen to be in his favour, and seized material gain without the exercise of any human qualities save a somewhat primitive common sense and caution (and often not even these—easy come, easy go!). As a human being, he remains relatively low in the scale of effective development. (That is, his higher side has been allowed to remain latent and unused, no matter how biologically evolved he may be.) On the other hand, the impecunious professor has made the most of himself. He has lived up to the natural en-dowments which a million years of differentiation from the ape has given him; and is infinitely farther removed from shapeless protoplasm—in point of range and content of consciousness—than the athlete is. He has known sensations and experienced perspectives which are forever closed to the primitive slugger or kicker, and has formed conceptions and attained a grasp on life in such a way as to raise his intrinsic status as an example of cosmic organisation. He is more of a man and less of a blind outcropping of diffusive natural force than the pounder or jumper or weight-lifter is. And it is simply absurd to belittle him because he has not wasted his energies on the purely artificial gestures of material luxury. What if he has patches on the seat of his breeches? Does that hurt him? He has preferred the vital to the external and trivial, and by dedicating himself to a high plane of effort and consciousness has experienced far more satisfaction than has the prosperous oaf whose pleasures are wholly external and superficial. By the same token, I can't understand your consciously expressed attitude about literary motives. Why anyone should (by implication if not by conscious and specific statement) approve a purely mercenary motive for writing, and scorn the real joy of creation for the sake of creation, is beyond me! I can't think that this attitude really colours all the subconscious forces behind your work, because the work itself seems to show evidence of genuine creative vitality—whether you admit it or not. Your stories are really vastly different from the pallid hack work of systematically mercenary writers like Otis Adelbert Kline, Hugh B. Cave, the later Seabury Quinn, and (alas!) the future E. Hoffmann Price if he doesn't watch his step and cling to his old non-professional standards. I simply can't read the crap Kline and Cave grind out—yet I find a real vitality and genuine interest in virtually everything you've produced so far. The difference, as I take it, is due to a certain real imagination and creative zest which you unconsciously put into your stories and poems despite all your conscious disavowals. As for money—of course everybody has got to make enough somehow to feed, clothe, and shelter him. So far, so good. But I have no use for the fellow who goes beyond that point and debases all his energies into a mere scramble for more and more money and more and more luxuries. There's a lot more to life than material luxury, and the wise man will prefer to content himself with plain living and preserve his intellectual and imaginative integrity. To me, the profit motive in human activity seems a damn shoddy thing. I don't believe you really exalt the profit motive as much as these random references would imply. Indeed—I guess you make it clear that you connect it with writing only because you don't regard writing as your main activity or natural outlet. Your enthusiastic scholarship in historical fields, and your vivid capture of the Texas atmosphere in splendidly written letters not designed for publication, are sufficient proof of your real *inward* taste for highly evolved activities as an end in themselves, without the lure of gold.

Your opinion that 'of all snobberies, the assumption that intellectual endeavours, attainments, and accomplishments are the only worth-while and important* things in life is the least justifiable' seems to me something demanding reflection. In the first place, I don't see how this assumption could possibly be less justifiable than the assumptions that wealth, social status, and other artificial bases of common snobberies, are of supreme importance. Certainly, sound intellectual or artistic attainment is much more of a tangible

---

*meaning, I presume, important to the individual. The most important things from the point of view of the community are those sets of government and construction which create an environment in which the individual may develop.

form of superiority than the possession of material wealth or the shadowy enjoyment of a certain artificial regard from the community. Secondly, I doubt if many mean to imply that intellectual-aesthetic development and experience form the *only* important* element in life. Certainly they form the *most* important single element according to the evolutionary criterion discussed some paragraphs back, but any careful student of life must concede that other important elements exist. (Although some of these other elements really fall within the domain of intellectual-aesthetic experience according to the broadest and least formal interpretation of that term.) Elements important to us are those producing a sense of expanded personality. Anything giving a consciousness of functions well performed is important in this sense. Altogether, I see what you mean by your assertion, though it would not occur to me to put as much emphasis as you do on the matter. It does not do to undervalue the highest product of organic development. Of course, *all* snobberies—i.e., ostentatious and contemptuous paradings of acquirements to the disadvantage of others, are essentially vulgar.

Again—I think you have a certain amount of misconception in commenting on my random illustration of relative pride in horses and books. (When I spoke of horses I scarcely had in mind the scientific breeder. Surely, I admit that the careful artificial evolution of a perfect organism is a feat of science and art calling for a goodly amount of well-justified pride.) I did not speak of books as mere material objects bought by the pound, but as parts of a collection slowly, carefully, and discriminatingly made—forming an outgrowth of their possessor's personality and reflecting—through their selection—his character, interests, and degree of taste. Nothing is so intimately a part of a man as his library. Certainly, it would be vain to take pride in a mere showy set of books bought for their fine binding. The pride is in the quality of the choice. But of course, what a library really gives is *satisfaction* rather than mere pride. It contains just what the possessor wants to look at most often, and comes to form his window or gateway to the larger cosmos. One becomes more attached to books than to anything else except old pictures, old scenes, and certain bits of old furniture. They come to represent what is familiar and beloved, and symbolise one's whole grasp of experience. Of course, not all the books one may happen to own come within this category. There are borderline books which are only semi-indispensable, and other casual volumes that one both acquires and parts with lightly. But a certain nucleus of one's library takes on the very fondest associations, and forms the very last thing that a really appreciative person would willingly sacrifice.

---

*i.e., important on the scale of quality of activity. All concede, of course, that everything is grounded (except for individuals of the ascetic-martyr type) on a certain irreducible minimum of bodily comfort and security.

Turning to politico-anthropological matters—I still insist that the modern conditions *called* "slavery" by rhetorical liberals are not in the least comparable to the conditions of *actual* ancient slavery or mediaeval serfdom. One must not be led astray by high-flown generalities. It is *details* that count. What were the daily conditions and limitations encountered by the real slave or serf? How do the daily conditions and limitations encountered by the modern majority compare with these? Actually, no comparison is possible so far as the majority is concerned. It is true that certain small minorities in certain specific regions and industries do at present suffer the conditions approaching *serfdom* (not slavery), but the number affected is not sufficient to justify wide generalisation—and more, the tendency of political reform is to improve rather than debase these unfortunate minorities. Fascism, while curbing certain types of open anti-governmental utterance, certainly does not press down painfully upon the average individual. The bulk of the Italian people go as freely about their business as they have always gone. Just *what is* the wild and untrammeled "freedom" that our modern radicals are so vociferously clamouring for? What is it that they *want* to do that they *can't* do? I am curious to know, for they never seem to convey a very clear idea. I don't see many honest and well-disposed people 'sitting in dungeons with their legs in iron stocks', nor do I see in the varied and active life of the modern average man anything resembling emasculation or reduction to the guinea-pig or rabbit stage. Just what do our "free souls" *want* to do? Ride bicycles on the sidewalks, disregard traffic signals and collide with other people's cars, play the radio at 3 a.m., shoot and carve people for fun, or what? If they despise artists who smudge on canvas and scientists who have a regard for truth, what is it that they *don't* despise? Do they esteem running amok with automatic pistols, setting fire to houses at will, pitching tents in the middle of the public streets, or what the hell? I've never seen anybody whom I could imagine as doing any differently from what he actually does do without any interference from anybody—and yet half of our young "intelligentsia" are clamouring for a mystical "freedom" which they imagine exists somewhere in the land of Cockaigne. In your case the idea of a wider "freedom" is more justifiable than in the case of the majority of protesters, for you have a definite ideal of frontier life with hunting, battles, and other accessories of the heroic age. But surely you realise that this is a mere matter of *preference*—that there could hardly be any *intrinsic* advantage in the barbaric ways of yesterday. If the wild and wooly frontier satisfied one set of natural instincts in man, it left a definitely greater number unsatisfied—so that the change to a settled and orderly life has almost undoubtedly brought far more advantages than it has taken away. True, there are a few individuals whose especial makeup inclines them naturally toward the frontier life and no other, just as there are others who could not possibly endure such a thing. But the majority are in between—able to adapt themselves to either wild or settled life, though on the whole getting more out of the settled than out of the wild. Such, at least, is my sincere opinion. You can appreciate my position when you reflect how purely *negative* all the prevailing criticism of society is. All that we hear is what people *don't* like. Never do we get a clear presentation of *precisely what they want.* If I saw a really coherent statement of the exact condition of life demanded by our protesting critics— what they think would fit natural human instincts better than existing institutions, and how they think such a set of conditions could be established,—I would be less impatient than I am with the habit of protestation. Part of the existing discontent, I really believe, is not so much with what *is* as with what people *fear is going to be.* In view of the admittedly flagrant example set by Soviet Russia this fear is perhaps not unreasonable—but I honestly fail to see that the western world is in danger of any such fate. Bertrand Russell's dismal picture is interesting and entertaining—but its exaggeration is obvious.[1] People have a tendency, when a slight change in conditions occurs, to imagine that this change is necessarily the beginning of an infinite trend in the same direction; but this belief is seldom justified. Though settled life and denser population naturally demand certain limitations of rural or small-town irresponsibility, there is no reason to suppose that there is any continuous trend toward increased limitations. Indeed, it is my opinion that most of the limitations added by the future will affect not the individual, but rather the forces of industry which now exploit the individual. There may of course be limits set on private fortunes, but it isn't likely that these will interfere with anybody's daily life. Standardisation of facilities will probably continue, but this tendency does not necessarily affect the individual. A determined and independent soul can steer clear of it. Suppose the world does have only one radio programme or newspaper? We don't have to listen to the radio, and we can find ways of checking up on facts. Our revered pioneer ancestors had neither newspapers nor radios, and we can emulate them in this respect if we wish. Remember one thing—that the ideal freedom to which you look back never existed (after barbaric times) except in certain special parts of the globe. Your frontier of Homeric strife, whose dramatic vividness all acknowledge, was never a *general* characteristic of our civilisation. In the settled parts of the globe—where a numerical majority of the population have always dwelt—the changes in degree of "freedom" have been very slight—and perhaps the decrease in certain directions has been equalled or overbalanced by increases in other directions. The real, vital changes brought by the machine age are (aside from the very real problem of technological unemployment) far more in the direction of overspeeded life (which the discriminating individual can dodge) than curtailed freedom of action. You can't construct a general graph of cultural trends by taking the exceptional conditions prevailing in one especial section, where a throwback to primitive times brought about a repetition of early changes such as most of the world went through many years ago. The abrupt changes which you, personally, notice, are those which most members of the civilisation are not now undergoing because they were ancestrally undergone in Saxon and Norman England. The bulk of us are *perfectly used* to the settled life which you find new and intolerable, and there is no reason why we should not be. It would be impossible to adduce any evidence in favour of a primitive state of life, intrinsically speaking. The only criterion of a mode of life, apart from the absolute evolutionary one which emphatically endorses civilisation, is the extent to which it suits the natures of those who pursue it. If it can be shown that the bulk of modern people are as well adapted to modern life as the bulk of early people were adapted to primitive life, then there is no ground for preferring primitive to civilised life. Such a preference can be no more than a purely personal emotion. I would prefer being a Roman of about 150 B.C., or a Devonshire squire of 1750, occasionally spending a season in London—yet I don't think those earlier ages were essentially superior to our own as a general thing. We have much which they lack. It is well to leave out all purely personal bias in estimating the relative status of two or more periods. Likewise concerning the restless, super-vital type of person. There is no need of idealising him. He served a useful function in his day—when conditions needed him—but his survival is not now necessary. Today it is a middle type which conditions demand—neither the excess-energy dynamo, nor the slothful and effeminate decadent. However, of the two extremes, the super-vital one is unquestionably preferable—and even intrinsically desirable when the super-vitality can be steered in the right direction. Altogether, I don't think people need really dread the future unless some major breakdown occurs. For the settled parts of the world, changes will be very mild and gradual so far as freedom is concerned; and any increase in the supervision of man's industrial life will probably be compensated for by a growth of greater leisure during which he will be subjected to no supervision at all except the common principles of decent law and order.

March 28.

The foregoing paragraphs have, in a way, overlapped into our discussion of civilisation versus barbarism. Regarding this discussion, let me say that I can understand perfectly a person's vaguely romantic feeling of kinship with some colourful barbarous age, and his dreamy, half-serious wish that he might escape from reality into some distant glittering world corresponding to his idyllic conception of that age. With that I could surely have no quarrel— for have I not said that I would like to be a Roman consul of Scipio Aemilianus' time,[2] or a rural squire of the middle 18th century . . . . ages which, in all details, I know were not essentially superior to ours? My sole reason for debate is what seems to be an underlying assumption on your part that the barbaric state is *intrinsically superior*—in a serious sense—to civilisation. This I most emphatically believe to be an erroneous assumption. Personal sentimental preference does not call for argument. The argument concerns only what appears to be your tacit position—that barbarism actually satisfied more of the normal human personality than civilisation does.

As I have said, I see absolutely no ground for a serious defence of barbarism. It was normal enough in its day—as an early stage in the social and emotional development of the species—but the instincts and emotions which it satisfied were only the cruder and more embryonic ones. The race grew beyond it. Today we find barbaric instincts mainly in small boys—for as we know, the developing individual roughly repeats the history of the species. The human embryo has *gills*—repeating the amphibian or aqueous stage in man's ancestry—and the infant is virtually a *savage* in his emotions. One stage later—the small-boy stage—finds us arrived at *barbarism*. It is then that all the cruelty, treachery, restlessness, gang spirit, callousness, etc. of the barbaric type becomes temporarily paramount in the personality. Emotionally, the barbarian was about 10 years old—and the modern boy of ten roughly repeats his psychology. But in the normal course of nature—if our endocrine glands are in working order—we outgrow this emotional phase. Other sides of our personality open up, and we develop instincts and emotions which the barbaric mode of life and thought cannot satisfy. Some of these new impulses are direct contradictions of some of the older ones, so that the barbaric state becomes not only unsatisfying but actually repugant to us. (That is, actual contact with the barbaric state would be. Of course, our imagination produces pictures of it—with its brighter aspects predominating—which strongly appeal to our aesthetic sense.) That is why the species outgrew barbarism in the first place. Barbarism failed to satisfy the whole personality of mankind as soon as that personality began to mature. It belonged to what we may call the small-boyhood of the race. There are still races backward enough to be satisfied with it, but for the Aryan it is definitely obsolete. It leaves the best part of our personality neglected and untouched—developing only the coarser part of life and cheating us out of the best of our human heritage. Whatever satisfactions have to be sacrificed in the climb to civilisation are crude and trivial indeed as compared with the rich rewards gained. The case is analogous to that of a boy growing up to be a man. True, he has to leave his carefree marble-playing and cat-torturing behind—but in exchange for these doubtful boons he gains a wealth of mental and emotional experience so incomparably superior to them, that he hardly (except in moments of whimsical sentiment) regrets his maturing. He who could be forever a barbarian is, in effect, one who would be forever a small boy—with a small boy's cruelty, callousness, thoughtlessness, ignorance, and general emotional underdevelopment. Both the barbarian and the boy are men in the making rather than fully made men. This phase of development is essentially temporary.

In saying that you would like to be a barbarian, you admit that you would have to leave a great deal of your present personality behind. But don't you realise that without that part of your personality—your imagination, perspective, etc.—*you could not be yourself at all?* All that makes any person—all that gives him his existing cast of thought and impulse and imagination—is a blend of his biological heredity and what his environment puts into his consciousness and emotions. Take any part of that blend away, and the person—as a definite personality—ceases to exist. I suppose what you mean is that you think your purely biological side, if stripped of all acquired impressions, would fit barbarism better than civilisation. While such a supposition is *conceivable*, I think its probability is distinctly open to question. In the first place, none of us can *really* picture what we would be without the acquired qualities which have become a part of our nature. And secondly, I have an idea that one's imaginative cast is at least partly biological—so that if you were to be suddenly pitched into the Celtic world of 100 B.C. you would not find the hacking and swigging of the ordinary tribesman a satisfying round of experience. That part of you which creates images of Valusia, Bran Mak Morn, Conan the Reaver, the crypts of Tsotha-lanti, the Elephant Tower, etc., would begin to get restless, so that before you knew it you would be breaking into the Druidic priesthood or becoming a bard of some sort—although probably not relinquishing the combative side of existence. It was just that steady overleaping of a narrow experience-range by the maturing mind and personality of man which caused barbarism to be cast aside as an immature and unsatisfying mode of life for an adult people. Of course, in any civilisation there are underdeveloped individuals—hordes of them—who would be better suited to barbarism than to the life around them. No one disputes that. My point was simply that I don't believe *you* would find barbarism at all satisfying if you were born into the midst of it. Or rather, (since in that case you would know of no other mode of life) that barbarism would not give you even nearly as rich and varied a life as civilisation, with all its admitted defects, is able to give you; that it would leave untouched whole areas of consciousness and imagination which mean more to you than you think, and which could not be atoned for by any such doubtfully advantageous "freedoms" as those enabling you to override the weak, kill and burn and torture, and wantonly distort living organisms into shapeless and sanguinary pulp. I don't think that you, or any other normally adult Aryan, would *really* wish to exchange civilisation's rich heritage for any such "paradise" of slashing and mangling and plundering as barbarism formed—not, that is, if you would pause for a really profound and searching analysis of what barbarism actually meant. Your statement that I "idealise" the present age is really hardly correct. I have repeatedly admitted its defects, and regretted certain losses in variety and imaginative richness which excessive standardisation may bring if not intelligently combated. But you undoubtedly exaggerate its undesirable phases out of all normal proportion. You speak of social injustices which affect only a small part of modern mankind (barbarism's cruelty affected virtually *everyone*—no highly developed human personality had any chance to do aught but suffer in a barbaric state), and which modern ingenuity is trying its best to abolish; and magnify the abuses of police power which *certainly* affect only a microscopic and definitely inferior handful of the people, (which are mostly confined to a very few sections, which seldom touch any but emphatically degraded types, and which are vigorously combated in all really civilised regions) and which at their worst are nothing as compared with the *habitual* cruelties and enormities of barbarism. It is not idealising, but plain fact, to say that most normal persons in the really civilised parts of the Anglo-Saxon world never experience these injustices and cruelties, and indeed scarcely know of their existence except through study. No person of my acquaintance has ever run afoul of the police. The real facts are against you—for all the extreme cases of cruelty which you cite take place in the *least* civilised parts of the country . . . . those parts which are *least* evolved out of the recrudescent barbarism of the frontier. The more settled and civilised a region is, the smaller the percentage of cruelty and ugliness in it. Modern wars, of course, are sheer reversions to barbarism. They can't be helped, for civilisation is still only partial and incomplete; but it is pointless to call a survival of the barbaric an attribute of civilisation. Wars occur not because of civilisation but in spite of it. They are a sample of the idyllic Golden Age to which so many romanticists love to look back. In my opinion, the whole trouble with your view of civilisation is that you have happened to encounter a very unfortunate local phase of it—a phase in which its full characteristics do not appear. We agreed in an earlier debate that the less settled parts of the Southwest represent an essentially *transitional* stage— in which neither the working equilibrium of frontier's folkways nor the working equilibrium of settled-life folkways has a chance to exist. Surely such a temporary condition of upheaval and change cannot be taken as a fair sample of civilisation. Its defect is not that it is too civilised, but that it is not civilised enough. That is why it experiences all these police and other injustices which are utterly unknown in the long-settled East, in England, or in Canada. Any place where a "prominent business man" could pound a weak boy to a pulp is surely not typical of the long-settled Anglo-Saxon world. Civilisation is where honest and well-disposed people have a reasonable guarantee of remaining unmolested as long as they behave themselves; and where a person does not have to go about armed, as if against savage natives, merely because he is not illiterate or insensitive. Civilisation is a place where human intelligence has tried to minimise the wasteful element of mere blind individual survival-struggle in order to let individuals at least partly attain and enjoy the objects of struggle. Incidentally, though, don't take *New York* as a typical specimen of civilisation. That especial place has moved past the zone of civilisation into that of definite decadence—being rotten, as it were, before it is ripe. One of the great problems of civilisation—still, alas, unsolved—is how to attain a well-rounded maturity without beginning to crumble at the edges. How, in a word, to become fully and permanently adult without incurring senescence. It may be an unsolvable problem. Probably it is. But that does not contradict the fact that a real civilisation, while at its peak, certainly does give mankind a richer life than any other form of social organisation. If you want to name really civilised places of long settlement in contrast with places where unsettledness lingers, choose towns where the polyglot, megalopolitan stage of decadence has not set in. The most thoroughly civilised town I have ever seen is Charleston, S.C. Others are New Orleans, Savannah, Richmond, Philadelphia, New Haven, Hartford, Providence, Worcester, Springfield, Boston, Portland, Quebec, Montreal, Toronto—and in the old world, the cities of the British Isles. Most of the towns of the European continent I would tend to call decadent. They retain many of the advantages of civilisation, but these are tinctured with the disadvantages of decadence—disadvantages, let me add, which are even more repulsive than those of barbarism. In many ways decadence tends to duplicate barbarism—as witness the cruelty of sadistic degenerates and the indifference to human life of urban gangsters—and it is unquestionably far uglier . . . . just as the senile second-childishness of a decaying nonagenarian is uglier than the normal childishness of a child. But remember that praise of *civilisation* doesn't mean praise of *decadence*. When we say a man is superior to a small boy we don't mean a doddering, superannuated wreck!

You ask where barbarism leaves off and civilisation begins. Well—of course the transition is extremely gradual. There is a wide border zone within which it is impossible to apply a hard and fast classification. All we can do is to point to certain tendencies as characteristic of each state, and apply a classification when those tendencies seem sufficiently prominent to warrant it. No modern anthropologist makes any essential distinction between the different flowerings of civilisation—Babylon, Egypt, Persia, Crete, Greece, Rome, and so on, all are one. Even China's civilisation may be an incredibly early offshoot of the same stem—as likewise those of Mexico and Peru may be. One cannot measure civilisation by any one accomplishment. As you point out, many definitely barbaric races had certain accomplishments like ivory-carving, boat-building, military skill, tribal organisation, special branches of ethics, etc. developed to a very substantial degree. Indeed, we cannot doubt but that the Aryan tribes of western Europe were really on the verge of becoming civilised in their own right—the Celts extremely so, and the Teutons some distance behind. Even without Roman conquest, it is virtually certain that Gaul would have become a region of settled towns in a century from Caesar's time, and that a few centuries later a really profound and autochthonous Gallic civilisation would have developed. What largely held the Teutons back was *climate*. Paradoxically, a cold or cool climate seems to retard a barbaric race in its development toward civilisation, but to enable that race's culture to reach the greatest heights and nearest approach toward permanence once civilisation has been attained. As to what civilisation is—I'd tend to say that it consists of settled residence in permanent homes, development of industries favourable to settled life, intelligent organisation of the people to avoid waste of energy and mutual encroachment, higher standards of knowledge and beauty, and a general tendency toward the encouragement of a full personality and the minimisation of those factors which interfere with full development. The tendency to form a sounder scale of *values* than barbarism possesses, would probably be included under the heading of higher standards of knowledge and beauty. As to barbarians—one cannot of course apply the term 'dull, mindless clods' to all of them. One may merely remark that their mode of life tended to make them *more like that* (in varying degree of course) than is the fully civilised man. Mere orgiastic animal reactions do not constitute much of a removal from the state of mindless, primitive matter, while callousness toward the mutilation of living beings marks close kinship with the inert and unorganised . . . . i.e., a flagrant lack of delicacy, nervous sensitiveness, and sympathetic imagination. Side by side with the bestial and mindless characteristics, of course, there existed the rudiments of those higher qualities which were to give birth to civilisation. As the race ascended in the scale, these qualities became emphasised; so that we behold the poetic mentality of the Polynesian and American Indian, the lyrical prowess of the early Aryan bard, the rising ethical conceptions (honour—discriminating *courage* as distinguished from brute belligerency and the absence of fear due to defective imagination—magnanimity—kindness—etc.) of many tribes, and other characteristics which lend a glamour to the later phases of barbarism. But we must not forget that all these desirable qualities are carried over without loss into the earlier and sounder phases of civilisation, while many of their undesirable concomitants are left behind. And decadence has to go a long way before they decline enough to annul the net gain caused by the change. To sum up—while recognising all the undeniable virtues of barbaric life, I cannot see how these can possibly overbalance the abysmal vacancies and hideous defects which coexisted with them. The worst and most beastlike sides of man were overdeveloped, and the best and most human sides were underdeveloped. When you compare the type of experience involved in killing and plundering with that involved in thinking and appreciating, you are ignoring so many irrefutable evolutionary facts and psychological values that the comparison cannot really count in an argument. The use of that mode of reasoning would glorify the lion, the crocodile, or the extinct tyrannosaurus rex above mankind—which I am sure you do not mean to do. The trouble with your whole argument is that you underestimate the value of the human side of life. You show this by your confident assertion (in connexion with Jack London) that "the aims, pretenses, and aspirations of artists are basically as ultimately empty, futile, and meaningless as those of the wallowing masses"—an assertion which ignores completely the real facts, both psychological and evolutionary, connected with disinterested intellectual and aesthetic effort, and the poignant and supreme satisfaction afforded to maturely developed personalities by the successful exercise of the faculties in these fields. It is useless to argue when basic facts are denied. You certainly have a fatal prejudice against the highest expression of the human personality which is bound to interfere with your formation of a correct social and historical perspective. In a way, I can see how you may have formed such a prejudice. Living in a region where immediate conditions give a high valuation to the qualities needed in the physical-survival struggle, you naturally tend, before reflection, to regard everything else as secondary. Moreover (just as you tend to take a special and only partly developed form of civilisation as typical of all civilisation) you have probably been unfavourably influenced by inferior exponents of the intellectual-aesthetic outlook—persons who represent not creative work itself, but only the *hollow attitudes of creative work;* and who in their posing adopt an attitude of depreciation toward other necessary phases of life. It ought not to be necessary to say that these poseurs of the "Greenwich-Village" type are merely to be ignored. They do not represent any rational civilised outlook. No responsible thinker tries to depreciate the solid human qualities (honour, kindness, courage, strength, perseverance, responsibility, etc.) upon which the foundations of all human institutions rest, or to belittle any individual because he may not represent the more complex expressions of personality. Any attempt at such depreciation or belittlement stamps one as an immature thinker. There is nothing whatever of this attitude in the position of the searcher who compares human values, inquires into the evolutionary status of each, investigates their place in the emotional life of every type of mankind, and finally tries to figure out just what it is that all the prevailing human struggle is for. If such an honest searcher ends up by saying that the supreme expression of personality is the exercise of the mind and of the aesthetically creative and appreciative faculties, he is by no means denying that other legitimate expressions exist, or that myriads of individuals can be admirable social assets without taking advantage of the supreme expression (that is, in its more separately formulated aspects). All that he means to say is that these things—mental and aesthetic life—have been found to form what all developing humans naturally tend to gravitate toward as the fullest way of satisfying the net resultant of their myriad conflicting urges; that the fullest and best-rounded life is to be obtained through them; that, therefore, the opportunities for their free exercise are the most logical goals in the human struggle; and that, all things considered, it is more sensible to uphold a social system in which these things can have free play (without any necessary injury to other aspects of life) than to uphold a system in which they must be sacrificed to antagonistic things demonstrably far lower in the scale of removal from primitive protoplasm. In all this there is no hostility toward less evolved types of life. Everyone knows that evolution is fragmentary and uneven; and the very man who insists on the biological superiority of mental life, and upon the encouragement of a state of society favourable to it, may freely and cheerfully confess to dozens of aspects of intellectual-aesthetic underdevelopment in his own personality. What he holds uppermost is the fact that, allowing for all defects, we really do get more of our thorough, permanent, and satisfying rewards from *fragments* of this mental life (no matter how small the fragment or fragments may be in any one case) than we do from anything else; and that the higher we may happen to be in the scale of emotional development (a scale on which larger and larger numbers of persons are gradually moving upward, so that it is to the interest of all to make safe the rewards desired by its higher types), the more completely will our thorough, permanent satisfactions depend upon this mental life. It would in any case be destructive and anti-human to encourage any form of social organisation other than that which brings out and favours the best in man—which sets him farthest above the other animals—and mature reflection shows that even the (at present) less evolved members of society have good reasons for insisting that no lower standard be tolerated. I don't see how you can, on the one hand, very logically refute this general position; or how you can, on the other hand, confound it with the cheap snobbery of those pseudo-intellectuals and mock-aesthetes who think that the reading of two or three cultural "outlines" gives them the right to despise all the plain citizenry of the planet. Heaven knows, I hate these posers as thoroughly as you possibly can! I recognise no types or classes in the ordinary relations of life, and admire all good qualities wherever I find them— irrespective of association with other qualities which I admire. Only the other day I ridiculed a correspondent who proposed a sort of neo-Nietzscheism with separate moral codes for "intellectuals" and ordinary folk.[3] But at the same time I have too high a regard for accuracy to let sentimental fallacies overcloud a general perspective of mankind and social organisation. It is clear to me that certain sets of qualities are connected with high degrees of evolution—the direction away from amorphous protoplasm, in which most of mankind seems to be moving—while other sets are connected with low or comparatively low degrees—the direction toward that amorphous protoplasm which we have left behind. And I believe it is only reasonable to insist that we favour the higher qualities—at the expense of the lower if necessary. It would be mere pretence if I tried to adhere to any other position, because I can't see that any other position has a leg to stand on. I assume you realise that I don't postulate any fixed connexion between highly evolved life and the *formal studies* expressive of it. That is, I assume you realise that I recognise high intellectual and aesthetic development in myriads of persons without advanced *formal education*. These naturally rational and appreciative people in all walks of life— people who act from reason and take pleasure in the exercise of reason, who delight in the beauty of flowers, landscapes, sunsets, and some forms of art, who act according to principles instinctively ethical, and who hate cruelty, encroachment, high-handedness, the defacement of the living form, and other stigmata of low development—represent just as high a degree of emotional evolution as do formal scholars and artists, and are just as much the beneficiaries of civilisation. It is for them, just as much as for the formal scholars and artists, that the upholder of civilisation is fighting. In estimating the elements of life, no serious comparison between thought, beauty, ethics, decency, and kindliness on the one hand, and blood-lust, thought-repression, predatory roving, ignorance, callousness, and bestial mangling on the other hand. No matter what bad qualities (like trickiness) tend to become associated with the first group, or what pleasant qualities (like unlimited freedom, the apparent straightforwardness which comes from stupidity and ignorance, and certain extremes of physical prowess) tend to accompany the second group, we cannot possibly do other than give our net preference to group I. Probably many persons allow their detestation of *trickiness* (and nobody detests it more than I!) to prejudice them unduly against the civilisation which seems to them to breed it. Against this quality they array the *directness* of the barbarian. Yet if they would exercise their judgment they would see that the contrast does not establish a true moral antithesis. *There are just as many really straightforward men in civilisation as in barbarism*—just as many who have the aesthetic or ethical sensitiveness to respect the natural rights of others. The only difference involved is in the *kind* of anti-social selfishness practiced by those *in both groups* who lack this aesthetic-ethical sensitiveness. In each case—that of the civilised man and that of the barbarian—the callously anti-social offender merely uses for his selfish ends *whatever weapon fits him most handily.* For the civilised man, trickery is the natural weapon. For the barbarian, brute strength. *But the motive behind both types of anti-social action is precisely the same.* You cannot say that a theft or injustice by trickery is any more contemptible or reprehensible than a theft or injustice accomplished through a brute strength too stupid and ignorant to exercise the trickery which it would if it could. It is no worse to swindle a man out of $500 than to break into his house, seize the $500 by brute strength, carve and mash him in "healthy, straightforward barbarian blood-lust", and depart after setting fire to the place. The attitude at the back of each criminal's head is exactly the same, and only a hopeless idiot or sentimentalist could—if he stopped to think—condemn the "tricky" civilisee while praising the "straightforward" barbarian. Yet we still find people romantically belittling the "tricky, complex" ways of civilisation, and praising the "simple, direct" barbarian. As a matter of fact, there are just as many men with *the real intent and psychology of straightforwardness* in civilisation as in barbarism. What makes barbarism *seem* to have more straightforwrd men, is the fact that those anti-social members who would be tricky if they could don't know enough to be, hence adopt bestial slashing and pounding instead of stratagem. Turn to civilisation, and you'll find that the ruthless tricky element forms no larger a proportion than the corresponding anti-social, ruthless element among savages. It is simply the anti-intellectualism of childhood which condemns acquisition by stratagem as opposed to acquisition by violence. Both forms involve merely the employment of the handiest weapon at hand. The psychology is the same, and the degree of reprehensibility is the same. That violent acquisition sometimes involves a form of courage is largely irrelevant. Many forms of strategic acquisition also involve courage, and there is no indication that it would not, if necessary, be employed in many others which may less often require it. *All* unlawful and dishonourable acquisition is reprehensible, and it really makes very little difference how it is accomplished. And yet I can understand something of the feeling behind the irrational prejudice. Trickery is so often associated with especially craven individuals and decadent races that its atmosphere is necessarily very repugnant. But we must not allow such atmospheric considerations to lead us into false appraisals destructive of a true social perspective.

As the argument draws toward its conclusion, I trust you do not fancy that I depreciate the great barbarians of history. Previous utterances ought to make it clear that I do not. Many of them, it is obvious, embodied substantial qualities of merit which are common to barbarism and civilisation, and still other qualities which are really civilised but which often appear in the later stages of barbarism. Their defects and callousnesses were not of their choosing, but were merely the accidents of an inevitable environment—the only environment they knew. For them I have the highest respect. But I cannot think that civilisation would have made them less eminent. An Arminius at the head of a Macedonian phalanx, or a Vercingetorix in command of a Roman legion, would have been no less distinguished than the Arminius and Vercingetorix whom chance placed as it did. What I object to in barbarism are its positive and unmistakable bad qualities—its appalling brutishness, insane ignorance and narrowness, and savage opposition to the most truly human fields of mankind's potential experience. And I don't see how any enumeration of its few advantages can suffice to whitewash it. Those forms which most closely approached civilisation, of course, (such as the near-civilisation of the Gauls in Caesar's time) are entitled to a respect which the more savage forms do not merit.

I don't think I even need to emphasise the fact that my argument implies no light or disrespectful estimate of your position. On the contrary, you can realise from the length and detail of my harangue that I do take your position very seriously indeed. It would be foolish to take other than seriously any position held by one of your scholarship, natural endowments, and imaginative attainments. I am merely trying to get a clarified perspective—to see how your tenure of your position can square with the absolute natural facts as I am able to envisage them. And incidentally, I am trying to make my own position clear, so that you will not attribute to me any opinions or standpoints which are not in truth mine. Throughout the argument you will probably accuse me of presenting civilisation in too favourable a light—but in reply to that let me repeat a previous assurance that I am not blind to its defects. My position is (a) that the number of people who suffer in civilisation is far less, and that the degree of their suffering is generally far less, than in barbarism; and (b) that civilisation expands man's natural capacities to the utmost, raising him as high as possible above other animals and satisfying his total impulses most completely, while barbarism crushes and restricts those capacities, dragging him toward the beast and offering very doubtful advantages in return. When you come to examine your own attitude toward human suffering, you will probably find that your exaggerated estimate of it arose from that same romantic-sentimental fallacy pointed out some paragraphs back, whereby so many persons *resent the evil caused by stratagem more than the evil caused by violence.* You are hostile toward the oppressions of civilisation because they are the result of calculation and organisation, and lenient toward the vastly greater oppressions of barbarism because these are the result of hacking and slashing and bludgeoning. But is this sentimental anti-intellectualism in any way justified by reason? I am sure you will eventually come to agree that it is not. I, too, despise the oppression of great corporations, and the maladministration of law by corrupt officials, and would do all in my power to abolish them—but this does not prevent me from also despising the oppressions of barbarian sea-rovers and plundering chieftains, the disgusting and subhuman tortures and mutilations blackening the record of barbarian folkways, and the fanatical outragings of human reason perpetrated by barbarian tribal and sacerdotal agencies. Judged by any theoretical ideal, all life is evil. I merely believe that civilised life is the least evil of the various alternatives known and open to us. And that goes only for our race. Other races, other ways. I am at one with those who lament the imposition of Aryan civilisation upon alien races who—like the Polynesians and the more advanced American Indians—were gradually working out ways of life of their own, fitted to their especial needs.

Much, of course, in the matter of a clear general understanding of these issues, depends upon a rational stand regarding basic human values. In time, I think your bitter anti-intellectual and anti-aesthetic bias cannot help abating; especially when you realise that a recognition of the evolutionary paramountcy of mental life does not involve any actual disparagement of other life-elements in their proper places, and that it does not involve any worship of the special scholar and artist types at the expense of other types embodying balanced development. And likewise, I hope it is plain that I would not even think of depreciating the sturdy qualities of honour, courage, strength, persistence, responsibility, kindliness, etc., which (as I do not merely *admit,* but positively *assert and insist*) must always accompany and supplement the purely intellectual-aesthetic qualities in any effective, desirable, and socially useful character. You might easily come to underestimate my profound and insistent regard for these sturdy qualities, because my recent arguments have not lain in a direction to bring them up prominently, and because I have been obliged to champion a parallel set of qualities with especial vigour. However, please be assured that I do possess such a profound and insistent regard. I wish you could see the arguments which I fire toward persons of the amoral intellectual-aesthetic type! And I fancy that an earlier part of this letter made clear my lack of all opposition to rational physical development, or to a well-proportioned pride in physical prowess.

As an ultimate conclusion to this harangue, let me say that I was paying you no left-handed compliment when comparing you with the celebrated Scottish anthropologist James Burnett, Lord Monboddo (1714–1799). Lord Monboddo was a graduate of Aberdeen, and of the German university of Groningen, and his two books ("Origin and Progress of Language", 1773, and "Ancient Metaphysics", 1779) are scientific classics of their period. As a virtual pioneer in the unworked field of knowledge regarding the origins of man and of human society, he arrived at conclusions truly marvellous in their anticipation of the results of later research—including that of the descent of man from lower animals. His conclusions—based directly upon nature, and fortified by a profound knowledge of the Greek natural philosophers—differed widely from the ideas prevalent in his day, and he had to withstand a great deal of badinage. Preference for a barbaric state of society was only one of his opinions—and perhaps the least well founded. On this topic he was vigorously—and quite justly—attacked by Dr. Johnson.[4] Of course, the amount of knowledge regarding barbaric times existing in the 18th century was not comparable to ours. Monboddo lived in an age when the romanticists—culminating in Rousseau and Chateaubriand—were busily constructing sentimental pictures of the happy "age of innocence", and of the "noble savage" as opposed to the "debased" product of a "corrupt" civilisation—an age before any of the great 19th century anthropologists had conducted their exhaustive investigations into the nature of savage and barbaric life. But for all that, Lord Monboddo was no pygmy! You err in damned good company!

Regarding the fear of cats and other small animals—it does not seem to be associated with any specific unpleasant experience, but is apparently innate. It may be hereditary in some obscure way—bringing up associations with the larger predatory mammals. Our fairly general repugnance toward reptiles is possibly due to ancestral memories of the great saurians, but more probably due to experience with poisonous existing specimens. The natural shrinking from insects probably arises from the same cause. Aversion to rats and mice probably arises primarily from our association of them with filthy and malodorous conditions. Among those who have feared cats—though in a mild and controllable degree—was the celebrated biographer of Dr. Johnson—James Boswell. Your own early attitude toward horses was clearly a result of experience—not an irrational phobia. My mother—who when 4 years old was chased and bitten by a large dog—had a similar attitude toward dogs. One of the most curious cases of phobia on record is that of Prof. William Ellery Leonard of the U. of Wisconsin,[5] who when a very small child was badly frightened by a locomotive which passed close to him on a station platform and scalded him with steam. He developed a most anomalous fear of locomotives, which he afterward transferred to other objects symbolically associated with locomotives. Phobias of various sorts have pursued him all his life, and he described them a few years ago in an autobiographical volume called "The Locomotive God". That book is eminently worth reading by anyone in this general subject. Incidentally—I certainly would enjoy the plenitude of cats which you picture at your place. I'd invite a good bunch of them in and have them around my study—to me there's nothing on earth half so companionable.

I surely hope you will sometime prepare that treatise on Texas's historical and political background—and it really seems a pity to deny it to a larger audience than one. To my mind, the only way to correct the conditions you deplore is to give them intelligent publicity. Let them be discussed widely, and an effective body of public opinion against them can begin to form. Nor should the coöperation of such bodies as the American Civil Liberties Union be scorned. The head of that organisation, by the way—Roger Baldwin[6]—is connected by marriage with Long's family. But of course, I think you're wrong in associating these evils with civilisation as a whole. As I pointed out once before, the real trouble is obviously *the unsettled state incident to a transition.* Previously you had a sort of equilibrium—a set of stable folkways worked out to meet the conditions of the frontier. Then the period of easy communication and diffused business interest brought about a new set of conditions which was sprung on you without adequate preparation. New adjustments and problems arose before the local psychology could be modified to grapple with them, and the former equilibrium gave place to a kind of chaos in which objects, methods, and standards are all at cross-purposes. Things move so quickly in the machine age that there has been no time for normal evolution. Surely you don't think that the painful and rapacious conditions which disgust you are typical of a mature civilisation! As I've pointed out, your police problems are things so unknown in the east (or in any settled region) that I thought the Gladewater Journal was exaggerating until you backed it up with personal observation. All this capricious high-handedness and readiness to interfere with personal inviolability and dignity is *not a result of civilisation.* It is, in fact, *the direct reverse of civilisation.* The trouble is, that having inevitably passed out of an *earlier* equilibrium, the region has not yet reached a *newer* equilibrium. In other words, in relation to existing realities *it isn't civilised enough.* Anecdotes like those you relate—the prominent business man making an insane and hydrophobiac attack on a mere impertinent and helpless youth, and the fact that persons who show signs of literacy are likely to 'have their ears kicked off' by local mobs—shows a condition of unsettled ethics very remote from civilisation, yet very obviously the cause of the arrogance and lawlessness in police officers which you erroneously attribute to civilisation. If the public peace and the inviolability of the human personality are not yet respected by the people, how can the people expect the officers of the law to hold a higher standard of ethics? This is a condition which needs *more civilisation all around.* It is too late to go back to the frontier. Knife and gun and fist cannot cope with existing problems. Therefore the logical thing is to outgrow the knife-gun-fist psychology as quickly as possible, and work for a *new equilibrium* which *will* be possible under the conditions of the future. It can be done—time itself will help, and intelligent publicity and propaganda will help still more. But the direction to pull is forward, not backward. What is needed is the sense of responsibility and civic adjustment and public order and non-encroachment characteristic of long-settled regions. You don't hear of these barbarities in Charleston or Richmond* or Philadelphia or Boston. In all these places, well-disposed persons go where they will without molestation from either police or mobs. Really—as a corrective to your unfortunately twisted idea of *what civilisation is,* I wish you could arrange to live for a full year in a genuinely civilised city of old traditions and settled folkways—*but emphatically not New York.* If you would do that, you would come to harbour an entirely new point of view regarding these matters—and what I say about civilisation would not seem so strange to you. You would certainly not find it an unpleasant experience, even though as a permanent thing you would probably (like most of us) prefer to remain in a setting long familiar to you. The main thing that would be impressed upon you would be that *civilisation does not mean bad government or oppression*—that bad government and oppression are earmarks of half-civilisation and defective civilisation. However—I realise that I have no right to prescribe courses for a region I have never seen or studied in detail. Although it is certainly true that the only desirable general direction of development is forward toward full civilisation and the ways of orderly settled regions, it may well be that just at present—amidst an ambiguous chaos— some of the old summary methods of the frontier would be effective in cleaning up bad conditions. The one criterion of methods is needs—and if the best way to deal with oppressive officers is to tar and feather them and ride them out of the country, or to liberate their unjustly incarcerated prisoners by force, then I certainly wouldn't discourage that as a temporary measure pending political readjustment and gradual social evolution. I trust, incidentally, that the House of Ferguson has been living up to its promises. You must pardon what looks like a relapse into our main theoretical argument— but I really couldn't resist trying to correct what seems to me a vital misconception on your part; a misconception liable to hamper your whole social-political outlook until it can be removed. I have lived 42½ years in an old and settled civilisation, and have never suffered from oppression or seen anybody suffer from oppression, so you can understand how strongly I am convinced

---

*Richmond's recent political arrests have been exclusively of self-announced communists, and you surely agree that such safeguards of the social order are scarcely unjustified.

of your mistakenness when you denounce civilisation as an evil to be lamented. Again let me say that, in my firm and honest belief, what you find so unjust and intolerable is not civilisation itself, but merely the chaotic period of transition marking a region's loss of an older tradition preparatory to the development of civilisation. I'll swear that in later years, when Texas achieves new conditions—when, that is, it becomes more like such long and thoroughly civilised states as South Carolina, Virginia, Pennsylvania, or Massachusetts—you will find most of your present sources of complaint entirely vanished. Your *present* stage is what we went through in Saxon or Norman times nearly a thousand years ago—for as I pointed out some time ago, the Eastern seaboard and especially New England was settled so rapidly and voluminously that no true "pioneer" period existed. It was practically an extension of settled, civilised, coördinated Old England over a new area—for the first emigrants were soon living in towns of several thousand inhabitants, or in thickly settled countrysides, with all the familiar social adjustments and principles of non-encroachment laid down by the English common law. If all this seems remote and irrelevant to you, you really ought to try the experiment of living for a while in a long-settled region.

I was greatly interested in your remarks supplementing the article on buffalo-hunters. The situation in Kansas was surely tense, and demonstrates the error of dealing with a problem before thoroughly appraising it. And I am reminded anew that all this lore of the epic days—extending over an imperially vast area and involving so many separate and often obscure legends—ought eventually to be summarised and given a clear, unified presentation by some writer erudite enough on the one hand, and stylistically skilled enough on the other hand, to do it justice. Who is a better candidate for that job than you? Certainly no one is more steeped in the history and spirit of the events, more sensitive to the dramatic sweep of the whole empire-building pageant, or more capable of capturing the stirring cycle in prose which comes close to poetry in imagery and fire.

By the way—I was quite astonished by your recent revelation that you are only 27. You must, then, have been only a youth of 19 when you wrote "Wolfshead" and other pieces achieving success and prominence in W.T. (and possibly elsewhere) That is certainly a very substantial testimony of brilliancy, for your 1925 tales were far ahead of any other 19-year-old's work that I've ever seen in the magazine. And your growth since then has been steady. I really wish you didn't take such a contemptuous view of literature—or rather, of the process of literary creation. You're really doing an important side of your own personality a grave injustice! By the way, I recall your collaborated story with Tevis Clyde Smith, and thought it vivid and excellent. I also treasure in my files his brochure—"Frontier's Generation"—which you sent me. I don't wonder that you have received inquiries about "The Road of Kings"—which, together with the "old ballads" and other alluring fragments at the head of your chapters, certainly forms poetry of the most genuine sort. These bits have a magnificently stirring rhythm and haunting imagery, and I really wish you would some day actually round them out into the epics and ballads to which they are attributed. What you say of Gottfried von Kalmbach interests me mightily. I suppose he is destined for the Magic Carpet rather than W.T.—and I hope you'll tell me when he appears, since I don't get the M.C. regularly.

March 29.

Yes—I always enjoy good museums, of which my modest wanderings have allowed me to see a fair variety. The collection in the old Cabildo at New Orleans has some notable items, and the industrial museum in the old court building (the duplicate of the Cabildo) at the other end of the square is also worth visiting. For art, the Delgado Museum in City Park is far from bad. The greatest museum centres of the country are probably Boston, New York, Philadelphia, and Washington, though many other cities have museums of special kinds which surpass any in these metropolitan centres. Here in Providence, for instance, we have three absolutely unique collections—the greatest library of Americana in the world (John Carter Brown Library of Brown Univ.), the greatest collection of American poetry in the world (Harris Collection in the John Hay Library of Brown Univ.), and the greatest collection of early printed books (before 1500) in the United States (Annmary Brown Memorial Library). In New Bedford, Mass., the Whaling Museum contains the world's greatest collection of whaling relics, plus a half-size replica of the old whaling barque Lagoda, fully and accurately equipped, and housed in a great hall. For Civil War relics, nothing can approach the Confederate Museum in Richmond, housed in the mansion (the old Brockenbrough House, a fine late-Georgian specimen built in 1818 and standing close to the grassy bluff at the end of Clay St. where Poe as a small boy used to climb down to bathe in old Shockoe Creek, which has since been filled in) occupied by Pres. Davis during the war. If your chief museum interests are arms and armour, I fancy the vast Metropolitan Museum of Art in New York would be your logical goal. A whole immense hall there is devoted to that one subject. Sorry you find a private collection prohibitively expensive.

As to my "education"—such as it is—ill health in youth made a sorry mess of it. As a child I was always dragging from one nervous breakdown to another, hence attended school only intermittently—piecing out with a private tutor, and with the home instruction picked up from my grandfather, mother, and aunts (my father died when I was very young). My longest quasi-continuous stretch was high-school—1904 to 1908—but even that was interrupted by a breakdown in the latter half of the 1905–6 term. I never attended college. I was to have gone to Brown University in my own city, but in the fall of 1908 I was so near a collapse that I couldn't attempt it.[7] I wasn't much better in 1909, and in the end I decided I'd better not try any more systematic instruction. Today I'm sorry I didn't, because I can see how one-sided my alleged education is. I am abysmally weak in modern languages, and mathematics, and in certain phases of history (such as that of the European Continent in mediaeval and modern times)—while my absence of training in economics and sociology is really a deplorable handicap to me in my efforts to understand the trend of these tense times, when so much of the motivation of nations, as well as their internal problems, depend almost wholly on complex economic consideration. If I seem to some people to *overvalue* learning, it is because I am so damned ignorant myself. We appreciate what we lack ourselves. What has redeemed me from a still worse ignorance is a fairly lively curiosity about things in general; which has led me to read up on various subjects, and to argue at great length with people who know more about things than I do. My first interests were in mythology of various sorts—Grimm's Fairy Tales, the Arabian Nights, and sundry popular versions of the Greek and Roman myths. Antiquarianism then—or rather, simultaneously—claimed my attention, and when six years old I used to go up in the attic of the old home and browse among the 18th century books exiled there from the library downstairs. (I have most of them still.) I learned the art of versification out of one of these—a manual of rhetoric published in 1797 and studied by one of my great-grandfathers in his day. My interest in the Graeco-Roman myths led me to search out the classics from which the popular versions were derived—and these I found in the form of poetical translations by Dryden, Pope, etc.—a kind of reading which got me interested in the age of Dryden and Pope and thus (in connexion with other things such as the old books in the attic and the old houses and traditions of Providence) led to the 18th century bias which I have ever since retained. When I was 8 I became interested in chemistry, and this led to a long period in which the natural sciences formed my paramount interest. Geography— geology—anthropology—physics—and above all astronomy, which left an indelible impress on me. I had many instruments (of which I still retain a good small telescope) and books on the subject, and for years (1906–1918) contributed monthly articles on celestial phenomena to the lesser local papers, besides issuing a small astronomical magazine (1903–1907) on a hectograph.[8] All this time, however, I was still greatly interested in weird literature. I first attempted stories and verses in 1897—age 7—and kept right along attempting although the results were 100% worthless. About this time I first encountered Poe, and became his eternal disciple. It was in the spring of 1905 that I first wrote a story worth reading—an effusion called "The Beast in the Cave", which involved a prodigious amount of study of Kentucky's Mammoth Cave. I still have it, although it isn't up to professional publication grade. The style is heavy and Johnsonese—pure 18th century. In 1908 I decided that fiction was not my forte, and destroyed all but two of my many crude tales. I was then busy writing popular treatises on astronomy and chemistry, which I later destroyed. Around 1910 or 1911 I began to take my versification more seriously than before—a great mistake since I could never be a first-rate poet. From then onward till 1917 I specialised in verse and general belles-lettres—always with an 18th century bias, and with some ambitions of achieving competence in the critical field. After 1914 I was greatly helped and encouraged by some amateur press associations which I joined—one of which (the only survivor of the two) I still belong to, as attested by the critical brochure[9] I sent you last autumn. But all this time I was not as sedentary or indoors-bound as one might judge from my health and interests. I managed to get out and around considerably, played with boys of my age, and did a vast lot of bicycle riding (which familiarised me intimately with the Rhode Island and Massachusetts countryside, and laid the foundation of my predominantly rural tastes) between 1900 and 1913. I could not, however, be sure of any continuous supply of energy; hence stuck close to home and did no real travelling beyond the Boston–Worcester radius. I did not resume writing weird tales till 1917, when some of the members of the amateur association saw the two I had saved from the flames and urged me to write more. The results were "The Tomb" and "Dagon", published later in W.T. This resumption was very gradual, though—for in 1918 (an off year in point of health) I wrote only one tale—"Polaris", which Wright later rejected. In 1919 I received the greatest literary stimulus I had had since discovering Poe—through my discovery of *Dunsany*. Under this new influence I began writing voluminously—though much of the stuff was rotten and unduly imitative of my illustrious model. I heard Dunsany lecture in Boston in October 1919. In 1922 the sudden and radical improvement in my health allowed me to *travel* for the first time. I visited ancient Salem (Arkham) and Marblehead (Kingsport), spent some time in New York, and got as far west as Cleveland. Meanwhile I had been doing a good deal of the revisory work which I still do. In 1923 W.T. was founded, and I had my first stories published professionally (except for two serials in a vile rag called Home Brew).[10] In 1924 and 1925 I was in Brooklyn, but an increasing hatred for the metropolitan zone brought me home to stay in 1926. My travels were slowly extending. In 1923 I got as far north as Portsmouth, N. H., and in 1924 I got down to Philadelphia. In 1925 I made Washington and Alexandria. In 1927 I explored western Mass. and got up to Portland, Me. In 1928 I got up to Vermont and down to Baltimore, Annapolis, and Washington, and visited the *nether world* for the first time—the Endless Caverns at New Market, Va. In 1929 I got down to Richmond, Williamsburg, Jamestown, and Yorktown, and also visited our friend Dwyer in ancient Kingston. In 1930 I made Charleston—also stopping in Richmond and visiting Petersburg—while in the autumn, as you know, I plunged north to ancient and incomparable Quebec. And so it goes. Florida 1931, Chattanooga–

Vicksburg–Natchez–New Orleans—and also Montreal–Quebec–Isle d'Orleans 1932. . . . But I fear my expansions of radius are about over, owing to financial trouble. This will be a bad year—indeed, I shall probably have to seek cheaper quarters than 10 Barnes before long. Well—all this has been education in its way. I never visit a place without reading up fully on its history and antiquities, and in that way my background gradually grows. Then again, many of my revision jobs involve so much research—or so many technical problems—that they help to swell my narrow store of ideas. My literary standards have definitely risen ---whether or not my own writing succeeds in keeping up with them. My first fictional period—that of florid, rhetorical stuff—ended about 1927. Then, beginning with "The Colour Out of Space", began my quasi-realistic period. Now I am in a sort of impasse again. I'm dissatisfied with my stuff, but can't agree just what to do about it. If I ever get time to write any more original tales, I'll probably do quite a bit of diverse experimenting.[11]

As for actual schooldays—I always liked school, although I didn't fit in with the discipline overly well during the fragmentary grammar-school snatches. In high school, however, I never realised there was such a thing as discipline. The teachers—a goodly percentage of them men—took the position that the pupils were near enough to responsible adulthood to be treated as adults, and in return for this compliment the vast majority—including myself—reciprocated by behaving like adults. Naturally we were expected to follow the time-schedule of the school—just as the teachers themselves were obliged to—and it was also naturally expected that we were not to shout and jump about the classrooms like infants or puppies. But we didn't regard this as tyrannical discipline because it was obviously reasonable. What school could be conducted otherwise? I don't recall, at high school, any of the senseless and arbitrary little restrictions which irked me at grammar school—and which seem to have existed in your high school. Nor can I cite any instance of disproportionate severity or arrogant authority-parading in the occasional cases of minor rule-infractions due to exuberance. Not all the teachers, of course, were equally well-liked; but there was nothing in my memory amounting to major friction. I really detested only one teacher—whom I had in algebra, and who found fault with methods of solving problems, even when correct, if the steps did not agree with his own. He *might* have tried to "ride" me (he especially disliked me because my methods were unorthodox) if I had not brought him up short the first time he became really offensive; but as it was, I was able to force a showdown—a blackboard demonstration of the actual correctness (which he wanted to deny by forestalling proof) of my method. After that a policy of dignified peace—though scarcely of cordiality—prevailed betwixt me and the gentleman. In another case I had a tilt with a history teacher, but made a good friend of him. He asked me what the native races of Europe were, and I told him Caucasian and Mongolian. That last didn't suit him, and he began to tell me that *Asia* was the only home of the Mongol. Then I reminded him of the *Lapps,* and of the original stock, at least, of the Finns, Magyars, and Turks. He was doubtful, but slowly began to see the light; and was afterward the most affable of beings. Another near-tilt was in the fall of 1906—with a fat old lady English teacher. I had handed in a theme entitled "Can the Moon Be Reached By Man"? And something about it (gawd knows what) led her to question its originality. She said it sounded like a magazine article. Well—chance was with me that day, for I had the ammunition to stage a peach of a tableau. Did I deny the magazine-article charge? Not so! Instead, I calmly informed the lady that the theme was indeed a verbatim parallel of an article which had appeared in a rural weekly only a few days before. I felt sure, I said, that no one could possibly object to the parallelism! Indeed, I added—as the good soul's bewilderment became almost apoplectic—I would be glad to show her the printed article in question! Then, reaching in my pocket, I produced a badly printed cutting from a Rhode Island village paper (which would accept almost anything sent to it). Sure enough—here was the selfsame article. And mixed were the emotions of the honest Mrs. Blake when she perused the heading—CAN THE MOON BE REACHED BY MAN? BY H. P. LOVECRAFT.[12] In studies I was not bad—except for mathematics, which repelled and exhausted me. I passed in these subjects—but just about that. Or rather, it was *algebra* which formed the bugbear. Geometry was not so bad. But the whole thing disappointed me bitterly, for I was then intending to pursue *astronomy* as a career, and of course advanced astronomy is simply a mass of mathematics. That was the first major set-back I ever received—the first time I was ever brought up short against a consciousness of my own limitations. It was clear to me that I hadn't brains enough to be an astronomer—and that was a pill I couldn't swallow with equanimity. But it's just as well to have one's ego deflated early. As for other studies—English rather bored me, because it virtually repeated ground over which my home reading had long ago ranged. Latin and Greek were my delight—although I had a long-standing feud with teachers of the former over pronunciation. My grandfather had previously taught me a great deal of Latin, using the traditional English pronunciation taught in his day, but at school I was expected to follow the "Roman method" which attempts to duplicate the actual pronunciation of the Romans. Instead of *Caesar* (Seezar) I was expected to say "Ky´sar". Cicero became Kikero, Scipio, Skeep´io, and so on. It got on my nerves . . . . . fancy pronouncing *juvenes urbium vicinarum* as *yoo´-way-nace oor-beoom wee-kee-nah´-room!* Ugh! Well—in this case the school won. I had to modify my method, untraditional as the change seemed to me. At least, it was a consolation to reflect that this odd way brought me closer to Immortal Rome itself! But the conflict was never quite settled—and even today I waver between methods, with nigh disastrous results. In Greek I had no quarrel—and didn't get beyond the first six books of

Xenophon anyhow. Ancient history I ate up avidly; aided by some previous acquaintance with the subject, and by my abiding love of Rome. Botany was a sort of neutral subject with me. German I frankly disliked. Above all else (except perhaps Latin and Ancient History) I revelled in physics and chemistry—subjects I was also studying at home. I had a small and pretty well equipped basement laboratory of my own, but the chance to use the great school laboratories was a rare delight. All told, I had a pretty good time at high school, and I look back on that period with considerable affection. Alas for the changes of time. Some of the teachers are dead, my physics-chemistry teacher is a lawyer now, and my old principal is in an insane asylum[13] (the one where my young friend Brobst is now a nurse). Eheu fugaces![14] Well—I live only two squares from old Hope St. High School now, and the building looks pretty much the same. The papers call it an 'antiquated fire-trap' these days—though I saw it built in 1897, long before I ever attended it. There's a symbol of senility—the decadence of buildings which one saw rising in one's far-off youth!

What you say of the "tough" schools of Texas is indeed interesting. Early rural New England had some rather hardy school conditions—overgrown youths who occasionally disputed the preceptor's rule with physical prowess—but it never got as far as *weapons* in these parts! To apply the ancient vaudeville gag—the canary-birds surely do sing bass where you come from! I have a delightful book about the district schools of Vermont in the early 1800's—but all the lusty anecdotes would sound tame beside the sanguinary chronicles of your halls of erudition. I can imagine a Texas mother packing her hopeful three-year-old off to kindergarten . . . . "Have you got your slate and pencil, dear? And your knife and six-shooter? Don't shoot teacher unless he shoots first!" But I assume that even now time has modified some of these virile folkways.

A research job took me to Hartford, Conn. three weeks ago, and I took delight in exploring the ancient suburbs of Farmington and Wethersfield.[15] Farmington is one of the most beautiful old villages I have ever seen—situate in a picturesque rolling country with splendid vistas, and adorned with magnificent elms. The house are very old—including one of the 17th century type with overhanging second story—and the steepled church dates from 1771. I stopped at a rambling inn whose nucleus was built in 1638, and no part of which is later than 1790. Wethersfield lies in a flat region, and has an immensely broad common lined with the greatest elms east of the Rocky Mountains. The houses are largely Colonial, and of typical Connecticut-valley architecture. Among them is the Webb house, where in May 1781 Washington and Rochambeau planned the Virginia campaign which ended in Yorktown. The brick church, built in 1763, was then called the finest in New England outside Boston. It was in Wethersfield that the Pequot War of 1637 started.

Well—I'll shut up for the time being. Doubtless my endless arguings will cause you to proclaim me a garrulous old bore—but as you see, the problems at issue vastly interest me and make me strive for light on the whole subject. At least, my arguments help me clarify my own opinions—and I feel sure you will realise the complete absence of any arrogant spirit in them.

Best wishes, and hoping to see more of your work soon—

Yrs. most cordially and sincerely

H P L

P.S. My "Dreams in the Witch House" will appear in the July W.T. I hadn't meant to submit it, but Derleth showed Wright a copy and he decided to offer $140 for it. "The Festival" will also appear soon as a reprint.

P.P.S. 18° below in Texas? Brrr! 10° above is the worst we've had this winter—and that's plenty bad enough for me! Spring is here now—but so far it has meant little save chilly rain.

Notes

1. British philosopher Bertrand Russell (1872–1970) spoke harshly of Soviet communism in *Bolshevism: Practice and Theory* (1920), based on a trip made to the Soviet Union in 1920.

2. P. Cornelius Scipio Aemilianus Africanus Numantinus (184–129 B.C.E.), Roman military and political leader who achieved great distinction during the Third Punic War (149–48) and in the Numantine War (133).

3. See HPL to AWD, March 23[, 1933] (*Essential Solitude* 554).

4. There are repeated attacks by Samuel Johnson on Monboddo's view of primitive man recorded in James Boswell's *Life of Johnson* (1791).

5. William Ellery Leonard (1876–1944), professor of English at the University of Wisconsin (1906–44) and author of many books of poetry and of translations from Latin and Greek authors. HPL's friend Alfred Galpin studied with him.

6. Roger Nash Baldwin (1884–1981), social activist and executive director of the ACLU (1920–50). He was married to Madeleine Doty, who was related to FBL's mother, May (Doty) Long.

7. Actually, HPL suffered a nervous breakdown in June 1908, just at the end of his third year of high school. He would have had to attend at least another year of high school before being eligible to attend Brown University.

8. HPL's astronomy columns ran in the *Pawtuxet Valley Gleaner* (1906–08?), the *Providence Tribune* (1906–08), and the *Providence Evening News* (1914–18). He had no columns in the intervening period. His hectographed journal was the *Rhode Island Journal of Astronomy*.

9. *Further Criticism of Poetry* (Louisville, KY: George G. Fetter, 1932).

10. "Herbert West—Reanimator" and "The Lurking Fear."

11. In 1932–33, lacking confidence in the merits of his work, HPL reread the classics of weird fiction, and in doing so took notes attempting to capture the essence of those works for his own use in writing new fiction.

12. The article appeared in the *Pawtuxet Valley Gleaner* (12 October 1906).

13. Charles E. Dennis, Jr., principal of Hope Street High School.

14. From Horace, *Odes* 2.14.1–2: *Eheu, fugaces . . . labuntur anni* ("Alas, the fleeting years rush along").

15. In fact, HPL was visiting his ex-wife, Sonia H. Greene. It was the last time he would see her in person.

[80]   [TLS]

[23 April 1933]

Dear Mr. Lovecraft:

I'm enclosing some of the latest views of places of which I've doubtless sent you pictures before.

Last week was the Fiesta de San Jacinto, which I find more wearisome each year. It was during the Battle of Flowers, the climax of the fiesta, that news came of the declaration of war on Spain. A hell of a time; bugles blowing, cannons rumbling at Fort Sam Houston, women fainting, men in uniform tearing away to take their proper places—an aunt of mine lived here then and saw it all. She saw them go and she saw them come—scare-crows in tattered uniforms, some of them, reeling in their saddles, marked by malaria and Spanish bullets and Filipino kampilans. The Spanish-American war was no picnic, regardless of what they say.

All the news of the Southwest blows through San Antonio. For instance, I've done a lot of reading on a certain subject here, and a letter from the hill country far away from here proved a strange coincidence. I'll quote it, in part.

"Dear Bob:

The feuds seem to be at a low ebb, about the only thing that happened was one brawl out on the high way between here and Burkett which ended by Odie L—— nearly cutting one bozo's arm off. Two more guys were threatening to fight, Odie urged them to let him have their knives, some way Odie got mixed up in the following encounter and did his whittling.

We went fishing Tuesday. One of the boys sat down by a rattlesnake when we first arrived, but the snake was too cold to move, so we killed him without any trouble, he only had two rattles and I didn't bother to take them. We were on the San Saba river first; a short distance up the river from us a gang of outlaws or gold prospectors were camped, they had enough guns to do credit to any army, they seemed to be digging for some reason or other. Every time one of us would get in sight they would go for their guns. I always despised a man who didn't have any confidence in me, so I didn't go near them.

Pink."

Typical letter from the postoak country. I know what those gun-toting gents were after. Gold—tons of gold. Enough gold to sink a battleship. No, it's not the liquor talking now, though this San Antonio booze kicks like an army mule. Gold. Los Almagres, Las Amarillas, La Mina de las Iguanas, the Lost Llano Mine, the Lost San Saba Mine, the Lost Bowie Mine. They won't find it, not if they blast apart the hills till the sky splits like Judgment Day. But it's there.

> "They were there, in the distance dreaming
> Their dreams that were worn and old;
> They were there, to his frenzied seeming,
> Still burrowing down for gold."[1]

The only way to find a lost mine is not to look for it. If it's meant for you to find, you'll stump your toe on it, or your horse will throw you into a bed of nuggets as big as ostrich eggs.

Coincidence, though, that just after I should have been reading so much about the San Saba mine, I should have heard tidings of its searchers from a man who did not suspect its existence. Not so strange, either; news of all southwest blows on the winds through San Antonio, which was the heart of Old Texas, just as at an earlier day it was the heart of New Philippines, and earlier yet, the heart of New Spain. A hundred years of Spanish life, and never a Saxon set foot on Texas soil. San Antonio was more Spanish than was Mexico City, for it was settled by grandees from the Canary Islands, chosen for their pure Castilian blood. No Indian mixture among them, as it was among the Mexicans.

What was I talking about?

I remember. The Lost San Saba Mine. They showed it to Jim Bowie. That was the doings of Tres Manos, the Lipan chief. His sight was stunned and dazzled by the immensity of the treasure—Bowie, I mean. He reeled, and his wits went from him like light flicked from a candle by a rifle bullet. His mind was numbed by what he had seen. Not the main vein; only the store room; gold bars stacked in a cavern from floor to roof, catching the sunlight glinting through the leaves and reflecting it like a sheet of pulsing flame. He rode all night; his horse fell under him, and he staggered on afoot. Tres Manos missed him from the tribe and was on his trail, but Bowie won that race. He was a Lipan by adoption. He had seen the red men trading silver and gold armlets to the merchants near the Presidio. For months he fought and hunted with Tres Manos' braves. At last they showed him the cavern stacked with golden bars that caught the beams of the sun in a net of flame. Tres

Manos was brave. He followed Bowie into San Antonio, met him and called him a traitor. Only his quickness saved him when Bowie's knife flashed from its sheath. They went back into the hill country but the Indians were waiting them. They never reached the mine. They fought all day and all night. Three or four Texans fell, fifty Indians. The white man retreated. They were far outnumbered. They fell back to San Antonio. Bowie fought his last fight in the Alamo. No white man since has seen the Lost Mine. But it's there, with untold millions waiting for the man who's meant to fine it.

> Under the grim San Saba hills
> It sleeps the years away:
> The gold that Don Mirando found
> When unnamed woods and nameless ground
> First heard the Spanish trumpets sound
> Like a doom on Judgment Day.
>
> But waving plumes and flying flame
> On shrieking winds were brought;
> Over the hills war-bonnets streamed,
> The lances flashed and the horses screamed;
> On Lipan arms the bracelets gleamed
> That Spanish hands had wrought.
>
> Cordovan boot and tinkling spur
> The hill-paths knew no more;
> Till Bowie reeled before the flame
> That put the bursting sun to shame,
> When to the hidden cave he came,
> And stood before the door.
>
> A grimmer sun, a redder flame
> In billowing death clouds rolled
> On Bowie and the Alamo.
> And from the north as sandstorms blow
> Burst a feathered and painted foe
> On the guardians of the gold.
>
> Scalps with their braids in crimson dyed
> Trailed from Comanche spears.
> The hills forgot the Lipan tongue,
> But not the songs the ancients sung,
> And out of the hills the conquerors wrung
> Spoils of the vanished years.

White men and red men, breast to breast,
In the birth throes of a state,
Blind in the gun smoke, slashed and thrust,
Screaming mad with the slaughter lust,
Grappled and died in the bloody dust,
With a frozen grin of hate.

The moccasin left a bloody track
From shore to mountain crest;
From room and beam the red sparks rained;
But the plow bit deep and the oxen strained,
And the red warbonnets dimmed and waned
Into the lurid West.

Like dim and ghostly caravan
Of painted shapes astride
Phantasmal mustangs, pass the years.
A crest of plumes each rider rears.
With sinking rains and drooping spears
The phantom horsemen ride.

Scant are the relics Time has left
To set men wondering.
A flint by careless boot heel spurned.
A skull by straining plow upturned.
A shattered kiln where once was burned
The ransom of a king.

And men forget the maddening lure
Which cast men's lives away;
Gaunt specters guard the gleaming tills,
The gold which seven caverns fills,
And under blue San Saba hills
It sleeps till Judgment Day.

Hell, I sure must be drunk, trying to write verse; excuse it, please.

Robert E. Howard

Notes

1. Henry Herbert Knibbs (1874–1945), "The Valley That God Forgot," ll. 3–6. In *Songs of the Trail* (Boston: Houghton Mifflin, 1920), p. 24.

[81]   [nonextant letter by HPL]

[82]   [TLS]

[June 15, 1933]
Dear Mr. Lovecraft:

Glad we got the physical-mental question terminated satisfactorily. However, you missed my point entirely on the matter of the financial success of a
profession. I was merely trying to point out that a successful man need not be
denied a real pride in his occupation just because it didn't happen to be of an
intellectual nature. You criticize me for saying that I "prefer a rich athlete to a
poor professor"; as a matter of fact, I didn't say that, though perhaps I might
have expressed myself more clearly. What I said was that *I would rather be the
rich athlete.* This implies no belittling of the professor. Ordinarily I would prefer such a man for a companion, rather than the other. God knows I have no
reason to look down on any man because he is poor. I have been poor all my
life, and so have all my friends. So much so that I am naturally antagonistic
toward the wealthy classes. When I said I had rather be a rich athlete than a
poor professor, I might better have said a poor author, which I am. If I could
make more money at something—anything—that would give me as much
freedom as writing does, I'd jump at it. However much I may theorize on
some subjects, poverty is something I don't have to weave theories about.
I've eaten the crusts of poverty all my life, and probably will all the rest of it.
I'd like to have more money than I have, and if that's mercenary, I care not a
bit. I wouldn't give a damn for all the fine clothes, social position, limousines,
yachts, and all that muck. But I would like to have enough money to assure
my financial independence, and the freedom which is my main passion in life.
I wouldn't sacrifice the freedom I have found in the writing game in order to
become wealthy—if such a thing were possible—but I would quickly sacrifice
whatever artistic ambitions I ever had. (I speak relatively; as you know, I am
no artist.) I've heard a lot of people say and write that money was not necessary to real happiness; but I've noticed those people were always such as had
never known what it was to be hungry, cold or thirsty, or wear ragged clothes,
or work in the blazing heat or the freezing rain and snow. I wouldn't give a
damn to be a millionaire; but I would like to be financially independent, and if
the course offered itself, I'd desert the writing game in a minute—if I could
have the same freedom that game has given me. But please don't think that I
look down on a man who hasn't been a success. Good God, one of the
grandest gentlemen I ever knew in my life was a pauper, with scarcely enough
clothes to cover his back. I was proud as hell to shake his hand and hear him
call me his friend.

As for being anti-intellectual—I must beg not guilty. I have no hostility
whatever toward either an intellectual or an artist. I am neither, but I recog-

nize their merits. You say I scorn the real joy of creation for the sake of creating. I did not say that I did. As a matter of fact, I do not. I realize that this very joy is the breath of life for many men, and I would not deny them that for an instant. If I get more satisfaction out of writing for money rather than creative joy, that's a purely personal matter, and does not detract from my admiration of those creations which spring from purely artistic motives. I probably did not make myself clear in this matter. As for the writing I do, I would be a hypocrite to pretend that I did not enjoy it. I should have enlarged somewhat on my remark that I would not write a masterpiece—supposing I could—unless I had a chance of selling it. That is literally true, but is not to be taken as a belittling of those who do write masterpieces without expectations of monetary gain. Remember that, such as I am, I am a professional writer. The money I get from my stories constitutes my entire income. I certainly couldn't afford to put in time on a "masterpiece" I knew I wouldn't be able to turn into cash. Naturally, I write loads of junk that won't sell. But I write it with the intention of selling it if I can, at least.

I have no quarrel with men who write solely for the joy of creation—and certainly no contempt for the purely creative motive. That would indeed be a startling reversal of the usual procedure!—for a lowly professional to dare to despise the motives of the artists. As I've said, I don't. There is no reason why I should. Sure, I approve the commercial motive in writing if a man finds it satisfying or necessary. But that doesn't necessarily imply contempt for other motives. Writing is no sacred profession, as far as I can see. If a man chooses to make a living by it, I see no reason why he shouldn't.

I was not aware that the expression "smudge their canvas" reflected any particular bitterness. Possibly I am unfortunate in my selection of phrases. I admire the good artist just as much as I admire any good workman; in fact, because of my interest in literature, I admire the artist's work more than I admire the work of other good workmen. But I try not to let my personal preference blind me to the merits of other good workmen. I have just as much reverence for the artist as for any honest and worthy person—and not an ounce more. I refuse to place art on a pedestal above and beyond everything else; I refuse to believe that a million generations of human beings have lived, suffered, toiled and died in order that certain men may make marks on paper or canvas. In a word, I do not believe that artistic expression is the sole and only reason for evolution. (I don't believe there is any human reason for evolution at all.) I could cite a hundred cases of self-sacrificing heroism which emphasize man's progress more strikingly than any book that was ever written or any picture that was ever painted.

I see no real reason why I should not "take a fling" at what I consider objectionable features pertaining to art and intellectuality. My desire for personal freedom, which has been the ruling passion of my whole life, and the ruling passion of my family for some three hundred years, you assured me was not sacred. (As a matter of fact I never said that it was.) Well enough; but having admitted nothing I value is "sacred," I see no reason why I should admit that some other man or men's gods are sacred, not even if those men have a string of Ph.D.s tied to their tails.

I grant each man the right of enjoying his chosen profession. I do not seek to belittle the importance of an artist's efforts to himself. If he derives pleasure in his work, then by all means let him engulf himself in it, let him strain out the last least ounce of joy and exaltation, and let him, if he can, become glorified and intoxicated in it. Thus far he has my hearty support, and more than once I have savagely defended the right of the artist to do this. You think I am hostile to artists because I do not worship them as much as others do; you should have heard some of the things I've said to persons who would deny them the rights I have outlined above.

That I detest certain artists—in the literary world, that is—I would scorn to deny. But it is not because they are artists; I'd feel the same if they were brick-layers. But it seems to me ridiculous to suppose that there are no charlatans, posers, and mountebanks in the ranks of art; or that even a sincere artist can not have objectionable characteristics. (I have an idea that plenty of artists are impelled as much by desire for prestige, praise and—yes, even money—as by the pure love of creation. That is no criticism. I have nothing to say against such people, or such purposes; but I see no reason to glorify or idealize artists any more than any other class of people.)

I do not possess an indiscriminate antipathy for intellectuals; for such men as, for instance, Harold Lamb,[1] I have only respect and a keen admiration. But at the same time I do not indiscriminately worship intellectuals, just because they are intellectuals. There are certain types of such that I detest. Of course, I have to judge them by their writings; if I were to meet them personally, I might find them to be the varnish on God's footstool—but I doubt it. I happen to belong to the class of people these erudite gentlemen center out for their most violent attacks. My tastes and habits are simple; I am neither erudite nor sophisticated. I prefer jazz to classical music, musical burlesques to Greek tragedy, A. Conan Doyle to Balzac, Bob Service's verse to Santayana's writing, a prize fight to a lecture on art. I read the wood pulp magazines and enjoy them. I laugh uproariously at slap stick comedy in the movies. I respect men's religion whether I believe in it or not. I am a 100% American and damned proud of it. I think the United States is the finest country on earth, and I wouldn't trade a quarter section of it for the whole land of Europe. I cheer and yell madly at football games, prize fights, and horse races. All in all, I qualify, according to the standards of the "professional intellectuals" as a Babbitt, a yokel, a moron, etc. These gentlemen are quite welcome to attack me and my kind as viciously and superciliously as they wish. But I'll be damned if I can see any reason why they should be loved and worshipped by the people they flay as boobs, morons and fools.

That clipping you sent me concerning the erudition of the presidential candidates is a good example. The writer implies that Hoover is unpopular with the people merely because he has read books. I have heard hundreds of people curse Hoover, and not one said anything about his culture. They didn't care how many books he'd read, or hadn't read. On the other hand, I have found a distinct admiration for education and for educated people among the most illiterate and common people. My God, when I think of the poor devils who have worked their fingers to the bone and starved and slaved, just in order that their children should have "book larn'in'" and when I read something like that clipping—why don't such gentlemen tell the other side of the story, once in a while?

If some of the common people tend to mistrust educated men, it is because they have learned by bitter experience that too often education and a glib tongue go hand in hand with crookedness. This was especially true during the early days of the West, following the taming of the frontier, when glib gentlemen with cultured phrases on their lips came from the "civilized" sections and swindled the illiterate but generally honest pioneers out of everything they owned. I've seen the same thing, myself, in newly opened oil-fields. It's easy to say that the people are fools to judge all educated men by a few superficially polished crooks. More than once I've seen references in publications wherein Eastern writers referred to certain noted Western gunfighters as "road-agents," "stage-coach robbers" and "railroad bandits"; if men of such unquestioned intelligence can have such a misconception of a type as to suppose that a man was necessarily a robber because he was a gunman, is it any wonder that illiterate and untrained people may be misled into accepting a certain stray phase of a type, as characteristic of the whole type?

Concerning artists—the efforts of an artist are of immeasurable importance to himself and to those interested in him and his efforts. That's as it should be. But he can not expect the world to accord those efforts the same worship he accords them. The average artist is no more important in the scheme of things than is the average lawyer, physician, engineer, farmer or politician. A painting is of no more importance to a painter, or a story to an author, than a bridge is to the engineer, a well-pleaded case to the lawyer, or a fine crop to the farmer. It seems to me that artists as a whole are prone to exalt themselves and their work beyond all natural proportions. How many, many times have I read something wherein an artist or an intellectual rent something certain people look on as sacred, seeming to aver that nothing human is sacred, or really important in the cosmic scheme of things. Yet many of them seem to maintain that their aims *do* have a cosmic significance beyond themselves, and beyond the lines of ordinary human endeavor— when they have already seemed to maintain that beyond these lines *nothing* is important, or of significance. I am ready to grant the importance of artistic endeavors to the artist; to grant it a general human significance equal to any other endeavor; beyond this I will not go. I believe that *all* human desires, aims and pretensions are ultimately futile and empty, leading from nothing to nothing; I do not exclude the aims of art. I repeat that they are as basically and ultimately futile as are the aims of all the rest of humanity.

As for basic facts, I do not think that my failure to agree with all the tenets of some special class of human beings implies any ignoring of such facts.

I said that intellectual snobbishness was less justifiable than other forms, because the more intelligent a man is, the less reason for folly. A social snob may be tolerated slightly, on the grounds that he was only a pin head anyway; intellectuals can not make that excuse, since by their own admission, they represent the highest type of mentality this planet is capable of evolving.

Incidentally, it need not be taken that I center out either artists or intellectuals for attack. If all such people were as courteous, reasonable, considerate, and honest as you are, I'd have no fault to find with anybody in the artistic-intellectual ranks. It is not your type of intellectual I have any quarrel with.

But not all are like you. As I've said, I have to judge the popes of art by their writing; but I have met a number of people who were their disciples, and people who wished to imitate them. And I have no reason to suppose that the writing I have mentioned did not reflect the natures and attitudes of the writers. I do not confine my dislikes to what I consider objectionable features in the classes under discussion. I hate anything, anywhere I find it, which smacks of a supercilious viewpoint, or a leaning toward special privileges—such as, for instance, the case of the correspondent who proposed separate moral codes for intellectuals. I do not, of course, suppose that such an individual represents either the artistic or the intellectual class, or even a small part of it. But I do know a little about human nature, and I know that in any superior class, regardless of how wise and reasonable its members may be, there is likely to rise up a desire for undue power and privilege. Regardless of the sneers of the sophisticated, my nature is truly Democratic. As long as I live, I will never cease to oppose special privilege and everything smacking of special privilege. A man is only a man, regardless of how many books he has read, or written. Neither wealth nor erudition gives him any more fundamental rights than is due any man. That's why I love the memory of the frontier; there a man was not judged by what he had or what he knew, but by *what he was*. Which, I realize, is somewhat bound up in what he *knew*, but you get my meaning.

As concerning human freedom, you can no more connect me with the wild-haired young Liberals you mentioned than you can connect me with those souls who believe that modern life is one sweet, long summer dream. I know nothing about them, I never heard one of them speak, and I never read anything any one wrote. I don't know what they want, and I don't care. What I want is impossible, as I've told you before; I want, in a word, the frontier—which is compassed in the phrase, new land, open land, free land—land rich and unbroken and virgin, swarming with game and laden with fresh forests and sweet cold streams, where a man could live by the sweat of his hands unharried by taxes, crowds, noise, unemployment, bank-failures, gang-extortions, laws, and all the other wearisome things of civilization. Failing in that, I want as much personal freedom as is possible under this system, and if I can't have at least as much as I have now, I don't want to live at all. I realize this sounds highly melodramatic. But my people have lived free lives for three hundred years, and the love of it is implanted in me too strongly for me to survive its uprooting.

Glancing over your remarks about what the young intelligentsia want, it seems to me that my unfortunate use of the word "smudge" is still rankling a little bit. You have probably discovered by this time that I do not despise artists. When I used the case of the dungeon and stocks, I was merely pointing out that mental freedom was useless—and largely impossible—without physical freedom. Your remark that you see few honest and good people sitting in stocks, would seem to indicate a conviction that rogues are the only people who ever see the inside of prisons. I must disagree with you. History would seem to indicate that many worthy men were imprisoned at various times. Plato, I believe, was once imprisoned by one of the Tyrants. In the case of political prisoners, I believe it is best to leave it to history as to whether they were worthy or not. If the prisoner dies imprisoned and his cause fails, he is likely to go down as a rebel and traitor; if his cause succeeds, he goes down as a martyr or a patriot, as the case may be. As far as that goes, I've known several men who, while not political prisoners at all, never the less spent some time in dungeons, and yet were honorable citizens. As for the guinea pigs, I admit freely that Americans are not yet committed to that status. But give them time. The trend just now is toward government control, and will probably reach a point (in fact I see not how any other alternative will allow civilization to continue) in which men are fed and cared for, and work for, and are protected by, the government. I look for a reducing of personal liberty, coupled with a condition approaching pampering as far as physical needs go. You must admit such a course is not likely to produce lions. I imagine the Romans would have resented the term "guinea pigs" just before the Goths rushed in and cut their throats. In a system where men are protected by hired forces, and waited on by machines, how can any real self-confidence and self-reliance be induced or long-sustained?

Speaking of what the Liberals want, you ask if they desire to ride bicycles on the sidewalks, disregard traffic signals, play the radio at 3 a.m., and shoot and carve people for fun. I gather that you are really inquiring just what *I* want. Well, in Cross Plains I can ride a bicycle on the sidewalk; there are no traffic signals; I can—and do—play the radio at all hours of the day and night, and I'd like to see anybody try to stop me; I have never yet shot or carved anybody for fun, but so far I have never been arrested for emptying my pistol into the air or using trash cans for targets in moments of alcoholic exuberance, and if we step outside the corporation lines, a friend and I can pummel each other unmolested by police interference. I don't suppose I would be allowed to pitch a tent, as you suggest, in the middle of the main street, but so far I have never experienced any overpowering desire to pitch such a tent.

I think the real reason so many youngsters are clamoring for freedom of some vague sort, is because of unrest and dissatisfaction with present conditions; I don't believe this machine age gives full satisfaction in a spiritual way, if the term may be allowed.

Your remark concerning newspapers and radios, and the fact that our pioneer ancestors did very well without them, surprised me somewhat. All along I have been contending that many of the products of civilization were immaterial, necessary only because the necessity was formed by their creation, and you seemed to oppose that view. Yet now you use an argument somewhat similar to mine.

As for the advantages of the frontier, that depends somewhat on the individual, I should think, and I refuse to believe that a choice of such a life implies an inferior nature. Naturally, the frontier was hardly the place for a man who preferred a life of scholarly ease; no criticism of such a man involved. But that a good many men did consider the frontier preferable to a more settled form of life is evident by the mere fact of its occupation by people from more civilized parts. There is a widely diffused idea that the frontier was settled by broken men, men who had proved themselves failures elsewhere, criminals and paupers. I think that fallacy was created and played up to flatter the vanity of the people who stayed at home. Of course there were criminals, paupers and failures in the westward drift. I'd like to hear of some phase of humanity where they were not present. I'd also like to know how it is supposed that these theoretical weaklings and misfits conquered one of the wildest and most ferocious environments this planet has ever seen. When my great-grandfather Squire Jim Henry started west he travelled in a regular caravan of great wagons, loaded with supplies, implements and furnishings, and negro slaves, and he took with him herds of oxen, steers, cows and horses, and a buckskin bag plump with gold coins. He was no broken man, seeking a place to hide. He was an adventurous soul, looking for new, unbroken and uncrowded land, because the wilds had more attraction for him than the teeming countries of men. And there were thousands and thousands like him.

I must repeat that it is not my intention to idealize conditions of barbarism—and here let it be noted that I am not speaking of the American frontier, but of the Gauls and Goths. The American frontiersman was not a barbarian; he was simply a highly specialized type. My conception of barbarism does not glitter, particularly. You deny that you idealize the modern age, yet at the same time accuse me of idealizing barbarism. Yet it is evident that I am doing with that state of being only what you are doing with this: pointing out the strong points, or what I conceive to be the strong points; naturally I'm not emphasizing the weak points; nor are you emphasizing civilization's weak points. You can't expect a man to argue against himself.

But if I exaggerate the sufferings in civilization (that's a compliment to my imagination, considering the plight of twelve million unemployed, whose condition can hardly be attributed to the Gauls and Goths) you are no less prone to exaggerate the sufferings of the Germanic barbarians. In the first place, your barbarian who suffers so bitterly is not a barbarian at all, but a Twentieth Century scholar brutally thrust into alien and barbaric environments. You make the mistake of thinking of and judging the barbaric age by modern standards; in a word, you project a bit of this century into that, instead of regarding that age in its true proportion—as a unit in no way dependent upon this age. For another thing, you seem to make no distinction between a Gothic barbarian, an Ashanti savage, and a Papuan bushman. The pictures you paint of Gaulish and Gothic conditions are more suited to the blood-stained courts of Dahomey and the Slave Coast, ruled by madmen. What constitutes human suffering? The German barbarians had their feuds and tribal wars; we have strikes, child labor, sweat shops, unemployment, gang-rule. And I doubt if a larger number of Germans were bumped off in tribal wars than are smashed up by autos and machinery in civilization. It strikes me as rather extreme to judge the people of a former epoch by the standards of this, and conclude that all were miserable and wretched because people of this age would be that, if thrown back into that age. I am not contending that there was less suffering in that age than in this; I am merely contending that the German barbarian was as well (or better) fitted to endure and overcome the hardships of his life as is the modern man. You said war is merely a hangover from barbarism. According to that, modern wars are planned and instigated by those among us who are least civilized, according to the intellectual standard. Yet I hardly think that the facts would prove that our wars are caused by day-laborers, cowboys, prize fighters, soda-jerkers, farmers, and other despised types. As near as I can figure it out, they are planned and started and carried out by the men who represent the very highest type of civilization—statesmen, politicians, kings, lords of finance, and diplomats. If it is absurd, as you say, to attribute war to civilization, it seems to me that it is no less absurd to blame all the defects of this system on survivals of barbarism. If our present civilization is possessed of so many enviable virtues, why all this unrest and turmoil? Why isn't everybody happy? Why are some twelve million people out of work and on the verge of starvation? When I say that I believe I would be as well off as a Goth as I am in my present condition, I am merely expressing an honest belief. Conceivably, people a thousand years from now will be as far in "advance" of us, as we are of the Goths, but I don't think moderns consciously suffer much because of that fact. Nor do I think the Goths consciously suffered because they were not "advanced" as far as a race was to be a thousand years later. I believe they were as happy as we are.

Let me here correct a mistake, caused no doubt by my vague manner of expression. Your remarks about "a weak boy" I take to mean the songster whose plastering I described in a previous letter. I should have given more details. The reason I didn't, was because I merely mentioned the matter in support of one of my arguments, and it did not occur to me to enlarge upon it. Doubtless the conclusion you reached was natural, because of my failure to make the matter more clear. The songster was beaten, not because he was "impertinent" or because the other man disagreed with him, but because he was shady in his business dealings. And he was far from being a weak boy; he was a man in full maturity, and bigger than I am; he weighed 225 pounds, and had the natural strength of a bull. The man who beat him up was smaller and well along in years. The songster lost the fight just because he'd neglected the physical side of himself. Nature gave him a powerful body, but he ignored it. If he was going to start trouble, he ought to have been able to carry it through. The people in this country feel that a man of strong healthy physique ought to be able to defend himself when it is necessary, regardless of his occupation. But it was not his culture that got him that beating. It was his crooked business dealings. I should have explained that, of course. However, I don't remember saying anything that would lead to the conclusion that a man would be beaten up simply because "he is not illiterate" or "insensitive," or that "persons who show signs of literacy" are slugged by "local mobs." What I actually said was: that the people would kick the ears off an artist as *quick as anybody else.* I thought my meaning was obvious, that if an artist's methods or manners were offensive, he would not be excused simply on the grounds that he was an artist. I did not mean— nor did I say—that an intellectual would be more liable to assault than any other man. It is simply that the people resent oppression or trickery in such a man as quickly as in an ordinary man—though naturally, no *more* quickly. I have lived in Texas all my life, and I have never known a man to be persecuted because of his education or his lack of it, or because of any creed, cult, belief or lack of belief. We have a few artists, even in Texas; and I never heard of them being manhandled because they were artists. I might also point out that no one has ever been hanged in Texas for a witch, and that we have never persecuted any class or race because of its religious beliefs or chance of birth; nor have we ever banned or burned any books, as the "civilized" Nazis are now doing in "civilized" Germany.

You, or any other honorable gentleman would be perfectly safe in Texas. Casualties among tourists are remarkably few. Several thousand strangers pass through the state yearly, and most of them escape alive. I have never yet seen an unoffending tourist scalped, flayed, or castrated, regardless of his erudition.

The case mentioned was simply that of a shifty character who got his just deserts. We certainly have no prejudice against artistic people. The people of Texas, taken as a whole, are neither pro-intellectual or anti-intellectual. When a man proves himself a worthy character, they do not grill him about his artistic appreciation before asking him out to dinner; nor do they give a crook any favors because he possesses intellectual talents. No; any man who conducts himself with ordinary decency can wander unarmed all over the state unmolested by the private citizens. Of course, there are sparsely settled parts where it is not wise to venture at random because of the possibility of raids from across the Border. But you can't blame the citizens of Texas for that. A gentleman is safe anywhere else. But a shifty, domineering, arrogant supercilious type better know how to use his hands, and that comment isn't limited to Texas. It holds good just about everywhere west of the Mississippi; and some places east of it, I imagine.

The fellow in question was beaten up because of his business methods. But if he'd been hammered because of his "impertinence" I'd consider that he'd got no more than what was coming to him. Was it particularly tactful, his saying that only dogs fought, to men who occasionally settled their differences with their fists? Would you enjoy being called a dog by a man because he didn't like weird literature? Are certain men to be allowed full privilege of abuse and insolence, while the men they insult are to be denied the right of retaliation? We have our rules and customs of courtesy and decency which we try to follow to the best of our ability—why should we allow somebody to ignore and trample on them, merely because he considers himself the possessor of superior culture? Don't you really think that there was some obligation of consideration on the other side, to be considered?

You need not fear that there is any lack of fair play in Texas. I doubt if you will find it more highly developed in any region. I never saw a helpless individual beaten up without a chance to defend himself; not by ordinary citizens, anyway. What the police do, is not our fault; and every region has its thugs and sluggers. I remember, for instance, a big fellow called Red, who was going down a street in a western town, and saw a couple of thugs abusing a weakling—something that might happen anywhere, since hoodlums are not confined to Texas. Red had never seen the victim before, but without hesitation he stepped in with both fists swinging, and knocked the thugs for a loop, getting, in the process, a knife stab that lacked only about an inch of finding a vital organ. Could any man, even in the "civilized" sections, have shown any more chivalry? That is no isolated case. I merely cite it at random; I could mention many more. But that will serve to illustrate my point.

Concerning your remarks about violence being as despisable as trickery, it may be that my comments on western outlawry (which I do not doubt have proved boresome) led you to believe that I take a too tolerant viewpoint regarding crimes of violence. I hardly think such is the case. It would be hypocritical for me to pretend that I did not feel a certain keen admiration for such men as John Wesley Hardin, Simp Dixon, Bob Lee, etc.[2] But I do not consider these men ordinary criminals, in the first place. Anyway, whatever crimes they may be said to have committed were more than balanced by the war they waged against the vandals who were looting the South at that time. A regard for fact forces me to the statement that most of the outlawry in the West was the result of conflicting forces engineered from the outside. The period of Southwestern outlawry at its wildest, was between 1865 and 1885; especially in the years immediately following the Civil War. Texas was in the grasp of the carpet-bag vultures, who were only intent on looting the state. Free niggers—more primitive and ferocious than anywhere else on this continent—were swaggering over the countryside, plundering, murdering and burning. The niggers and the carpet-baggers had Federal soldiers behind them. Resistance against oppression resulted in outlawry; men were hunted like mad dogs simply because they tried to protect their property and their lives and the lives of their family. And they were trying it on the wrong breed. Wars? I could tell you of wars; of ambushes and midnight raids and men kicking at the ends of ropes, and rolling out of their saddles in the teeth of a blast from the thickets. In such conditions the men I have mentioned grew up; they were neither thieves nor train-robbers nor hiwaymen, though a few, because of the conditions under which they lived, became such in later life. Take John Wesley Hardin. At the age of fifteen he shot a nigger who was trying to kill him with a club. For that he was declared outlaw, and hunted most of his life.

And so with many western "outlaws." Sometimes it is not easy to judge a man's actions. In a long settled country, with well defined rules of conduct, it may be possible to say just exactly when a man is "right" and when he is "wrong." Such was not the case in the early West. In the big range wars of the '80's and '90's, there was a certain amount of right on both sides. But the main trouble was just as it is now: absentee ownership. The big ranches fell into the hands of Eastern and British corporations. The owners knew nothing about local conditions and cared less. They wanted money to be made from beef, and some of them didn't care how it was made. An unsavory breed sprang up—gunmen, hired by the owners and managers to protect their interests. Which is the least civilized: a man who goes out with a gun and openly fights for his property, or a man who hires a thug to do his shooting for him?

Turning to another point, I take up your argument concerning theft by trickery or by violence. You are, of course, correct in most of your assertions. The same motive impels the highwayman as impels the swindler; I think none would deny that. Naturally, I had rather a man would simply swindle me out of $500 than to knock me in the head and take it away from me. On the other hand, I'd really have more respect for the latter, than for a man who would writhe his way into my trust, and take advantage of my friendship. By respect, I mean it in a relative way; I have no respect whatever for a highwayman;

even less for a swindler. I think the real reason so many people are prone to despise shifty crookedness more than physical brutality in these matters, is because of the taint of treachery that usually accompanies the former (and quite often the latter, of course).

It is not a good idea to generalize or theorize too quickly on this thing, because it has phases which shade into each other, and involves highly intricate ethical convictions and traditions. For instance, when a mob broke into the jail to lynch the Marlow boys many years ago; the prisoners were powerful, desperate men and were armed with pipes and chair legs. One of the mob was brained in his attempt to drag them out. They held the jail, and the mob dared not come in after them. The mob at last scattered, leaving the boys unharmed.[3] Why did they not fire through the door and windows? What was the difference between hanging and shooting? Only in the minds of the mob—shooting was murder; hanging was—well, I doubt if any of the men could have given their reasons clearly. But they simply could not shoot down in cold blood the men they had come to hang. Later a man brought in Boone Marlow's body, and claimed the reward. He had met Marlow, he claimed, and shot him down. The reward was paid. Later it was found that the man had poisoned Marlow, and fired the bullets into him after he was dead. What was the difference between poisoning and shooting? But they indicted the man for murder and sent him to prison. The difference was *treachery*—a difference sometimes intangible and nebulous, but never the less a real factor that can not be ignored. The motive behind an act is not the only thing to be considered; the manner in which the act is carried out must also be considered. And rightly or wrongly, the Anglo-Saxon has a distaste for treachery, or for what he considers treachery.

I have a scar on my wrist; the fellow who put it there was trying to sink his knife into my throat, instead of my hand. A few years ago I was examining my saddle, and found that somebody had cut the stirrup leather nearly through, cutting from each side, and leaving only a shred of leather in the middle. It was well up near the frame, and hidden by the fender. It was merely by chance that I discovered it. It was, moreover, on the right side. No chance of me discovering it when I mounted, by breaking the leather as I swung up. But the first time my horse started bucking, or running, and my full weight was swung onto my right stirrup, the leather would have snapped, leaving me with a broken leg or a broken neck. The same motive was behind the knife that scarred my wrist, and the knife that cut my saddle leather. Both men wished to maim, cripple or kill me. But my feelings toward them are quite different. I have no grudge against the man who cut my hand; whenever we meet, we shake hands and talk over old times. But if I ever find out who it was that cut my saddle, I'll be tempted to part his hair with a pistol butt. One was open in his attack, and I had a chance to defend myself. The other was subtle and underhand; he tried to get me without risk to himself, and without giving me a chance. It's the old business of treachery again.

Returning to our discussion of barbarism, you say the trouble with Texas is, she isn't civilized enough. Yet nine tenths of her troubles rise from attempted exploiting of her resources—and her citizens—by individuals and corporations from those very sections which you praise so highly as examples of true civilization. If those individuals and persons of corporations are possessed of the virtues you ascribe to highly civilized people, the actions of many of them have certainly been inconsistent. Please realize that what I say of the state's exploiting by alien individuals does not apply to those good and honest citizens of many other states who have come and settled in Texas and have adapted themselves to their new environments and made fine citizens of the state. Some of my best friends are among these. But there *are* vandals and vultures who would bankrupt the state to fill their purses, and practically all of them are from the very sections you speak of as being so highly civilized. Not that there are no native vultures; but they are generally working for or with the others.

In the last few years thousands and thousands of people have come into Texas from the East; from New York, Virginia, Florida, New Jersey, Pennsylvania, New England. Some of them were fine folks; and some were definitely not. I found that the percentage of worthy citizens among them was not substantially different from that of the same amount of native Texans. Take a crowd of them, and a crowd of native Texans, and you'd find just about the same elements in each bunch. I've had business dealings with hundreds of these people, and though their viewpoints in many ways differed from that of the Texans, I didn't find much fundamental difference in them. Some were good, some bad, just about the same proportion that would make up an equal number of Texans.

I appreciate your interest and wish to remove what looks like a twist in my thinking; but I have no desire to spend a year in any city, though I'd like to visit those Eastern towns you mention. I really can't see what advantage I'd have in them that I wouldn't have in San Antonio, except such things as bigger museums, finer theaters, more opportunities to attend lectures and the like, which, though very enjoyable, are not absolutely necessary to my pleasure. Of course I was only a kid of thirteen when I was in New Orleans, but I can't remember that it differed in any startling way from San Antonio; it was just bigger and smelt worse. I've never been molested by anybody, cop or otherwise, in San Antonio. In fact, when I was down there this time, I found them—such as I talked with—quite affable and willing to oblige. There were complaints of corruption, but I heard none of the police brutality to individuals, such as are so common in other parts of the state. The fact is, San Antonio is more completely in the hands of the native Texans than are other cities in the Eastern part of the state—a fact which would not tend to support your argument that abuses are due to lack of native civilization. Another thing—conditions were never as bad in Texas as they were during the Sterling regime, an administration openly under the complete domination of interests in the East. Since the Ferguson election there has been a complete shake-up of the police force in Fort Worth, and some changes in other parts; the whole Ranger company which worked in the East Texas fields was dropped from the force—the work of the *Gladewater Journal,* or I miss my guess.[4] I'm not trying to say that everything is hotsy-totsy and all abuses by and corruptions of authority have been wiped out. But there seems to be a start in the right direction, at least; and such reforms as have been made, have been the work of native Texans, or men who have become Texans by settlement and honest desire to work for the good of their adopted state.

Texas is Texas, capable of developing her own civilization and her own culture. Her history is unique; and she does not need to copy anything or anybody. She is not an imitation or a duplicate of something in the East, or in the West, or somewhere in Europe. Some inhabitants of Dallas proudly call that town "Little New York." That's nothing to recommend it. New York is New York, and no copy of something else; Texas is Texas, and no copy of something else. That's one reason I like San Antonio. Nobody ever tried to call it Little New York, or Little Boston, or Little Charleston, or Little Madrid, or Little Barcelona, or Little anything. I do not by any means belittle these cities; I simply do not wish to be a copy of anything. I don't want to be somebody's understudy, and I don't want my state to think she has to imitate somebody else. And she won't, in spite of the efforts of a tiny minority who would like to make the state over on lines laid down in Greenwich Village; natives, too, I hate to say; natives, but not true Texans. Once we were *Texicans*; then we were *Texians*; now we are *Texans*; some time I'll explain the difference.[5] I had rather been a Texican than the king of Europe; but I at least intend to remain a *Texan.*

Thanks very much for the kind things you said about "Wolfshead" and other early attempts. I was eighteen when I wrote "Spear and Fang," "The Lost Race," "The Hyena"; nineteen when I wrote "In the Forest of Villefere" and "Wolfshead." And after that it was two solid years before I sold another line of fiction.[6] I don't like to think about those two years. I wrote my first story when I was fifteen, and sent it—to *Adventure,* I believe.[7] Three years later I managed to break into *Weird Tales.* Three years of writing without selling a blasted line. (I never have been able to sell to *Adventure;* guess my first attempt cooked me with them for ever!) I haven't been any kind of a success, financially, though I have managed to get by. I could have studied law, or gone into some other occupation, but none offered me the freedom writing did—and my passion for freedom is almost an obsession. I honestly have paid the price of freedom by living with Spartan simplicity, and doing without things I really wanted. Of course, I've always hoped to some day make more than a bare living out of the game, and I was beginning to do that, when the markets started cracking up.

Writing has always been a means to an end I hoped to achieve—freedom. Personal liberty may be a phantom, but I hardly think anybody would deny that there is more freedom in writing than there is in slaving in an iron foundry, or working—as I have worked—from twelve to fourteen hours seven days out of the week behind a soda fountain. I have worked as much as eighteen hours a day at my typewriter, but it was work of my own choosing, and I could quit any time I wanted to without getting fired from the job. Yes, writing has been more of a means to an end than it may be with some, but it is not to be thought that I have any contempt for it. Is it likely that I would despise a profession to which I have devoted the best years of my youth, and which I expect to follow the rest of my life? When I said that writing is merely a means of making a living, for me, I spoke the truth; but I hope I am good enough workman to enjoy my trade, and to take a proper pride in it. Just because I use the profession as a means of support does not necessarily mean that I despise it.

When you seem to read hostility towards literature in my remarks, remember this: that I was first to light a torch of literature in this part of the country, however small, frail and easily extinguished that flame may be. I am, in my way, a pioneer. To the best of my knowledge I am the first writer to be produced by a section of country comprising a territory equal to that of the state of Connecticut. In the last few years large numbers of youngsters have taken to writing; some of them show real merit; some have already far surpassed me. But I was the first writer of the post oak country; my work's lack of merit can not erase that fact. By first, I do not, of course, mean in point of excellence, God knows; I mean in point of time. There are some real writers growing up in this country now, whose work will be read and applauded long after my junk has passed to the oblivion it will earn. But when I set my hand to my chosen profession, there was none other in the land except me. At least if there was, I never heard of him.

It seems to me that many writers, by virtue of environments of culture, art and education, slip into writing because of their environments. I became a writer in spite of my environments. Understand, I am not criticizing those environments. They were good, solid and worthy. The fact that they were not inducive to literature and art is nothing in their disfavor. Never the less, it is no light thing to enter into a profession absolutely foreign and alien to the people among which one's lot is cast; a profession which seems as dim and faraway and unreal as the shores of Europe. The people among which I lived—and yet live, mainly—made their living from cotton, wheat, cattle, oil, with the usual percentage of business men and professional men. That is most certainly not in their disfavor. But the idea of a man making his living by writing seemed, in that hardy environment, so fantastic that even today I am sometimes myself assailed by a feeling of unreality. Never the less, at the age of fifteen, having never seen a writer, a poet, a publisher or a magazine editor, and having only the vaguest ideas of procedure, I began working on the profession I had chosen. I have accomplished little enough, but such as it is, it is the result of my own efforts. I had neither expert aid nor advice. I studied no courses in writing; until a year or so ago, I never read a book by anybody advising writers how to write. Ordinarily I had no access to public libraries, and when I did, it was to no such libraries as exist in the cities. Until recently—a few weeks ago in fact—I employed no agent.[8] I have not been a success, and probably never will be. But whatever my failure, I have this thing to remember—that I was a pioneer in my profession, just as my grandfathers were in theirs, in that I was the first man in this section to earn his living as a writer.

I hesitated to say all this stuff. Some of it sounds a great deal as if I were boasting. Please believe that such is not my intention. No one realizes my work's lack of merit better than myself. I have no reason in the world to feel any vanity over my paltry accomplishments, and probably never will. The only reason I have made these remarks is for the purpose of making my position clearer in the case of writing and literature in general, a position about which I have doubtless been so vague as to give rise to misconceptions concerning it. As for any hostility I might feel toward artistic literature—the sincere praise I have repeatedly showered on your own work ought to convince you that I have nothing but admiration for such literature, when not accompanied by the hokum that certain artists invest it with. I had no reason to praise your work unless I meant what I said. When I expressed my keen admiration for your stories and poems, I was expressing my deepest and most sincere feelings. No, I am not hostile toward art or intellectuality; if there is any hostility, it is directed toward the bunk from which these things are no more free than are any other forms of human endeavors. I am not hostile toward the artistic class; but I will admit some bewilderment as to what is required of me by a class which rejects half my ideas and aspirations as empty sentimentality, and the other half as gross commercialism.

What you said of museums, interested me much. As well as your remarks concerning your education. Your remark concerning your "ignorance" is something with which I must take issue. If you are "ignorant" then no man on this planet can boast an education. What if you do lack some technical knowledge on some subjects? Great heavens, no man could hope to master *all* subjects, if he had a thousand years to live. Judging from your correspondence, you have more real education in more different matters than any man I ever met or corresponded with, or heard lecture. I am very sorry that you suffered such poor health in your youth. I have always been brutishly healthy myself, but I feel the keenest sympathy for those who are not. I note with admiration the varied interests of your childhood. You were studying the classics at an age at which I could scarcely read or write. Your scope, both in travel and in study, has certainly been much wider than that of the average man.

Our feelings in school, again, differ. I hated school, not because any particular tyranny was practiced on me—I wouldn't have stood for it, anyway—but simply because the whole system irked me. Sitting still in one place for hours at a time got on my nerves. Having to go and come at certain times irked me; I hated for my actions to be controlled by the ringing of a bell. The fact that these things were necessary had nothing to do with it. School, any way it is looked at, was a restriction of my freedom. I accepted it as a necessary evil, and got through with it as quickly as possible, and I'll never forget the wild and passionate feeling of relief that surged through me as I bounded out of the building where the graduation exercizes had been held, with my diploma in my hand, and halting on the lawn, expressed my pleasure at being through with school, and my opinion of the whole works in language more picturesque than choice. The passing of ten years has not dimmed that feeling in the slightest. Yet there was a good deal of comedy in my last year of high school; I look back on it, not with any pleasure, but with some amusement. I attended Brownwood High, and it was overcrowded—fairly flowing over with students. Next year they built a Junior High and took care of the surplus, but that year it was like a sardine can. We had to gang up, two or three to a seat in the main study hall. The Senior class was given separate study halls, but they were eventually abolished, because the students didn't keep order any too well. Some of them were mean as the devil, but most were just exuberant kids, overflowing with a superabundance of vigor and animal spirits. My biology class was the biggest in the school, and all the unruly spirits that could got in there. The teacher was a poor misfit who didn't know his stuff; that is, he was a good biologist, but he couldn't handle students. They gave him hell. The very last day of school, for instance, while he was trying to lecture to the class, certain unregenerate spirits kept galloping past the door, firing various objects at him, such as old shirts wadded up and soaked with water, to the hilarious enjoyment of the class. At last he shut the door, and then they locked it from the outside and he had to telephone down to the janitor to come and open it. I had no part in harassing the poor devil; but he never gave me a square deal if he could help it, so I didn't much give a damn what they did to him. The class in which I graduated was the biggest that had ever graduated from a Texas high school, up to that time.

I was much amused and interested by your account of your tilt with the English teacher concerning your astronomical essay. It was in truth a dramatic situation, and one I wish I'd had a chance to duplicate at some time or other. But the only place my stuff was appearing when I was in school was in the school paper—and some of it was barred from print by the teacher-censors on account of a certain Rabelaisian tang that would creep in in spite of myself.

I had a hell of a time with mathematics. I blundered through algebra, geometry and trigonometry without learning a blamed thing about any of them. The only reason I passed my last year's math was a combination of luck and a teacher's laziness. The final exam was split in half, part to be taken one day and part the next, the results to be added on the basis of 100; thus, if a scholar made 100 on the first exam, he was given 50, etc., the results of both exams to be added. I made 60 on the first exam, and came in the next day to take the rest of it. The teacher was there alone, to my surprise, leaning back with his feet on a desk. I told him I was there to take my exam. He asked me what I made; I told him; he said then my grade was really 30, and asked me if I could improve that in another exam. "Hell, no," quoth I; "I worked the only problem in the book I could work, yesterday." He then asked me what grades I made in other subjects—they ran something like this: English 80, science 100, economics 85. He allowed that we'd let it go and say nothing; and call my mathematics grade 60, which would pass me.

I never studied Latin much, and disliked it intensely; my old antipathy for anything Roman. The only reason I ever took it up was because I knew it would help me in Spanish; but I never got a chance to study Spanish. I had a short course in agriculture once, which interested me immensely, and I made very high grades in it, as well as in its various branchings, such as the grafting of trees, etc. But I was unable to continue it, and I've long ago forgotten all I learned. I've also forgotten what elementary science I learned, as well as the business English, commercial law and business arithmetic I learned in the business college. I generally made my highest grades in history and science, though I found the latter of scant interest, as a general thing.

Things I have discovered to be of most use, I learned mostly without formal teaching. What little knowledge I have picked up in a rudimentary manner here and there was mainly the result of reading for amusement. Yet that is not the word, either. As a boy and a youth in my 'teens, I read purely for the love of reading. I can say with confidence that no man, however mature, ever loved reading for its own sake more than I. I did not read because of any particular urge for learning, or to merely pass the time, or to escape the realities of life. I read simply because I loved reading for its own sake alone. The printed page was like wine to me. Books were scarce in the country. I could not go into a library or book store and select what I wanted. I had to read whatever came to my hand; and I did, and generally enjoyed it supremely. Perhaps that accounts in part for my still rather indiscriminate taste. If I had tried to pick and choose in my early youth, damned little I'd have ever read. I was not critical; I never tried to analyze what I read; I was simply and sincerely grateful for whatever chance put it into my hands. Often I would read a book through, and without pausing, turn back to the first and read it through again—sometimes repeating this three or four times. As a youngster, I would sometimes skip a paragraph here and there, in order to thrill over its newness when I re-read it. My own library was generally the largest in the place I lived, but it was small. I generally was given a book on Christmas and on my birthday. Occasionally between times a book was bought. For the rest, I borrowed whenever I could. My main source of reading material were the hand-made bookcases which served for libraries in the country schools. Each tiny school had one, and the contents were small, but varied. In the summer I regularly raided those "libraries." During the long summer vacations which usually lasted six or seven months, schools and bookcases were kept locked and barred. Then I made my raids. Occasionally I could obtain the key and permission to read the books so guarded. But refusal did not halt me. In my passionate quest for reading material, nothing could have halted me but a bullet through the head. With a flour sack tied to my saddle-horn, I raided isolated school houses far up the creeks, in the hills, and in villages. I jimmied the doors or windows of the buildings, and pried the locks off the solidly made book cases; if that failed, I removed the hinges. Then with my flour-sack saddle-bag full of books, I departed in a cloud of dust, oblivious to the maledictions sometimes directed my way. I did not steal those books. I always returned them in as good shape as I took them. But I had to read, and I did read, even in the teeth of threats to have the law on me. It was a matter beyond my control; literature, of one sort or another, was meat and drink and the wine of Life to me.

It may seem from the above that I spent most of my time reading; as a matter of fact, I did not. I only wished to. Books were scarce, and often to procure a book, I had to ride many miles on horse-back. Then, naturally, I had a certain amount of work to do. However, as my father had his practice and did not attempt to run a farm, I had more leisure than the average country kid. I lived pretty much the average life of the time and place. Then (as now) I had more enemies than friends, but I did not lack companionship of my own age. I played the rough and savage games popular in those parts then, wrestled, hunted a little, fished a little, trapped a little, stole watermelons, went swimming, and spent more time than all in wandering about over the country-side on foot or on horse-back. But I would have done all these things less if there had been more for me to read. I am glad, in a way, that there was not; as it was I permanently impaired my sight reading in all kinds of light, and if I could have done so, I might have pored over books too much—that is, to the damage of my health. Though a certain restlessness of my nature might have always prevented that.

Magazines were even more scarce than books. It was after I moved into "town" (speaking comparatively) that I began to buy magazines. I well remember the first I ever bought. I was fifteen years old; I bought it one summer night when a wild restlessness in me would not let me keep still, and I had exhausted all the reading material on the place. I'll never forget the thrill it gave me. Somehow it never had occurred to me before that I could buy a magazine. It was an *Adventure*. I still have the copy. After that I bought *Adventure* for many years, though at times it cramped my resources to pay the price. It came out three times a month, then. I earned my first money when I was ten years old, but between that time, and the time when I began to find comparatively steady employment, at about the age of seventeen, there were many stretches of enforced idleness when my pockets were empty. I was never one to make undue calls on my father for spending money. During the idle stretches, I skimped and saved from one magazine to the next; I'd buy one copy and have it charged, and when the next issue was out, I'd pay for the one for which I owed, and have the other one charged, and so on. So I generally owed for one, but only one. I inherited a distaste for debt which is still strong. But I beg your pardon. I did not intend to inflict so much personal reminiscence upon you.

I should also beg your pardon for the drunken maunderings I seem to have remembered sending you from San Antonio. When I'm in drink, I ought to have sense enough to keep away from the typewriter. I trust the contents did not prove offensive.

I was interested in your account of your new quarters, and am glad you find them so satisfying.[9]

Concerning the lost San Saba mine, which I evidently touched on in my maunderings, I probably exaggerated the legends—yet it would be hard to do that. There was such a mine once, and the Spaniards worked it. Beyond that, all is vagueness and myth; but men still look for it. My friend Pink Tyson ran into a gang hunting for it down on the San Saba River awhile back, and one of them, a white bearded taciturn old timer, drew his gun every time a stranger came near the camp.

I went south in the latter days of March, taking my mother with me, because I wanted her to escape the discomforts of a dry spring in this country which is always accompanied by stormy clouds, high winds and sand storms. She was born and spent her childhood in a more eastern part of the state,[10] and though she has spent many years in West Texas she has never become accustomed to sand storms. On the other hand, they don't bother me, because I became accustomed to them in infancy and early childhood. We spent a few days in Austin, then went on to San Antonio, where we spent the month of April. It was my intention to stay longer, but the intense heat caused us to change our plans, and we returned to West Texas during the first part of May. I wish we could have stayed longer, because my mother has many congenial friends in San Antonio, and enjoys our visits there. For myself, while I like the town better than any I have ever seen, a week is long enough to satisfy me.

I am definitely a country dweller. Cities, after a short time, even cities no bigger than San Antonio (which would seem little more than a village to an Easterner) oppress me. I feel caged, and imprisoned. This may seem utterly fantastic to a city dweller, but is real enough to me. After all, I see no reason why my preference for the country is any less sound or more sentimentalistic than a city man's preference for the city, if there is anything in heredity or environment. To the best of my knowledge, no man or woman in my direct line of ancestry ever made his or her permanent home in a city; certainly not on this side of the Atlantic; and I was born and raised in the country.

After returning home, I spent some days in Fort Worth and Dallas, and for the rest, my sojourns have been limited to wandering around in the hill country, especially down in Brown County, to the south, on the shores of the new Brownwood Lake.[11] That lake has a fascination for me. Some friends of mine and I have discussed tentative plans for building a fishing shack up in the hills, on one of the broad arms of the lake, in a secluded spot, but it takes money, and money is always short. I don't know whether we'll do it or not; probably not. But there is a sort of fierce grandeur about the scenery there, especially when I know the country and its history so intimately, which attracts me. But hell, shacks will spring up on the shores, and resorts will be built, and the whole effect will be spoiled by the usual spewing of humanity out over the landscape. If I had the money, I'd buy—but hell, what am I maundering about.

Thanks for what you said about my verse. If it ever sees the light of day, I'll have to publish it myself, because (outside Wright who occasionally buys a fantasy) I've never found a publisher who would touch it with a fifteen foot pole. They don't want it at all.

Lately I've been hammering away at various things, trying vainly to make new markets. A British house asked to look at a collection of my weird stories, with a view of possible publication in book form.[12] I sent them a batch, but I haven't the slightest idea in the world that anything will come of it. Literary success is a persimmon that hangs out of my reach.

However, despite my own personal disappointments, I get some pleasure out of the fact that sensible people seem to be getting the upper hand in my state. The racing bill was passed, the law against prize-fighting repealed, and beer seems to be a cinch in the coming vote. All these things will add immensely to the revenues and prosperity of the state.

But I'm rambling too much. Looking back over what I have written, it might be well to summarize it, something as follows:

1. As concerns the matter I touched upon first in this letter: I do not judge a man's merit by his financial success. I do not look down on a man merely because he has failed to make as much money as somebody else. My own preference for commercial writing implies no scorn for those who possess the artistic motive. Leaving my own feelings out of the matter entirely: there are those who are dependent on the income from my writing. To abandon it in favor of a pursuit of art (which in my case would mean working

without any monetary return at all) would be to sacrifice their welfare. I can not, and will not, put art ahead of the needs of my family.

2. As for artists and intellectuals: I do not deny the sincerity of the purely creative urge in artists. I simply refuse to exalt art and artists beyond what I feel is a normal and natural proportion. Nor do I feel any hostility toward an intellectual simply because he is an intellectual. Only a fool undervalues knowledge or sneers at learning. I have no more use for anyone who sneers at everything smacking of intellectuality, than I have for anyone who sneers at everything that does not smack of intellectuality. The fact that I detest certain individuals and types among the intellectuals does not mean that I have any-thing against the *class* they represent. If I take "flings" at them occasionally, it isn't to be wondered at. Men who devote most of their lives to attacking the idols of other people shouldn't be surprised if a few bricks are heaved at theirs.

3. Concerning civilization and barbarism: I really think you are taking this matter a bit too seriously. You surely realize that I am not making any at-tempt to undermine or overthrow civilization! My personal feelings can scarcely matter much one way or the other. In fact, I think your resentment in this matter is based on a feeling that my attitude implies a depreciation of certain ideals and pursuits for which you have a passion. I believe that you feel you are defending your personal pursuits, preferences and ideals as much as civilization. Let me hasten to assure you that I have never intended to im-ply any depreciation of anything you value. I have never consciously uttered a word of criticism of any of your personal preferences or pursuits. When I have occasionally defended some of my personal preferences, it did not in-volve any criticism of yours. I keenly realize that different sets of conditions, hereditary and environmental, produce different sets of values and different modes of thinking. And I do not suppose that any one such set is likely to produce values and thought-processes sounder and more superior than all the others.

It may be true that my viewpoint is too much affected by local condi-tions. I lay no claims to being a cosmopolitan. However, the term "local" may admit of some discussion. I think that certain conditions and characteristics are more wide spread than you realize. Conditions that may seem at first glance to be merely isolated products of my township or county may—and in some cases do—exist to a greater or less extent all over the West. You will find that the characteristics of most people west of the Mississippi tend to resemble those of Texas more than they resemble those of New England or New York.

However, that comment is merely incidental. The point is, that nothing I say is to be taken as a criticism or depreciation of any of your personal choices or preferences.

I hope, also, that our argument has not caused you to doubt the sincerity of my admiration for your own artistic accomplishments. I think I have made it clear that for your type of artist, I have only the highest respect and admiration.

As always, I experienced the keenest enjoyment in reading your latest story. "The Dreams in the Witch House" is truly magnificent, from the title (a splendid bit of imagery in itself) to the very last line.[13] I shall doubtless re-read it many times, as I have your other splendid stories. You certainly dominated the current *Weird Tales;* indeed, it might be said that you had *two* stories in the magazine, since "The Horror in the Museum" reflected your style and power in every line.[14] Both stories were indeed fine, and I hope more of your work will appear soon. I make bold to remark that you are one of the very, very few men in the world who could handle "Brown Jenkin." With the average writer, he would have appeared merely ludicrous, a fantastic image from a dream. But you invested him with a startling reality, and a crawling horror, that made him spring out in appalling clarity against a background of twilight mystery. He is, indeed, one of the most powerful and grisly creations that have ever stalked through the shadow-haunted twilight realms of your tales. By the way, thanks very much for the allusions to Von Junzt's "Nameless Cults" in both the stories.

And thanks, again, for the kind things you said about my work. I'll send you that copy containing the yarn about Von Kalmbach, when it appears. I hope that my arguments have not proved too boresome or objectionable. I scarcely need to remark that I do not under rate your arguments on points whereon we differ, and that I have the highest respect for your point of view.

And so, with best wishes, I am,

Very cordially yours,
REH

Notes

1. Harold Lamb (1892–1962) was an American novelist and short story writer who published many stories in *Adventure* and went on to write many historical novels, including *Tamerlane, the Earth Shaker* (1928) and *The Crusades* (1930–31, originally published in two volumes as *Iron Men and Saints* and *The Flame of Islam*), both of which were in REH's library.
2. Simp Dixon was a cousin of John Wesley Hardin. Bob Lee (d. 1869), a former Confederate officer, fell out with Union authorities in North Texas in 1867, arousing the enmity of Lewis Peacock, a Union supporter. Lee was killed in 1869, but the feud continued until Peacock was shot from ambush in 1871.
3. The five Marlow brothers were arrested and jailed in Graham, Texas, in the fall of 1888, accused of stealing horses in Oklahoma. After their release on bond, law officers received a warrant accusing Boone Marlow of a murder in Vernon, Texas, in 1886. When the officers attempted to arrest Boone, a gunfight broke out and Sheriff

Marion Wallace was killed. Boone Marlow fled, but his brothers were returned to the jail in Graham. Knowing that there was talk of lynching them, they broke out of the jail on 14 January 1889 but were recaptured the following day. On 16 January, a mob tried to take them from the jail for lynching but the brothers stood them off. Charlie Marlow hit one of the mob, Robert Hill, causing the man to strike his head on a stone wall; he died two days later.

Federal authorities told local officials to transport the Marlows to Weatherford. On 19 January, the four brothers and two other prisoners were leg-shackled and put aboard wagons, along with federal deputy Sheriff Ed Johnson and several guards. The Marlows would allege that some of the guards were among the mob who tried to lynch them. The wagons were ambushed by a mob near Dry Creek, about two miles from Graham. The brothers jumped from their wagon and wrested weapons from the guards, most of whom fled, and beat off their attackers. Alfred and Llewelyn (Epp or Ely) Marlow were killed, Charlie was seriously wounded. George suffered minor wounds, but managed to free himself and Charlie by cutting off the feet of his dead brothers, and the two survivors, along with one of the other prisoners, were able to make their way to their farm and barricade themselves in a cabin until federal authorities arrived to take them to Dallas.

Boone Marlow's body was brought in to Fort Sill, Oklahoma, by three men generally described as bounty hunters, in January 1889. A doctor discovered that he had actually been poisoned, with two shots fired into his head to make it look as if he had been shot in self-defense. The three killers were arrested but released on bond and apparently never prosecuted.

Charlie and George Marlow later moved to Colorado and for a time served as deputies. REH's story "Law-Shooters of Cowtown" includes a mob scene probably inspired by the story of the Marlows.

4. S. W. Adams of the *Gladewater Journal* roused considerable interest around Texas—purportedly disseminating one million copies of a single issue of his paper in 1932—for his criticism of the oil policies of Governor Sterling.

5. As REH is using the terms, "Texican" would refer to a settler in the Anglo-American section of the Mexican province of Coahuila and Texas, prior to the Texas Revolution, "Texian" to a citizen of the Republic of Texas, and "Texan" to a citizen of the State of Texas (i.e., after annexation by the United States). As used by most authorities, "Texian" is the common term for both of the first two senses. "Texan" did not actually come into the English language until about 1860, and many used "Texian" well into the 1880s, but in general usage "Texian" is the preferred term before, and "Texan" after, admission of Texas to statehood.

6. "Spear and Fang" was accepted in the fall of 1924 (published in *WT*, July 1925); "The Lost Race" was accepted c. January 1925 (*WT*, January 1927); "The Hyena" was accepted c. December 1924 (*WT*, March 1928); "In the Forest of Villefere" was accepted early in 1925 (*WT*, August 1925); and "Wolfshead" was accepted c. October 1925 (*WT*, April 1926). Actually, it was only about one year between these and REH's next sales: "The Dream Snake" (*WT*, February 1928) and "Sea Curse" (*WT*, May 1928) were both accepted in early fall 1926.

7. "Bill Smalley and the Power of the Human Eye," rejected by *Adventure* and *Western Story* (see *CL* 1.309). No story by REH ever appeared in *Adventure*.

8. REH retained Otis Adelbert Kline as his agent during the spring of 1933. He continued to sell directly to *WT*, while Kline worked on breaking him into other markets.

9. 66 College Street, where HPL moved on 15 May 1933.

10. Hester Ervin was born in Dallas, 11 July 1870; her early years were spent there and in Fayetteville, Arkansas, and Lewisville, Texas.

11. Brownwood Lake was created by damming Pecan Bayou above the city of Brownwood. Started in 1930, the project was completed in 1933. The reservoir had been filled by flooding in 1932, but the water was released to enable completion of the dam. Deliberate impoundment began in July 1933. See letter 58, n. 3 (p. 329).

12. Denis Archer wrote REH regarding this collection on 19 May 1933. REH responded in a letter dated 15 June, sending "Wings in the Night," "The Tower of the Elephant," "Kings of the Night," "The House of Arabu," "The Valley of the Lost," "The Scarlet Citadel," "The Horror from the Mound," and "The Children of the Night."

13. Published in *WT*, July 1933.

14. HPL revised this story for Hazel Heald.

[83]   [nonextant letter by HPL]

[c. late June 1933]

[84]   [TLS]

[c. July 1933]

Dear Mr. Lovecraft:

I am sending on to you the enclosed manuscript, according to instructions. I read it the same day I received it, and I hardly know how to express my admiration for the splendid work you and Mr. Price have accomplished. I was most intrigued by the personalities of "Etienne de Marigny" and "Ward Phillips"![1] And hope these fine characters will be used again.

My sensations while reading this story are rather difficult to describe. The effect of *reality* was remarkable. Some of the speculations were over my head, at the first reading—not from any lack of clarity, but simply because of their cosmic depth.

The Dhole-haunted planet of Yaddith conjures up tantalizing vistas of surmise, and I hope you will use it in future stories. I hope, too, that you'll decide to get poor Randolph Carter out of his frightful predicament. I remember "The Silver Key"—yet remember is hardly the word to use. I have constantly referred to that story in my meditations ever since I read it, years ago—have probably thought of it more than any other story that ever appeared in Weird Tales. There was something about it that struck deep. I read it aloud to Tevis Clyde Smith, some years ago, and he agreed with me as to its cosmic sweep.

I should be answering herewith your recent—and as always, interesting—letter; but I'm swamped with work just now. However, I hope to answer it in full soon. Our points of disagreement are not so radical as I had previously thought.

Thanks for the picture folder, and please present my best wishes to Mr. Long. I here enclose a few snaps taken at old Fort McKavett, which lies in Menard County, 155 miles southwest of here, three miles from the head of the San Saba river, mentioned in tale and fable, and in connection with the Lost Bowie Mine, mentioned in a previous letter.[2] McKavett is fascinating—a village of ruins and semi-ruins, people living in the old unruined barracks and soldier's quarters, among the remnants of other buildings which have not stood the test of time. I was in too big a hurry to get much of its history, or many pictures, but I hope to return there some day for more data. The fort was established in 1871 by the Federal government which was foolish enough to station negro troops there; their arrogance led to a fierce and bloody war between the fort and the inhabitants of the country—a wild, hilly, rocky, thickly timbered expanse—in which the natives had the best of it; and in 1883 the fort was definitely abandoned. Don't bother to return these snaps; I have duplicates of them.

Cordially,
Robert E. Howard

Notes

1. The ms. was of "Through the Gates of the Silver Key."
2. One of the photos sent to HPL is reproduced in *The Last Celt* (p. 389). REH's inscription reads: "Ruins of Fort McKavett, July 9, 1933; I like this snap; it makes me feel kind of like a Vandal or Goth standing amidst the ruins of a Roman fortress or palace."

[85]

66 College St.,
Providence, R.I.
July 24, 1933

Dear R E H:—

I was delighted to receive your interesting letter of the 15th, with its wealth of clarifying material and its account of your recent movements. My own chronicles of the period are meagre and dismal, as a result of the disaster about to be related.

The fascination of my new colonial abode persists. It is ineffably glamourous to come *home* through a carved colonial doorway like that on my bookplate, and sit beside a white Georgian mantel gazing out through small-paned windows over a sea of venerable roofs and stately foliage! I forget how minutely I described the place to you—but I probably mentioned that it is in a quaint grassy court behind the Brown University library on the steep dividing hill, and that it has all the traditional features of the colonial house—fireplaces, mantels, chimneys-cupboards, wide floor-boards, old-fashioned latches, six-panel doors, rear wing with different floor level, etc. The windows have no cords and weights, but are fastened by a side spring in the old colonial way. My aunt and I occupy the upper half—consisting of 5 rooms (besides bath and kitchen) on the main (2nd) floor, plus 2 attic storerooms. My own especial quarters consist of a large southwest study and a small adjoining bedroom. My working desk is under a west window affording a splendid view of the lower town's outspread roofs and of the mystical sunsets that flame behind them. Outside—in the rear and on the west—are picturesque, village-like gardens—those behind being at a higher level than the front of the house. In front there are some flower-beds, a hedge, and a row of old-fashioned posts to keep off vehicles. Altogether, it is just the sort of place I have longed all my life to live in. Now I hope to hell I can scrape up enough cash to continue here indefinitely—at least, till the climate drives me south. Astonishingly enough, this whole flat costs only as much as my *one* room and alcove in Barnes St.—and the neighbourhood is really just as good, though not quite so wholly *residential* on account of the college. Like Barnes St., it has a distinctly *small-village* atmosphere which is astonishing in view of the city's size. That is one of the great charms of Providence. Only a stone's throw from my door in three directions are grassy, unpaved lanes bordered with bushes, while on every hand are quaint colonial houses with moss-grown bank walls and rambling terraced gardens. It is almost impossible to realise that one is in a modern city. A short distance away, in a bend of a nearby street, is an intact old farmhouse with its tangled and picturesque farmyard untouched by any urban influence. No city but Providence could afford a spectacle quite like this . . . . nor would I wish to live in any other city. Though not an actual *country* enthusiast like you, I am definitely a *villager* or *small-towner*. I hate a treeless, gardenless, formally built-up city as much as anyone alive, and would mourn to see Providence lose its village-like aspect. I doubt if heredity has very much to do with such matters, but as a matter of fact my own lineage is entirely rural up to a relatively recent date. My paternal ancestors lived in the English countryside till 1823, and my maternal ancestors in the Rhode Island countryside till 1874. And the part of Providence where I was born was very close to what was then the edge of the settled district; so that in youth I played largely in open green fields and shadowy woods, and knew intimately the sights and sounds of typical old New-England farms. To this day I make for the open country every summer afternoon when I can possibly get there.

Well—so much for that. Now for the disaster to which I referred. On June 14th my aunt broke her right ankle while descending the stairs to answer the doorbell during my absence, and has since been confined to bed with the injured member in a heavy plaster cast. She was at the hospital for three weeks, and is now at home with a nurse in constant attendance. For the past few days she has sat up a bit in the afternoon, and in about another week the cast can come off—allowing her to be up and around on crutches. How soon she can walk freely is still doubtful—it won't be till autumn, at any rate. Truly, a delightful sort of housewarming! This matter has tied me up considerably, since I have to be here on duty every afternoon while the nurse goes out— except by special arrangement. When my aunt is up and the nurse goes, I shall be even more tied—for on account of my aunt's inability to get down stairs I shall have to be constantly on hand to answer the doorbell. I have had to forego all long trips, though certain short ones have proved of interest— and I have had quite a number of exceedingly pleasant visitors. Today I hope to get to Onset, near Cape Cod, where Frank B. Long and his parents are spending some time. I shall stay over tomorrow (perhaps accompanying the Longs on a motor trip to Provincetown) and return Wednesday morning, when my hosts will start back for New York.

My first visitor this season was none other than our dashing friend E. Hoffmann Price, who hopes to get around to see you later in the year. He came in his 1928 Ford juggernaut just before my aunt's return from the hospital, and we had a festive and enjoyable four days. Young Brobst was over twice—on one occasion staying all night for a session of triangular literary and philosophical discussion, punctuated by a trip to the ancient hillside churchyard (which I have probably mentioned before in letters) at about 3 a.m. On July 2nd Price brought his juggernaut into the service of antiquarian exploration by taking me all through a Rhode Island rural region which— despite my residence less than 30 miles from it, and my ⅓ ancestral connexion with its old stock—I had never before explored in person because of the absence of all public transportation facilities. This was the ancient "South County" or "Narragansett County" west of the bay, which I once mentioned to you as a region of large plantations and black slaves—exactly like the South—before the revolution. I think I spoke of the fame of Narragansett cheeses and Narragansett pacers in the old days, and of the wealth of legendry still clinging round this ancient seat of a mellow and patriarchal culture. This was the rural hinterland which looked to Newport—across the bay—as "the town". Although socially and economically akin to the South, the Narragansett country did not copy Virginia or Carolina designs for its plantation-houses, but employed the native New-England gambrel-roof farmhouse design on an unprecedentedly large scale. Even the townhouses of the planters in Newport (mostly in Water, now Washington, St.) tended to follow this pattern. The natural scenery of this territory is unprecedentedly fine, though the choicest bits are never visible from the travelled highways. On this occasion we began with the unspoiled Colonial seaport of Wickford (which I had seen many times before) and worked south through the magical countryside. An especial high spot was the gambrel-roofed snuff-mill on Narrow River where in 1755 the eminent portrait-painter Gilbert Stuart was born. This has recently been restored to its original appearance and working order in every detail, and a very pleasant custodian showed us all about and worked the great water-wheel and grinding machinery for our benefit. I enclose a card of the mill—representing it as it was when Stuart was a child dwelling there. Another thing we saw was the last surviving perfect specimen of the great plantation-houses—the Rowland Robinson house, built in 1705 and situated most impressively amidst a grove of gigantic, centuried willows. It is now inhabited by a very cultivated connoisseur who showed us all about—letting us see the fine interior woodwork. Still another sight was the abandoned "Glebe" or rectory of the Rev. James MacSparran, (1727),[1] which lies on a deserted road, with its succession of terraces and courtyards spectrally embowered in a lush profusion of vines and briers. This region, like the South, was largely Church-of-England; and the churches (as in Maryland, Virginia, and the Carolinas) were situate in the midst of the country to accomodate the planters in their coaches rather than the relatively few villagers. Dr. MacSparran's church was formerly near his "Glebe"—on a spot called "The Platform", where a ghoulish-looking churchyard still remains. After the revolution, however, the decline of plantation life forced the churches to transfer their activities to the villages—and this edifice, built in 1707, was removed bodily on rollers to Wickford, where it still stands in excellent condition. On the high hill above the Glebe we visited "Hannah Robinson's Rock"[2]— around which a pathetic legend clusters, and from which can be obtained perhaps the finest landscape vista in New England—winding blue river far below, green meadows and woodlands outspread, white headland church in the distance, and the remote gleam of the mystical, half-glimpsed sea. Last of all came the utterly unchanged colonial village of Kingston with its great elms, ancient houses, centuried court building, 1746 inn, and general atmosphere of well-preserved antiquity. It is the same today as when men in periwigs and small-clothes assembled there for His Majesty's quarterly assizes. On our way back we paused at the quaint old fishing village of Pawtuxet (6 m. s. of Providence, but now connected with it by a continuous street network) so that Price might sample a typical clam dinner. As you may imagine from what I told you about my attitude toward sea-food, I remained an interested but unparticipating spectator. Price, by the way, holds a very high opinion of you and your work—so that our conversation contained much which would have gratified you could you have overheard it. He is now visiting a friend of Clark Ashton Smith's from California, to whom I showed ancient Newport—taking my first boat trip of the season. I anticipate a pleasant time with Long around Cape Cod today and tomorrow.

Glad you and your mother have had some pleasant travel, and wish you might have stayed in San Antonio longer. The new Brownwood Lake country must be fascinating—but as you say, it is likely to become spoiled with cheap resort and bungalow developments.

I wish you luck with your British collection of stories. Possibly a collection of mine might have more of a chance in Great Britain than here. Glad you enjoyed the Witch House and Museum story. Another tale which I revised for the "Museum" author, and which Wright has accepted, brings in von Juntz and his black book as almost the central theme.[3] It concerns a mummy found in the crypt of a Cyclopean stone temple of fabulous antiquity, volcanically upheaved from the sea. Of late my programme has been too feverishly crowded to permit me to write anything new, but I hope to get things more under control later on. By the way—I enclose a circular of Clark Ashton Smith's new brochure of weird stories, all of which are splendid. I advise you to pick up this item—and also the book of poems at its reduced price.[4] Both are highly unusual and meritorious. I hope to see your von Kalmbach tale when it is done, and am sure it will be a highly unusual production.

The summer here—except for a few hot days—has been disconcertingly cool so far, but I have managed to keep tolerably comfortable with an oil heater. Whenever weather and opportunity have coincided, I have (as usual) taken my work out to the woods and fields for performance.

And now I must pause in order to take the New Bedford motor-coach. The Longs will meet me at New Bedford with their car. I shall carry my correspondence with me, and may continue this epistle there. If so, the ensuing parts will be on a smaller paper. Perhaps, though, I shall get no chance for correspondence—in which case I shall pick up the threads here Wednesday or later. Weather looks favourable for a good trip—and I hope my hosts will include in their plans an exploration of some of the quainter byways on the Cape.

Later—July 31

Well—the trip gave me no chance for writing, and when I got back I found an engulfing stack of mail awaiting me. Had an interesting session with Long—as our joint folder doubtless apprised you—though the weather was adverse throughout my Cape Cod sojourn. Cold and rainy—so that much of the time had to be spent on the piazza of the place we stopped. We did, though, include one motor trip—through the rather attractive countryside to Hyannis. Cape Cod is very pleasant, though I really think it is rather overrated as compared with other parts of [text dropped?] . . . well-preserved old houses, ancient mill, slender white steeple, and luxuriant greenery. I am now about to welcome another guest—James F. Morton, curator of the Paterson Museum—with whom I anticipate a pleasant half-week of delving among the antiquities of Rhode Island. Weather has turned warm and pleasant since my return, so that I have done most of my writing in the open air.

By the way—I enclose a circular from a new weird magazine to which Clark Ashton Smith and I [are] contributing.[5] There is no pay for contributions, but we are glad of a chance to get printed copies of the tales all other magazines have rejected.

Regarding our controversy—your recent letter leaves most of the points much clearer than before; in many cases resolving apparent philosophical differences into mere differences in taste. As for the status of art—by which I mean not only the process of creation but the whole development of personality which includes appreciation and general tasteful living—I don't know that I called it the 'only reason for evolution'; for indeed, evolution is a matter of chance which has no reason or object. Rather did I suggest that it is simply something which is *characteristic* of those types which are most evolved. It does form a very great factor in the life of all highly evolved persons, so that without it many of the best types would no longer care to exist. But I feel sure that any recognition of its high place did not involve any intentional depreciation of other forms of activity—the constructive and the administrative, for example. Also—I hope I made clear my thorough realisation that art has its fringe of boastful charlatans, whose prime motive is prestige, and who use the name of art to solicit a homage to which they are not entitled.

As for the attacks which certain types of philosophically-minded thinkers make upon certain simple pleasures and attitudes involving an only average complexity of emotional organisation—I hardly think these are typical of all profound thinkers, or even that they are as far-reaching as they seem when they do occur. It must be admitted at the outset that many of the commonplace pleasures and attitudes of the majority are in truth very naive and quasi-childish—in other words, that they unquestionably involve an extremely narrow area of thought and feeling, so that a broadening of the personality would cause them to lose much of their hold on one's interest. This cannot possibly be denied—hence it is useless to object to the basic classification of such pleasures and attitudes as relatively inferior. Where the rub comes is in the concrete application of this general truth—i.e., when one attempts to classify an entire personality according to the sources of its pleasure. Here the really wise thinker exercises a sense of proportion, and realises how variable, contradictory, and oddly compartmented the human personality is. He realises that the average individual may have all his effective cerebration and erudition concentrated in certain areas, thus leaving the other areas relatively unsupervised by the consciousness. Such a type may well be deeply intelligent and tasteful in its major field, yet retain a thoroughly uncritical childishness in such secondary fields as that of sheer pleasure-seeking. In other words, we cannot properly judge a man by his recreative interests—which always have a tendency to reflect a lower grade of taste and intelligence than his best. While we can and must concede that certain *pleasures themselves* are inferior (and in view of the sound, abstract, and impersonal basis of classification—a sheer matter of cosmic is-or-isn'tness—no one has any reason to *resent* this grouping, whether it involves his personal predilections or not), we cannot justly say that all men who follow such pleasures are inferior. Indeed, if we use practical observation instead of mere theory, we shall find that many demonstrably superior men are strongly devoted to the very diversions which arbitrary theorists ridicule. Thus the error of the Mencken type is one arising from a defective sense of proportion which fails to consider the one-sidedness, variability, and contradictoriness of mankind—that is, so far as the Mencken type attempts to classify men rigidly according to their pleasures. Actually, however, the critics are not always as sweeping as they seem to be. They often realise how many superior men turn to light and frivolous diversions at intervals (with a full realisation of the lightness and frivolity of what they pursue); that their criticism is really not directed toward everyone who adopts such diversions, but only toward those who actually regard their frothy pastimes as supreme or important ends. A rational critic of this kind will often pronounce a certain sport or attitude childish—yet will at the same time recognise that many highly cultivated men (and perhaps himself!) enthusiastically follow it. We all have our blind or insensitive or unawakened spots. Of course one may add that all critics are by no means correct in their grouping of superior and inferior sports and interests. Often a seemingly inferior pastime may involve poetic or associative factors whereby the enjoyer's pleasure is really of a vastly higher grade than appears on the surface. To sum up: on the one hand it is by no means true that all thorough thinkers, as a class, condemn the followers of simple sports and interests; while on the other hand, it is certainly unfair to blame those who, after a study of all the factors involved, and leaving out all personalities, cannot help pointing out the very slight intellectual and aesthetic content of certain widespread popular interests and attitudes. It is irrational and unjustified to think less of these critics because their honest and searching observation forces them to establish judgments apparently unflattering to our chance array of surface tastes. I, for instance, have no taste in music and like the cheap popular songs of my youth—yet I never think of resenting the honest judgment of a real musician when he explains to me how undeveloped my taste is. It is only an egotist and emotionalist—whose life hinges on things other than reason—who resents the impersonal, abstract judgments which now and then seem to deflate certain pet attitudes into which he has carelessly drifted. I certainly don't see why I should think less of a man when he chances to 'show up' a naive or weak spot of mine.

Harking back to the matter of the place of aesthetic development in life—a good many confusing definitions on both sides are undoubtedly involved. No one has ever claimed that the artist is more important in the maintenance of some sort of civilisation than is the farmer, mechanic, engineer, or statesman. It is, on the other hand, generally recognised that these possibly simpler types are supremely necessary to the preservation of that well-ordered material fabric which underlies a high civilisation. That much is axiomatic. However, when we consider the vast enlargement of life made possible by the expansion of the personality under the influence of art; and realise how infinitely more worth living is a life enriched by such an expansion; we are certainly justified in censuring any civilisation which does not favour this process. It is not that we regard art or any other thing in life as "sacred", but that we recognise the importance of something which naturally forms the chief life-interest of the most highly evolved types. Art certainly *is* more intrinsically removed from the unevolved protoplasmic stage of organic reaction than any other human manifestation except pure reason—hence our grouping of it as one of the "highest" things in life. By "highest" we do not mean "most important to survival", but simply "most advanced in intrinsic development." There is no attempt on the part of rational thinkers to give art (or anything else) a "cosmic significance"—the case is merely one of recognising a certain degree of removal from the amoebal stage. As for the validity of evolutionary degree as a criterion of value—even that is admitted to be *purely relative* in a cosmos which is probably no more than a directionally perpetual vortex of alternate or intermingled building-up and breaking-down. However, it is none the less a fact that such a *basically relative* criterion can be adopted as *to all intents and purposes absolute* when applied locally to the human species. From our point of view (and that is the only one which matters to us) there is something quasi-intrinsically superior about the impression-gathering and sensation-correlating condition of a complexly evolved organism as distinguished from an unevolved organism. We feel an instinctive superiority in conscious and sensitive things like man (which represent the direction *toward* which organic mutation is at present moving) as opposed to relatively unconscious and insensitive things like starfish or stones (which represent the direction *away from* which organic mutation is at present moving). Whether or not there is any cosmic logic in this feeling, it is subjectively valid for all of us— and that is all that is necessary. We need not call the qualities of "superiority" and "inferiority" anything more than a matter of human preference . . . . . but we know that we naturally consider a man as "higher" than a protozoön. On that—empirically, if you wish, yet without doubt sensibly—we base our preferences. It is according to this scale that we find art and involved intellection the "highest" of human activities . . . . . "highest" because they are the *most human* and *least protozoic.*

Regarding politics and sociology—the utter complexity of human nature, and the tremendous doubtfulness and variability of all social problems, make it impossible and unscientific to be dogmatic on any point. All the individual knows is that he is here—on this planet, with his own fortunes to carve out. His problem is simply how to make the tedious ordeal of living most worth enduring for himself—and to this end he must consider all sorts of systems and grouping with other individuals, tracing out their probable ultimate effects upon him. This task is complicated by the fact that many different natural types of human being exist, so that the "best" system for one type does not always coincide with the "best" system envisaged by another type. The result of this diversity is of course a ceaseless struggle—perhaps to be later abated when a clearer general knowledge teaches methods of compromise whereby the ends of each type may be achieved with a minimum of encroachment on other types. My own views of social organisation change constantly as new evidence and fresh trends appear from year to year—the only persistent factor being my settled conviction that the best civilisation is that which gives the freest play and greatest encouragement to the highest (i.e., most evolved) attributes of mankind. I have no *class* sympathies whatsoever, since I do not believe in classes except as temporary and accidental phenomena. All I sympathise with is *excellence in the individual—*for after all, *the individual is the only basic human reality.* "Mankind" is a mere myth or working hypothesis—but *individual men* are actualities to be dealt with. The effect of my position is to make me rather an outlaw among all groups of orthodox social and political thinkers. Proletarians and democrats curse me for upholding a standard of civilisation which *accidents of previous history* have identified with the artificial and temporary institution of aristocracy; whilst aristocrats and plutocrats curse me just as loudly for my lack of enthusiasm for the arbitrary barriers and inequalities of resource-distribution which *they* believe to underlie all high standards and true civilisation. Between the two groups I am absolutely impartial, since I think in terms of neither. I think only as an individual.

Regarding the various social devices roughly grouped together under the head of "special privilege"—I am not disposed to lay down any arbitrary or blanket laws. We must remember that the abstract and rigid thing called "justice" is only an illusion, and that an entire group may often profit in the end by allowing certain advantages to a few advanced members. This is a question where blind fanaticism has no place—we must neither love nor hate, but simply *reason* coolly and farseeingly. Actually, there are fields where all arbitrary preference is indeed definitely out of place. It is grotesque and impracticable, for example, that either birth or wealth should affect any individual's opportunities for advancement; or that carelessly determined groups should be allowed to monopolise resources and wield disproportionate power. On the other hand, it seems to me equally foolish that a man's intrinsic development should not win him definite advantages in the social order—especially as concerns the exercise of *power.* This, it may be added, is as much for the sake of the social order as for that of the individuals concerned; since it is obvious that our complex and mechanised society can never be properly governed—or even comprehended—except by the minority of highly endowed (in point of natural intelligence and strength of character) and intensively trained (in problems of science, administration, economics, etc.) products of sound breeding and thorough education. There is no doubt in my mind but that the cultural norm of any nation ought to be as high as possible, and that all participation in government ought to be restricted to those who can pass rigid examinations in natural aptitude and acquired comprehension of political science. Modern problems are too intricate to be handled by any other sort of person—I myself, for example, am so ignorant of economics, engineering, finance, and other basic governmental essentials, that no really enlightened nation ought to allow me to vote or hold office. What is more—we now understand so well the suicidal deadlocks caused by the diffusion of authority among many individuals (no matter how well qualified each may be), that we are forced to recognise the need of compact and highly centralised dictatorships in the increasingly complex world of the future. Even with the choicest kind of an electorate we cannot hope for effective government unless the vital matters of immediate policy are in the hands of a well-ordered group empowered to take action without delay or cumbrous consultations and agreements. Parliamentarianism—the child of the Middle Ages—is helpless before the problems of the machine age. The best we can do is to have a choice electorate select a very few powerful officials for terms of reasonable length, giving them a free rein except when basic national aspirations seem likely to be contravened. Not only is this necessary to ensure the survival of the whole group, but it is likewise the only way whereby the average or humble individual can be assured of a chance for a decent life and normal opportunities. We know now that under the machine age any policy of laissez-faire individualism means only the crushing and starvation of the weak or unlucky man, and the corresponding concentration of wealth among the minority of strong and lucky men . . . . . and nothing but a highly intelligent dictatorship can ever evolve and enforce anything so complex and delicate as a planned economy and deliberate allocation of resources.

As for the matter of *freedom*—I do not think that any thoughtful system of government wishes to curtail this element beyond the degree necessary for group-survival. It is impossible for an industrialised nation to return to the agrarian-handicraft stage typified by the frontier and its transient conditions; nor is it logical to assume that frontier conditions were necessarily superior, as a whole, to those of a more settled order. Advantages have vanished, but other compensating advantages have appeared in their place—so that the net result is at least highly debatable. As a matter of fact, the frontier was a cruelly unjust institution—at least as much so as modern plutocracy. It gave everything to the physically strong and took everything from the physically weak or slow—irrespective of the finer qualities of mind and spirit which have at least *some* chance of recognition in most settled civilisations. Devotees of the frontier err in their over-simplification of human values—laying all stress on the material and assertive virtues, and ignoring the more delicate qualities which make life worth living for the highly evolved. This is not to minimise the worth of the frontier culture in its day—*when it was necessary*—but merely to warn against the exaltation of this or any other transient development-phase as an arbitrary ideal. No one respects more than I do the strength and ability of the men who tamed the wilderness—but I feel sure that these very men, as indicated by the conquests they made, did not wish the wilderness to continue as such. They envisaged for their descendants a civilised world like that of the Eastern States out of which they came; and I believe they would feel astonished if they knew that some of these descendants reject the ultimate gift and yearn for the unsettled years of violent struggle. In eulogising the heroes of the heroic age we are all too apt to lose sight of the ultimate future for which they fought. However—let it be admitted that the course of national development has not been by any means what it ought to be, and that in many cases certain qualities emphasised by the frontier have been allowed to die out too completely. I am far from claiming that the frontier has nothing to teach modern civilisation. All I maintain is that the *entire body* of frontier culture is not necessarily superior to the present as a whole—though in its day it represented the best equilibrium achievable under the given conditions, and produced some of the strongest types observable in our national history.

As for the alleged horrors of civilisation—I have never said that innocent men are not imprisoned now and then in the course of the years, but merely that this evil is a *very rare one* in the settled civilisation of modern Anglo-Saxondom. Indeed, all the evidence seems to indicate that the *most* oppression and unrest occur where the degree of civilisation is *least* complete. The simple fact is—as attested by any normal resident of any normal eastern city—that *virtually everyone lives his life through without any adverse contact with the law*. This is a *fact* which no amount of *theory* can get around. I know what I've seen—I'll be 43 on the 20th of next month, and in all the years I've lived I've never had any legal trouble or known anybody else who has had. It's no use to hark back to past ages of political or religious disorder for cases of oppression—or to cite foreign instances like Nazi-ridden Germany. These things don't represent the Western civilised norm—and *even they* do not involve nearly as much tragic waste of life as the barbarism of tribal antiquity or the unrest of the frontier. What we are talking about is the normal Anglo-Saxon civilised community—England, Ontario, Massachusetts, Virginia, South Carolina, New Zealand, or New South Wales—and there it is certain that unjust imprisonment is one of the rarest of all phenomena. What happens in certain border zones where settlement is less complete is hardly a criterion—even if much of this trouble is due to the machinations of those who themselves dwell in settled regions. That's the hell of human nature . . . . . men are predatory at heart, even amidst the stablest of social orders. It is only the force of the social order which holds them in; hence if they have power in regions outside the radius of that order, they are apt to let loose their pent-up lawlessness. That is why it is important for every region to achieve a settled social order as soon as possible. But meanwhile the fact remains *that in long-settled regions the law does not interfere with the normal individual.*

As for a possible reduction in human stamina under an increasingly complex civilisation—there probably is a peril of such a trend. It need not, however, be as rapid or extensive as some fear; since many counteractive influences can be supplied through psychological and physical exercises. It is not altogether necessary that a man be in constant hazard of death or starvation in order to develop a worthy character—history shows that the great civilisations have virtues of their own; not always identical with barbaric virtues, yet not always excluding some of the traits admired in ruder ages.

Regarding the question of *liberty*—it seems to me that most of the existing unrest comes simply from the *transitional* nature of the present age. It is not that the amount of personal latitude in the age just closing had any especial sacredness, but simply that we always cling blindly and irrationally to what we have been used to. Man has never—since he has been man—had perfect liberty. The amount he has is always a compromise—being as much as he can safely possess under the given conditions of the moment. The exact degree of freedom granted by the early-American civilisation was merely a chance product of temporary economic conditions. There was never any guarantee of its permanence—but we merely became used to it because conditions permitted it to remain for a considerable time. Now the inevitable social drift makes necessary a very slight change, lest people defeat themselves by getting in one another's way. The new equilibrium is no less logical and justifiable than the old—since each is simply an adjustment to existing conditions. But our restless souls resent it because it is *different*. This, however, is merely the present generation's emotion. The next generation will be used to the new state of things, and will harbour a new norm of liberty based upon them . . . . nor will this be intrinsically any less logical than the older norm. It is simply a matter of point of view—actually, a little more regulation will not destroy anything of real value in the process of living. The amount of latitude left to every normal man is still enormous . . . . vastly greater than that possessed by the average citizen in many of the earlier civilisations.

I do not see why my light opinion of newspapers and radios surprised you—since these purely mechanical and material things have almost nothing to do with the psychological refinement which is civilisation. Great art and great philosophy have flourished without them, so why should the friend of culture deify them? I respect only *quality*, and attach no importance to accidental offshoots which may or may not accompany a certain degree of advancement. As a matter of fact, the cultural value of most newspapers and all radio programmes is slight to the point of actual negativeness.

As for Gothic barbarism—which I certainly do not fail to distinguish from the savagery of the inferior races—I still do not see how it can be held as equal or superior to a settled civilisation. It is true that the members of such a barbarism did not view it with our eyes, and that they were adapted to its conditions more completely than we can readily realise; but even so, the undevelopment of vast sides of the personality, and the habitual outrages against the integrity of the physical body (not restricted to rare war periods, or offset by the careful surgery and occasional humaneness never wholly absent from modern warfare) must have made an average far below that reached by the mentally active and relatively humane civilisation of modern Anglo-Saxondom.

I note the facts regarding the fate of the 225-lb. songster; and agree, in view of the circumstances, that he tended to deserve something of what he received. Dishonesty is a violation of the most precious element in real civilisation, hence no friend of civilisation need defend anyone guilty of it. And it would also seem that his attitude lacked the basic courtesy and considerateness which form an essential part of true cultivation.

Concerning the general history of violence in the southwest—I realise that in former times it was an inevitable result of unchosen conditions. The horrors of "reconstruction" after the Civil War were probably the most insane and widely-extended negation of civilisation practiced in any Anglo-Saxon nation during the lifetime of people now surviving (a negation made possible partly through fanatical vindictiveness and callous corruption, and partly through a sheer popular ignorance of what was going on); and nothing but praise is due to the extra-legal forces (such as the Ku Klux Klan under Gen. N. B. Forrest) which helped to nullify the menace and preserve a real civilisation in what may yet prove to be the most important and long-enduring part of the American fabric. It is natural that the struggle in the pioneer Southwest should be more violent and sanguinary than in the older South east of the Mississippi, and no one can criticise the emergency measures adopted for the defence of home soil and institutions. It must always be remembered that the pro-civilisationist's criticism of violence is applied only to *unnecessary* violence. Violence exerted in defence of one's integrity and institutions is desperately *necessary*, hence receives only admiration and respect. It is the mere *wanton* waste of life—in adjusting problems which could be otherwise adjusted—that one is inclined to lament.

As for the 'trickery versus violence' question—there is certainly much to say on both sides. Certainly, trickery is the more *ignominious*, since it involves that element of duplicity and evasion which the Aryan instinctively hates; yet violence can assume extremely repulsive forms—especially when exerted by the strong against the weak, or under circumstances where the danger of equal combat is either wholly or partly evaded. The anecdotes you cite are of intense psychological interest and significance—each really worthy of development as a short story . . . . not a didactic story with a moral, but a purely artistic story illustrating the subtleties of human feeling.

About your spending a year in a settled and orderly city—I didn't imply that you would prefer it to your present environment, but merely suggested that it would prove a valuable broadening influence by showing you how free from oppression and arbitrary injustice an old and traditionally organised community is. Very probably a Texas city like San Antonio would furnish a similar illustration if thoroughly known and analysed. I don't doubt but that the parts of Texas controlled by real natives are far better managed than those where outlanders dominate—for after all, there is no rule worse than callous alien rule. Unfortunately—as I mentioned before—civilisation does not seem to improve the anti-social qualities of men when they are dealing outside their own compact radius. The perfectly law-abiding (in Massachusetts) Massachusetts man becomes a predatory pirate when driving a land deal in Idaho, while the punctilious (in Virginia) Virginian thinks nothing of ruthlessness when developing an oil field in Mexico. The only way to defeat this sort of cultural backsliding is to develop in the exploited regions a protective and law-enforcing native civilisation just as thorough and effective as that of the invaders' respective homelands. Then the invaders, faced with the same kind of inhibitions to which they have been conditioned at home, will begin to subside into the patterns which their heritage has taught them to follow among their fellows. I am glad that the Ferguson administration is establishing changes for the better, and hope that progress may continue solidly even if gradually. You are certainly right in preferring a purely autochthonous civilisation to any sort of importation from outside. Each region's culture ought most emphatically to be its own—a genuine outgrowth of local traditions and institutions, and resembling others only through elements of common inheritance and degree of settled law-abidingness. I am glad that San Antonio remains true to the heritage of its own soil, and hope it will continue thus. Incidentally, you raise interesting distinctions in your reference to *Texicans, Texians,* and *Texans.*

Still Later—August 5.

Morton's visit held up my correspondence, but we had a damned good time. Aside from our continual and congenial debating we took many rural walks and antiquarian pilgrimages, on one occasion seeing an ancient well with great wooden sweep . . . . from which we paused to drink in memory of the past. This walk ended up at Greenville, an unspoiled village which holds much of the atmosphere of the 1820 period. Another time we visited the colonial seaport of Warren, down the East shore of the bay—incidentally stopping at a place (quite a rendezvous of our gang) where 28 varieties of ice cream are sold. We had six varieties apiece—my choices being grape, chocolate chip, macaroon, cherry, banana, and orange-pineapple. Afterward we walked south to Bristol, another quaint 18th century seaport. Still another trip was to old Pawtuxet—where, as with Price, I watched Morton eat a shore dinner. On the last day of the visit, we took a boat trip to Newport—

spending most of out time on the rugged sea-cliffs. The enclosed card will give you some idea of the rocks and surf on which we looked down from our exalted perch—a perch which 200 years ago was a favourite of Dean (later Bishop) Berkeley as he composed his famous "Alciphron", or, "The Minute Philosopher". We had splendidly hot weather all along—thermometer around 90°—though Morton didn't appreciate this bounty of Nature as much as I did. Now it has turned cool again, and I shiver wistfully. From here Morton goes to Vermont and New Hampshire to climb mountains.

My aunt's plaster cast was removed Thursday night, but the doctor says she must remain in bed for a week more. I am still largely tied down, and shall probably be so till winter . . . . when liberty is of no use to me! Had an invitation to New Hampshire, but will probably have to decline.

Had a letter from the Knopf firm yesterday, asking to see a few of my tales with a view to possible book publication. I sent about seven—though after my experience with Putnam's and the Viking Press I realise how little such requests mean.[6] These fellows are merely scouting around to make sure that they didn't miss anything good—but they didn't really want the kind of stuff I write. Sooner or later this batch will come back with the usual polite regrets.

Your references to your early writing interested me extremely. Undoubtedly you have a thoroughly innate and really powerful literary gift, for not many could hammer out a vivid and effective style as soon as you did. I am sure you need not regret the sale-less years, for these probably played as important a part in your development as any of the more visibly fruitful years. I surely hope—and indeed believe—that you will be able to make a permanent profession of writing, for its flexible schedule would seem admirably suited to your temperament. It seems to me that you have a happy ability to suit editors without sacrificing that zest of composition which means literature of some sort or other—a combination generally indicative of success. I can appreciate your position as a local pioneer of writing, which is all the greater proof of your genuineness of impulse. In view of the lack of stimuli in your environment, your persistence from boyhood onward is certainly of the greatest significance. I note the school reminiscences with interest. Mathematics seems to have been our joint bane—as it was with Arthur Machen. Though there are notable exceptions, I think that persons of imaginative inclinations tend to be weak in this field. As for forgetting—I fancy that even the things which have completely vanished from your consciousness have left a strong impression within, and have given your powers of effective thought a facility which untrained minds must necessarily lack. Still, I suppose your extensive voluntary reading was really the greatest formative influence. Your perseverance in that field was surely remarkable in the highest degree, rivalling some of the classic anecdotes told about obstacle-conquering students. Sorry the process injured your vision—and glad the injury didn't go farther than it did. I trust you have corrected the strain with proper glasses. The scarcity of magazines in your region seems singular as compared with the inexhaustible plethora of them—good and bad—hereabouts.

In reading over your summary of your side of our debate I am impressed with the fact that we are beginning to understand more of each other's positions. After all, the major differences are purely matters of different emotions—as fortuitously determined by temperament and environmental accident. If I were to make a similar summary of my own position, I suppose it would run something like this:

I. I value aesthetic and intellectual activities highly because they are beyond doubt an expression of the most thoroughly evolved part of the human personality.

II. I value civilisation above barbarism because I feel that it utilises human personality to the full instead of involving a waste of man's most highly evolved faculties.

III. I think that the most precious possession of a highly evolved man is his freedom of thought and expression; and that conversely the worst hardship he can suffer is a curtailment of that freedom, either through overt censorship or through the obligation of writing insincere material to suit commercial editors.

Speaking of literary insincerity and repulsive hack work—Long has just sold a wretched "confession" tale to the equally wretched Macfadden outfit for $100.00.[7] He isn't signing his own name, though the company insist on his giving them his full name and address for filing. It gives him a nauseated feeling to reflect that his name is even secretly connected with such a piece of abysmal tripe—but he wants the cash badly!

First issue of *The Fantasy Fan* came the other day. It looks sadly amateurish, though the editor promises better things to come. No further news of the other new weird magazine (said to pay ½¢ per word) which the agent Lenniger says is about to appear.

And now I must tackle some less interesting items of my piled-up correspondence. Hope these pages haven't proved too boresome. I see that a new Conan story is announced for the Sept. W T, and shall be on the lookout for it. Congratulations, by the way, on the vote accorded your vivid and excellent "Black Colossus". With every good wish—

Yrs most cordially and sincerely,

H P L

Notes

1. See letter 13, n. 4.

2. Hannah Robinson (1746–1773) gazed out at Narragansett Bay from a large boulder at Tower Hill Road in South Kingston, Rhode Island. Hannah had eloped with her teacher, Peter Simon, whom her father had forbidden her to see. They reconciled over the matter only after Hannah had become deathly ill.

3. "Out of the Aeons."

4. *The Double Shadow and Other Fantasies* (1933), and *Ebony and Crystal.*

5. The *Fantasy Fan,* edited by Charles D. Hornig.

6. HPL submitted "The Picture in the House," "The Music of Erich Zann," "The Rats in the Walls," "The Strange High House in the Mist," "Pickman's Model," "The Colour out of Space," and "The Dunwich Horror" in his letter to Allan G. Ullman of Knopf dated 3 Aug. 1933 (ms., JHL). HPL had heard from Putnam's with a similar request in 1931, and Vanguard in 1932 (HPL mistakenly referred to this publisher as "Viking" in later years).

7. Unidentified.

[86]   [nonextant postcards by HPL]

[87]   [TLS]

[ca. September 1933]

Dear H.P.L.:

I was very sorry to hear of your aunt's accident, and hope she has progressed well toward her recovery. Elderly people's bones are not prone to knit as well as those of the young, and such injuries are the more serious. I trust she will suffer no permanent ill effect.

My father recently had a small mishap which might well have proved serious, but for his promptness in acting. He had just lanced an infected foot, and laid the lancet on a small table, when it slipped off and fell on his foot, sticking through the shoe and the flesh, into the bone, and cutting a small artery. The danger lay, of course, not in the actual cut, but in the corruption on the blade. Nothing like that ever happened to my father before, in thirty some odd years of practicing medicine. He instantly tore off his shoe—which was full of blood—and split the wound wide open, letting it bleed as much as it would. Then he scraped the bone itself with a lancet—all this without anything to lessen the pain, not even novocain. If you've ever felt anything rasping against the naked bone, you'll know how it felt. He cleansed the wound as well as he could and dressed it, then drove thirty miles to obtain novocain, when he had the wound further enlarged, and more of the bone scraped. This done, and his foot re-dressed, he drove back home, and went about his business without more ado. He was out late that night making calls, up early and at work the next morning, and in fact never did slacken his work or slow up on account of the mishap, the wound of which quickly healed. Not bad for a man well past sixty. But all the men raised on the Southwestern frontier in the old days possess vigor and stamina impossible to the modern generation.

Price wrote me concerning his visit to Providence, of which he spoke with great gusto, praising you very highly indeed. I feel very much honored that you and he should have discussed my work. I read with the greatest of interest your accounts of the localities visited during his trip, and am sure that the country is packed with fascinating scenes and traditions.

I've had little opportunity for travel, since returning from San Antonio last spring, and such trips as I have taken have been more in the nature of business and necessity than pleasure, though I did enjoy some of them. I've been to Dallas three times this summer, and hope I won't have to go again for awhile, at least, for of all the towns in Texas, I like that one least. Naturally, as the road from the west leads through Fort Worth, I visited that town each trip, which was all right, because I like Ft. Worth. Ft. Worth, as I've probably mentioned, lies about 165 miles east of Cross Plains, and Dallas lies thirty miles east of Ft. Worth. The towns are nothing at all alike, except in external appearances, and the fact that all modern cities are more or less alike. But Dallas looks east and south, while Ft. Worth as definitely looks north and west. The prosperity of Dallas is founded on the rich agricultural lands and timber lands of East Texas, while Ft. Worth owes her very existence to her packing-plants and stockyards—in a word, to the cattle men of the West. Her slogan of "Where the West Begins" is not an idle saying. Geographically, West Texas begins in the western part of this county—Callahan; economically and politically, it begins just east of Ft. Worth. Between Ft. Worth and Dallas—thirty miles—lies the most densely settled district in Texas—379 people to the square mile—which compares to some sections in Eastern states. The country is slightly rolling, and very rich, lying in the Eastern cross-timbers. Small farms, dairies, and the raising of prize hogs and poultry make up most of the business. It's almost like traveling through one wide-spread town between the cities, the farms and houses are so close together. There are three small, thriving towns—Handley, Grand Prairie, and Arlington, in which last is located the famous Arlington Downs, the most noted race-tracks in the Southwest. Dallas stands on the banks of the Trinity River, as does Ft. Worth. After traversing the rich, densely populated country between those cities, the contrast is greater when one strikes west from Ft. Worth. Abruptly you come into open country, a broad, rolling, tree-less expanse, of great ranches, and considerable distances between towns. That's the Grand, or Ft. Worth, Prairie, one of the important physiographical divisions of the state, and in reality, merely a continuance of the vast Central Plains of America, which roll down from Canada nearly to the Coastal Plain. I was born on the western edge of that Prairie. On the west the country changes abruptly again into a wild region of timbered hills, which, alternated by short stretches of

plains, continue several hundred miles until they meet the great western uplands.

On one trip to Dallas I intended going on up to Durant, Oklahoma, but
circumstances prevented. I turned south instead, into the rich blacklands of
Ellis county, one of the leading cotton counties in the state—in the world, for
that matter—and got my first glimpse of the beautiful old town of Waxa-
hatchie, where is located Trinity University, which my father attended when
he was a young man, and the university was located at old Tehuacana. Returning to Ft. Worth, I didn't return directly to Cross Plains, but followed the
Grand Prairie up to Decatur (an old town remembered by me in connection,
especially, with a great-grand-uncle who lost his arm in a blue blizzard hauling
supplies from Decatur to the frontier settlements of Montague county back
in the early days) then to Jacksboro, once the jumping-off place for the buffalo hunters, and celebrated by them in tale and song, and eventually back to
Cross Plains, by way of the oil belt country. On that particular trip to Dallas I
visited the jail where the famous Harvey Bailey[1] was confined, but got no
opportunity to look at him; a fellow with me was a personal friend of the
Federal attorney who was working on Bailey's case, but we couldn't find him,
and I don't have any idea we could have gotten a glimpse of Bailey, if we had.
The jail was heavily guarded, but since then Bailey has managed to escape,
though recaptured the same day in Ardmore, Oklahoma.

Another trip I took of some small interest was to Stamford, 135 miles
north west of Cross Plains, where the big annual West Texas rodeo and cowboy reunion takes place each third, fourth, and fifth of July. On the way I
stopped at old Fort Griffin, on the Clear Fork of the Brazos, now almost
vanished, and presenting no such elaborate ruins as McKavett. But in its day
it was the toughest, wildest, and wooliest town west of the Mississippi. The
barracks were on a hill, the town at the foot. Seven men have been hanged in
the same oak tree there, at one time. There John Selman, later slayer of John
Wesley Hardin, got his education in deviltry. There, after the Civil War, came
General Sherman, inspecting the frontier forts with a small escort, and scorn-
ing warnings of Indians. He pulled into Fort Griffin about the time they were
bringing in the bodies of a gang of teamsters the Comanches had caught, and
looking at those scalped and mutilated horrors, the intrepid general turned
pale and shook violently, realizing the narrowness of the chance that had let
him escape from a race capable of making war even more hell than he could.
Thereafter he travelled with as big an escort as he could gather, and ordered
more troops sent out to the frontier forts.

Outside of the above mentioned trips, and others here and there within a
radius of forty or fifty miles, I've done no traveling this summer. The trouble
with Texas, it's so big you have to travel forever to get outside the state, and a
man doesn't get much credit for traveling when he doesn't cross his own
state line. When I say, for instance, that I've been to Brownsville, and back, it

doesn't sound as if I've been anywhere. Yet it's as far from Cross Plains to Brownsville as it is from New York to Quebec. Cross Plains is in West Texas, and so is El Paso, but it's over five hundred miles between the towns. Not many weeks ago I drove three hundred miles between 2 O'clock in the afternoon and 2 O'clock in the morning, from east to west, and never got out of Central Texas. If I'd travelled on the Atlantic seaboard as much as I've travelled in Texas alone, I could have covered every mile of coast between Miami and Eastport, three, or possibly even four times. That isn't any conjecture. I've figured it out. But my chances of ever even seeing the Atlantic sea-board are so scant they're not worth thinking about.

The summer's been reasonably warm, though the record for the summer was only 115 in the shade, and it never got over 112 in these parts. Of course it never gets as hot anywhere in Texas as it does in Oklahoma and Kansas. But we've had a drouth almost all summer which has destroyed the gardens and injured crops a great deal.

I haven't heard from the Britishers, and am on the point of writing them a letter. I'm pretty sure they'll turn my stuff down. I understand that "Worms of the Earth" is to appear in the "Not at Night" series. I've been laying off to get the book that published my "Black Stone" but haven't ever got around to it.[2] Yes, I got both Smith's brochure and his book of poems. Both were splendid, as I told him. Yes, I did indeed enjoy your latest story in Weird Tales,[3] and was glad to see the readers voted you first place—as indeed, I was sure they would. I feel honored that Von Junzt's hellish book should have such a prominent place in the story you mentioned as revising for the author of "The Horror in the Museum." Lately I've been trying to write detective yarns, something entirely new for me, and haven't had much success—in fact none, so far, except for a short yarn, "Talons in the Dark", written in San Antonio last spring, and which Kline, as my agent, sold to a magazine called Strange Detective Stories. Kline has been a big help in teaching me the technique of detective story writing; whether I am able to profit by his teaching remains to be seen. (Kline marketed another yarn for me since I wrote the above.)[4]

Concerning our discussion of esthetic and artistic values, or however it might be termed. First I would like to take up the—perhaps unimportant—matter of "resentment." In a previous discussion you quite obviously deeply resented what seemed like an attack on artistic values and other things you prized; rightly enough; yet now you denounce me as irrational, emotional and egotistical because I resent—or seem to resent—attacks on certain things I happen to prize rather highly. I really don't see much consistency or logic in this position. I fail to see that it is any less my privilege to defend my tastes and ideals than it is another man's, even if I am not an artist.

As a matter of fact, I don't resent being told that certain of my preferences are inferior; I rarely object to being called a God damned fool because I happen to have preferences that certain people despise or depreciate. In a word, I merely object to what you point out as "attempts to classify an entire personality according to the sources of its pleasure." Nor am I sure that certain portions of my brain are dead or petrified because of certain preferences. It seems to me that a capacity for enjoying certain simple thing[s], when combined with an ability to appreciate the "higher" things as well, is, if anything, the indication of a broader, rather than a narrower personality. If I can enjoy (for instance) both Service and Baudelaire, I see no reason why I should feel inferior to the man who can enjoy only Baudelaire, any more than to the man who can enjoy only Service. You must admit the scope of enjoyment is broader, whatever is to be said about the esthetic value. It strikes me that the life of a man who is able to enjoy only things with a high esthetic value is about as narrow as that of a man who is able to enjoy nothing of esthetic value. I'd hate to be one of those exalted beings who feel that they would be ruined and debased forever if they descended from their pedestal and soiled their togas by doing something or enjoying something that wasn't "superior." It's really a matter of indifference to me whether or not my preferences, pursuits and desires are "superior" according to some arbitrary standard. I know what I like, and what I want, and that's enough for me; all I object to is any assumption that I *don't* know what I want, because my desires don't chance to correspond with those of "superior" people; and that my aspirations are less sincere and less important to me than those of the exalted ones are to them.

As for art itself—maybe there isn't any attempt by rational thinkers to give it cosmic significance, but when I reflect on all the stuff I've heard and read about "inspiration", "touch of divinity", "the divine in Man" etc., etc., and other things I can't remember, it seems that the idea of cosmic significance is not altogether foreign in the minds of some. Undoubtedly art is an evidence of man's evolution from the amoeba. But art is no more characteristically human than some other things (some less savory than poetry and painting, for instance). When a man overcomes all his primitive instincts and even stifles the fundamental instinct of self-preservation and sacrifices his life for another—that's just as "high" as art. And if we consider those things characteristically human: well, treachery, and chicanery, and sex perversions come under the same head. When a man swindles his neighbor out of all his money, then poisons him and seduces his wife, he is demonstrating his removal from the amoeba just as much as the artist is by his work. His actions are just as characteristically *human* as the work of the artist. It ought to be evident that the only creature on the planet capable of such detestable treachery and duplicity is man. Therefore, we are quite justified in calling such a man "superior"; i.e. superior, for instance, to an ordinary ploughman who demonstrates *his* kinship with the worm by toiling day in and day out with his hands; honesty and decency does not necessarily enter into it, if we are to follow the procedure laid down, because honesty and decency are not exclusively human characteristics. Most animals have them in larger abundance than man. It is just as impossible for an amoeba to crack the stock market and beggar thousands, plot and start a war in order to acquire valuable concessions, and having exhausted himself with debauchery, turn to perverse pleasures, as it is for him to paint a picture or write a book. Therefore according to the procedure in question, we are quite as fully justified in recognizing as the highest being possible a thief, a whole-sale murderer and a degenerate, as we are in recognizing the artist. We are a modest and self-depreciating breed of life; all the characteristics of honesty, courage, loyalty, and determination, which are possessed by most animals to a greater extent than by ourselves, we term "human" characteristics; while our most typical characteristics, such as thievishness, sensuality, cowardice, dishonesty, ingratitude, and general baseness, we dub: bestiality, beastliness, swinishness, animal-like. We call our enemies swine, dogs, skunks, etc. I never saw a dog, hog or pole-cat commit any of the crimes and vices that human beings perpetrate day after day. We even seek to set our few fundamental virtues aside and gild them with the divinity which we all seem to have a sneaking idea is ours, under one name or another. So courage directed by "reason" is superior somehow to courage inspired by "instinct." And the honesty of a man is superior to the honesty of a dog; because, apparently, we recognize the fact that, before the man does an honest act, he is forced to overcome his reason which, being characteristically human, naturally impels him to be a thief. So, likewise, we maintain stages in human development as well, and the virtues of a "superior" man are held to be of higher type than those of the "inferior" man. We have not yet reached the point where the superior man is supposed to exude perfume instead of sweat, to bleed ichor instead of blood, and to void ambergris instead of dung, but I expect that revelation almost any time. Between the fundamental religionist who goes into foaming rages over the idea of evolution, because he can not stand the thought of kinship with a monkey, and the artists who strains his guts to prove his distance from the protozoa, I see no basic difference; both seem outcroppings of the idea concerning the divinity of man.

You are quite right about the necessity of each individual working out his own system of living, according to his own necessity—the trouble is that each of us is prone to regard his particular system as the best one, not only for himself, but for everybody else. So we scrap and fight among ourselves, and when one of us chances to be elevated above the herd, he immediately bends all efforts toward hammering and pounding as many people as possible into his particular pattern. Quite often he sincerely believes it is for their own good; carried to extremes it leads to massacres, because it is quite possible for a man to honestly believe that people would be better off dead than not conforming to his particular pattern. And we are all prone to exalt our faults as virtues, and condemn our neighbor's virtues as faults, if they don't agree with ours. As for individualism, we have no ground for dispute there, as far as I can see. I quite agree with you in regard to the importance of the individual—

in fact, one of our previous causes of disagreement, I thought, was what I supposed to be a depreciation and belittlement of the individual on your part. I see now that I was wrong in my supposition. I reckon I'd be called an individual thinker (if the term "thinker" could be applied to me at all) because I'm certainly not connected or affiliated with any political organizations claiming to be either the pillars of democracy or the pillars of republicanism. I simply believe in the fundamental equality of men; I recognize the fact that certain men will always be shrewder, or stronger, or braver, or more intelligent than others. But if anybody has any rights, everybody has those rights. I do not, in this instance, especially refer to the ballot. I would not particularly fight the innovation of a system whereby only the properly trained could vote, *providing* that ample provisions were made whereby any man could so train himself. Not that I would expect such a system to do away with present evils, or even alleviate them to any great extent. Human nature isn't changed by glossing it with a veneer of culture. Make the ballot the reward of study in the special line of economics and government, and a powerful minority would soon manage to get full and exclusive power in their hands, and either limit the actual voting numbers of the population, or else direct it to their own ends, just as is done in every other form of government. The rulers will always be three or four jumps ahead of the ruled, regardless of how well educated the latter are, or become. The tendency of the human race is toward caste—to form aristocracies of one sort or another; this runs the gamut from the beggar in the gutter to the plutocrat in the swivel chair. I've seen casers that would scarcely speak to any but casers, tool-dressers who curled the lip of scorn at all laborers except tool-dressers or drillers. When I was a soda-jerker the hairy-handed sons of toil who did the work of men and mules together, despised me—as they despise the white-collar workers—with a deep and abiding scorn which was on several occasions very nearly the cause of broken heads. Nor is it otherwise among the great ones of the earth, only they try to conceal it with the veneer of diplomacy. Financiers look with scorn on poverty-stricken artists; artists despise men who avowedly wield pen or brush for a living; and so on, and so on. Educate men for the ballot, and in a few generations it would be suddenly discovered that only a certain caste ever managed to pass the examinations required for such a reward. Undoubtedly the present system is rotten and could be improved upon; but I doubt if any system of high education will ever bring Utopia.

Concerning freedom and liberty: I don't suppose that anybody ever said that man had "complete" freedom. Terms are always relative—except when somebody takes refuge in philosophical completeness, if I may use a vague term. Naturally, man has always been bound by certain natural limitations, as he always will be. What is freedom for one man is not necessarily freedom for another. The trouble is, as I pointed out awhile back—each man is likely to consider himself capable of determining just which amount of freedom, and what kind of freedom, is good for his neighbor. All men being subject to natural limitations, it is easy enough to take the philosophical stand that freedom is an illusion and never existed. By that means of argument you can prove the same of anything—including Art. Arguing from that standpoint, the writer who works five or six hours a day, or at least directs his work as he wishes, and toils at a congenial task, is as much a slave as a farm-hand pushing a plough through rocky ground from sunup to sundown. However, if it were suggested that these philosophers abandon their professions to gaze on a mule's tail from dawn to dusk, a howl would go up that would shake the stars in their firmament. And if these persons were forced to work with their hands—or with their heads at some uncongenial task—for sixteen hours a day, they would speak most bitterly of serfdom and oppression, as if indeed, freedom and its lack did exist except in the minds of such romantic emotionalists as myself. Like most philosophical sophistry, it falls down when put to a material test. As for what constitutes real value in life, that is merely a matter of opinion, and however much one may feel that his particular values are the ones of real worth, he can not, or should not, expect people living under different conditions and in different environments, with different ways of thinking, to accept his standards without question.

As for the frontier: what if it was a chance product, a temporary result of blind conditions? What if it was transient? Is that in its disfavor? How many conditions and ages of mankind were not chance products? Surely you don't think this particular age, for instance, is any more permanent or less transient than any that have gone before? As for the injustice of the frontier—well, show me an age where injustice didn't exist, or a condition of mankind from which it was absent. You say that it took everything from the physically weak to give to the physically strong. That statement is entirely too sweeping. The intelligence had its place on the frontier as everywhere else. The leaders were not only the strongest men physically, they were the strongest and most able mentally. Life on the frontier was not a blind, brainless scramble where men got by through a sort of bestial ferocity and mindless muscularity. As a matter of fact, the life required a certain amount of physical fitness, so naturally the leaders were generally men who combined brain with brawn. What's wrong about that, since conditions evolved the system? In every age and under all conditions, the leaders and the most successful among men were those who were most fully adapted to their particular age and conditions. You yourself unconditionally demand that fullest rewards be given to those men who most nearly represent what you believe to be the most perfect adaptation to this age. Why condemn in one age, what you uphold in another? Looking at it from another angle: you condemn the frontier because you say it gave all to certain characteristics and ignored others—obviously of the artistic type. Well, is that much different from the system of today? The modern world gives its richest rewards to those possessed of the ability to grab money, and

I've never heard that the most typical representatives of that type necessarily combine with their money-grabbing ability the characteristics mentioned. Wherein are Sam Insull, Andy Mellon, J. P. Morgan, and the others superior in esthetic qualities to Sam Houston, Old Hickory, Abe Lincoln, and Bucky O'Connor?[5] Sam was a great lover of poetry and paintings, at least; Old Abe was not without artistic appreciation; and O'Connor died with a quotation of Walt Whitman on his lips. Do you reckon Sam Insull would quote Whitman or Shakespeare or anybody else with a bullet through his neck? Anyway, Edgar Allan Poe didn't suffer want and die in poverty on the frontier. If he'd been there, somebody would have shot a deer for him, somebody would have showed him how to build his cabin, and helped him do it—in emphasizing the undeniable brutalities of the frontier you lose sight entirely of those qualities which made the conquest of the wilderness possible—the loyalty of men, their readiness to shoulder each others' burdens, their honesty, kindness— because a man could split an Indian's head at five hundred yards didn't mean he'd go over and beat and rob his neighbor because that neighbor happened to be physically weaker than himself. Intelligence—there's as much room for the exercise of the intelligence on a farm, today, as there is in a studio, though I don't expect any artist to believe that. And the men of the best intellects were the leaders on the frontier just as they are everywhere else. The better qualities—when my grandfather came to Texas in the late '60's, he made plenty of money farming, and he became, in part, a money-lender—a term which conjures up a stooped drone humping over his money-bags. My grandfather's office was his store, his porch, the saddle of his riding-horse— anywhere he happened to be. A rancher might ride in from a ranch a hundred and fifty miles away, and introduce himself. My grandfather never had seen him before. He'd state his needs, and the Colonel would haul out his pouch and hand him the money. The rancher would state the day he would return and pay, and ride off. No witnesses, no notes, no rituals whatever. Half the time the Colonel didn't know how much money he had out. But in those early days he never lost a penny. The men who borrowed the money paid it back—in Texas, when and where there was no law strong enough to have forced them, and no witnesses to bring down the scorn of the people on them, if they defaulted. If that honesty isn't an evidence of "finer feelings" and "social balance" etc. etc., then I don't know what is. Oh, of course, the Colonel eventually lost money—when the state began to fill up with smart gentlemen from the civilized sections who knew all about business methods. But he never lost a cent to the old timers.

As for the urge of the frontiersmen to make over the new country into a duplicate of the states they had just left—if that was so, why did they bother to come west in the first place? Why did they keep moving on, many of them, as the country filled up around them? They had the pick of the land; why did they not stay and build up something to look like something they'd long before abandoned? Exalt the frontier? Yes, I exalt it. The older I get the more I realize the glory of it, the true worth, the iron in the men and women who enacted it. My feeling toward it is founded on principles and realities no less vital, real and solid and sound than yours toward the long settled country in which you were born and reared. As for the relative "superiority" of our different emotions, it's not worth discussing. My worship of the frontier, if it can be called such, is in no way a belittlement or depreciation of your environment or tradition. But my feeling toward the frontier is by no means an isolated exhibition of faulty thinking on my part; the frontier tradition is not a dream or a legend; it is a living, vital element which, whether people of the older sections like it or not, colors and flavors the every-day life of the West, and will continue to do so for many generations, possibly as long as any remain of the old stock. And the West, as a glance at any map will show, is by no means insignificant or unimportant in the development of the American nation.

As for our perennial discussion of civilization and barbarism, I really did not mean to imply that false imprisonment was a characteristic of civilization, or that many men were falsely imprisoned. I should have made that clear. My remarks concerning the merit of some men, when imprisoned, was really in the nature of a philosophical aside. I wished merely to call attention to the fact that a man could be imprisoned as a felon in one age, and acclaimed a martyr or a hero in the next. And that a man, even when legally convicted and sentenced, was not necessarily an all-around scoundrel, even when guilty of the crime of which he was accused. When I said I'd known men who served sentences and still made good citizens, I didn't mean to imply that they were falsely sentenced; I was in reality referring to certain men who killed personal enemies in moments of passion, and having paid the price the law demanded, resumed their places as respectable citizens. I was merely asking that it be recognized that because a man has served time in a cell, it does not necessarily follow that he is an utter villain, steeped in sin and iniquity. As for the police, I have never questioned your assertions in regard to the integrity of the Eastern police. Anyway, police corruption and brutality anywhere forms but one of the many unsavory elements of modern life, and even where such vice is most flagrant only a few people suffer.

And having made those comments, I think I have disposed of the matters wherein I am supposed to theorize. There are some things in this system you can't dismiss as theories. You can't dismiss twelve and a half million men and women without work and on the point of starvation as theories. It would be well for the capitalists, perhaps, if they could be so dismissed. As for the "alleged horrors" of civilization—if you would inquire into the condition of some of these people, and if you had ever seen what modern machinery can do to the human frame, you'd realize that all the horrors are not "alleged." I doubt if it would make much difference to a man whether he was disemboweled by a Gothic sword, or had his entrails ripped out of him by a buzz-saw.

As for going back to past ages for cases of oppression—it's as fair for one side as it is for another. I'm not comparing the yesterday of some other section to the Texas of today. I'm not merely saying that witch-burning and religious persecution does not exist in Texas today. I say that it *never* existed here, even in the most primitive times, when, according to the civilized standard, Anglo-Saxon Texans should have been howling savages. I'm not trying to make out my people as saints; I merely rebel at the implication that all the vices incidental to mankind are limited exclusively to a special section of the continent. If it's logical to cite the barbarities the people of my section *have* committed, it's equally logical for me to defend them by citing the barbarities they have *not* committed. I was merely pointing out that, barbaric as we are supposed to be, there are and have been things done by "civilized" people of which we were never guilty.

You say that Germany is not typical of Western civilization. Why not? Wherein is Germany less civilized than England? It seems to be a characteristic among civilized people, that each advocate of civilization maintains that his is the only true civilization. I have heard an intellectual declare that Germany was the only truly civilized country in the world. You make out a logical, sensible and in many ways unanswerable case for English civilization; *but* the German, the Russian, the Italian, the Japanese each presents arguments in favor of his particular civilization just as logical, sensible and unanswerable.

Looking at your remarks again: if only England (obviously excluding Ireland, Scotland, Cornwall, Man and Wales), New England, Virginia, the Carolinas, Eastern Canada, New Zealand and New South Wales, are deserving of being termed "civilized", while the rest of the world is barbaric, then it is certainly a mistake to speak of this as a civilized age at all, and the term "civilization" loses its international and national significance, and must be considered merely as an isolated local phenomenon, too restricted in extent to merit any particular consideration from the world at large.

Taking up your remarks concerning newspapers and radios: I quite agree with your estimate of the average newspaper, and do not differ radically with your opinion of radio programs. And yet it would be erroneous to say that *all* radio programs are entirely without cultural value. I will freely admit that nine-tenths of them are utter bosh, and frequently so to the point of disgusting one. Yet there are a few people on the air with really artistic ideas, struggling—mostly in vain—against the inundation of commercial bunkum spilled out. Leaving out certain programs which I personally enjoy, but which I realize have no particular esthetic merit, I have heard some things which were not without such merit. I have heard, among other things, such plays as "The Blue Bird", "John Ferguson", "Cyrano de Bergerac", "Antigone", "The Admirable Creighton", "Tartuffe", "Trelawny of the Wells", "The Iron Master", and a number of Shakespearean plays.[6] Of course I had rather see these things on the stage, but as my chances of doing that are so slim they are practically non-existent, I was grateful for the opportunity of hearing them over the air. And I am further grateful to the radio for reviving and giving to the world many old folk-songs and legends of the cow-camps, the cattle-trails, and the southern mountains. Then I have heard the music of Wagner, Beethoven, Liszt, and other masters, played by the finest modern musicians, and some splendid recitals of poetry.

I see that your next paragraph deals with our barbarism-civilization debate. It is not my intention to minimize the suffering attendant upon barbarism. Barbaric life was hell; but so is modern life. So was any life, in any age. I am not particularly saying that all the madness, insanity, griefs, diseases, social turmoil, and social injustices are the result of civilization; I merely say that they do exist under a system which calls itself civilized. And I don't believe that all the suffering I've observed in my short life (enough to sicken a man's soul) can be attributed to the victims' lack of proper civilization, or was a consequence of them living in a region suffering under the frontier tradition. What about (for instance) the recent strike riots in Pennsylvania, and the sweat shop scandals in Connecticut?[7] You can't blame them on the frontier tradition. And according to the papers at least, people commit suicide, go insane, and generally have about as uncomfortable a time of it in the East as they do in the West.

Let us for an instant consider the conditions of the Germanic barbarians as well as we are able to do so, from a distance which will prevent us from ever gaining a completely correct viewpoint, whichever side we may be on. Your main indictment (aside from their lack of esthetic development) is what you have called "outrages against the integrity of the physical body." That integrity again, is not always to be considered sacred. Under certain conditions it may even be said that no man has any right to the integrity of his body unless he can defend it. The modern governments reserve the privilege to annul the individual's right to life and limb, in war times. When the primitive German or Gaul went on the war path he went with more enthusiasm, with more reason, and with more assurance of personal, material gain, than the modern soldier goes to war. As for casual mutilations, I have never discovered that the Germans practised ceremonial speyings and castrations as certain other races have done—and in some parts, still do. They did, indeed, practise human sacrifice to a certain extent; but the civilized Romans were not guiltless in that respect. And I strongly doubt if the number of men and human offered up to their gods exceeded the number of men mutilated and killed in modern mines and factories. And I don't believe that insanity, disease and degeneracy were anything like as common among the tribes along the Rhine as among moderns. There were doubtless famines; but no race as physically powerful and as mentally active as the Germans could have developed under conditions of continual undernourishment. Venereal diseases obviously were extremely rare, or possibly even unknown entirely, at least among the most primitive tribes. Turning now to war. For what reasons did the German tribes go to war? Was it, as moderns are prone to suppose without bothering to ascertain the true fact, merely because of a blood-thirsty ferocity? I quote Professor Eduard Heyck: "Their one desire was to secure a permanent settlement upon good arable ground; this was an indispensable condition."[8] Their advance westward and southward was, obviously, not in the nature of aimless raids, for blood-stained loot, but merely to find a place where they could obtain or secure a decent living: the same motive which has driven men since the first ape-man drifted southward before the glaciers, to the present Japanese overflow in Manchuria—the latter named movement of which you declared yourself to be in perfect accord, since it was necessary to the existence of the Japanese nation. Why, then, was the onslaught of the Germans upon their neighbors in more fertile ground any more despicable or blame-worthy than the invasion of Manchuria and Korea by the Japs, or the invasion of the American continent by the Anglo-Saxons? It was the hard conditions of life which forced the Germans onward until they trampled a civilization which had already forfeited its right to survive. When the civilized Chinese set the Huns in motion, and the Huns in turn drove the Eastern Teutons before them—in that crush of nations, where were the Lombards, the Vandals, the Franks, the Saxons, and the Goths to go, if not over the crumbling lines of a rotten civilization? There was suffering in such wars; there is suffering in all wars; the barbarians wrought less destruction on their civilized enemies than many civilized races have wrought upon vanquished barbarians—the Spaniards upon the Aztecs and Incas, for instance; read inside accounts of French rule in Syria and Algeria for a good idea of how civilization deals with her barbaric subjects. The Romanized peoples probably suffered less from the Germans than the Germans themselves, and the Slavs, suffered from the Huns, Avars or Yen-yen and Bulgars. As a matter of fact, the refusal of the great masses of population to even resist the oncoming hordes, shows that they had already suffered so much under their civilized Roman rulers, that any change would be considered for the better. The Vandals took Africa with little trouble, encountering, in fact, resistance only from the Roman garrisons there, and from the wild Berber tribesmen who have disputed with every master from Cyrene to France. The Vandals were looked on, apparently, as an improvement on the corrupt rule of the Romans, and but for the unfortunate circumstance of their conversion to Arianism, would probably never have encountered any obstacle in merging and mingling with the native Africans. I have it on the authority of Professor Heinrich Shurtz,[9] that after the invasion of Spain by the mixed bands of Vandals, Alani and Suevi who overthrew the Roman bureaucracy, the coming of the Visigoths as allies of the Roman governors was not looked upon by the natives as the return of rescuers. In fact, hordes of the natives fought on the side of the Suevi, and upon their defeat, abandoned their homes, and fled with them to the mountains. An evidence that the people of Romanized Spain did not look upon either the invasion of the barbarians as an unmixed curse, or the return of Roman authority as an unmixed blessing. Also, that even in those days, the ideal of personal freedom was not limited to the dreams of certain idle romanticists. But the idea is that there was not, in the minds of the barbarians (with the possible exception of the Anglo-Saxons) any definite plans for the complete destruction of the Roman people or the Roman system. Even in Britain, it might be discovered that the apparent ferocity of the Saxons resulted from the equally ferocious resistance offered them. The Britons *had* to be exterminated, in order to be conquered. I am not trying to pretend that the barbarians were not ferocious in warfare, destructive, and in many cases simply blood-thirsty. I am merely seeking to point out that the overthrow of a rotten civilization by barbarians is not necessarily more tragic and bloody than the overthrow of barbarians by civilized men, or the conquest of one civilized nation by another. The conquests of the Germans were scarcely more devastating and brutal than Alexander's sack of Thebes, Rome's destruction of Carthage, or the mutilation of Belgium in the last war. All wars are ghastly. And it must be admitted that the overthrow of Rome, and the events attendant thereupon did not represent what you might call the norm of Germanic barbaric life. That sudden crush of nations was at least as abnormal as the modern depression. Otherwise the expansion would have been more gradual. Such expansion had been going on, for centuries, with resultant wars and unrest as the different tribes collided with one another; but the sudden bursting of the barriers resulted from, as near as I can learn, the westward drive of the Turkish Huns. Leaving that aside for the moment, to look again at the question of suffering among the barbarians (and not among the civilized races who were overthrown by their onslaught) I am not by any means certain that their suffering was greater than that of modern man. They were giants physically; disease was rare; their food, if not always abundant, was at least sufficient for their needs, and evidently they could digest anything; they fought among themselves, occasionally for love of war, but more often through necessity, but they enjoyed fighting, so that was no hardship; their religion called for a violent death, so that was no hardship either. The mere fact that they expanded so greatly in numbers and importance shows that their lives were not unmixed rounds of suffering and agony. A race can not develop under conditions too adverse; compare the squalid Yakuts of Siberia, with the Ottomans of Western Asia—people of the same stock and blood, but developed under different conditions. As for the Germanic lack of artistic values—I'm not inclined to believe that modern artists get any more satisfaction out of expressing themselves in their modern ways, than the German scalds and minstrels derived from telling their legends and composing and singing their sagas. And I'm not convinced that the proportion of honest artists among them was much less than it is in the present day. You must admit that the number of true artists is never great, in any age. And that reminds me of one question: if modern conditions are so conducive to artistic work and expression, and if so many people, as you say, are able to revel in esthetic enjoyment and development, then why is it that this age is producing so few literary men, of any real value, and so few real masters in any branch of art? The Golden Age of Florence, from 1250 to 1500, and the Elizabethan Age of England certainly produced more artists of worth than this age is producing; and from what I've read of them, fifteenth and sixteenth century Italians and Englishmen were at least as "barbaric" in their ways and manners as modern Texans. I know that I, at least, would have felt a damn sight more secure in Texas, even during the Mexican and Indian wars, than I'd have felt in Italy of the middle ages, or England either, for that matter. And I have always understood that security is one of the conditions and evidences of civilization. This is another question: at just what period did barbarism cease to be, and civilization begin? If the American west is not to be considered civilized, why are we to consider European countries of a few centuries ago as civilized? There was more cruelty, ignorance, injustice and intolerance practised in the best of them then, than was ever practised in any part of America.

Which, in a way, brings me back to the custom of violence. It is quite true that nothing is more revolting that the physical oppression of the weak and helpless by the strong. Wanton brutality is hated as much in the West as it is in the East. It is just a matter of deciding just what violence is necessary, and not actually wanton, and that, like everything else, varies with different sections. What would be unnecessary on the streets of Boston, may very well be the only solution to a problem in the Guadalupe Mountains. Just as certain laws may be unimportant in the Guadalupes, though they bulk very important in Boston. Men have to be guided by necessity rather than an absolute abstraction of what is "right" and what is not.

Which likewise brings up the question of law-abidingness of this section. I am not sure that we deserve the accusation of lawlessness. You can't condemn the inhabitants of one corner of the continent merely because all their customs and traditions don't exactly coincide with the customs and traditions of some other corner of the continent. If some Texans, past and present, have broken the law, you might reflect that an even greater number have— and do—risk their lives in upholding the law. We have an organization down here known as the Texas Rangers which is not without some reputation. And the men composing it are not valiants imported from some "civilized" section to keep the lawless natives in order. Without exception, they are native Texans. When one thinks of Bill Longley, John Wesley Hardin, Curly Bill, etc., it might be well to also remember Jack Hayes, who, after breaking up the outlaw gangs of early Texas, went to San Francisco, and, as city marshal, cleaned up the town almost single-handed, whipping out both the hoodlums and the gone-to-seed Vigilantes; of Captain Henry Love, who hunted down and hanged the famous California bandit Joaquin Murietta; of John Poe and Pat Garrett, who hunted Billy the Kid to his death; of John Slaughter, who brought law and order into the bandit-haunted hills of Cochise County. Cape Willingham[10] was probably the wisest and most intelligent law-officer the West ever saw; but for him Tascosa would have been another Dodge City. Why, as far as that goes, John Wesley Hardin himself was deputized in Abilene, Kansas, to hunt down a Mexican murderer who was too tough for the Kansas officers. Wild Bill Hickok had a warrant for John's arrest at the time, which he would not or could not enforce; he swore the young Texan in as a special officer, and Hardin killed the criminal before another sun set. It is not alone as killers and outlaws that Texans left their mark on the West; they made good officers where ever they went. Even today you will find them all over the western country.

When Glen Hunsucker, nineteen year old bandit, and ten times as desperate as "Machine Gun" Kelly[11] ever thought of being, was shot down in a fight in Lincoln County, New Mexico, (Billy the Kid's old stamping ground) not many weeks ago, in which fight a New Mexican officer was also killed, the papers mentioned that he was a Texan. Which was true; what most papers did not mention was the fact that the Lincoln County officers who killed him and captured his companion, Perch-mouth Stanton, were also Texans. Reynolds, who tore Hunsucker's guts out with a charge of buckshot, was from this very county—Callahan. And McCamant, who aided Reynolds in capturing Stanton, was from an adjoining county.[12]

As for lawlessness, possibly you base your argument on the rather lengthy list of homicides Texas furnishes each year. Not all of these are crimes—not as far as I'm concerned. I certainly don't consider a man a criminal just because he kills a personal enemy in a fair stand-up fight. Some of these killings are a result of blood-feuds going back thirty or forty years. The men who engage in them are by no means necessarily criminals. Another thing you have to remember is that some of these killings are done by honest citizens defending their lives and property from thugs and hoodlums—many of whom are not native Texans at all. It must be remembered that Texas is the literal crossroads of the Continent, and that each year thousands upon thousands of transients drift back and forth across the state, criss-crossing from north to south, and from east to west. To mention a few international highways, there are, for instance: No. 81, running from Winnipeg, Canada, to Laredo, and on to Monterey and Mexico City; No. 75, from Winnipeg to Galveston; No. 80, from Savannah, Georgia, to San Diego, California. It is the Southern Route from coast to coast. (That route once ran right by this house, until the present highway was designated and built.) There is a constant drift of people over these highways, as well as over the railroads. Then, each winter, there is a great drift of hoboes southward, as well as more respectable tourists. In the fall, workers swarm into the great cotton fields; in the summer they come to the grain fields; winter and summer they surge into the oil fields; negroes come in from the east, Mexicans from the south. Paupers come looking for work and mild weather; millionaires come to build lodges, mansions, or new fortunes. And between these extremes are all sorts of people, good, bad and indifferent. Some remain permanently; some drift through without stopping; many pause here and there, only to roam on. How, under such conditions, can the section be expected to present the tranquil and unruffled appearance of the older localities where life runs more placidly? And why the natives of Texas should be wholly blamed for all the infractions of law that take place in this state is more than I can see. On one transcontinental highway, within fifty miles, I have seen cars the license tags of which announced them as being from New York, California, Iowa, Arkansas, Arizona, Georgia, Tennessee, Pennsylvania, Rhode Island, Kansas, South Dakota, Toronto, Canada, Central America, Sonora, Mexico, and South Carolina. With such a continual drift across the state, how can the officers of the law keep up with all of them? The officers in certain sections are indeed, in need of improvement; but they have their problems in this case. When you hear of some especially atrocious crime happening in Texas, pause to consider that the perpetrator may well be a Californian, a Virginian, an Iowayan, or a New Englander. Incidentally, I want to remark here that the only confirmed wife-beater in this town is a "gentleman" from Virginia; and that the most brutish and cold-blooded murder ever committed in the town was the act, not of a native, but of an Englishman, of breeding and family, who had been an officer in the British Army.[13] I knew him well, as well as his victim—his wife. Naturally I do not conclude from this that all Virginians are wife-beaters, or all Britishers murderers, any more than I suppose New Englanders to be particularly sanguinary because John Brown and Henry Plummer were natives of New England; and it might be realized that for every Texan who leads a life of outlawry, there are thousands of quiet, honest people who go about their business and never kill anybody, rob a train or stick up a bank. Take this recent business of the Urschel kidnapping;[14] how many of the outlaws are Texans? Bailey is a Missourian; Machine Gun Kelly is a Tennessean; Bates is, so far as I know, a native of Colorado; Kelly's wife is an Oklahoman; and the Shannons are also Oklahomans, originally at least, to the best of my knowledge.

I see most of them were pronounced guilty, and probably will get all that's coming to them, as is right. It'll be a relief, I imagine, to Kirkpatrick and his family; Kirkpatrick, as you know if you've followed the affair any, was the man who took the money to the thugs, and identified them at the trial. I understand the Kirkpatricks have lived in fear of his daughter Rita's young child being kidnapped by gangsters in revenge. Rita was in my class the year I graduated; I remember the first time I ever saw her, it was a class election of some sort, and I voted for her simply because she had a Celtic name.[15] That was before her father got all his dough; he worked for T. B. Slick, and when old T. B. retired, he made Kirkpatrick present of a million dollars, just for a gift. But T. B. could spare it; he was worth hundreds of millions.[16] The richest man that ever came to Cross Plains, which is saying plenty, because during the booms millionaires were thicker than flies. I was thrown among them in my daily work, and maybe that's why I have no great love for the ultra-rich to this day.

Getting back to law conditions, I'm not sure that I wasn't too hasty in saying that present unpleasant conditions were due to a period of transition. Texas has always been in a period of transition, changing from something to something else. Even before the Anglo-Celts came in from the east, there had been change—priests building missions in the wilderness, Indians submitting to conversion, then rebelling, and hostile tribes sweeping down to destroy the budding Spanish land-owners' civilization. Then there was change from Latin to American dominance, during the first of the period in which there was transition from Spanish to Mexican rule, with resultant chaos. The white settlers changed their government by force of arms, and had to adapt themselves economically, too. There was transition from wilderness to farms, and during that time many were changing too, from agriculture to cattle-raising. others from the grain crops of the mid-west to cotton growing. On the heels of these transitions, before they were complete was the Civil War and the necessity of adjusting conditions to the reality of free niggers, free labor, and the abominable carpet bag rule, which latter was soon kicked out bodily. But another change was necessary, in shifting the cattle market from New Orleans and Shreveport to the towns of Kansas. Steel ribbons of railroads creeping westward brought a wild prosperity, and the cattle-pauper of the day before became the cattle-king of the next day. Herds rolled north and westward, to Kansas, to Montana, to Canada, to New Mexico, filling the great empty lands with cattle and men, peopling the west, stocking the ranges—even before this movement was done, there came the squatters, the small farmers, with their wire fences, cutting up the ranges, ruining the great cattle barons; the necessity of fencing, of adjusting to smaller, more cramped conditions; of cowboys to find a new range, to become farmers, to settle down in small humdrum jobs—great God, no wonder so many of them turned outlaw. Then the growth of towns, the intricacies of business, and then the rush of oil booms, and all the time smaller changes, like the irrigating of the Lower Rio Grande, to change brush-wood wastes into blossoming orange groves, and the opening of ports, new markets and new industries. Transition? Why, heavens, there's never been anything else in Texas! In the years I've been in this section I've seen it change from a purely agricultural section to an industrial and oil producing section, and back again to an agricultural country. And less than a generation before I came here, it had changed from a cattle country to a farming country; and a generation after I am gone, it will change again into a land of irrigated gardens and intensified stock farming. Post oaks are the blight of this country, them, and lack of water. In the early days, this was all rolling prairies and bare hills, covered with sweet mesquite grass, and with myriad springs and creeks that ran all year. Fencing land ruins springs; the plowed dirt washes into the creeks and chokes them up. Weeds always follow the white man, and they stifled the grass and drove it westward. The Indians kept the land burnt off in each proper season and kept off the post oaks. The land was fat and rich, an ideal cattle country. But the farmers came and fenced and ploughed, and the post oaks grew, and the springs dried up, and the land washed and became poor and sterile. It's hard to blame the old settlers because of their carelessness. For generations they'd been pushing leisurely westward, with always plenty of land when they wore out one farm. Suddenly they woke up and realized that there was no more free land; and their descendants are only now beginning to learn how to build up the land and make it rich again. Oh, I suppose I shouldn't bore you with all this stuff. It must seem very tiresome to a dweller in an industrial section. But after all, the food of the nation does come from the soil. I've gotten clean off what I started to say, which was that Texas is, and always has been, in a state of transition difficult to appreciate. Young as I am, I can show you well established towns the sites of which I remember as bare prairie; and I can show you clusters of empty rotting buildings, deserted and forgotten, which I remember as prosperous towns. This very town of Cross Plains I have seen grow almost overnight from a population of twelve hundred to one of ten thousand, and slump back again to about fifteen hundred. I have seen paupers become millionaires almost in a day, and I have seen millionaires become paupers just as quickly. And the end of chaos and transition is not in sight; neither I nor my grandchildren will see it; because the natural resources of the state are scarcely touched, and there are ten thousand developments yet to be conceived and accomplished. All this leads to the faulty conditions of the state; certain types of men swarm here intent only on making quick money and big money, and going back to where ever they came from, and not at all scrupulous as to how they make it; they are met by a certain type of native who is as much an outlaw by nature as the old-time bandits, but whose methods are different; and these types combine their forces to the detriment of the honest inhabitants of the state, native or immigrant. Where there are opportunities of making gigantic fortunes quickly, there is bound to be a greater attraction for crooks and unscrupulous individuals than in places where life runs more slowly.

Well, as usual, this letter is dragging out longer than I intended. Let me go back over my comments for a general summing up, also to see if I missed anything, and possibly to clear up any point which seems hazy because of my always faulty manner of presentation.

As for "superiority": aside from matters of sheer necessity, I am guided in my preferences by my likes and dislikes, and not by a criterion of evolutionary degree. I am indifferent as to whether my choices are superior according to this standard or not. But the attitude of some critics is insulting.

Concerning art: I am by no means convinced that art is any higher than certain other forms of human activity, even according to the evolutionary standard. Such men as Michel Angelo, Poe, Beethoven, Cellini, Shaw are no more highly evolved than such men as Saladin, Napoleon, Genghis Khan, Robert E. Lee, Sam Houston, Thomas Jefferson, or James J. Corbett[17] for that matter. The whole trouble with the viewpoint of purely mental workers is that they invariably underrate the mentality of other types of persons, and the intelligence required by other types of activities.

As I made clear in the last letter, I have no hostility against artists. If I had my way, a fund would be set aside for their benefit, whereby they would be relieved of the necessity of doing uncongenial work for a living, and could devote all their time to their art. I honestly feel that the governments of civilization owe them that much. Certainly they deserve something of the sort more than the money-hogs of capitalism deserve to get all the riches of the system into their filthy hands. In a more sane system of distribution I feel certain that the value of artists to civilization will be recognized and their economic problems provided for—or rather the solution of those problems. Of course, a few slick pretenders might muscle in on it, but it would be better to support a few masqueraders than to let other real artists be so cramped by poverty and necessity as to hinder their production. It certainly wouldn't be "charity" on the part of civilization to provide a living wage for persons who are at least as important in the scheme of things as the fat-bellied capitalistic barons who at present build their fortunes on the backs of others—including these same artists. I respect the artistic complex, and I have no hostility for intellectuals as intellectuals, though I have neither respect nor patience for their habit of condemning as "sentimental," "romantic," and "irrational" every and all ideas, emotions and preferences that chance to fall outside their own particular set of ideas, emotions and preferences.

As for liberty: since my ideal of freedom certainly includes that freedom of thought and expression which you value so highly, obviously the only cause for dispute is the fact that I value physical freedom more highly than you do. The fact that "absolute freedom" is nonexistent doesn't mean that there are no varying degrees of freedom.

With regard to things of "real value" in life; I don't recognize the right or ability of any man to lay down arbitrary rules as what are and what are not of value; the best any man can do is to define what things make life worth living for himself, while realizing that his indifference to or contempt for certain other things doesn't keep those things from being highly valued by other types of humans. The only intelligent attitude in this matter is one of broad tolerance.

Concerning the frontier: it is not my intention to gild it with a false lustre, or to consciously belittle other conditions of mankind; but, considering my own mode of life and environments, and my hereditary traditions, I don't see how I could logically feel any other way towards it than the way I actually feel.

Thanks very much for the fine post card views you sent me. As always I found them most fascinating. Quebec must indeed present an intriguing old world aspect, different from anything I've ever seen. The Mexican towns on both sides of the river, while strikingly different from American environs, still do not—to me at least—suggest the old world nearly so much as these views you send me from Canada. Of course I have to get my ideas of Europe from pictures and reading, etc., but Mexican scenes have a distinct personality all their own, which is, allowing for the natural touches of Spain, as new world as American scenes are. The Aztec is stronger in the Mexican than the Spaniard is. Indeed, some of the scenes remind me more of Oriental places I have seen pictured, than European.

I liked your "Festival" reprint in the current Weird Tales. Indeed, I believe I like it as well as anything else I ever read of yours. It will quite overshadow my Conan yarn,[18] but being overshadowed by your stories is no disgrace. I particularly like the subtle implication of an alien race, the ancestors of the central character. I wish you'd enlarge on that theme in another story. And I wish you'd write some historical tales. You could do them finely. That bit of yours in Long's serial[19] showed how magnificently you could handle a tale with a historical Roman setting. I envy you your knowledge of history. With it, if you wished, you could roam the ages at will, dragging figures out of obscurity to gild with fictional lustre, lend new attributes to old heroes or drag false gods off their pedestals. There is no literary work, to me, half as zestful as rewriting history in the guise of fiction. I wish I was able to devote the rest of my life to that kind of work. I could write a hundred years and still there would be stories clamoring to be written, by the scores. Every page of history teems with dramas that should be put on paper. A single paragraph may be packed with action and drama enough to fill a whole volume of fiction work. I could never make a living writing such things, though; the markets are too scanty, with requirements too narrow, and it takes me so long to complete one. I try to write as true to the actual facts as possible, at least, I try to commit as few errors as possible. I like to have my background and setting as accurate and realistic as I can, with my limited knowledge; if I twist facts too much, alter dates as some writers do, or present a character out of keeping with my impressions of the time and place, I lose my sense of reality, and my characters cease to be living and vital things; and my stories center entirely on my conceptions of my characters. Once I lose the "feel" of my characters, and I might as well tear up what I have written. And once I have a definite conception of a character in my mind, it destroys the feeling of reality to have that individual act in any manner inconsistent with the character in which I have visualized him. My characters do and say illogical and inconsistent things—inconsistent as far as general things go—but they are consistent to my conception of them. But what I started to say was, I wish you'd write some historical stories.

But whatever you write, I can say with complete conviction that it will be a magnificent literary feast which I will admire with all sincerity. And I hope to see more of your work soon in Weird Tales. With the best of wishes,

Cordially,
REH

Notes

1. Harvey Bailey, a confederate of George "Machine Gun" Kelly in the kidnapping of millionaire Charles F. Urschel in Oklahoma City (see n. 14), was arrested on 12 August 1933, at a farmhouse near Paradise, Texas. He escaped from the Dallas County Jail the morning of 4 September, but was apprehended later that day in Ardmore, Oklahoma. He had been assisted in his escape by a deputy sheriff.

2. "Worms of the Earth" was published in *Keep on the Light* (1933), "The Black Stone" in *Grim Death* (1932).

3. "The Dreams in the Witch House" (July 1933).

4. "Talons in the Dark" was published as "Black Talons" in *Strange Detective,* December 1933; the other story REH mentions was probably either "People of the Serpent," published as "Fangs of Gold," or "Teeth of Doom," published as "The Tomb's Secret" under the byline Patrick Ervin, both in the February 1934 issue of the magazine.

5. REH apparently refers to William Owen "Bucky" O'Neill (1860–1898), not Bucky O'Connor, a fictional character. William McLeod Raine (1871–1954) wrote about both. O'Neill was a former sheriff of Yavapai County, Arizona, and was serving as Mayor of Prescott when the U.S. declared war on Spain in 1898. He enlisted in Theodore Roosevelt's Rough Riders and was made captain of Company A. He was killed in action at the Battle of San Juan Hill. According to Raine's "Taming the Frontier: 'Bucky' O'Neill" (*Outing Magazine,* June 1905, p. 292), O'Neill "quoted Whitman on the battlefield," but most accounts of his death suggest he died instantly when shot.

6. *The Blue Bird* (*L'Oiseau bleu,* 1908) by Maurice Maeterlinck; *John Ferguson* (1919) by St. John Ervine; *Cyrano de Bergerac* (1897) by Edmond Rostand; *Antigone* (c. 441 B.C.E.) by Sophocles; *The Admirable Crichton* (1902) by J. M. Barrie; *Tartuffe* (1664) by Molière; *Trelawny of the Wells* (1898) by Arthur Wing Pinero; *The Ironmaster* (*Le Maître des forges,* 1883) by Georges Ohnet.

7. Striking coal mine workers in Pennsylvania had rioted in late July and early August, leading President Franklin D. Roosevelt to call for a moratorium on strikes, to allow his recovery efforts to work. In Connecticut, and throughout the Northeast, textile mill owners were replacing employees with women and young children, paying as little as $1.00 per week and requiring them to work long hours.

8. Eduard Heyck (1862–1941), German historian. Heyck wrote only in German; no books of his were translated. REH derived the quotation from *The Book of History* (q.v.), vol. 8 (*Western Europe in the Middle Ages*), p. 3431.

9. REH refers to Heinrich Schurtz (1863–1903), German historian and author of *Urgeschichte der Kultur* (1900) and other works on primitive societies. REH derived his

information from "Spain and Its Conquerors," in *The Book of History*, vol. 9, pp. 3508ff.

10. Caleb Berg "Cape" Willingham (1853–1925), Texas rancher and lawman. He began working for Charles Goodnight in Colorado in 1875, and in 1877 was brought to Texas to work on the newly established JA Ranch. In 1879 he went to work for the LX ranch to help solve cattle thefts, and in 1880 was elected sheriff of the newly established Oldham County. He later moved to Mobeetie and for many years was associated with the Hansford Land and Cattle Company and their Turkey Track Ranch.

11. George ("Machine Gun") Kelly (1895–1954), notorious American gangster during the Prohibition era. His crimes included bootlegging, armed robbery, and kidnapping.

12. Glenn Hunsucker and Ed (or John) "Perchmouth" Stanton, sought for the murders of Swisher County, Texas, sheriff J. C. Moseley and Wise County, Texas, deputy sheriff Joe Brown in January 1933, were surprised by New Mexican officers on 16 July 1933 near Ramon in Lincoln County. Hunsucker and deputy sheriff Tom Jones were killed in the gun battle. Stanton escaped but was captured the following day. Contemporary newspaper accounts consulted do not identify the person who shot Hunsucker nor the weapon used; it is possible REH got his information from other sources. Alexander S. McCamant was sheriff of Lincoln County; census data show Texas as his birthplace. He may have been from Graford in Hood County, though that is not adjacent to Callahan. Hubert T. Reynolds was McCamant's deputy (and son-in-law); he was originally from the northwestern part of Callahan County. REH might have been cheered to know that, while the 1930 census showed Hunsucker living with his mother in Quitaque, Briscoe County, Texas, he was actually born and raised in Oklahoma.

13. After failing in efforts at reconciliation, Jack Ellis, known to locals as an Englishman, shot and killed his wife on 29 May 1926. According to REH's account in a letter to AWD of 1935 (see *CL* 3.336), "She ran out of the house with him behind her, threatening her with a shotgun and she begged a boy who was passing in an automobile to take her away. But Ellis threw his gun on the boy and bade him mind his own business. Then he turned on his wife and the first charge struck her in the thigh and flank, so she staggered to the steps of the porch and sank down, with her hand on her wound, begging for her life. But he placed the muzzles of the gun between her breasts and blew the life out of her; then he laid down the gun and went into the yard and cut his own throat with his knife. And there he lay long, spurting blood like a stuck hog and groaning and no man would soil the hands of him by touching him, until at last there came a doctor who was from Kansas and who sewed up his wound and saved his rotten life. . . . I hoped he would hang before the first snow flew; but he only got ninety-nine years."

14. Millionaire Charles F. Urschel was kidnapped by armed men from his home in Oklahoma City on 22 July 1933, and released on 31 July after payment of $200,000 ransom. Harvey J. Bailey, George R. "Machine Gun" Kelly, Albert L. Bates, Kelly's wife Kathryn, and her parents Mr. and Mrs. R. G. Shannon were all arrested for their parts in the kidnapping.

15. Rita Kirkpatrick was in the graduating class of Brownwood High School, 1923, as was REH. She was Class Secretary, and served on the staffs of the newspaper and yearbook.

16. Thomas Baker Slick (1883–1930), sometimes referred to as "King of the Wildcatters," was one of the most notable independent oil operators in the U.S. When he died in 1930, he left an estate estimated at $75 million to $100 million.

17. James J. Corbett (1866–1933), nicknamed "Gentleman Jim Corbett," American boxer who became the heavyweight champion of the world by defeating John L. Sullivan in 1892. He was defeated in 1897 by Bob Fitzsimmons.

18. "The Pool of the Black One."

19. See letter 19, n. 9.

[88]   [ANS][1]

[Postmarked Providence, R.I.,
25 October 1933]

Abundant & prodigious thanks for the marvellous set of rattles which came this morning. Never before have I seen so vast an outfit. They must have come from old Yig, the Father of Serpents, himself! I'd hate to encounter their erstwhile wearer in his prime! Needless to say, they take a top-notch place in my near-museum. ¶ Have enjoyed your recent tales, all of which capture to a phenomenal degree the atmosphere of unhallowed antiquity & malign alienage. ¶ My aunt is much better—all around on a cane now—so that I am less tied down than before. Have taken many rural walks through the autumn scenery, & shall probably visit Long in N Y next month. Photographed my colonial abode the other day—will send you a print shortly. ¶ Saw a demonstration of *television* last Saturday. Very vague & flickering. ¶ After a dismal rainy season in Sept. we have had a mild & pleasant Octr. Winter, however, is in the offing, & outdoor activities are near their end. ¶ Best wishes—& thanks again for that marvellous & patriarchal set of rattles!
—H P L

Notes

1. [Front: Unknown.]

[89]

Out on Prospect Terrace,
Slightly north of 66 College St., with
the spires, domes, and chimney pots of the
lower town outspread below me to the west.
November 2, 1933

Dear R E H:—

. . . . . The summer here was cooler than I like, with a maximum of 97°, attained on only a few days. It is obvious that W. Texas has greater extremes than R.I., for you have spoken of winter temperatures below our lowest, as well as of summer levels above our highest. It never exceeds 100° here. The seacoast is not prone to extremes, and one can note the difference even in interior New England. The other day my friend Cook—who has left Boston for N. Montpelier, Vermont—reported a 12-inch fall of snow and a temperature of 12°! Our autumn has been very mild, so that I've had many outdoor trips to compensate for the confinement imposed by my aunt's illness. It has been my habit to take a 'bus out some main road, then alighting and striking across country on foot till I reach another 'bus-traversed road along which I can return. In this way I have tapped some remarkably wild and unspoiled regions—many of which I never saw before. Despite the east's dense population, a vast amount of open country exists here and there—and the wilderness increases rather than decreases as people drift toward the larger towns. Some of the stretches I've been seeing are much as they were 200 years ago—with narrow, winding roads bordered by brier-twined stone walls, ancient gambrel-roofed cottages on rocky hills, and sweeping vistas of wood and pastures with here and there a glimpse of shining river or steepled village in the background. Last month I came across a very old house built by a linear ancestor of mine—the Thomas Clemence house just west of the city (1654),[1] with massive, plastered stone chimney, and a perfectly working *well-sweep* in the yard. For the past 2 or 3 evenings I've been enjoying the great round Hunter's Moon that comes up over the rock-ridged eastern hills at sunset. It blends exquisitely with the outspread landscapes of hill and meadow and forest and adds a touch of the weird to a scene already beautiful. But of course this is the very end of the season. No more continuous mild weather can be expected, tough there may be isolated days of more or less pleasantness.

I am delighted to hear that "Worms of the Earth" will appear in the new "Not at Night". With "The Black Stone" last year, you are surely becoming quite a fixture! Hope the book plan won't fall through. Glad you obtained Klarkash-Ton's "Double Shadow" and "Ebony and Crystal". In the latter, "The Hashish-Eater" is a marvellous piece of work. Glad you have begun to place detective tales—Kline seems to be a great teacher of the formula, judging from the help he has given Price. He is also a marvellous aid in marketing. As for my "Festival"—I liked it when I wrote it, but today it seems a bit strained and over-coloured to me. Adjectives and descriptive touches are laid on too thickly—there is a pervasive extravagance about the whole thing. In intimating an alien race I had in mind the survival of some clan of pre-Aryan sorcerers who preserved primitive rites like those of the witch-cult—I had just been reading Miss Murray's "Witch-Cult in Western Europe". It might be possible to enlarge on this theme—introducing a character descended from the cult stock who did not know of his ancestry till reminded by certain messengers sent to summon him to the tribal rites. As for historical tales—I am not sure how well I could do them. They are certainly fascinating, but they demand a *minute and specialised* knowledge far beyond any acquirements of mine. And further, I have not much of a knack at story writing except where the weird is concerned. It is possible, though, that I may use a Roman setting in certain weird tales—probably some in which a character covers long time-intervals. The thing which I would probably enjoy most in connexion with history would be bringing utterly separate culture-streams into anomalous contact—as in having a Roman washed across the ocean on a derelict galley and land amidst the Mayas, or having a Greek cross the great deserts to China. But the scholarship needed to write a really good historical tale is utterly dizzying in its extent. Hardly any moderns succeed in really recapturing the spirit of a former age. Indeed, despite all the Roman tales in existence, the only fiction which actually captures anything of Roman life is that of Edward Lucas White. ("Andivius Hedulio", "The Unwilling Vestal".)[2] You yourself are splendid in historical fiction, with a sense of pageantry which marvellously vivifies your work. I mentioned on my card how greatly I enjoyed the tale of Gottfried von Kalmbach. I envy you your knowledge of the history of eastern Europe and of the middle ages generally—a sadly weak spot in my equipment. One thing I'd like to see more often from your pen is fiction based on the old southwest—of which you have so encyclopaedic a knowledge. I see that in next month's W T something of the sort is scheduled.[3]

I am at a sort of standstill in writing—disgusted at much of my older work, and uncertain as to avenues of improvement. In recent weeks I have done a tremendous amount of experimenting in different styles and perspectives, but have destroyed most of the results. The one tale I have finished—"The Thing on the Doorstep"—is now starting on a circulation round which will include you. You'll get it from Smith, and can forward it to Price. During the summer the Knopf firm broached the idea of issuing a book of my stuff, but it all fell through like the Putnam fiasco of 1931. More recently a man in Asotin, Wash.—one F. Lee Baldwin—has proposed the publication of my "Colour Out of Space" as a separate booklet. I have gladly acquiesced, though I doubt if much will come of the matter.

My Quebec trip was certainly a great event—giving me 4 days of uninterrupted heat and sunshine in the picturesque citadel of the north. You are certainly right in judging, from pictures, that Quebec is the most distinctly and emphatically Old-World city on this continent. There may be South American towns reflecting something of old Spain, but all the Mexican views I have seen indicated a very different aspect. Race and climate in Mexico differ so extensively from those in Spain that architecture can hardly be parallel. On the other hand, Quebec has always had a purely French population, and its northern climate dictates houses of much the same type as those of northern France. Postcards of Honfleur, Rouen, Chartres, St. Malo, and other towns of France contain little or nothing that could be adjudged exotic in Quebec. Indeed, the French in Canada followed ancestral patterns more closely than we in New England did. We quickly evolved certain forms very different from anything in England, and preferred wood as a construction material to the brick and stone of our forefathers. Even in the later period of conscious and sophisticated architecture the various English colonies had styles of their own, whereas the French-Canadians followed Norman and Breton models faithfully. In the 19th century, though, some independent Canadian forms occur. The Spaniards in St. Augustine—although without any Indian mixture—made no attempt to follow real Spanish architecture. However, the old houses did once look more Spanish than they do now—since the present pointed roofs (of a West-Indian type also found in Charleston) were added during the British period, 1763–1783. When the Spaniards came back in 1783 they seemed to prefer the new British roofs; for they not only let every one remain, but followed that style themselves in subsequent building. (Actually, it was a vast improvement—leaving the upper stories much cooler than the flat Spanish roofs had done.) In New Orleans there is a certain old-world atmosphere, yet the architecture is purely local—like nothing in Europe. French and Spanish influences are blended, and modified by West Indian ideas, as nowhere else in the world. No—Quebec is about the only American city which would not feel out of place in Europe. The nearest thing to it in that respect would probably be some of the very compactly built cities in New England and the Middle Colonies. There are some districts in Boston and New York and Philadelphia and Baltimore and Alexandria and Richmond where the closely-packed brick houses of the middle and later 18th century look pretty much like the London houses of the same period—even Providence has a neighbourhood or two of the sort—but this does not apply to the cities as a whole. However—Boston is easily second to Quebec in this respect. It is without question London's closest counterpart on this continent. In the days before cinema companies built their own scenery, the streets and squares around Beacon Hill were often invaded by camera troupes seeking "London Exteriors". Salem and Marblehead, on the other hand, are all of the New World—embodying Massachusetts local idiosyncrasies to the full.

Well—as I have said, I had a great time in Quebec. I covered all the familiar sights and unearthed some new ones, besides taking several suburban trips. I never got tired of the place—the great city walls and gates, the lofty citadel, the frowning ramparts, the dizzying cliff, the winding, climbing ways, the ancient houses, the gleaming silver spires, and the breathtaking vistas of outspread roofs, verdant countryside, broad blue river, and distant purple Laurentians. I always get a special kick from the northern atmospheric effects, which never reach as far south as Rhode Island. The clouds assume fantastic forms, and have a curious, phantasmagoric behaviour at dawn. On the evening of Labour Day I saw one of the most impressive sunset phenomena imaginable—the roofs of the city ablaze with red-gold light, yet in the southeast, across the vast river, a low hung rain-cloud darting bolts of lightning to the distant countryside beyond Lévis. And due east, over the green, sun-gilded Isle d'Orleans, a pallid fragment of rainbow whose upper end was merged in the thundercloud.

I stopped in Boston both going and coming, and made a side-trip to Salem and Marblehead on the return-trip. In Salem there was something which would have interested you—a perfect reproduction of the earliest huts of the settlement (1626 to 1630 or so) in all their details, making an exact picture of that very brief period which involved actual pioneering. Houses and accommodations were crude, tools were primitive, crops were uncertain, and the Indians were always a source of uneasiness. But since very little of this utter crudeness existed after 1630 or 1635, it is to a great extent forgotten. Salem's new development, however, is designed to perpetuate the memory. These huts are designed with the utmost antiquarian accuracy after a study of all available records, and follow the original modes of construction throughout. They are of the original size, and include every variety—bent-bough wigwams copied from those of the Naumkeag Indians,[4] cabins of clay-mottled upright logs, crude board huts with wooden chimneys, and finally the first small houses built from European models. It is interesting to observe that some of the early cottages have *thatched roofs*—although this mode of construction was soon forbidden because of the danger of fire. These present reproductions are set in a park by the harbour's edge, and the landscape around them has been developed to imitate that of the earliest Salem settlement. Besides the houses there are barns, sheds, and reproductions of the earliest industries—blacksmith shop, saw-pit, fish-drying works, etc. etc. Also gardens of the primitive sort, with all the medicinal herbs so highly prized in early New England. Altogether, this is without doubt the finest and most vivid representation of the Atlantic coast's pioneer age which America can boast. It was a liberal education to me—for despite my familiarity with the late 17th and 18th century scene, the age of the 1620's and 1630's was pretty sketchy to my mind. There certainly ought to be corresponding exhibits in other colonial sections—New York, Virginia, and South Carolina. I couldn't get postcards this time, but hope to do so on my next Salem trip.

The next-best thing to this reproduced village is the set of miniature models of early New Amsterdam in the new municipal museum of New York. These include scenes from the first pioneer age, when the settlers of 1626 built their 30 cabins, fort, and horse-driven treadmill along the virgin shore of the East River.

Which reminds me—I've just had an article in young Talman's Holland Society magazine which may interest you . . . on Dutch influences in New England.[5] I'll enclose a copy when I get home—or in a later letter if I haven't any on hand now. I've lent quite a number with a request for return, but if you have any permanent use for the thing you're welcome to keep it. I find that very few laymen seem to know about the Dutch hold on the Maine coast from 1674 to 1676. Probably this is because the region in question was, at the time (despite a previous English occupation from 1629 to 1635), virtually a part of French Acadia—so that it is popularly thought of only in connexion with Canadian history.

By the way—on my outbound trip I visited a very ancient house—1637—in the seaward Boston suburb of Winthrop, which lies on the northern peninsula enclosing Boston Harbour. This old dwelling—the farmhouse of Deane Winthrop—is broad and low, with great exposed beams and an enormous brick chimney with a secret room in the base. I had never seen it before, though I had long meant to do so.

Nov. 5, 1933

Three days have elapsed since the start of this epistle—and I must ask pardon for the inferior penmanship beginning during the second sheet. At that place my best pen dropped and suffered injury, so that secondary pens had to be brought into play. None of these substitutes is really satisfactory—hence the visible result. My best pen is promised for tomorrow by the repairer and I only hope it will be restored to something like its original state. I've told you of my great difficulty in getting a decent pen. This one was given me by a friend who found the flow too free for him—though for me it was just right. If it isn't in good shape tomorrow I'll let the repairer try again—or send for a new point—for a pen like that can't be duplicated!

Regarding our many-phased controversy—I have read your arguments over many times, and with a deep appreciation of their force and cleverness. One thing I especially appreciate about them is their solid sincerity and first-hand derivation from observation and experience. I always respect such arguments infinitely more than I do the lightly-based and often-changed arguments of habitual theorists, whose opinions come largely from unverified reading and waves of academic fashion. It has always been my position that a thinker ought to get at his subject *directly*—applying pure reason at first-hand to the actual facts and phenomena instead of letting his judgment be influenced by prior opinions or conventional fashions. This you do to a gratifying degree, so that—whether or not I can concur with your final deductions—I always find your arguments full of meat and rich in starting-points for various trains of significant thought—a thing I could never say of the glib, ready-made harangues of those who merely echo Croce or Santayana or Briffault or Marx or Ellis or some other authority.[6] There is a lightweight quality about second-hand opinion which can't be escaped. These fashion-followers forget that the authorities whom they parrot did not derive their original opinions in this easy way. An opinion which is serious with its first-hand creator ceases to be serious when it is mimicked without sufficient basis in experience.

Now as to the question of *resentment*—of course, it is just as irrelevant in one party to an argument as in another. If I seemed to convey a different idea, I surely made a mistake in phraseology. There is no need of *condemning* resentment on either side, unless it actually obscures some point of the case; for its trouble is simply *that it has nothing to do with the actual issue*. It is doubtless natural for an arguer to display a sort of exasperation when his opponent seems to him to be contravening common reason and attacking the foundations of everything which makes life valuable to persons above the simian grade, but this exasperation is simply a side-issue. It has no part in the argument, and neither strengthens nor weakens the case of the man who displays it. *The only thing of importance is the truth or untruth of the various contentions.* Each arguer ought to strive to be as detached and impersonal as possible—acting merely as a collector and channel for objective evidence. And if he can't quite succeed, then the only thing to do is to ignore his *emotion* and study his *evidence* just as though the former did not exist.

Thus if I did express an adverse opinion of any emotion displayed by you, my expression was surely out of order, as you maintain. It is your privilege to ignore my opinion (if such) just as I ought to have passed over your emotion. *Both* are essentially side-issues—waste products cluttering up the one pertinent business at hand . . . i.e., *the search for truth itself, irrespective of its labyrinth of preconceptions and associations*. It really doesn't matter how clumsy I am as an arguer—and I probably am clumsy enough!—provided I can manage to get some real evidence across despite the penumbra of superfluous matter. I am not trying to defend myself—it really interests me relatively little whether I'm a good arguer or not. All I am trying to do is to clear away the cobwebs enshrouding certain basic standards of value in order to get at the truth. I had rather be a poor arguer on the right side than a good arguer on the wrong side—and I'd rather be on the right side even if I have to change former opinions in order to get there, than on the wrong side even though glib rhetoric might make it seem externally the right one. So forget *me*, and any expression of *personal* opinion that I may have made in the past or may make in the future. Heed only the *evidence* that I adduce from sources which reason indicates as reliable. No person can be more than a classifier and transmitter so far as truth is concerned. Truth is truth, irrespective of anybody's affirmation or denial, knowledge or ignorance. If I say that the sun is hot, the vital thing *isn't what I think* of the sun's heat or coldness, but simply the question of whether the sun is hot or cold. I have no part in the matter, except as a possible conveyer and correlator of data. The job of forming a final verdict from the evidence has nothing to do with me. It's your job alone—a case of your independent mind confronting the mass of available facts. All I can have done will have been to bring forward and arrange some of the facts for your perception and consideration—and it can hardly matter whether I do it gracefully or clumsily so long as you do get the facts and act on them independently. Of course we all have secondary considerations and emotions mixed with the primary issue in arguing, but these are simply to be ignored.

I had hoped that my argument was free from all offence; for certainly, no lack of respect for your position (a position whose sincere first-handedness, as just pointed out, I particularly admire) was at any time intended. While I do consider many of your beliefs at variance with sound standards, there is nothing of disrespect or belittlement in such an opinion, since it is notorious that minds of the highest development are often on the wrong side of a very plain question. The factors determining any individual's belief are complex and innumerable; and in view of the multifarious views held by eminent thinkers on nearly every question under the sun, it can certainly be no affront to tell anybody that his position seems to be utterly wrong. To say to a man "your belief is foolish" is *not in any way* akin to saying "you're a damn fool". Often circumstances are such that a very superior mind may harbour a delusion while a very inferior mind (through the chance circumstance of never having been exposed to the delusion, or through lack of enough imaginative sensitiveness to be deluded) will be absolutely free from it. In such a case a wise man will have a damn foolish opinion, while a damn fool will be perfectly correct . . . . . yet that doesn't make the sage less wise or the fool less foolish. Such is the paradoxical nature of human thought. Well—as I've said, I *thought* I had made the non-offensive and non-arrogant nature of my attitude quite plain—but if I *didn't*, let me express my sincere regret thereat. Possibly my language was careless and ambiguous through the very *absence* of an offensive intention—having no idea of being offensive, I didn't imagine that any loose expression of mine regarding this or that opinion could be interpreted as over-vehement or objectionable.

In the matter of personal tastes, I thought I made clear the distinction between the question of the superiority or inferiority of some *things* to other *things*, and that of the superiority or inferiority of the *persons who like or dislike certain of these things*. This distinction is really supremely important, because it marks off a *matter of basic abstract truth* from a *totally unrelated matter* of superficial, snobbish, and essentially erroneous judgment. At first I could not understand why my explicit drawing of this distinction did not seem clear and satisfying to you, but upon a closer reader of your text I think I can ascertain the trouble. You seem to take my objection to "the classification of an *entire* personality according to the sources of its pleasure" as a tacit assertion that *certain parts* of a personality are to be judged by their pleasure-sources; i.e., that a man who finds any pleasure in cheap popular songs cannot possibly have any real musical sensitiveness. Well—my wording may easily have given such an impression, and if so I hereby express regret. Actually, of course, the matter is not nearly as simple as all that. (But didn't I say something to indicate my appreciation of this point?) It is well known that the pleasure-appeal of any one given thing can be of one or more *entirely different* sorts, among which the aesthetic or intellectual is only a single item. Thus *the same thing* may cause pleasure (a) because it satisfies the intellect, (b) because it excites the aesthetic sense, (c) because it is physically agreeable, (d) because it promotes some definite secondary end, (e) because it arouses agreeable *associations* either consciously or subconsciously . . . and so on. Now obviously, many things of the utmost trashiness or triviality, intellectually or aesthetically considered, may easily give the wisest and most sensitive persons the keenest of pleasure *on other than intellectual or aesthetic grounds*. A grown man loves the trivial nursery tales which remind him of his happy childhood; a musician may love the tawdry barber-shop ballads which he sang in expectant, adventure-dreaming adolescent days with cherished companions now long dead. It is not that the grown man takes the nursery tales seriously, or that the musician thinks "In the Shade of the Old Apple Tree" real music. It is simply that these crude, unaesthetic things exert an emotional pull all apart from the aesthetic. Now only a total damn fool could claim that the grown man is literarily stunted because he likes the nursery tale, or that the musician has certain petrified cells because he feels tenderly toward 1905's sentimental yowling. Indeed, I don't see how I could have conveyed the notion that I harbour such an idea! The only thing which would proclaim these people as partly petrified would be the grown man's assertion that the childish tale is a serious expression of life, or the musician's belief that the tin-pan song forms intrinsically a genuine expression of emotion. It does not argue defective taste to be tickled by a jingle of Eddie Guest because it reminds us of something pleasing, although it does argue defective taste to accept such junk as serious emotional expression.[7] In the latter case, serious acceptance requires a defective receiving equipment because the material is so vapid, stale, ill-formed, and unrelated to anything in life or human feeling as intelligently understood, that it could not produce any response at all from a sensitive or well-developed receiving equipment. However, be sure to remember that this has nothing to do with a pleasure or liking unrelated to intrinsic quality. And more—don't forget that even an actual defect of taste in this one field need not argue an all-around inferior or undeveloped personality. Many a man who thinks Guest's crap is poetry has a splendid taste in music or painting, or possesses scientific or executive attainments of the highest order. We are all creatures of various compartments, and how few of us are uniformly developed! All this ought to show you that my attitude has nothing in common with the undiscriminating superciliousness of the self-conscious "intelligentsia". What *they* claim has nothing to do with any opinion of *mine*. I am quite indifferent to the assumption or possession of superiority by *persons;* my only interest being in the honest recognition of basic cultural values and in the moulding of collective national policies to uphold those values. If you saw me at close range you'd realise how utterly antithetical to the personal snob type I am. I never even think of judging *individuals* by any formal standard, and value all sorts of persons (many of the simplest rustic sort) for various reasons. I know the sort of languishing exquisite whom you associate with rigid aesthetic standards, but I can assure you that this type sickens me as thoroughly as it sickens you! What interests me in connexion with the cultural problem is wholly the large question of political, economic, and social organisation. I believe that a civilisation ought to choose those policies which allow its members to develop their natural human capacities to the utmost, as the Egyptians and Greeks and Western Europeans have done, rather than those which suppress and limit the development of the personality, as was the case in various Oriental and barbaric nations, and as tends to be the case in modern mechanised America with its dominant commercialism and speed and quantity worship. I don't ask any given individual to be other than what he wants to be; but I fight (and rightly, I believe) any general attitude of hostility to the *principle of human civilisation*—the principle which allows at least a certain proportion of the race to realise to the full the natural possibilities which biological development has given them. That's where I stand, and I don't see much resemblance between this position and that of the spectacled sissy who stops his ears whenever a hand-organ plays!

Regarding *values*—I fear it will be hard to reduce so complex a subject to concise simplicity, but perhaps I can convey a little more of my position than I did before. First—we must clearly recognise that any civilisation has to maintain several *parallel sets* of values in order to run along smoothly. There are some sets of merely *relative* values—values based on good practical or emotional adjustment *under a given set* (conceivably changeable) *of conditions,* or in relation to a (conceivably obsolescent and vanishing) past heritage. Other values are more absolute and permanent—physical values based on the (practically definite and fixed) biological welfare of the race. When these different sets of values conflict as they often do, preference is usually given the set which has the most permanent effect—which proves itself more consistently satisfying over long periods. The question of *qualitative status* does not often arise among these local and limited values.

But we cannot get far without correlating our local values and perceiving that through them all runs a thread of unspoken feeling which virtually forms a value in itself. It is more or less vaguely a component of most of the local values, yet has a separate existence of its own. This feeling need not be described pompously or grandiosely, but it is in general a sort of *recognition of the desirability of advancement in the biological scale*. It is of course quite meaningless (as are all other human feelings) in a purely objective and cosmic sense, but it is so universal among terrestrial organic beings that it may empirically be accepted as *quasi-absolute*. Indeed, the process on which it is based is *actually absolute,* for there is no mistaking the trend toward complex and effective organisation represented by the various steps of life-formation between a protozoön and Albert Einstein, or between a sunfish and John Keats. The only *subjective* and therefore non-absolute thing about this human preference for dogs over snakes, men over dogs, white men over niggers, and sensitive, intelligent men over vegetative or animalistic clods is the fact *that it is a preference.*

The *difference* and *direction* involved are unmistakable and beyond dispute. We *know* that a highly developed man is a more influential and effective figure in the cosmos than a caterpillar is, and that he extracts from his environment a wide and predominantly emotion-expanding range of impressions which the caterpillar has no means of receiving. This is beyond dispute. The only question is, whether we shall *prefer* the state of conscious, sensitive mankind to that of unconscious, insensitive caterpillardom. Now nobody attempts to establish any *cosmic* ruling in this matter. In the automatic, impersonal cosmos of force and electrons it would probably be meaningless and irrelevant to apply *qualitative* distinctions to any of the local condensation-nuclei. When, therefore, we speak of "high development" as a *desirable* thing, it is understood that we read no more than *a virtual unanimity of human feeling* into the matter. This much, however, cannot be denied. The feeling that a horse is worth more than a goldfish, and that a man is worth more than a bull is so profound and universal that all challenge is useless. Be it sensible or not, it *exists*—and no amount of anti-civilised feeling can remove it. We must heed it not because it is "sacred" or "absolute", but simply because it *is*. It is part of us—we can't shake it off if we want to—and *there is simply no sense or point in constructing a social system which does not recognise it*. Of course, most pro-barbarians of the Lord Monboddo type try to dodge the question by admitting this universal value up to a certain point, and then claiming that its exact application is impossible. For example, they will say that it is indeed right to prefer men to squirrels, but that any attempt to prefer developed men to undeveloped men—or to prefer man's developable side to his primitive and non-developable side—is carrying the principle too far. However, there is no logic in this position—and (which is even more important) it is not borne out by actual human feelings. There is no mistaking the universal preference for a widely expanded and deeply sensitised life over a fragmentary existence in which most of the capacities for human sensation are left untouched and wasted. Even when certain types of person express a dislike for one or more lines of human development because they have been made to feel at a disadvantage by certain persons of high or ostensibly high development (this motive seems to be inextricably associated with most cases of anti-development sentiment), they show in their attitude toward *other* lines of human development, and in other quite unconscious reactions, that they continue to hold the basic value which they outwardly repudiate. For example—a teamster who has been tricked by a shrewd swindler may call down curses on the whole tribe of quick thinkers, yet he will pummel any fellow-teamster who calls him a fool. An awkward youth who has been teased by more polished boys at school may declare war on all human codes of manners, yet he will be sickened by any crudity beyond a certain point—which he ought to condone if his repudiation of the whole standard-system is genuine. *Human valuation of high development is universal.*

I have perhaps been tediously repetitive in treating of this matter, but it has been necessary because of the pivotal nature of the issue. Since you take so bold a step as to challenge the virtually undisputed basis of valuation in the universe, it is up to me to meet you on your own ground (a ground I profoundly respect and invariably recommend) of first-hand unconventionality. Let it never be said that I tried to bluff through an argument by citing some universal axiom without a rational examination. I despise as much as you do the blustering thinker who fancies he can win a debate by dragging out a common opinion and shouting, "Why, this *can't* be disputed—everybody says it's so!" Like you, I agree that *anything can be disputed*—hence I feel it necessary to bring up plenty of rational support for my assertion *that degree of development in a direction away from the amoebal and the primitive is* (to all intents and purposes, as a matter of subjective human reality) *the supreme human criterion of worth.* You will, I believe, concede that I have not accepted this standard hastily or thoughtlessly, or cited it without mature consideration. I do not see how it can be denied or ignored, hence cannot understand the logic of the anti-civilisationist's position unless he claims that his preferred system of killing and burning and drinking is a higher form of human development than a system which encourages order, decorum, and the exercise of the intellect and the artistic sense. That question may well form a second chapter of the discussion. First, though, the question of human development as a standard must be fought out.

Before leaving the subject let me repeat what I said about *values in general* a few paragraphs back. I pointed out that although *degree of human development* is a sort of *basic, underlying, ultimate value,* there are *many other sets of more or less local values* both relative and semi-absolute, *which coexist with this ultimate value and are generally more or less coloured by it.* Now of course we all know, as a matter of common sense, that even the supreme value cannot be of much use unless supported by a suitable array of other practical values. Hence it ought to have been clear from the first that in singling out a criterion of *ultimate* worth I had no intention of minimising the other values which pertain more directly to the business of *immediate* welfare—the business of *physical survival* which must necessarily precede qualitative advancement. Indeed, I *thought* I made an explicit statement to that effect. Who can deny that a race must keep itself alive and healthy before it can advance? Truly, the *importance* of the social virtues (order, courage, stamina, etc.) is so obvious that it scarcely seemed necessary to affirm it. They are more important to the existence of mankind than is the quality of high development, and the only reason we regard the latter as qualitatively superior is that the fact of existence would be essentially meaningless without it.

In a word, the recognition of one certain value as *paramount* does not in any way deny the existence of other equally (and perhaps more immediately) important values on whose coöperation the effective functioning of the paramount value depends. It does not deny the fact that sheer qualitative development can be very ineffective and unbeautiful when insufficiently backed up by other phases of human character—or that there are cases where, in a net adding up, a specimen of high evolutionary quality with other phases notably deficient must necessarily rank intrinsically lower than a specimen less highly evolved but richer in energy, endurance, or some other essential endowment. Nobody is disposed to question the value of a Gothic church's foundation-stones and buttresses, even while pointing to the towers, traceries, rose windows, and finials as the elements of emotional exaltation which caused it to be built. We say that these towers and traceries are "higher" types of expression than the mechanical supports because they are the actual emotional products which formed a reason for the church's building. There would be no need of mechanical supports if there were no higher structure to support. And yet the higher structure could not exist without the supports. All this is recognised—so that when I say a nation ought to bend its policy toward the maintenance of a high standard of aesthetic and intellectual development, *I take it for granted that an equally high standard of order, courage, endurance, etc. must be cultivated.* Without these latter qualities no nation can long be worthy of respect, whatever its mental or artistic height. Do not forget that I take this for granted—that I prominently assert it and always have asserted it. Never for a moment have I considered a civilisation valid unless it has these sturdy qualities *in addition to a high qualitative goal.* That's what I mean by civilisation—a condition of high aim, plus the effective character needed to back that aim up and make it an unconquerable reality. I reiterate this matter somewhat tediously because I fear I have underemphasised it in the past. I have a feeling that you don't realise the great extent to which I respect those sturdy aspects of character which are paramount with you. Where I differ from you is merely that I insist on the harnessing of the sturdy qualities, if possible, to a goal really worthy of them. They are such noble upholding agents, that it is really an insult to them to devote them to any cause less than the support of a civilisation designed to give human potentialities the highest development and freest play.

Another point to clear up is that of *the real nature of high human development.* Regarding this, let me say that I do not wish to place aesthetic effort on any higher plane than pure intellectual effort. In my opinion, aesthetic and intellectual activities rank about equal. Each class has isolated points in which human capacity seems to reach its height, and I would hesitate to one above the other. Thus I think a pure scientist can be fully as exalted a type as a pure artist. Willem de Sitter[8] and A. C. Swinburne differ only in the kind and direction of their development. Great executives and administrators of course rank equally—being scientists in their essential attitude. The greatest military leaders are on the edge of this class, though the relative singleness and simplicity of their problems and their occasional lack of really broad-visioned motivations makes their position less certain. But the point is that I don't attempt to identify the highest development of mankind with art. Art is merely one of several manifestations of the highest stage of development. The development itself is far more generalised and inclusive. Biologically, it is simply an increased complexity and irritability in certain groups of cells. Culturally, it is an awakening of the natural capacities and sensitiveness of the human being, so that his combined consciousness and feelings embrace as large a variety of points of contact with the external world as possible. The whole thing is merely an increased differentiation from the inert, automatic, insensitive, and unconscious condition of the lower organisms. A recognition of this principle is, you must admit, widely different from the blind worship of art as "the divine in man" which you so justly ridicule. Let me add that whenever I insist on the practice of "pure art" it is only in contradistinction to an insincere pseudo-art with ulterior motives. I'm not implying that art is any more worthy an object than scientific research, but am simply protesting against the debased practice of whatever one has set out to practice. If the person had chosen some other line of effort and followed it *sincerely*, I wouldn't blame him. And if he were following that other line *insincerely*, I'd blame him as much as if he followed art insincerely. I'm sure you see what I mean.

Now as for your specific arguments—there is a fallacy in your citation of certain crimes as *typically human* acts to range beside art and science as evidences of removal from the beast. True, the *more effective performance* of anything is typically human; but the instincts behind most crimes are wholly primitive. None of the *fresh motivations* characteristic of aesthetics and of pure science are present in these cases. In the opposite matter of sacrificing one's life for another, we see not a suppression but a replacement of instincts. In certain cases, of course, there is a purely automatic action without any actual realisation of the consequences. In other cases, religio-moral illusions give one the impression that he is displaying superiority by following a sacrificial course—the ego has a tremendous stimulus compensating for the immediately ensuing loss of life. In still other cases, a distinct aesthetic factor—a sense of art in living—furnishes the requisite ego-stimulus.

However, in condemning crime and praising sacrifice you must remember that the accepted estimates of each of these categories are purely human and conventional. If you are not willing to accept degree of development as a qualitative standard, you can hardly accept the standards which denounce some acts as "evil" and praise others as "noble". *Why* do you condemn cheating and praise sacrifice? What causes you to echo these popular verdicts unquestioningly, when you demand elaborate proof before accepting evolutionary advancement as a supreme general standard? Why do you blindly assume for granted that the type of nerve-and-gland reaction expressed in the conduct called "honest" and "decent" is in any way *necessarily* desirable from a larger point of view? You blame me when I *seem* to be equally uncritical in accepting intrinsic development as a parallel standard.

Of course the answer to all this lies in what was said of *different sets of values* a few paragraphs back. Actually, the conduct called "sacrificial", "honest", or "decent" is of no significance *cosmically*—any more than basic development is. Socially, however, these courses tend to promote group-survival—hence have been surrounded with praise and exalted (with and without religious trimmings) as virtues. Also, some phases of them are forms of ego-exaltation, symbolising a personal strength which raises the possessor above evasion and subterfuge. Thus most of our values are born. Of course these ethical values are valid, because of the social function they discharge—and one freely concedes that sheer development would be ineffective without their aid—but to take them for granted as "divine" is as foolish as taking art for granted as "divine". Nor does the fact that they are necessary foundation-stones at all lessen the worth of the development factor which they help to sustain.

This invalidates your argument that other animals are "superior" to men simply because (in your opinion) they are more "honest" or "decent" than men. What if they have these purely relative virtues to a greater extent (as careful zoölogists, I think, will dispute)? Does that mean anything as scaled against their intrinsic inferiority? Of course I see what you are trying to establish—that man creates his own illusion of superiority by claiming those of his traits which he likes as "human" and dismissing those which he doesn't as "beastly"—but I fear the point isn't quite made, and that it isn't quite relevant even when made. For the fact is, that the sort of superiority I was assigning man isn't the moral sort which forms the subject of his own claims. I was merely pointing out, as an outsider, certain points in which he shows a definite differentiation from other types in the direction of greater complexity. I wasn't even thinking about such local and relative values as "honesty", "decency", etc. I merely stated a definite and measurable fact regarding man's increased cellular complexity and sensitivity and the augmented points of contact with the external world thereby opened up to his consciousness and feelings. *This augmentation of contact-points—this increased life-area—is all I meant by the expression "purely human" or "more human".* It is sufficient—for it embraces all the difference between a gorilla and Epicurus or Plato. That difference speaks for itself—it is enough to relegate the entire moral factor to complete negligibility.

As to your claims regarding the virtues of lower animals—a matter aside from the main issue yet withal interesting—of course I am no naturalist, but I believe most of your points could be successfully attacked. Lower animals have the same natural greed and ferocity that man has; and if they get less through unscrupulous means, it is merely because they don't know enough. Man cheats more for two reasons—because he is more capable, and because some of his number erect standards higher than those of the other animals, to which the inferior specimens can't conform. If man as a whole did not strive to be better than the beasts, his narrower-visioned members wouldn't be (in some ways, if your allegations be true) worse than the beasts.

On one issue you entirely miss the point. You compare the position of the man who exalts *the basic quality of development* with that of the theist who insists on the "divinity" and special separation of mankind from the rest of the animal world. There is no parallel. What the theist does is to draw a wholly *arbitrary* line at a certain point separating *one* species from *all others* without any special evidence. He divides man and ape, but ignores the gulf betwixt ape and jellyfish . . . which naturally is pure idiocy. On the other hand, the man who scientifically exalts the human over the simian stage of development *is equally ready to exalt the simian over the ichthyic or amoebal stages*. These attitudes have no kinship. What the man of sense exalts is *not mere humanness, but the whole trend toward complexity which distinguishes consciousness from primal inertia.*

Turning from the abstract basis to its concrete social applications—I possibly differ less than you think from your own position. While I refuse to lose sight of the fact that "justice"—even more than other human values—is purely a local and tentative conception without cosmic authority or any widespread foundation, I agree that this conception has certain practical and aesthetic qualities which make at least a rough application of it of considerable social value. Thus I fancy that, whenever it is possible to exercise a principle of equal rights in human relationships without lowering the development level of the foremost specimens, such an exercise is well-founded and sensible. It seems to me that the cardinal principle of any society ought to be that of giving all types as great a latitude as they can have without mutual interference or retardation of the most advanced types. The only particular guarantees I would demand for the more evolved elements would be that the group refrain from imposing the cultural standards of the cruder classes (as in Soviet Russia) as the official standards of the whole civilisation. As for political methods—I still think that a fascistic dictatorship, with the dictator elected by vote of those who pass suitable examinations in relevant subjects, would form the least of possible evils. Of course, corruption can never be obviated; but as I pointed out before, the *extent* of its ravages can certainly be *checked* through the tacit acceptance of a given set of political and social standards. For example—years ago, municipal sanitation and relief of poverty were so ill-defined and hazy that no standard of enforcement could be maintained. A corrupt administration could virtually cut off both if it chose. Today this is impossible. Public standards have risen, so that *no city administration, however corrupt, would dare to cut off the water supply, sewer connexions, and vaccination service, or allow relief applicants to starve.* It is understood that such things *must go on.* The cash *must* be raised somehow, so that the administration has to squeeze its graft out of other items exclusively when these departments have been squeezed to a certain fixed minimum. Failure to meet this minimum would result in a political overturn, impeachments, and probable rioting. Well—this same principle will undoubtedly extend to other fields. The public, under the spur of necessity, will evolve a code of necessary employment-spreading, remuneration, unemployment insurance, old-age pensions, and the like; defining and fixing *certain permanent obligations of the government to every individual*—universal, generally understood routine obligations as binding and as widely enforced as the present obligations touching urban sanitation and destitution-relief. With the pressure likely to exist during the next decade, these obligations can probably be made ample enough to ensure every citizen at least a mediocre job or its monetary equivalent. And that solves the *really acute* problem of government. Let the government be as corrupt as it likes—it can't go below this minimum. That is settled. It must fork over just so much, and depend on good management outside this limit to furnish the graft. No matter to what ends a "powerful minority" could bend the government, they couldn't bend it beyond the given pale without arousing an upheaval which would probably unseat them. And there are many reasons why a government elected by a trained and intelligent voting body would be apt to be less crude in the direction of its corruptness than the average government seated by the present haphazard methods. Satisfaction is of course a natural tendency—for it is perfectly normal for the like-minded people to hang together. What, indeed, of interest have unlike-minded people to say to one another? But it won't do any harm if it can be kept from becoming too marked in the economic field. It won't make a bit of difference whether or not the government of a nation will come to rest in the hands of a small group, so long as a certain standard of economic distribution is maintained. Let those who will make the laws, so long as those laws ensure civilised standards, and square meals and food and shelter and clothes and warmth for everyone. It is certain, though, that the effect of an enlightened electorate would be to seat a government infinitely more effective than any which could be seated in any other way. There could be no system worse than that in which the voters have no real knowledge of any of the issues. Whatever evils might remain, would be just so much less, and fewer, by reason of the change. With certain objects permanently defined (as suggested above) by public opinion and constitutional enactment, there is absolutely no question but that those objects could be achieved infinitely better and quicker by a government of trained men chosen by trained men, than by a parcel of rhetorically glib and half-educated platitude-mouthers chosen by an emotion-swayed mob of illiterates or foisted on that mob by shrewd and selfish business and financial interests dominated by the profit motive.

Regarding the matter of *freedom*—I don't quite grasp the *bearing* of your new argument on it in relation to your older arguments. You state, and rightly, that one who can subsist by 5 or 6 hours of congenial daily toil is not as badly tied down as one who is obliged to work 16 hours at a crushing and uncongenial task. You say that only the latter has the right to complain of the lack of freedom. Well, *if this excessive imposition of industry is what you mean by "lack of freedom", then I have never disputed the point.* This is something which I did not know was under discussion. I thought that your complaints were like those of most moderns—simply against the necessary regulations of collective life. When, nowadays, we hear of the "cruelly inhibited nature of American life" or the "galling yoke of oppression imposed by civilisation" it is usually from some idle member of the "intelligentsia" who is irked because he can't get drunk and break windows without being arrested, or play his radio in an apartment-house at 3 a.m. Naturally, there is nothing to do but dismiss such complaints against the inevitable. Of course, I didn't think your complaints were quite as baldly frivolous as this—but from various remarks I thought they belonged, albeit remotely, to something of the same category. That is why I called into question what seemed to be your ideal of indiscriminate license and anti-social disorder.

If, however, it is the weight of excessive toil imposed on the followers of certain occupations which you deplore, then *I am heartily with you*—as all enlightened sociologists are! But in this case you are *absolutely dead wrong* as to the effect of social evolution on the matter. There is not an iota of question but that mechanisation *will promote rather than limit the leisure of the manual worker.* This is as nearly a certainty as anything in human life. The whole trend of mechanisation calls for the artificial spread of employment (of which the NRA is a beginning) and the assignment of shorter hours to each individual.[9] That this system will eventually reach agriculture there is no doubt, for the tendency is toward large corporation farms manned by shifts of workers as in factories. Employment must be spread artificially here as well as in commerce and manufactures, hence compulsory short hours are merely a matter of time. In the face of the virtually universal recognition of the hour-shortening effect of the machine age, I don't see how you can possibly maintain that modernity subtracts from freedom instead of adding to it. Indeed, the workers of Russia deify the machine as their liberator. That is the one redeeming feature of mechanisation, which half-reconciles us to the havoc it causes in other departments of life. It certainly does promise relief to the overworked labourer, whose plight under the old order was admittedly disproportionately severe. The much-idealised frontier was a cruel and grinding taskmaster as contrasted with the mechanised world of the future, for despite its bloodshed and violence it certainly imposed upon all the very hardest kind of life. Thus *your new argument absolutely changes the whole aspect of the discussion on this point.* To the idle complainer of the intelligentsia, I admitted that civilisation checked *his* kind of "freedom", but argued that the loss was inevitable and not to be complained of by adults. To *this new complaint* (of the excessive labour assigned to certain classes of workers), however, one must extend full sympathy and agreement; disagreeing only as to the influence of civilisation—which is a vast liberator instead of an enslaver. Under the old non-mechanised civilisation there was no way in which a man without especial shrewdness or talents might keep himself alive except through endless, back-breaking toil—the "brother to the ox" stuff immortalised by Millet and Markham.[10] This kind of man had no freedom in the "free" world idealised by the intelligentsia, but he will have in the "enslaved" machine world of the future . . . . because the effect of intensive mechanisation has been to plunge him, together with millions of his more capable brothers, into so hopeless a plight that an artificial rescue from above has become necessary in order to avert wholesale starvation and probable revolution. The present year, just before the beginning of the new administration's remedial programme, marks the low point of the workman's fortunes in America. The tendencies crushing him under a "free" or laissez-faire economic system were steadily growing, yet the "free" system of Hoover individualism was unchecked. Now, under the "slavery" of a governmentally regulated economy, there will be a steady but slow trend toward relief. There is tragic irony in the workman's picture of a *government* which "crushes" him. Poor man—it is *not government*, but the *natural alignment* of a "free" and fluid society which presses down the weak! "Freedom" means concentrated power for the strong and servitude and starvation for the weak. *Government*—which he calls "slavery"—is *the only possible avenue of rescue he has.*

Thus whatever sort of a case the financially secure romanticist may have against order, civilisation, and mechanisation, it is clear that the real friend of the labouring class has no case at all. Order, civilisation, and mechanisation are the workman's best friend—they alone will save him from the long hours and gruelling toil which have always been his.

Concerning the *frontier*—let me readily admit that I may be all wrong in any picture I may have formed. As I have often said, I have virtually no *first-hand* data except from your own absorbingly interesting accounts, hence am likely to fall into all the errors of perspective common to a distant commentator without a wide range of information-sources.

If I seemed to say that the frontier gave its rewards solely on a basis of physical strength and murderous temperament I was of course putting the matter extravagantly and erroneously. What I meant to say (be it correct or not) was merely that it *tended* to do so to such an extent that even its members could scarcely have regarded it as a well-balanced condition worthy of permanent establishment. It was glamourous and heroic *as long as it was necessary*—like a bravely fought *war,* which to some extent it was. Yet while unreservedly admiring it, and respecting the sturdy and brilliant characters which it developed, we could hardly wish for its perpetuation any more than for the perpetuation of a glorious war. It gave America a stirring Iliad, and reënacted the old Aryan struggle on a new soil for new prizes—but even those who love the Iliad would mourn if the Homeric Age had not finally given place to the Age of Pericles. Such, I repeat, was the opinion I had formed from the limited data at hand. Naturally, it may be wrong—and in any case it does not conflict with my always-held parallel belief *that countless single elements of pioneer psychology and custom do indeed form precious additions to the American culture-stream.* I have never even thought of disputing this latter point—and indeed, I have always held frontier days in tremendous respect and admiration. Don't get the idea that I fail to appreciate a titanic chapter in American history merely because (on present information) I don't think its precise conditions are adapted to permanent retention in a settled nation. I fully appreciate the part played by intelligence in success on the frontier, and realise that kindness was not absent. It is very possible that the whole scene was much more orderly and rational and effective than my fragmentary information has led me to realise. Nor am I blind to the stupidities and ill-proportioned rewards existing in most civilisations. My objections to the frontier as a permanent form of society are based wholly on what I have heard of its cruel waste of life, inefficiency in achieving goals (i.e., clumsy steps needed to effect what civilisation readily effects), subtly callous psychology (disregard of human life and bodily integrity), neglect of many vital sides of the human personality, and so on. Of course I realise that these things are inevitable attributes of a formative period, and that they were offset by certain compensating virtues fostered by the conditions (quickness, courage, straightforwardness, resourcefulness, and so on); but I cannot feel that their permanent enthronement is justified— especially since it is by no means certain that their modification needs to be accompanied by a decline of their companion virtues.

I do not list the *intrinsic transientness* of the frontier as an objection, as you seem to assume. I simply point out that the special folkways of the frontier were adapted only to a sparsely populated region with certain economic conditions, and that both the sparse peopling and the given economic conditions were necessarily transient. It is not that the present period is necessarily any more fixed than the preceding, but simply that it and all of its possible successors are of a nature not permitting the frontier folkways to survive. We can't have "six-shooter justice" in the sort of thickly populated and quick-transportationed country which will certainly remain until the next collapse of all civilisation. It would not work even if it were ever more than a necessary evil. The Chicago racketeers illustrate what it becomes under modern urban conditions.

As for your claim that the old frontiersmen did not wish to extend and duplicate the civilised east which they left—I don't think history will bear it out. It is clear that all of them did their best to establish the institutions of the America they had known. That is, all the responsible men of character, like your own ancestors. They founded estates, set up courts, schools, encouraged industry and prosperity, and left many evidences of their dreams of a wider America with busy centres of activity in its new portions. That these solid founders wished to perpetuate a regime of sparse settlement, insecure life and property, violence as an arbiter, and all the rest, is hardly within the realm of probability. That they personally relished the adventurous role of founders, preferring it to the settled careers open to the at home, is hardly an indication that they desired the new territories to remain in the perpetually infant condition of being founded!

Your own idealisation of the frontier, I would judge from the information at hand, proceeds primarily from a strongly *moralistic* attitude. That is, you consider certain traits of frontier character so important and valuable, according to the standards you accept, that they overbalance all adverse traits, including the total lack of development of important sides of the human personality. Whether such an attitude is valid and sensible or not, I will not attempt to determine—particularly since my knowledge of actual frontier conditions is so slight. As I have freely admitted, I know only certain fragments. I don't know how *universal* the wanton killing was, or how callous toward life and limb people *really* were. Perhaps my picture is outrageously exaggerated. And anyhow, remember that I recognise the frontier as a necessity in its day. Those who formed it acted the part of heroes—they could not, under the conditions, have acted better than they did. *Never think that I am belittling the old frontier in its day, when I question the desirability of its folkways in a world which can get a richer life from other folkways.* Indeed, I once explicitly suggested that the real old frontier had certain compensating adjustments which made it vastly more desirable than is a belated survival of its lawless psychology in a rapidly settling-down and industrialising region. I have never condemned violence *when it is necessary*. Indeed, I have often cited cases where I think it is both necessary and desirable. (the *old* Ku Klux Klan of 1866–9, for example) All that I object to is the needless and out-of-place violence to which persons of callous psychology resort when less wasteful methods would be infinitely better. There is a difference between the grim need which drives a cattle man to open fire on a band of armed thieves, and the simple wantonness and stunted sensibilities which make that man's arrogant son shoot and stab and punch promiscuously around the village streets in the course of disputes which were frivolous to begin with, and which could easily be settled peaceably by the exercise of a little ordinary sense. The former case is of the justifiable violence of the real frontier; the latter represents the wholly reprehensible hangover of the psychology of violence in a milieu which no longer demands it. I respect the one, but feel amply justified in condemning the other.

Concerning the Texas of today—remember that I know nothing of it except from the information which you yourself have furnished. I told you that these glimpses were a vivid dramatic revelation to me, insomuch as I had never suspected how different conditions are from those of the east. All that I know of lawlessness in modern Texas is what you and the *Gladewater Journal* have reported—largely the high-handed acts of officers of the law, which are—in degree and frequency—absolutely unknown here. It was only in an effort (admittedly tentative in view of my limited data) to explain these singular brutalities that I suggested their origin in the residual violence-psychology of the frontier. That I might be all wrong, I freely conceded. All I was sure of, was that such things are *not* products of civilisation, since they are *least* known where civilisation is *most* settled. I note with great interest what you say of the swarming transients as a lawlessness-factor in Texas; and would not be surprised if this influence, rather than the frontier residue, were responsible for the unique tactics of the police. Incidentally, (as I said once before) I appreciate most thoroughly the tremendous valour and stamina of the early law-enforcement officers; who had so little aid at their disposal, and who faced such formidable opponents.

Your knowledge of some of the characters in the recent Urschel kidnapping episode is highly interesting. Incidentally, my young correspondent J. Vernon Shea of Pittsburgh has met Urschel himself—a ruddy, heavy-jowled man of quick intelligence—in the course of a business transaction which his father had with the now celebrated magnate. Urschel's family, as described by Shea, has had quite a colourful history. His brother-in-law got his start by marrying an Indian oil heiress—who with grim opportuneness was drowned shortly after the wedding while out in a canoe with the bridegroom. There was no open accusation or indictment—and the bereaved husband inherited the oil money and promptly married a white girl! Urschel was married to the man's sister, but later both brother and sister died, and now Urschel has marred the widowed second wife.

What you say of *change* as a permanent factor in Texas is extremely interesting. Certainly, no other region could produce quite such a record of vivid and powerfully contrasting pageantry. The rise and fall of towns must have had an especial element of drama, for bleak and deserted streets are hard to best for the sheer aura of desolation. It is easy to picture the effect of such a setting on an alert and sensitive mind growing up in its midst—and I doubt if you would ever find a less dynamic atmosphere fully satisfying. But I hope the law of change will not prevent your especial region from winning the settled agricultural prosperity at which it is now aiming.

Getting overseas—when I said that Germany is not typical of western civilisation I was not thereby attacking it, since there is no reason to consider western civilisation superior to the culture of China or ancient Egypt or perhaps other groups. I was merely stating a fact involving neither praise nor dispraise. If I said that Germany is *less civilised* than England (not merely less typical European), I was speaking too strongly; for I am certainly not one of those emotional thinkers who praise everything about their own group and condemn everything about others. As a matter of fact German culture is distinctly superior to English in many ways—I wish we could borrow points here and there. The German mind has a searching and systematic *thoroughness* probably unparalleled in the modern world, so that its scholarship in most fields is wholly unapproached. No one can get at basic facts and ultimate relationships like a German, and no one else has half the capacity for patient and accurate detail. In music, too, the Germans hopelessly outdistance us—so that no comparison is possible. They have a keen, adventurous spirit in aesthetics, so that they anticipate many modern developments—whether or not one likes the latter. In science they have never really lost the lead, though the United States is their strong rival there. Even in the practical application of science they are very hard to parallel in ingenuity. In education—until very recent times—no one else could come near them. Half the cultivated men in Providence whose college years fell in the '80's finished off at some German university. In short, just as I said during the war, when I'd have been glad to knock the whole bunch to hell, there is no sense in trying to picture German culture as other than absolutely first-class.

But the fact remains that German civilisation, high as it is, is not typical of the western world. It has an underlying adolescent or sentimental quality which stems from its tribal heritage instead of from the classical stream which touched virtually all the other western nations. It is probably a result of Germany's having never—except for the Rhineland strip—been part of the Roman Empire. All nations which spring from Rome have a balance and adulthood obtainable nowhere else. We nearly lost it through the Saxonisation of Roman Britain, but the Norman conquest brought it back to us at second or third hand. France has more of this quality than we—which is perfectly natural considering her closer connexion with Rome. What we have inherited so especially is only one side of the Roman culture—the sense of political order. It is not a matter of egotism and biassed perspective to say that we have this quality developed to a maximum, because we know that other races have other qualities more highly developed. Germany excels us in intellect, France in general taste, Italy in artistic capacity, China and Japan in decorative taste, Russia (pre-war) in literary depth, and so on. Political genius simply happens to be our strong point (that and *poetic feeling* are the two great English qualities), and Frenchmen and other foreigners admit it as freely as we assert it. Germany's lack of equal maturity in this field argues no general inferiority. If we beat her there, she beats us in scholarship, historical research, music, and dozens of other fields. Germany's difference from the western world proper is shown in subtle little ways—in naive psychological appraisals, heavy-handed state policies, odd misconceptions of the really western nations, and a tribally Teutonic attitude toward war. One has only to look at the Nazis' uncivilised extremes—the destruction of books, the attempted suppression of scientific truths distasteful to the government, and the naive ethnology of the Jew-baiting circus—to realise that performances like this could never occur in the western world. It isn't that only England and America wouldn't stage such a thing. France, Italy (even with Mussolini's strongest extremes), Spain, Holland—none of these countries could even imagine such a negation of the liberal thought which means civilisation. Even Austria, part of the original German fabric, will be very slow in falling into line—for Austria has been extensively westernised. Both pre-war Kaiserism and present Nazism display something entirely non-western.

However—it remains to be seen whether these peculiar differences represent unmitigated evils. It may be that they are attributes of a genuine cultural youthfulness involving a stamina and resilience we have lost. Time will tell. Germany's culture is too deep to be permanently hurt by Hitlerian restrictions, and I for one will forgive Der Schön Adolf much—even that moustache—if he can act as a focus for national feeling and help to stave off a collapse into communism.

All this ought to shew you that I had no intention of calling the long-settled Anglo-Saxon domains the only civilised regions. What I said or meant to say was simply that these regions have most maturely developed the *political* side of civilisation . . . . only one of many sides, of course. The great accomplishment of the Anglo-Saxon when he has a chance to settle down is that he can manage his affairs without shouting and stabbing and shooting and knocking people over the head. He is adult in the art of self-management. But of course, in other arts the Frenchman or the Dutchman is more adult than he. For example—we are congenitally unable, as a group, the face the real facts of human motivations. We pompously drape everything in a cloak of moralistic hypocrisy, so that when we steal Indian lands, it's always 'for the savage's own good', when we snatch half of Mexico it's to 'free it from oppression', etc. Our unwillingness to recognise the stark unmoral forces of the universe as they are proves us children in an important phase of life—just as the Germans are children in another phase. It's all 50–50—no one culture-group in all Aryandom is really superior to another when all the points are reckoned, and we can't afford to look down on the Chinese or Japanese, either. What makes some nations more prosperous or successful than others is largely the circumstance that their special aptitudes chance to be of a practical instead of abstract or imaginative sort.

Incidentally—I didn't mean to say that all radio programmes are 100% trash, any more than that all newspapers are. I know that many excellent features are sandwiched in amongst the hokum—available to anyone with patience to search them out, and with a machine powerful enough to command a good variety of stations. You've certainly had excellent luck in locating substantial features.

Reverting to the civilisation-barbarism question—nobody wishes to minimise the sufferings of certain small minorities in the various civilised nations; but the fact remains that these most assuredly do not suffer any more than they did under barbarism's crushing conditions, while it is also true that the *proportion* of those who suffer is infinitely *less* than under barbarism. In barbaric and mediaeval times the weak were crushed without mercy, and subjected to indignities unthinkable in the civilised world of today. The advance of civilisation is all clear gain for them, except during the transitional periods when new methods temporarily disturb the economic equilibrium. As civilisation has advanced, the lot of the weak and lowly has steadily improved. The oppressions of mediaeval times, and the utterly inhuman tortures and punishments (branding, ear-cropping, etc. etc.) which persisted even up to the 19th century are only memories now—so obsolete that the slightest attempts at partial revival excites instant notice and loud protest. Prison conditions are so much better than in the past that comparison is absurd, and now even the age-old economic burden is about to be attacked. Civilisation alone will be able to effect the artificial apportionment of labour, and the system of doles and pensions, which for the first time in history will give the weak a measure of comfort and security. Pennsylvania miners and Connecticut sweatshop workers may have their hour of suffering (less than was their habitual lot under barbarism) *now,* but before long civilisation will give them a peace they never had before. And if it's too slow in coming, the millions dispossessed by the present laissez-faire-plus-mechanisation tangle will help them seize it by force. Don't forget that *only civilisation, with its mechanical quantity-production, makes any such step toward the equalisation of resources possible.* In the agricultural-handicraft society of the past, or the pastoral-nomadic society of barbarism, *there is no possible way of producing resources enough to care for everybody's comfort.* In order to give even a few strong leaders an adequate life with ample resources, vast multitudes have to be crushed into submission and worked like oxen. Any attempt at equalisation of resources *would allot so little to any one person, that the misery of the poor would remain unabated, whilst the rich would simply be dragged down to the common level of complete misery.* In practice, a new group of the strong would of course establish a fresh corner on resources and rise on the shoulders of the oppressed multitude. The only thing which offers any promise of escape from this frankly and openly oppressive system is the institution of *quantity production* which civilisation and machinery have brought. At last—*for the first time in history*—it will be possible to let every single inhabitant of an industrial nation have a decent share of the collective resources without reducing everybody to uniform destitution. The almost limitless multiplication of resources due to civilised technology is what will make this a workable reality. Meanwhile remember that the number who acutely suffer at present is very small—and that until the existing crisis it was vastly smaller still. Contrast this minute minority with the vast hordes acutely oppressed under more primitive systems!

As for the matter of the integrity of the physical body—there is no comparison between the accidental injuries (carefully guarded against, and given the benefit of solicitous medical treatment) of industry or the very few additional diseases of civilisation, and the wanton, callous butchery of barbarism. The psychological element alone creates an impassable gulf. Today violations of physique are uniformly regarded as calamitous, and given every conceivable safeguard and remedy. Among barbarians, life and limb were held in no respect whatever. War, of course, is common to both civilisation and barbarism—yet despite the greater ravages of modern weapons, civilisation works so hard to reclaim the victims that its score is undoubtedly higher. And as for diseases—*all the advantage is on civilisation's side.* For every person stricken with a new disease in civilisation, thousands in barbarism suffered and died like flies from old diseases which civilisation largely holds in check. In our own lifetimes we have seen cholera, typhus, and yellow fever wane almost to zero in the regions touched by civilisation. Barbarism is a welter of death, crippling, and suffering. Only a little while before the settlement of New England a plague had swept away nearly ¾ of the Algonquin Indian population—nor are the annals of any barbaric group essentially different. I don't think that the physical flourishing of a race's surviving members can give much of a key to the sufferings of its weaker members. When a race leads a hard life in an environment not essentially unfavourable—that is, when the hardship comes from mode of life alone and not from any crushing outside handicap of milieu—the tendency is for the weak to suffer and perish, but for the strong to flourish. Eventually, of course, the predominance of the strong will cause strong types to be more frequently reproduced—but this racial improvement is achieved at a high cost. It is when a race meets an environment utterly adverse to all life that it becomes stunted as a whole.

But the main point, of course, is the fragmentary, impoverished mental and imaginative life of the barbarian—a circumstance which causes ¾ of his personality to go to waste and remain undeveloped. In this connexion don't get the idea that I'm referring merely to the specific exercise of the arts. I'm referring to the whole complex field of cerebral awareness, exercise, and gratification. The barbarian trains only a few of the cells he possesses—even when he exercises arts of a rude, simple kind. No matter how great his innate capacity, he remains relatively imprisoned in a narrow dungeon of simple impressions, with no key to the richer, more thrilling experience of wide intellectual and imaginative contacts with the world in which he moves. He is losing the better part of life and gaining virtually nothing in exchange. That is why I doubt if any exaltation of barbarism—despite all the Rousseaus and Monboddos—can ever really stand the test of common sense, enlightened opinion, and a realistic sense of proportion.

By the way—in one place you speak of *human sacrifices* among the Romans. This can hardly be called accurate except in theory. The only Roman rite in historic times which called for human offerings was that of Jupiter Latiaris, and in dealing with this a policy of evasion was always followed. If an actual killing was made, the victim was *invariably* a criminal sentenced to death, so that the "sacrifice" meant only a special time and place for a legal execution scheduled in any case. If the chosen "victim" was not a criminal, his "escape" was invariably arranged for. The nearest other Roman approach to a religious killing was of course the case of the priest of Diana of the

Grove at Aricia, who was always a runaway slave who had challenged and slain his predecessor in single combat, and who was in turn subject to death challenges from any other runaway slave who aspired to supplant him. As Macaulay puts it—

> The priest who slew the slayer,
> And shall himself be slain.[11]

The pseudo-sacrifices to Jupiter Latiaris ended with the establishment of the empire, though the priestly combats at Aricia (which were really in no sense sacrifices) lasted till the triumph of Christianity.

What you say of the Germanic tribes is of extreme interest. I myself don't think that their triumph was a calamity, since the empire was obviously going to seed in a melancholy way. The old race-stock in Italy was wholly mongrelised and rotten, though one regrets the change in Roman Gaul, where the last phase of classical civilisation had attained a very substantial if not brilliant flowering. What I really wish is that the Germans should have filtered in more slowly and regenerated the race stock without breaking the continuity of the ancient civilisation. Of course a vast number had done so before the final invasions—but one could hardly expect complete absorption when the number and importance of the invaders became so great. The fall of the *civilisation* (not the *empire* or any of its races) was the real calamity—though this might have occurred without the barbarians. To think of the decay and darkness and ignorance of all the dreary centuries between 400 or 500 and the stirrings of the Renaissance is a melancholy process. Life held comparatively little of value in those narrow, superstitious, squalid days, though of course there were certain vague stirrings and a few special oases in the universal night. However, the Saracens were without question the foremost civilised people from the 8th to the 12th century. In the 12th century—the age of the Gothic cathedral—the darkness becomes less dense. As for the conquest of Britain—modern historians and ethnologists, led by Sir Arthur Keith and Arthur Weigall, tend to think that the Roman-Cymric extirpation was more cultural than physical, so that the modern Englishman has far more of the Briton in him than has usually been supposed.

Turning to the present—you ask why this age is not more fruitful in creative genius, if a settled civilisation tends to promote the flowering of the human spirit. Well—the answer is really threefold. First—this age is one of singular transition, hence is scarcely settled in a psychological sense. The last really settled period—when standards and prospects were definite—was the Victorian age. Everything is uncertain now—standards, beliefs, economics, and even the future of the social order—hence despite material developments there is really a half-barbaric unrest in the air. Second—an unusually large share of contemporary brains has gone into science instead of aesthetics. This really is a remarkably active period in scientific history—many different branches of knowledge having been almost revolutionised since 1900, and our whole perspective on the structure of space and the workings of our own minds having been spectacularly altered. Third—the need of readjusting aesthetics to bring art and literature into touch with our wholly new concepts of life and human motives has forced the last 20 years to be gropingly experimental rather than confidently constructive. It is almost superfluous to point out that our whole sense of values and our whole feeling of relationship to the universe has altered utterly since the decline of genuine belief in religion, so that many of the emotional appeals of former times are no longer effective or significant. And what is more, modern psychology has completely changed our attitude toward our own motives, revealing to us the utter falsity of many of our old assumptions regarding the nature of human feelings and the basic reasons behind various manifestations of human conduct. We can no longer write of emotions and motives in the old way, as simple conscious things; for we now realise their utter complexity and their dependence upon hidden, unconscious factors. All our human valuations have been subtly changed, so that art founded on the old assumptions would seem childish and comic. This means that artists must for a long while do very little more than feel around in the dark for fresh approaches to the task of expression. They must find out through trial and error what sort of expression can reach our genuine emotions and ring true in light of what we now know about ourselves and about the cosmos. And that is exactly what most of the younger artists are doing. Naturally, their experimental results can hardly be of value as yet. Meanwhile the pallid echoes of older artists working in the dying tradition seem faint and unconvincing because the world of thoughts and feelings which bred that tradition has passed away. Certainly, this is a trying and unsatisfying age to live in!

As to the reason why a vigorous mental life could flourish amidst the violence and insecurities of mediaeval Florence and Elizabethan London—one may reply that it takes a lot to kill off a really powerful urge toward cerebration. Actually, violence is not necessarily fatal to mental effort in any supreme degree. The reason that barbarians have so little cerebral life is not, directly, because they use violence. Rather may we say merely that the conditions which breed violence tend also to breed ignorance and callousness. But this is not always the case. The causes of social habits are complex, and no fabric is ever uniform. Just as I said in comparing different European cultures, the strong points of various groups differ. A nation can have a high degree of civilisedness in one direction—such as mental or artistic effort—and a defective civilisation in another direction, such as government or public order. That is the irregular way mankind is made up. The old mediaeval cultures were tremendously uneven as they pulled out of the Dark Ages; combining a never-quite-killed thread of distorted mental and artistic tradition transmitted from classical times by the church, and an utter callousness in matters of social order bequeathed by the barbaric tradition of violence. When the cultural recovery began—first through the rediscovery of Greek thought as transmitted at second-hand by the Moors, and later through the influx of Byzantine scholars and scholarship from the crumbling Eastern Empire, it was perfectly natural that intellectual and artistic development should precede the social and political. For one thing, the new stimuli were all on the side of mental rather than political life. And for another thing, the standard of social and political order had never been as high as what we are accustomed to expect today. Even the Roman civilisation at its best had crude and weak spots which modern western civilisation has gradually ironed out. the flaming up of an irresistible intellectual and artistic revival which outstripped material civilisation was to be expected when the new influences struck western Europe, since the soil (so to speak) was ready for it. After all, there had never been a *complete* repudiation of mental ideals; so that the *mood* and *attitude* of learning was already in existence to build upon. When the revival was in full swing, there was nothing which could check it until the superstitious side of the race brought forward the piety of the Reformation, with its obscurantist accompaniments. Paradoxically, it is very probable that the intoxicating sense of freedom caused by the casting off of mediaeval shackles and the fuller flowering of the human spirit had for a time a directly *anti-social* effect on society. The individual was so delighted at the discovery of himself—so long hidden through ignorance and ecclesiasticism—that he forgot the existence of a social fabric and began kicking up his heels all along the line. This was the more natural because the Middle Ages had caused all his sense of order and obligation to be bound up with the now-weakened element of religion. However, as we have seen, the mental impulse was too strong to be checked or even seriously retarded by the adverse material environment. One great stimulus it had was the lure of the unknown—the sense of new and mysterious vistas—brought up by the opening of the Western Hemisphere. Intellectual excitement was everywhere—men were opening up and discovering so many long-dormant sides in their personalities that no single obstacle or defect could count.

As to the line between civilisation and barbarism—that is of course very ill-defined. Civilisation simply means *the ample development and utilisation of man's innate capacities,* and nobody can set up a narrow boundary line with unmistakable civilisation on one side and unmistakable barbarism on the other side. Human development is always uneven, as we have just noted. Many mainly undeveloped nations and groups have one or two phases of very high development, while many mainly well-developed groups have one or more crude spots. Thus groups which we must regard as "barbaric" often have certain *qualities* which we must regard as "civilised" or characteristic of civilisation, whilst groups which are clearly *civilised as a whole* frequently possess certain aspects which are obviously *barbaric,* or characteristic of barbarism. Classification of definite groups is primarily a matter of practical convenience in forming quick estimates, and there are many borderline cases where nothing but custom determines common usage. Ordinarily we seem to take steady agriculture and city-building as a kind of convenient trade-mark of civilisation; so that we call the mediaeval Europeans civilised but depressed, call the tribal Gauls and Teutons barbaric but advanced. How accurate this is, we can hardly say—but the nomenclature does not matter if we keep the actual facts independently in mind. As for the American west—of course no one seriously tries to classify it as other than a part of the Anglo-Saxon civilisation. Even in its wildest days, it was simply a fringe of civilisation with a high percentage of atavistic barbaric attributes called forth by necessity. Today, with its educational system, regional culture, orderly cities, and coherent economic life, it is as civilised as any typical European nation according to the average of the last thousand years. We do not call it a "barbaric region" merely because a few decreasing attitudes of somewhat barbaric cast (disregard of life and limb, indifference to order, etc.) may or may not faintly remain in its remoter reaches as a residue of its emergency period.

Your summary forms an admirable key to your views, and I appreciate the coherent fabric of belief which it reflects. It points out the root of many of our divergences of standards and opinions. Obviously, the main cleavage is your refusal to accept the basic standard of human development—the joint condition of complex and sensitive cell-structure and utilisation of that structure in enlarging and intensifying contact-points with the external world—which I regard as self-evident and automatically valid through the instinctive recognition of mankind. You consider an acceptance of that standard a 'laying down of arbitrary rules as to what things are and are not of value'; whereas I consider such an acceptance *a mere heeding of a natural fact*—a mere observation of an inevitable and existing condition. I have explained at some length *why* I consider the matter as I do, so that you can scarcely accuse me of unreasoning arbitrariness in intention. My position can be summed up by a concrete illustration—the difference in intrinsic quality between the pleasure of sucking one's thumb and the pleasure of discovering an important scientific principle. You claim that no one "has a right" to call thumb-sucking any "lower", intrinsically, than advanced scientific discovery—but I believe that an actual and quasi-absolute qualitative distinction exists in nature. Corresponding cases might involve the contrast of playing in a sand-pile with the absorption of imaginative impressions from the Odyssey; or the contrast of reading *True Confessions* with the formulation of a system of equitable government. I believe that the facts of nature make it foolish for us to try to dodge a recognition of *intrinsic quality* in human moods and activities—and I think I have adduced enough data to shew that my belief is at least neither hasty nor capricious. Remember, of course, that I do not deny the parallel importance of those practical and moral qualities which you choose for exaltation—

strength, courage, honesty, etc. I merely point out that, apart from all ethical or utilitarian phases, there certainly does exist such a thing as intrinsic quality (based on advancedness of structure, and on the full development and exercise of that structure—two separate factors) in human thought, feeling, and expression. I believe the importance of this point justifies the detailed attention given to it earlier in this letter.

Of course, I do not advocate any *compulsion* toward higher and away from lower life-levels, except where the actual retardation of the race is involved. I believe in letting every person seek, so far as practicable, that milieu and set of moods and activities best adapted to his tastes and capacities. I merely insist that a qualitative classification is possible.

As a final observation—you err if you think I classified *art* as any higher than *pure intellection* . . . . or *I* erred if I inadvertently gave that impression. Also—it is a mistake to fancy that I underrate the intrinsic intelligence of certain types who do not achieve visible results. I *tried* to make it clear that what I mean by *civilisation* or *personal development* is not a matter of any *biological* improvement, but simply a FULLER UTILISATION of the capacities already in the brain. *Of course* vast numbers of biologically superior men live out their lives on a relatively low plane through lack of the development of what is in them. It is this *waste of human capacity* which I deplore. Conversely, many a man of only mediocre mind has been raised to levels of usefulness and fruitful enjoyment through the civilised and cultivated exploitation of the limited capacities he does possess. It is this *adequate utilisation of human capacity* which I exalt and recommend.

In comparing the net quality of individuals one must reckon *both* their innate biological endowment and the use to which they have put that endowment. Often two men of equal brain capacity will differ infinitely in *quality of personality;* since one will have let his mind lie fallow, attaining only a very limited number of sensitivenesses and points of contact with the world, whereas the other will have developed his sensitivenesses and contacts until his whole life is expanded—so that the net *activity* (as distinguished from *capacity*) of his brain is magnified a thousandfold, while his satisfying adjustment to—or grasp of—the facts, images, and phenomena of the universe soars out of all proportion to the chained ignorance and unrewarding darkness of the other man's rudimentary range. Thus with Michelangelo and Jefferson and James J. Corbett, all of whom you cite. Just how different or how nearly equal their brain-capacity was, we shall never know. It may very well be that nature gave them all a precisely equal endowment. What we *do* know is that, for one reason or another, Michelangelo and Jefferson developed an enormous number of their points of sensitiveness and achieved an enormously broad and significant contact with the world around them, while Corbett (unless he had thoughts and moods and activities of which he left no record) was content to let his faculties function with relative narrowness in certain simple channels, so that he never utilised as personality-nourishment the rich and varied fare on which the other two throve. The number and arrangement of images in Corbett's brain (however fine its *structure*) was meagre and simple as compared with the image-archives of Michelangelo's and Jefferson's brains; and his cerebral activity, if measured in energy-units, could not compare with that of either of the others. The external world he envisaged was a narrow, meaningless, uncorrelated, and unsatisfying one as compared with Michelangelo's and Jefferson's worlds. He lived with only part of his brain whereas they lived with all of theirs. And yet he may have been just as highly evolved a biological specimen as either of them. Incidentally—as a man of brilliancy and good sense in an ordinary way (which I believe he was), Corbett would probably have been the very last person to regard himself as *great,* or to compare his accomplishments with those of eminent scientists, scholars, soldiers, artists, or statesmen. A case of extremely high intelligence devoted to relatively trivial ends is afforded by the magician Houdini, for whom I did some revisory work in the two years preceding his death. He was content to let his mind and taste function intensively in a very narrow and trivial range; becoming a peerless showman yet remaining surprisingly crude and undeveloped in other fields. He was blind and unresponsive to enormous areas of life—yet when his mind attacked any given problem it was easy to observe its lightning speed, invariable accuracy, easy tenacity, and broad, sharp, effective correlating power. There was a case of waste for you—a first-rate intellect which might have given its possessor a rich glow of comprehension and achievement in science, scholarship, or philosophy . . . . yet wasted on a narrow, trifling field which gave no rewards beyond those mediocre, superficial ones of professional satisfaction and tawdry popular distinction which many a crude bullfighter or brainless cinema hero achieves.

Thanks extremely for the cuttings. The epic of Addron College surely attests the strength of Texas's impulse toward the upholding of civilisation! The Carmichael letter is very sensible—and the beating incident very grave if the police were really responsible. The Chicago false arrest must have been woefully embarrassing, though it was obviously a very non-typical mistake as judged by the ordinary conditions in settled cities. The article on public school boys in England surely contains some disheartening points if the indicated trend is really decided and universal. Of course, a decline in mere *mischief* may be due merely to the wider outlook and earlier maturity of modern boys; but the lack of honour, courage, and truthfulness is surely a serious and menacing condition which bodes ill for the future of our civilisation. I have seemed to see occasional parallel tendencies among members of the post-war generation, though I am always slow to generalise from sporadic phenomena. Trends may form only temporary reactions, or be confined to certain classes and localities. Still, it is very possible that the race is beginning to shew age and decadence.

As for the world's wholesale mechanisation—no one hates its cultural implications worse than I. It has destroyed traditional elements of adjustment and relationship which can never be replaced, and has definitely impoverished life by rendering many factors in the natural environment meaningless. Over against this is the fact that nothing but mechanical quantity production can ever create enough resources to make an equitable social apportionment possible. It is a pity that we cannot manage machinery instead of having it manage us. If we were more truly civilised—with a keener sense of values—we would undoubtedly try to restrict its use to the supplying of *genuine needs;* discouraging the introduction of standards which exalt meaningless material luxury, trivial mechanical devices without intellectual or imaginative value, and the empty elements of speed and quantity. But I fear we haven't enough sheer intelligence and taste to effect such a restriction. "Plain living and high thinking" is too exalted a standard for a confused and already somewhat tainted race.

I am finishing this tediously long epistle on Nov. 6. Hope I haven't bored you quite to death! At any rate, I'm sure you can see the total absence of any arrogant or offensive intent in my arguments.

I've told you on postcards how keenly I appreciate your recent tales, with their glimpses of elder worlds or obscure corners of history.

. . . .

Yrs most cordially and sincerely—

H P L

Notes

1. Outside Manton, Rhode Island.

2. Edward Lucas White (1866–1934), author of the weird collections *The Song of the Sirens* (1919) and *Lukundoo and Other Stories* (1927), achieved celebrity with a series of historical novels set in the ancient world, including *Andivius Hedulio* (1921) and *The Unwilling Vestal* (1918).

3. "Old Garfield's Heart."

4. *Naumkeag* is also an old name for what is now Salem, Massachusetts.

5. "Some Dutch Footprints in New England."

6. HPL refers to the philosophers Benedetto Croce, George Santayana, Robert Briffault, Karl Marx, and Havelock Ellis.

7. Edgar A. Guest (1881–1959), British-born American poet who published verse prolifically in newspapers and collected them in many books, but who was scorned by critics for superficiality and conventionality of thought and expression.

8. Willem de Sitter (1872–1934), Dutch mathematician and physicist; Algernon Charles Swinburne (1837–1909), British poet.

9. The National Recovery Administration, one of the earliest of Franklin D. Roosevelt's programs to alleviate unemployment. It attempted to stabilize prices and wages through cooperative action between business, labor, and government. It was declared unconstitutional by the Supreme Court in 1935 and officially dismantled on 1 January 1936.

10. HPL refers to a painting by Jean-François Millet (1814–1875) commonly referred to in English as "The Man with the Hoe." This served as the title for an immensely popular poem by American poet Edwin Markham (1852–1940), first published in 1899 and expressing sympathy for the manual laborer.

11. From Thomas Babbington Macaulay's "The Battle of the Lake Regillus" (*Lays of Ancient Rome*, 1842), ll. 175–76.

[90]   [TLS]

[3 November 1933]

Dear HPL:

Glad you liked the rattles. The owner got his head shot off by an acquaintance of mine, one Tom Lee,[1] on the upper reaches of the Jim Ned, the scene of several bloody Indian fights in the past. Knowing I was anxious to procure a good set of rattles to send to you, he saved them.

An even bigger snake was bagged by a friend of mine down in Brown County this fall, but the discharge of his shotgun blew the rattles all apart and destroyed some of them. They found fourteen, and there's no telling how many were destroyed. The snake, according to what I heard, was as thick as a man's arm. Talking of phobias—there was a fellow with my friends when they came onto the snake, and he was shaken so badly by the incident that he trembled like a leaf, and his teeth chattered for perhaps half an hour afterwards. I'll admit there's something unnerving about the slimy brutes. I'll never forget the time that I came clambering up out of a creek bed, reached up to pull myself up on the bank by a tree limb, and took hold of the tail of a water-moccasin which was sunning itself on the branch. They say you can't do but one thing at a time, but I did, or rather my various members acted simultaneously and independent of each other. My left hand released the snake, my right drew my knife, and my legs gave way and precipitated me down the bank.

I'm glad to hear your aunt is recovering nicely, and hope her complete recovery will be soon.

Thank you very much for the kind things you said about the yarns in *Magic Carpet*. "Alleys of Darkness" isn't much of a yarn, but I do like "The Shadow of the Vulture." I tried to follow history as closely as possible, though I did shift the actual date of Mikhal Oglu's death. He was not killed until a year or so later, on the occasion of a later invasion of Austria, in which the Akinji were trapped and destroyed by Paul Bakics. The incident of Suleyman's fete to celebrate his "victory" and his proclamation concerning his campaign is among the most curious episodes of history, which is often ironic.

We had our first cold spell yesterday—November 2. Up to then it had been clear and warm, though rather too dry. A rain accompanied the cold snap, which will help the grain a great deal. I always hate to see winter come. If it's warm, it's cloudy and rainy all the time, and if it's dry, it's cold as the devil, with dust storms and blizzards. I won't be able to make it south this winter.

I've read a copy of *Fantasy Fan,* and subscribed for a year. I enjoyed Smith's tale, and of course, I reread your "Supernatural Horror in Literature" and was glad to see the readers of weird fiction are going to have the opportunity of reading it. I treasure the magazine of Mr. Cook's in which it originally appeared, and re-read it from time to time, also for the purpose of quoting extracts to my various correspondents (giving full credit to the author, of course). I'm looking forward to seeing *Unusual Stories.* I let Crawford have a yarn called "The Garden of Fear." Hope he'll be able to build up the magazine into a permanent publication.

Cordially,

REH

Notes

1. Thomas D. Lee was an older brother of REH's good friends Dave and Dock Lee.

[91]   [TLS]

[mid-November 1933]

Dear HPL:

I am so submerged in work that I must postpone the answering in full of your extremely interesting letter, until I can give it the attention it deserves, but this is just a note to assure you that I did not mean to imply that I had ever taken offense at any of your remarks. I have had no reason to. I have never encountered the slightest trace of arrogance in any of your positions. If there has been any misunderstanding it has probably resulted from my slowness of perception and clumsiness of expression. All I ever asked of anyone in a debate is that he credit me with as much sincerity as himself; as you grant me that, there is no cause for resentment.

Thanks for the material, especially the picture of the house, which is the first picture of the sort I have ever seen. (First hand snap shot, I mean, of course; thanks to you I have quite a collection of post card views of New England architecture.) It is a most interesting example of architecture. The greatest difference I notice between it and the houses of this section is the doorway, and the absence of a porch. Of late years small porches or practically none, have been the fad in the Southwest but in this country a broad, deep porch is really necessary for coolness in the summer, shielding the interior of the building from the glare of the sun.

Thanks for the loan of De Halve Maen. Talman used to mail me a copy, but I didn't get it this time. I read the article you mentioned with much interest; it was news to me. I admire your extensive grasp on New England history, and the lucidity with which you expound it.

I'm enclosing a piece written in an idle moment which I thought you might find amusing.[1] No particular hurry about returning it. I don't expect to sell the thing, though if I'm ever able, I may include it in a book of sketches and try to find a publisher.

Cordially,
REH.

Notes

1. "The Beast from the Abyss."

[92]   [nonextant letter by HPL]

[93]   [TLS]

[3 December 1933]

Dear HPL:

Glad you found the cat article of some amusement. As I said, it was written in an idle hour, and with no intention of precipitating any philosophical argument. I merely recorded a few of my observations regarding felines—an animal for whose physical side I have a deep admiration, whatever my opinions of his moral aspects may be.

Your essay was read with great interest; it was clever and well-written, though it seems less a defense of cats themselves, than a glorification of people who idealize cats.[1] However I can not regard seriously any attempt to classify peoples' mentality by their like or dislike of cats, or dogs.

I also read your remarks in your letter with equal interest, particularly the battle-scenes. Don't let Mr. Osterberg's refusal to strike a prostrate foe fool you;[2] it wasn't chivalry on his part; it was merely recognition of his foe's strategy; he knew that to strike would be to lay himself open for the disembowelling stroke that is a feline's most dangerous weapon. Dropping on the ground and coming up inside the other's guard is a trick old as Thebes. As for their lack of scars, you won't find many cats wearing these tokens of battle. Not one cat in a hundred has the guts for a finish fight. I've seen a big rat run a fighting tom clean out of sight, and I've seen at least five hundred cat-fights in which not one drop of blood was spilt. There are exceptions; the big Persian I mentioned was one. But I never saw any cat display the high brand of sheer courage that I've seen dogs display repeatedly. And I've owned over a hundred cats in my time.

I have three cats at present—the article I sent you was months out of date—and a few others hang around: one of the latter a big yellow tom which I am sure is a son of the Persian. The most interesting one is a little devil I found starving in a post-oak grove and brought home. I found him the day before beer became legal in Texas,[3] so I named him Bebe, which stands for B.B. which in turn means, "Before Beer". When I found him he was so weak he could only take a few steps at a time, but I fed him up. He was funny looking: scrawny, bow-legged in front and knock-kneed behind, pigeon-breasted, with enormous green eyes and huge ears, and, after I had fed him, a pot belly. I never saw such a greedy devil in all my life. He seems to be perpetually ravenous; he's a good hunter and devours numbers of birds, mice and rabbits, but he never fails to greet me with a yell and a gaping mouth that seems to accuse me of skimping his feed. Even when he is scarcely able to walk from gorging he wears the same expression. He is still bow-legged and pot-bellied, but he's growing into the most powerfully built feline for his pounds and inches I ever saw. His breast is particularly broad, and his wide braced front legs gave him a stance I never saw in another cat. He is fairly intelligent, and as courageous as any cat is—which is seldom very much. If you could see him and his mates spitting, squalling, yelling, gorging and gluttonizing as they tear into the raw chicken guts given them I believe it would give you a new angle on feline grace, dignity and fastidiousness. As for beauty—nothing I ever saw in the shape of a cat could equal the sight of a big gray buffalo wolf floating across the road and clearing a high stone fence with the ease of a wind-blown tumbleweed one still dawn.

Thanks again for the chance to read the feline defence.

R E H

Notes

1. "Cats and Dogs."
2. The reference is to a cat whom HPL called Count Magnus Osterberg, putatively the Vice-President of the Kappa Alpha Tau fraternity. See letter 100 n. 9.
3. Sale of beer became legal in Texas at midnight, 14 September 1933.

[94]　　[nonextant letter by HPL]

1934

[circa January 1934]

Dear Mr. Lovecraft:

I enjoyed very much your account of your travels along the East Coast,[1] and am glad you were able to make the trips. As to our debate: it had not occurred to me that any expression of resentment I have made could be taken to be directed at yourself. When I expressed a dislike for certain individuals who have made themselves obnoxious in the smooth-paper publications and elsewhere, I thought it was clear whom I meant.

As for values, I have finally recognized what you have [been] driving at for some time, in your objections to most of my positions. You say I "refuse to accept the basic standards of human development". That is hardly correct. It would be more appropriate to say that I have questioned some of your conclusions as to what constitutes the criterion of human development. You apparently feel that I have, in disagreeing with some of your ideas, denied the whole system of human valuation; that I lump everything into a chaotic jumble, in which there is neither superiority or inferiority. That clears up matters quite a good deal. I had not realized the trend of your arguments, simply because it did not occur to me that my position could be interpreted as you have interpreted it. I must be infinitely clumsier in expression than I had thought, even. However, because I question the correctness of some of your conceptions of the universe, it does not necessarily follow that I deny the existence of the universe. In the first place, considering it from a cosmic sense (and if I am not mistaken it was you who first brought up that consideration, in asserting that something I valued had no cosmic significance) considering the cosmos as a whole, I am convinced that things *are* a meaningless jumble, that a caterpillar is as important as a man, that a baboon is as significant as an artist, and that it means absolutely nothing to the universe whether a man is an imbecile or a genius.

Yet at the same time I recognize the vital importance of a scale of values in so far as human affairs are concerned, in the relationship of the human to other humans. The idea that I repudiate such valuation is so radical, so utterly fantastic, that I did not for a long time recognize it as such. As far as human preference goes, my every action reflects my recognition of such a scale. Yet it certainly isn't a simple scale. It has occurred to me that probably you got your idea of my "repudiation of values" from my remarks about "superior" individuals. Well, I never denied the superiority of some types of men. I was merely questioning what I *thought* was your conception of a superior man. I felt that you narrowed the field of superiority too greatly. In a word, it seemed to me that you considered as inferior all types of men not definitely identified with the esthetic-artistic occupations—I mean the formal expres-

694   ❦   *A Means to Freedom*

sions of the arts. It seemed to me that by "high development" you meant participation in the arts, and that your "superior" man was simply a formal artist. It was—and is—my conviction that a man can be a superior type of human without having any formal knowledge of literature, sculpturing, music or painting. I said, it is true, that I did not believe that art, even judged by human valuations, was any higher than some other things. Yet in your recent letter you yourself say that you consider science, statesmanship, and other intellectual activities of an equality with art. Well, naturally I did not suppose that, when I said I thought there were other human activities on a level with art, I did not, I say, suppose that it would be concluded that I was referring to the making of mud pies or the twiddling of one's thumbs. I did not specify science, statesmanship and the like because I thought the matter was obvious. When I said there was as much room for the exercise of the intelligence on a farm as there is in a studio, I was not depreciating the studio, I was merely replying to what I felt was a tendency on your part to underestimate the intelligence required by non-intellectual pursuits. No doubt my statement seems to you utterly fantastic and radical; but if you were to visit an extensive farm, scientifically managed by a student of agriculture, you would realize the truth of my remark. It is not that I have ever denied that art is one of the superior pursuits; I simply demand the recognition of the high development of other types of endeavors and individuals. You have said that it is impossible for an inferior man to be a poet, a great novelist or a great painter. It is equally impossible for an inferior man to be a great physician, engineer, general, statesman, agriculturist or football coach. If we disagree, it is not over the fact of human superiority, but over just what constitutes that superiority. If by artist, one means a man who has attained the highest development possible in his particular line, whatever it may be, then undoubtedly an artist is the highest type of man. But if by artist one means merely a person recognized as a pursuer of the formal arts (literature, painting, sculpturing, etc.) then I deny that it necessarily follows that he represents the ultimate peak of development. He *may*, but it is not a certitude that he *does*. I believe that there are doctors, lawyers, judges, farmers, athletes, business men, soldiers who are superior to many formal artists, in that they are scientists or artists in their own lines. Nor do I believe that a really great artist is necessarily any greater than a great statesman, a great economist, etc. But isn't that much what you said, in your recent letter? You have said that art is "merely one of the several manifestations of the highest state of development." Well, isn't that just about what I've been saying? I've intended to convey that idea, at least. It seems to me that your whole assumption of my position as a repudiator of human values is based on my refusal to exalt art above everything else in the universe. Yet, since you yourself place certain other things on an equal level with art, that argument is scarcely valid.

Returning for an instant to superiority, I am surprized to note that you do not judge individuals by formal standards of superiority. I had supposed that you judged them by no other standard. I am sorry if I misunderstood your position, but at least I had some reason for the supposition. Throughout our debates the very first objection you generally voiced to anything with which you disagreed was that it was of an inferior type, and you seemed to find it objectionable when I remarked that I was guided by my likes and dislikes rather than by considerations of superiority or inferiority.

As for my supposed idealization of morals (which I certainly do not "blindly" accept as "divine", realizing they are merely human conceptions without weight in the cosmos at large), this idea is as baseless as was the assumption that I worshipped physical strength as a supreme value. If I have placed a good deal of emphasis on the moral code of the frontier, it was not because I have any over-inflated feeling toward these morals, but it was simply in answer to some of your former arguments. You seemed to take the attitude that only in a super-civilized, long-settled section was a high standard of morals possible. In our previous arguments about civilization, you used these very things as an argument in favor of your conception of civilization. There was nothing said then about there being any possibility of over-valuing honor, honesty, courage, social-balance and integrity. But when I had proved beyond the shadow of contradiction that these characteristics existed on the frontier of yesterday and in the West of today as highly developed—and in some instances more highly developed—as in long settled sections, you attacked me for "idealization" of such characteristics! I narrated instances of these characteristics not because I over-valued them but simply because you seemed to assume that they were the exclusive properties of the long settled districts. It was yourself who first brought up the question of morals, ethics, or whatever they call them, by implying that only in such environments as England and the East Coast can they exist. As a matter of fact, I do place a high value upon these characteristics, because without them life would be unbearable, and in many cases impossible. Theoretically I do not value them above sheer intellectuality, but in actual every-day practice I do, and so do you, and every other normal minded man. It is easy to put this to a test: simply go down on the street, select a stranger at random, and tell him first he is neither a scholar, an artist or an intellectual; then tell him he's a liar, a thief and a coward. See if you don't notice a slight difference in his reactions. Or to put it another way: if you had to choose between two men for a business associate and daily companion, and one was a thief, an embezzler, a wife-stealer, a liar, and a swindler, although a man of high intellectual accomplishments, and the other was a man of ordinary intelligence, but a man of high integrity and honor, which would you choose to work with? The fact that the world as a whole recognizes something of the sort is shown by the fact that it is not a crime not to be an intellectual, but that men are sent to the pen for stealing horses and burning houses. I never suffered from any man's lack of artistic appreciation, but I have suffered from men's lack of honesty and the recognition of obligation. I prefer to associate with honest men, even if they lack intellectuality in its formal sense, than to associate with a thief, a liar and a rogue, even if he were the finest poet or artist in the world. I may recognize his merit, but I don't want to give him a chance to skin me. If the practical application of this is idealization, then every intelligent man in the world is an "idealist."

Concerning the lower animals, I have no doubt that, as you say, my observations could be refuted by scientific theory. Any statement can be so refuted. I have, it is true, noticed shadows of almost human depravity in animals—treachery, greed, cowardice, perversions—but I never saw an animal whose whole life was devoted to these things. And I never saw any bestial trait that was not possessed in greater volume by humanity. You say I say that animals are "superior" because "in my opinion" they are more "honest." I didn't say, or mean to say, that. I merely said that animals possess all the characteristics of courage, kindliness, and honesty that we are taught are the exclusive possessions of the human race. And this can't be refuted by "scientific theory" because I'm speaking from first-hand observation. You assume that all crimes are animalistic, reflecting a human tinge only because of greater intelligence. But I've seen acts of cruelty and revolting brutality committed by humans transcending anything ever done by an animal, and at the same time requiring no more mentality than the animal would require to commit them. I'm not entirely devoid of experience with the so-called lower animals. I've spent all my life in the country and in small towns, among horses, cattle, hogs, dogs, cats and less domesticated beasts. And it is my judgment, borne upon me by experience and observation, that the average animal is a cleanly, decent, respectable and altogether worthy citizen compared to the average man, when judged by moral standards. This is possibly beside the point, as you mentioned. I probably brought it in in the first place because I thought your idea of a "superior man" was the conventional one—that a person highly developed in art and intellectuality was necessarily possessed of superiority in all other ways—that, for instance, the courage or integrity displayed by such a man is somehow of a higher type than the courage or integrity displayed by a man of less intellectual development. Anyway, if we are to accept the "purely human" as an absolute standard, why don't you exalt lepers and syphilitics? I understand they are purely human types.

Concerning governments: I have always been a staunch supporter of Roosevelt and his policies. To my mind, he is taking the only course by which the country can be saved from utter chaos. It is merely the action of lopping off a crushed limb, to keep it from destroying the whole body. Whether he can prop up a system rotten from its foundations is a question, but he deserves plenty of credit for trying.

Concerning freedom, there is no need to get a new slant on my conception of it—which is simply that there was more personal freedom on the frontier than there is in modern life. I thought it was obvious why I brought in the example of the five-hour writer and the sixteen-hour farm hand. I was simply replying to your sweeping statement that freedom is a myth. Complete liberty is, of course, impossible, but degrees of freedom exist, as I showed by the above example. I am quite aware that modern machinery is supposed to usher in an age of leisure—though I can assure you that that hilarious millennium has not yet quite arrived in this country, at least. To note in passing—tractors cut a farmer's work in half; well and good; but if he must raise twice or three times as much as he formerly did in order to make a bare living, where is the gain? That's what broke the farmers; doubling and tripling their production in order to meet the mounting prices of finished commodities, without getting any more for their raw products. The more they turned out, the less money they got, and the deeper into the mire of debt and bankruptcy they sank.

But I haven't presented a new angle of the question of human freedom. I have merely answered your statement that liberty was a myth. According to that way of looking at it, a man in prison for life is as well off as a man with an income which even frees him from the necessity of work. If freedom is a myth, and the desire for freedom merely an empty romantic whim, as you intimate, then I was a sap to quit picking cotton, jerking soda and smashing baggage to become a writer, because (according to your views) I was as free working from twelve to sixteen hours a day, seven days in the week at jobs I hated as I have been as a free lance writer. Never the less, whether you are right or not in dismissing my passion for freedom of mind and body as a romantic fallacy, the fact remains that I have enjoyed greater freedom as a writer than I did as a soda jerker, cotton picker, rod toter, counter-jumper, etc. This is a *fact* which no amount of philosophical theorizing can refute. I understand this position, of course, it is the popular conventional one; when a man makes an effort to get out of the day-laborer class and into a field even remotely connected with literature, he is supposed to say that he made the attempt because of a pure love of art burning like a holy fire in his bosom. If he had any other reason for changing his occupation and is honest enough to say so, he is immediately condemned by the votaries of art, and his motives depreciated. I have persevered in my endeavors to become a writer mainly because that profession offered me more freedom than I had working at other jobs. My reasons were akin to those that brought my ancestors to America from Ireland; that drove my great-great-grandfather from the hard life of a day laborer in New York to the ownership of his own plantation in Alabama; that drove my grandfather from carpet-bag ruled post-war Mississippi to the open lands of early Texas. An ideal that rules the lives of generations is no empty pose.

And just as I have struggled for a maximum amount of freedom in my own life, I look back with envy at the greater freedom known by my ancestors on the frontier. Hard work? Certainly they worked hard. But they were building something; making the most of opportunities; working for themselves, not merely cogs grinding in a soulless machine, as is the modern working man, whose life is a constant round of barren toil infinitely more monotonous and crushing than the toil on the frontier. He's not building anything. He's simply making a bare living. My grandfather Colonel Ervin, my great-grandfather Squire Jim Henry, and various other members of my family built up comfortable fortunes on the frontier, and they didn't work any harder than I'm working for a bare living; not as hard as many intelligent men are working today for crumbs. You say I idealize the frontier. It isn't idealization to state mere facts, however much at variance with the popular conceptions they may tend to be. In narrating the drawbacks of the frontier, you have completely lost sight of the most dominating thing of all—the opportunities the new country offered, the chances for a man building a career and a fortune. There was the real democracy. Poverty wasn't degrading. The man, not the dollar, was the measure of merit. Why shouldn't I look back on the frontier with envy? My people thrived there, most of them did well and were prominent men, they had a real place in the world. It wasn't until the country began to be "civilized" that they lost their wealth and their hold on events. When you demand that I prefer this age to that, you are demanding that I state a preference to a system in which I'm barely surviving, to one in which I would in all probability have amounted to something in life. I can understand your antipathy to anything approaching frontier conditions; but if you can feel that you would have fitted into the picture better in early Eighteenth Century England, there's no logical reason why I can't feel that I would have fitted better in middle Nineteenth Century America.

I am ready to admit that the workman in a modern city is probably freer, and certainly his working conditions are better than they were in that same city a generation or a century ago. But it's useless to compare the urban, industrial worker with the pioneer. As for my "complaints" as you call them—it never occurred to me to designate your criticisms of the frontier and the modern West as "complaints"; nor do I see any reason why my criticisms of modern life and systems should be so designated.

You seem to group my remarks concerning freedom with those you call "the idle intelligentsia." I see no reason for that. I am certainly not one of the intelligentsia, and no one who knows the amount of work I put out daily ever accuses me of being idle. Moderns seem prone to judge human freedom by radio and traffic lights. Invariably, when I have remarked to a city-dweller that I dislike the (to me) restrictions of city life, I am asked with some heat if I want to run through traffic lights and play the radio all night. I can only reply that I always try to comply with existing rules and regulations where ever I am. If I prefer to live in a region where such rules and regulations do not exist, because they are not necessary, I see no reason for resentment on the part of people who don't mind these things. You call my ideal of freedom "indiscriminate license and anti-social disorder." It occurs to me that perhaps you base that idea on my remark that I wished I had lived on the frontier. Perhaps you think that constitutes an admission that I would have enjoyed the life of an outlaw. But if I wanted to be an outlaw, I wouldn't have to yearn for the old West; I'd simply go to some super-civilized Eastern city and become a gangster. Don't you realize that the freedom of the West meant more than lack of restraint by law? It meant freedom from crushing taxes, from crowds, the hurry and rush of urban life, from the monotony of the sweat-shop or the office, from never-varying routine, from snobbery and from being merely a cog in the machine. It meant a thousand things that apparently is beyond the comprehension of the modern urban dweller.

I don't get the drift of your assertion that my "idealization" as you insist on calling it, of the frontier, is based on a "moralistic" attitude. If moralist means one of these pious creatures that go around sticking their snouts into what's none of their business, I certainly can't qualify. If I'd ever had any prudishness in me, I'd have lost it in the oil boom towns. Anyway, this isn't very consistent with your conception of my "ideal of anti-social license." How can a man be a blue-nosed Puritan and a red-handed outlaw at the same time?

But if we are to judge freedom by radios and traffic lights, and if the desire to play a radio at unseemly hours perturbs the super-civilized, I wonder how they'd fare in some of the oil boom towns I've been in, and lived in— with gambling joints, booze dens, dance halls and whore houses going full blast, the town wide open, dope peddlers on every corner, drunken roughnecks shooting craps on the side walks and brawling in the alleys, somebody getting stabbed or knocked in the head with monotonous regularity. I never lived in a boom town quite as wide open as that one in which whores walked down main street stark naked soliciting business, but I've seen nearly everything else that was raw and elemental. I can't say that a wide open boom town is my ideal of a place of residence, but I'd a damn sight rather live in one than in a place where, apparently, a man would be arrested for disturbing the peace if he burst into a lusty whistle.

Concerning the frontier again—I have never suggested that frontier methods be applied to modern problems. I have never expressed a wish that the frontier had continued in all its pristine aspects until the present day. I have merely expressed my personal admiration for it, my wish that I had lived then instead of now, and offered facts to show that conditions were not so awful as moderns appear to believe. As for what you call "six shooter justice" I can't remember ever having advocated anything of the sort for modern conditions.

I never denied that the pioneers built up the country as completely as possible. I merely pointed out that many of them kept moving on into new country. That was in reply to what you seemed to imply—that even to them a settled life was unqualifiedly superior to a frontier life. I didn't say they wanted the country to always remain frontier; yet the fact can not be denied that many of them, as soon as the country began to settle up around them moved on into fresh country. If, as you imply, there is not and never was any advantage the frontier possessed over the long settled portions, then why, in the name of common reason, did anybody ever go west in the first place? Why did they ever leave the land of milk and honey along the Atlantic coast?

As for violence it seems incongruous that you should conclude that I uphold the butchery and oppression of helpless people because I am a "moralist." I should think a moralist would be anything rather than an upholder of violence. Naturally you are justified in condemning the "arrogant son" (of the cattleman) who wants to "shoot and stab and punch promiscuously around the village streets," but I don't know where you got the idea that I was fond of such a character, or the idea that such a moron would be tolerated, much less condoned, anywhere in Texas. I've known plenty of bullies in my life, but the worst ones ordinarily had sense enough to stay in their own class; of course they are allowed more license in oil-boom towns than elsewhere, because men are too busy grabbing money to give a damn what goes on. But even there there's a limit. The dumbest, most ignorant and most offensive man of this type I ever knew seldom molested respectable citizens and when he did finally step over the line and try to assault a decent citizen, he got his brains blown out before he knew what was happening. I know, because I heard the shot that dropped him.

I'll admit that there seems to be more fighting in Texas than there is in the East. But whether *crime* is a result of a frontier tradition is at least doubtful. New England, I noticed not long ago, did not have a single hold-up or burglary in 1932; that's a fine record; but Idaho and Nevada made the same report, and they are even newer than Texas. Most of the so-called crime in Texas consists of killings among private citizens who are not to be classed criminals, despite hot-house conceptions of "law and order."

There are causes for feuds in the Southwest that obviously can not exist in the East. One thing that seems to puzzle Easterners is the number of fights and killings over fences in Texas. Why fight over a fence, when it is so easy to determine exactly where it should legally be placed. Well, there is a slight difference between building a stone wall around a three-acre field, and running the fence-lines around a fifty-thousand acre ranch. Early surveys were rather casual, and likely to admit of argument. Some deeds run back to Spanish land-grants, and often there is no way exactly to determine where one man's land ends and another's begins. Each man considers that he is right, and is determined not to be done out of a foot of what he considers his rightful property. This is not criminality—or if it is, then all our ancestors whom we admire for defending their home-land on this side of the Atlantic and the other, are criminals too. Again these men have a heritage of sturdy independence—doubtless a handicap in a super-civilization—but nevertheless a tradition from sires who defended their rights with their rifles because there was no other way to defend them. When it is evident that there is no legal way to decide the question, one man is likely to go move the fence back—perhaps not over a foot, certainly not an inch over what he considers the rightful boundary. The other man comes and moves it back. Then there is likely to be a killing; not because either man is at heart a criminal, but simply because each man believes he is right, and is ready to defend what he considers his own property. Another thing that Easterners seem to feel is terrible is the fact that men have been killed for leaving gates open. But if some of the men who so violently condemn these actions would have to ride for several days and nights gathering up several hundred head of half-wild cattle from the thickets, ridges, hollows, and river country, and then maybe lose a large number of them, they might feel slightly different about it. Especially after it had happened a dozen or so times, and was the result of deliberate malice.

It seems to me that, as a whole, the people of the long-settled regions are prone to condemn without proper investigation such actions and habits as are not common to their own sections. They seem to take it for granted that anything that indicates a criminal nature in their orderly society likewise constitutes criminality anywhere else. Instead of considering the matter with an open mind to discover just what motives, reasons, and traditional thought-habits lie behind these "crimes" they seem to take the position that the west is full of blood-thirsty devils who burn and slaughter for no other reason than mere brutal depravity. One reason travellers from the long-settled sections who used to carry back terrible tales of abuse and oppression ran into trouble is, and has been, the tendency of these people to look on western customs and habits as nonsensical and mere whims. Of course, most travellers in the West are sensible people. But there is a type of human who sees only nonsense in any custom or way of thinking that differs from the customs to which he is used. They would bitterly resent a Westerner coming to their country and trampling on any law or regulation; but they seem to think that they are privileged to violate any code of the West they wish, and when they get hurt, they set up an awful howl. Their excuse for their position is, that these customs are not necessary in their particular locality, therefore they represent mere whims that not only can, but should be trampled with disdain. They are motivated, of course, by a smug conviction of superiority; with the idea that anything different from what they have always been accustomed to, is wrong. And in the past some of these people have suffered from their arrogance. The average Westerner will take more off a stranger, especially a stranger from the East, than he will off an acquaintance or another Westerner. But there is always a limit to any man's patience.

I remember a number of cases in point. There was a big cattle magnate from Boston, back in the days when the beef corporations were crushing out the small independent ranchmen, who owned a big ranch up in the Panhandle. Billy the Kid and some of his boys, who had been stealing cattle in the Panhandle to sell to Old Man Coghlin of Tularosa,[2] stopped by this man's ranch and stayed several days, fraternizing with the cowboys and naturally eating with them. It was the custom in those days; hospitality was almost a sacred obligation; if a man stopped at your ranch, you made a place for him at your table without asking him who he was or where he was from. The West could never have been settled without this custom. The capitalist mentioned, whose name was Torrey,[3] was away at the time, and when he returned, Billy and the boys had ridden on to Tascosa. Hearing that his cook had been feeding them, Torrey went into a towering rage and gave orders that if they returned they were not to be given food or a bunk. The Kid heard of this, and when Torrey rode into Tascosa, caught him in front of a saloon, and asked him if he had given such orders. Torrey replied that he was not in the habit of harbouring outlaws. Thereupon Billy shoved his gun into Torrey's belly and told him if he had any last requests, to make them. Torrey, they say, bellowed like a cut yearling, begged for his life and invited the Kid to eat with him whenever he wished. Billy then laughed and put up his gun, for he never had any intention of shooting the fellow in the first place. Torrey was merely acting as it was probably proper to act in Boston; but because anything is proper in Boston, doesn't mean it's proper in Tascosa. Torrey refused to adapt himself to his environment—until he had to. Who was he to trample on a respected custom of the country? John Chisum was a bigger man than Torrey, and did infinitely more to bring law into the wild places than all Torrey's ilk; and he kept a great table set day and night for who ever might chance along. Sometimes a fleeing outlaw would eat breakfast there, and the posse chasing him would eat dinner at the same table. And if John Chisum respected the custom—indeed no other course ever occurred to John—then certainly Torrey was not much degraded by observing it to some extent.

As an aside, I want to say that generosity was a dominant characteristic of those days, and the men who lived in them. Even the most lawless and brutal of the cattle-barons of the old school showed a free-handed lavishness, as a rule, that reminds one of the generosity of certain ancient kings. In that respect they certainly differed from the breed of money-barons that later followed them. I've set and watched oil-field millionaires squabbling over pennies—I mean that literally—and reflected on the old-time cattle-barons and mining-kings and empire-builders who used to strew their paths with silver and gold dust, and give away whole town-sites, and feed whole villages, and the contrast often made me burst into sardonic laughter which would cause these glorified misers to stare at me. They had no more sense of humor than they had other than the entrails of a fish.

To return to what I was speaking of: it seems evident to me that when a man is travelling in a strange country, he should respect its customs, even if he disagrees with. If I ever travel in a long-settled section, I shall certainly endeavor to comply with its rules, even if I don't understand them. I'll suppose that the people living there knew enough about their own problems to formulate logical regulations. But some of the people coming West don't seem to think that at all, though there is less friction of late years, since more and more the whole nation tends to become standardized. Some of these people seem to feel that we ought to pass and enforce all the laws which govern the long settled sections, and some of which are wholly unnecessary in the West. About a year ago, for instance, a certain Florida judge in a tirade against lawlessness, demanded that the people be disarmed. That all guns be taken away from everybody not peace-officers. He did not limit his demands to his own section, or to the long-settled sections. He made a blanket-demand that all guns be taken from the people. Well, if that is done, the proper procedure should be to post placards all along the Mexican border in Texas, New Mexico and Arizona, something to this effect: "Notice to all Mexican outlaws, white renegades, murderers, bandits, and killers generally: you are cordially invited to visit the isolated ranches and border villages and there burn, kill, torture and rape to your hearts content, since the people have been disarmed and rendered helpless and have no means of defending themselves; with the compliments of a civilized judge who has never been out of calling distance from a policeman." Nor did this erudite gentleman attempt to say how ranchmen, farmers and sheep men were to defend their animals from wolves, bears and mountain lions—with theories of good government, I suppose.

Going up the Rio Grande valley a couple of years ago, I saw a car with a Kansas license stopped at a government inspection post, and a gunnysack of oranges taken from it. The people in the car seemed much disgruntled, and undoubtedly had some bitter things to say about fool Texas laws when they got home. But the law is a sound one, and prevents the spread of a certain destructive insect that preys on citrus fruits, and also sees that defective fruit is not taken out of the Valley and sold. If the Kansas people had merely had their oranges properly sacked, inspected, and tagged, they could have taken out all they wanted. I never had any oranges taken away from me. A law concerning oranges is scarcely necessary in Kansas; and likewise, there are doubtless laws peculiar to Kansas which are not needed in Texas. There used to be a law—may still be for all I know—which made it a penitentiary offense to carry a pair of pliers, or any kind of a wire-cutter in Texas. That sounds foolish, perhaps, but there was a good reason for that law. When the country began to be fenced up, there was so much wire-cutting that it caused several bloody feuds, and began to assume such proportions that even the lawmakers took notice. Of course, the law hasn't been enforced in many years, and if it's still on the statutes it's because they haven't bothered to erase it. And by the way, I just remembered one Kansas law, which, if enforced in Texas would be tough on the Mexican populations—the law against the eating of snakes. As a matter of fact, the long-settled portions always had a rather exaggerated idea of Western lawlessness, which accounts, probably, for the misfortune of a good many young fellows who thought when they hit the West they could rob, steal and shoot to their hearts' content. The odds were always against the outlaw, in the long run, except in those cases where the outlaw had the sympathy of an entire countryside because of his stand against some foreign oppressor, like the big Eastern and British cattle-trusts, or the carpetbaggers of an earlier date.

To return to my original theme, for another example of refusal to respect the customs of the country. When the factions of the bloody Lincoln County War came to an agreement, Billy the Kid drew up the terms of peace, and one of his men took the treaty to the leaders of the other faction for them to sign. When this had been done, they went into a saloon to celebrate the armistice, and were accompanied by a travelling salesman from some Eastern state. This man, for some reason, began abusing the Kid and his warriors as bloody outlaws. He was entitled to his opinion, of course, but he showed very little tact, as one of the men of the party was the warrior Billy had sent in with the treaty. This man objected to his remarks, and said (according to what I have heard these were his actual words): "You're not in a civilized country where you can say what you like without fighting." The drummer retorted that he had a right to criticize outlawry, anywhere. The next instant he was down on the floor with a bullet through his heart. In those days (and even now to a certain extent) in the West a man either conducted himself with almost formal politeness and courtesy, or he fought. There wasn't any half-way about it. He was allowed all the freedom of speech he desired, but he had to be ready to back up his words with his fists or his guns. A man didn't hand out insults unless he was willing and ready to fight it out. The drummer should either have kept his mouth shut, or he should have been ready to shoot. Apparently he wanted to air his views without suffering reprisals. He thought he ought to be allowed to say just what he thought. Good enough; but it ought to be remembered that in an atmosphere of such freedom as the West enjoyed, one man is as free as another. If one man is free to hand out verbal insults, the victim is free to retort with a knife or a sixshooter. I remember when the oil fields first came into being in this part of the state, and the farm boys and ranch hands began to turn to tool-dressing, there was considerable friction at first between them and the drillers and bosses from other sections. These men tried to curse the boys out, and were surprized when they found a knife in their ribs, or a rock splintered over their heads. They apparently were accustomed to cursing and abusing their employees, and it amazed them to find men that resented it. They learned their lesson, however. Things have changed somewhat, even in my time. When I was a kid in school, unless we were actually fighting, we were studiously polite to each other, and scrupulously observed various conventions of courtesy. Now I hear youngsters—and older men too—jawing heatedly with each other, and never a knife drawn nor a blow struck. Fighting isn't nice, but it's preferable to wordy wrangles.

Then there was the case of Lord Adair.[4] The Irish lord had made some big investments in the cattle business—beef was being exploited in Texas then as oil and farm products were later and the British companies were dipping their hands in the pot—and he and his wife were visiting the famous Goodnight ranch on the range of the South Paladuro. Goodnight was the nobleman's partner.[5] Goodnight and his waddies were out on the round-up and he sent Cape Willingham, one of his vaqueros, into the ranch for the mail. Willingham was a real man—later sheriff of thirteen Panhandle counties at once; and those are big counties. He was in my opinion the best sheriff Texas ever had, for he kept Tascosa from becoming another Dodge City, and maintained the maximum of order with the minimum amount of bloodshed; therein he differed from Wild Bill Hickok who never arrested a man if he had the slightest excuse for killing him. Cape came into the dining room of the big log ranch-house, dusty and sweaty from the branding-pens, with his bandanna and chaps on, and naturally Mrs. Goodnight set him a plate. At this Lord Adair, who was eating with his wife at the table, went into a fine British fury. He was not going to eat with hired hands, not he! Mrs. Goodnight answered with some surprize that she and her husband always ate with the punchers. But the Lord would not be pacified; he bellowed with outraged pride, and insisted on finishing his meal, with his wife, at another table. Naturally that didn't please Cape very much. As far as manhood went, he was so far above this monocled Irish monkey that there was no comparison. But I doubt if Cape thought of that. He was not conceited. But he had been insulted, and the men of that day didn't meekly swallow insults. A short time later the Goodnight men started the drive to Dodge City, and Lord Adair accompanied them. No, I'll take that back. Adair didn't go up the trail; I doubt if he could have stood the grind, even in a wagon. He merely went to the camp where the steers were being held after the round-up. It started raining and a blizzard began to blow, and along about one o'clock one morning Cape Willingham came in from his night-herd guard, and saw the tipi under which his Lordship was snoozing. He piled his lariat over the top of the tent and dashed off into the night with it. The next thing was Lord Adair scudding for the mess-wagon in his night-shirt through the sleet and freezing wind, screeching like a locomotive. They say he exhibited hysteria and seemed extremely upset. He demanded that Willingham be fired (the usual vengeance of his type) and probably was pacified somewhat when he saw Goodnight pay Cape off, and Cape head for Tascosa. He didn't know that Cape was being given a vacation with pay. Lady Adair had more sense than her husband; she survived him by many years, becoming known as the Cow Queen of the Panhandle, and was respected and liked by everyone. She wasn't a snob like he was, and thought it not beneath her dignity to eat with the men who worked for her.

Of course, this rule works both ways. Men have been killed in the country in which they were born and raised, because they either could not or would not change their ways and adapt themselves to changing conditions. Sheriff Bill Tilghman met his death in that manner.[6] He was the best law officer Oklahoma and Kansas ever had, to my mind. He killed only as a last resort. It was he who captured the famous Bill Doolin; and the outlaw admired him so much that he once prevented one of his men (Red Buck, or Weightman, a cold-blooded murderer) from shooting Tilghman in the back, when they had the drop on him. In 1924, when Tilghman was an old man, he accepted the job of marshal in an oil-boom town in Oklahoma, though warned by his friends that he was up against a brand of criminal he did not understand—the modern gangster rat. There was a Federal prohibition enforcement agent drunk and raising hell up and down the streets, and Tilghman, after urging him to go away quietly, arrested him bare-handed; and then, after disarming him, made the mistake of turning his back on him; the Federal officer, having gotten his training in civilization, drew another gun he had concealed, and shot Tilghman in the back. I often think of that contrast: Doolin, the outlaw, the bandit, robber, and killer, striking down Red Buck's rifle, and exclaiming: "Would you shoot a brave man in the *back?*" And the civilized officer, himself sworn to uphold the law, shooting down an old man from behind with no more warning than a copperhead.

You mention "inefficiency in achieving goals" as an objection to frontier life. Undoubtedly the people of the new countries made mistakes, and blunders. But don't people of the long settled sections ever make mistakes either? Do they always meet every problem that comes up with a perfectly rational and ideal solution? Or do they have to grope a little, sometimes, and experiment, just as the old pioneers did? It would clarify matters if you would give me some definite cases where the pioneers could have solved problems more rationally than they did.

As a starter, I'll cite a few cases myself for your solution. And remember these were actual human episodes, not philosophical questions to be debated calmly in a quiet study, with groceries and libraries and banks and policemen within call; they were questions of life and death, fought out under the naked sun, in the dust and the glare of the open lands, with sweat and muscle-ache, and perhaps blood. Here is a thing that cost lives in the old days often enough: two herds, being driven toward distant ranges or markets, meet at a muddy water-hole in the midst of the parched wilderness. A drouth has endured for months, turning the whole country into a barren inferno under a molten sky. For days the steers of both herds have staggered through that hell. They are mad for water; all night they have lowed and bellowed piteously, pushed on in a desperate effort to find a creek or spring. Now they have found it, but both herds have arrived simultaneously. There is enough for one herd, not enough for both. It is far to the next water. The herd that drinks will reach the next hole and survive. The other herd will leave its bones on the plains. Each herd represents the total fortune of its owner. Owners and cowboys have toiled and labored gigantically through heat and snow and sand storm and driving sleet. The boys have not been paid for months; they will be paid only when, and if, the steers are sold at the market for which they are headed. One herd must perish and its destruction means bankruptcy for its owner, and means that the boys have worked for nothing. How would you solve that problem? I'll give you another. Again a drouth is on. It is the day of the open range, but a ranchman has built his house near a spring. In order to preserve that water, and keep his steers alive through the long months of drouth, he fences that spring. That saves his steers, but dooms the steers of his neighbors. He defends his fence with his rifle, they fight to cut it and save their own stock. How would you solve that problem? Here is another that was the beginning of many a range feud: two cowboys, riding the open range on the round-up for neighboring ranches, come upon an unbranded calf. There is no way of identifying it, but each is convinced that it belongs to the herd of his employer. Here a principle is involved, just as in the case of the fence I mentioned earlier in the letter. The calf, as a piece of property, matters little. Either would give it to the other for beef, were its ownership absolutely established. But there is no policeman or magistrate to call in and arbitrate the matter. Each man carries his independence and his honor on his hip. Either feels that if he allows the other to take the calf, he will be allowing his rights to be trampled on, and feels that in the mind of the other will always lurk a suspicion as to his courage. The usual solution was blazing guns and a range war on. How would you solve that problem?

I do not, and have never advocated the perpetuation of the frontier as a permanent condition, nor have I advocated the solving of modern problems after the fashion of the frontier. I have merely said that I wished I had lived in those times instead of now, and pointed out certain things that certain temperaments would consider advantages the life has over the modern, mechanized life. That doesn't suggest that everybody would find a frontier life more to their liking. I certainly don't object to your personal preference for the long settled sections. All I argue against is: what seems to be your conviction that my desire to have lived in the early days is merely a silly romantic whim, unrelated to any traditional thought stream; what seems to be your conviction that no intelligent man could honestly prefer the life of a pioneer to that of a dweller in a long settled urban center; what seems to be your conviction that frontier life was such a state of unqualified misery and nightmare that even the boldest pioneers were frantic to escape from it.

As for the first, I see no reason why I should be classed with those city-bred youngsters who get their ideas of the West from high-colored romantic fiction, and form a vague, dazzling conception of glamour. My desire to have been a pioneer is no different from the impulse that drove my ancestors westward. If it is a silly whim, then every man that ever crossed the Alleghenies was motivated by a silly whim.

Concerning the next reason: we are all prone to question the sincerity of preference expressed for any environment differing radically from our own. It is hard for any of us to understand how anybody could like something we don't like, or prefer living in an environment different widely from that to which we are accustomed. That is a bit of provincialism of which we are all more or less guilty.

As for the third: I make no attempt to deny that the average modern urban-dweller would find frontier life anything but a nightmare. But that the settlers suffered as much as the urban-dweller would suffer, is a position that can not be supported. I had a first-hand example of that when I was a child out on the South Plains, which were being over-run by a rush of colonization from the eastern parts of the state, and from other states. Some of the colonists, from softer sections, found the going pure hell. I could tell you tales of madness and suicide that would lift your hair. But the country was also full of hard-bitten old cattlemen who had come out there in the seventies and eighties, and their sons and grandsons. These men didn't go crazy or shoot themselves. They were a lusty, hearty crew, who apparently enjoyed life to the utmost. They didn't find the country too hard for them; they loved it, they loved the life, and they wouldn't have lived anywhere else on a bet. I did not say, or at least I did not mean to imply, that all the settlers wanted to keep the frontier in its wildest, rawest state. I merely suggested that to certain temperaments, (not inferior by any means) the wild, open life of the naked countries appealed more than a settled, urban life. This can not be denied, it is proved by the vast numbers of settlers who kept following the fringe of the frontier clear across the continent. I have offered these facts merely as a sort of explanation of my craving for the early times, which you seem to find so inexplicable. I merely wished to show you that certain types of men found the frontier more satisfying than the settled regions, and that my statement of desire for the life, was not an isolated example of twisted "idealization" but simply an echo of a thought-force that motivated thousands of men, many of my direct ancestors among them. It was a nomadic urge, in a way; a desire for freedom not necessarily expressed in defiance of law and order, but the desire to wander over new lands unhindered. And a man could roam in the early days. To travel now he needs money, else he becomes a mere hobo. But then he could saddle his horse, or hitch his wagon and be off to California, Montana, Arizona—or where ever he wished. Freedom from the tyranny of money—that's one thing I mean by the freedom of the old days. Freedom of new, fresh, fertile land. I don't suggest that the ways of the frontier are better for everybody, I don't demand that everybody—or anybody—place the same value on the freedom of those days that I do. I simply say that I wish I had lived then; not because of some vague "moralistic" conception, but simply because I know my particular temperament would have found more satisfaction in those days; and because my material gains would very probably have been greater than they will be in my actual life. Of course, it's idle to wish for something impossible. But we started talking about what age we would have preferred, could we have chosen our own environment. You said you would have found more content in early Eighteenth Century England; I said I'd find more in middle Nineteenth Century America. When you questioned whether my choice was "sensible and valid" I merely gave some of the reasons for my choice. It did not occur to me that they would be taken as a demand for the frontier conditions to be perpetuated permanently, or the application of pioneer solutions to modern problems.

Concerning violence in the modern West: it occurs to me that each section has it's own particular brand of violence. In Texas, outside of occasional hold-ups and robberies which are too wide-spread over the whole country to be branded as an institution of Texas alone, about all the violence that occurs is fight between citizens, growing out of old feuds often enough, and the outrages sometimes committed by the police. For the latter there is neither excuse nor palliation. But it is a question whether the private killings of the state weigh in the balance so very overwhelmingly against some of the things done in other sections. For instance, we have no gang rule in Texas. A man like Barrow[7] may hide in the hills and evade capture for a long time, but his life is that of a hunted wolf. A gang-boss like Capone wouldn't last long enough to get started. Many of the killings in Texas are those of robbers—frequently enough from other states—killed by officers are private citizens while attempting to commit robberies. We have never had a scandal here like the abominable "Vice-squad scandal",[8] nor anything remotely resembling "Welfare Island."[9] We never had anything like that business in Maryland a few months ago, when Ritchie sent out militia to arrest the lynchers.[10] True, lynchings occur occasionally in Texas, and once a courthouse was burned during the process. But even then, the courthouse was burned merely because that was the only way of the getting the nigger out. The mob did not then go up and down the street smashing automobiles and assaulting newspaper men. We never had anything like that Beacon Hill affair in Boston, where, according to the papers, an anti-Nazi mob fought with the police for some time trying to break up a Nazi lecture.[11] It may surprize you, but the whole keynote of the Southwest, of that part west of the Mississippi, at least, is easygoing tolerance. That's a characteristic of the whole west, with the possible exception of California, which has been flooded with people from other sections. Texas police may arrest a Communist and club him in the jail, at the behest of agitated capitalists, but the ordinary citizen would never dream of interfering with a man's speech, whether Socialist, Communist, Nazi, Fascist, or what ever. That business where the New York Communists broke up a meeting of Socialists protesting the slaughter of their brothers in Austria[12]— that couldn't have happened in Texas. And though we've had strikes down here, in the industrialized sections, they have never been accompanied by the violence that accompanied the mine strikes in Pennsylvania.[13] In fact, when I look at the world today, with the East seething with political unrests and economic clashes (to judge from the newspapers) with the West Coast in much the same state, the turmoil of the mid-western farmers, with Europe seething like a volcano, mobs rioting in "civilized" France, working men, women and children being slaughtered in "civilized" Austria, a madman running wild in "civilized" Germany, it looks to me as if Texas is just about the calmest and most tranquil part of the world.

I note with interest your remarks pertaining to German culture, and find no point of disagreement, except that I doubt if Germany's throes are a result of cultural youth; it seems more like decay and senility to me.

Concerning radios: since writing you I've had the pleasure of hearing a number of splendid dramas: "The Scarecrow" by Percy McKaye (was it?)[14] a most strikingly weird and haunting thing; the dramatization of one of Poe's stories—I forget the name, but it was about a phantom horse that haunted a royal German family; a remarkable German play about a bell that was lost in a deep lake, and others of less weird interest. I'd like to be able to get a more modern and more powerful machine, but even so find it easy to get such stations as Jacksonville, Louisville, Birmingham, Denver, Salt Lake, Phoenix, San Francisco, etc. Some notable men talk over the air; I've heard Irvin S. Cobb,[15] Gandhi, that Irish poet—AE I believe he calls himself[16]—and the inventor of "Fu Manchu"[17] among others. Alexander Woolcott is a regular feature, and I like to listen to him occasionally, though I can hardly endure his effeminate voice.[18]

As to barbarism and civilization, I did not mean to intimate that more people suffer under civilization than under barbarism. I merely suggest that the barbarian does not suffer as a civilized man would if forced to live under the same conditions as the barbarian. I argue against what you seem to imply: that a civilized life of itself produces no conditions that lead to suffering. You can hardly blame sweat-shops and strikes and business depressions and unsanitary tenements and ghettoes on the Goths and Vandals. You may say these things are not "civilized" and maybe they aren't, but nevertheless, they are characteristics of what we have been taught to regard as settled, civilized life, and they did not exist either on the American frontier or among the Teutonic barbarians. You say the number of people who are suffering because of this depression is very small. I can hardly agree with that. Some ten million unemployed is scarcely insignificant, even in a country of this size. And there are many millions more who find themselves almost unbearably pinched, even though they are not classed among the unemployed.

Concerning disease and accidents: I freely grant the magnificent gains made in medical research. That is one thing that reconciles me to modern life. But don't forget that the race also grows weaker. I don't know how prevalent sickness was among the Germanic barbarians, and undoubtedly they had plagues that swept off thousands. But it is also very sure that they had more resistance than we moderns have. If not—if they had had all the ills we have, all their plagues, and the modern's lack of stamina, they would all have died. There would have been no Aryan race. I judge of their hardihood by the American frontiersman. Sickness was rare among them. Along the rivers and in the lowlands they had typhoid and malaria and the death rate was pretty high in malaria, and they also had an occasional scourge of typhus or cholera that wiped out many. But they were essentially a healthy race. Even in the lowlands of Arkansas, where some of my lines dwelt, people seldom died with anything except typhoid or malaria. And out further west, in these highlands here, for instance, casualties from sickness was so slight I doubt if you'd believe me if I told you just what percent of the people did die from disease. This is still a healthy country, compared to some, but it can not compare to the early days. I know what I'm talking about; I've seen diseases increase during my own life time. The medical profession had to keep step with the increase of disease, to counterbalance what appeared to be a loss of hardihood. As for the weak suffering in the Teutonic countries—I doubt if many weaklings were born. I know few were born on the frontier. Suppose the German weaklings did die early? It has not been long ago that I read an article by a noted scientist questioning the desirability of preserving the lives of weaklings, and hinting that science might find it necessary, not only to provide against the bearing of such weaklings, but to exterminate such as were born.[19] If a civilized scientist can consider the artificial weeding out of the race, why condemn the barbarians who supposedly followed the same procedure? What about the civilized Spartans? Didn't they bump off their weaklings at birth?

Concerning accidents, doubtless a greater proportion of the Germans died violent deaths than is common among moderns. What I pointed out, though, was that they considered that no hardship. It was part of their religion. I think you underestimate the casualties of mechanized life. Statistics show that for the year of 1933, 89,500 lives were lost in accidents, and there were 6,500,000 non-fatal injuries which, however, maimed or disabled. To this can be added hundreds, possibly thousands of injuries never reported. 30,500 were killed by automobiles alone. In fact, the great majority of the accidents were connected with machinery in one way or another. I do not say that the hazards of modern life are greater than those of barbaric life; I do say that the hazards of industrial life show statistically to be greater than the ordinary life of the frontier, which moderns apparently consider the very pinnacle of peril and hazard. I have lived in agricultural sections, and in industrialized sections. And I can declare with certainty that the number of men killed and maimed in this country, for instance, during its most highly industrialized era, was infinitely greater than the number who suffered in wildest frontier days.

My contention is that on the one hand you underestimate the actual development of the Germanic barbarians—that you place them on too low a scale of humanity—and on the other that you minimize the actual sufferings of modern people. I do not, as you seem to think, admire the Germanic tribes because they were on the bottom rung of the ladder; my admiration is not based on their lack of development; I believe they were far more highly developed than you give them credit for, and I believe they were developed to a point where life as one would have been more satisfying (to one of my temperament, if born among them) than would have been the life of a Roman plebeian, a medieval yeoman, or a modern European peasant or American tenant-farmer. I can not believe that the singers of Beowulf and the Sagas, the builders of the dragon-ships and creators of Thor and Odin and Valhalla, the forgers of the swords and armor which I've seen reproduced in pictures—I can not believe that they were in reality the stunted, stupid, miserable, dull creatures you picture them to be, with no feelings above filling their bellies. How did such clods manage to father the civilization of which you are so proud? The heritage of Greece and Rome had to fall on fertile soil to come to life again, regardless of how strong it was. When I speak with admiration of the Germanic tribes, I am not necessarily exalting savagery. When I speak of my admiration for the Goths it doesn't necessarily follow that I'm upholding the customs of the Australian bush-fellows, or the Borneo pirates.

I note your next argument contains reference to what you feel is my "refusal to accept the basic standards of human development." I have already explained my position there. My remark about the inadvisability of laying down arbitrary rule as to what things are of value, had no connection with "the basic standards of human development." It was called forth entirely by your statement that further and more rigid regulation of individual life would not hamper anything of value. If you had said "anything of *artistic or cultural* value" I would not have disagreed with you. But your statement was too sweeping, when considering just what things are of value to the individual.

Let me give an example. Recently a law was passed in Texas against hitch-hiking;[20] as I understand it, it even forbids walking along the highways from one town to another. Now tramping the highway has no cultural or artistic value. There are millions of people this law won't affect. On the other hand, there are thousands who will suffer bitterly from it, if it is enforced. And it serves no real purpose. The millions who are not affected by it, on the other hand are not aided in any way. It is simply another cramping of the life of the individual. If you say that no artistic or cultural aim is hindered, I am ready to instantly agree with you. But if you maintain that tramping the highway is without value to the individual, I am flat against you. Outside of the principle of the thing, this law will work a savage hardship on many men. Of course, most of them are laborers; but even a laborer wants to live and keep food in his belly and clothes on his back. I have many friends who, lacking suitable employment at home, go to the wheat fields of the mid-west in season, to the cotton-fields of the Panhandle, and into the further western states yearly, working at seasonable occupations. They can not afford to own automobiles, and they earn so little in any event, they can not pay their fare on buses or trains. So they ride the rods or walk, and if anybody gives them a ride, so much the better. I myself have tramped the roads for many and many a weary mile; coming home from school, and going back to school, going to other towns for magazines or to consult libraries, or for scores of other things vitally necessary to my life. Certainly the right to walk the highway unmolested is of value to me, and a man who has no need of tramping it himself, has no right to deny its value to me. There's no use to say that modern life does not cramp the individual. It is not unbearable now, if they'll stop within reasonable limits. But nearly every magazine I pick up contains some attack on some phase of human liberty of thought or action, by some scientist, politician or intellectual who either has some axe to grind or else has no particular need himself of the phase of freedom he denounces.

Considering it again, I am not so sure that even cultural and artistic things will not suffer as civilization "advances" along its present lines. You seem to take it for granted that Fascism would guarantee absolute freedom of thought and mental research. I wonder if this faith is justified. I don't notice any hilarious renaissance emanating from Germany or Italy or Austria resulting from the exhilarating freedom of dictatorship. It had always seemed to me, erroneously perhaps, that suppression of speech and thought generally accompanied dictatorship. Admitting that the forbidding of such material things as highway-tramping, the possession of arms, the right of laborers to strike, or to choose their type of work, the right to cross a state-line without being thumb-printed and having to pay a tax—admitting all these and a hundred other things are of no artistic value, will not affect the stream of formal culture, still, what assurance have you that you will be allowed to speak, write, study and think exactly what you please under a dictator? Over-regulation of men's physical life is generally followed by over-regulation of their mental life.

In mentioning Jim Corbett along with Michel Angelo, I was merely pointing out that it would be as impossible for an inferior man to be a Corbett as it would be for an inferior man to be an Angelo. That prize fighting is not to be compared with Angelo's artistic triumphs goes without saying. Nevertheless, Corbett can not be called an inferior man; certainly his accomplishments can not be compared with Angelo's. Nevertheless, Corbett was as supreme in his line as Angelo was in his. It is no mistake to call Corbett great; he was great; not as Angelo was great, of course. But great in his own line. That's all I'm trying to get at; that supremacy in almost any line is a sign of superiority, in that it marks off the possessor from the inferior herd. Of course, there are varying degrees of superiority. I never denied that. I merely object to the assumption that only a superior man can attain supremacy in literature, painting or sculpturing, while any bone-headed dunce can be a great boxer, a great football coach, a great acrobat, a great business man, a great navigator, or a great soldier. Of course only a very superior man can master the arts; but only a superior man can be a Jim Corbett, a Pop Warner, a J. P. Morgan, a Magellan, or a Jeb Stuart.[21]

Your mention of Houdini interests me. You blame him for being a showman when he might have been, in your opinion, a scholar, scientist, or philosopher. How do you know he would have derived more pleasure out of being a scholar, scientist or philosopher than he did as a showman? Now, don't get to thinking again that I'm questioning the superiority of these things over showmanship. I'm simply questioning the assumption that *any* man would get more satisfaction out of being a scholar, scientist or philosopher, than he would out of being something else. As a born showman, Houdini was undoubtedly happier as the supreme artist of his profession, than he would have been in anything else. You don't take differences of temperament into consideration. Because scholarship, science and philosophy are superior to other things, doesn't necessarily mean that any man of intelligence would be happier following one of these pursuits than at any thing else. I had a cousin once who was an acrobat. He showed early evidences of real talent in art—portrait painting especially. His natural talent in that line was really remarkable. His mother offered him every inducement to follow painting as a life career, offered to send him to Italy to study art, and gave him every advantage possible. But my cousin laughed at the idea. He didn't want to be an artist, he wanted to be an acrobat. The love of the game was born in him. The thrill of it, the joy of it were to him infinitely more vital and important than anything art had to offer. He *was* an artist, in his line. He became an acrobat, and one of the finest of his day. When he was twenty-one, a fall from a thirty foot trapeze ended his life. But I don't blame him for taking up acrobatics, if that's what he wanted. There is a concrete example of a man of high intellect and artistic talents, who found his fullest satisfaction in something not connected with the formal arts. And I say he was right in his choice. I do not say that acrobatics are superior to painting. Of course not. I say that a man ought to do whatever gives him the most pleasure, the most satisfaction. I *know* that my cousin Dave Thomas[22] got more joy and satisfaction out of his few years as an acrobat than he could have gotten in a lifetime as an artist. So I say he was right in selecting the calling that gave him the most pleasure. The fact that I myself, would never select acrobatics before any form of art, has nothing to do with it. I don't expect others to follow rules laid down for myself. You can say that certain activities are superior to other activities; that's right; but that doesn't necessarily follow that the superior activity will *always* give a man the fullest possible satisfaction. Human nature is too complex; temperaments differ too greatly. Nor is innate capacity an absolute index to preferences. My cousin had the capacity to become a great artist. He chose to become an acrobat. I've known plenty of men who had greater natural capacities in lines other than the pursuits they deliberately followed. I certainly don't belong with the bunch I've been naming, but to use a concrete example of a very humble kind: in high school I showed something of a knack for biology; certainly my science grades were infinitely higher than my English and literature grades. I have reason to believe that I had more capacity for biology than I have for literature. My teacher—who detested me as human being but seemed to appreciate my laboratory work—suggested that I take up biology as a career. Now undoubtedly biology is a career superior to writing fiction for the wood-pulps. But it wasn't a question of superiority with me; it was a question of what I enjoyed most. I wanted to be a writer; I didn't give a damn about being a scientist. I chose the wood-pulps, and I do not in the slightest regret my choice. I might have gone much further as a scientist, but I know very well I wouldn't have enjoyed the life as much as I have that of a writer. If I ever said anything about "arbitrary" standards, that's probably what I meant—the assumption that a certain pursuit necessarily offers the fullest satisfaction to *all* sorts of temperament, merely because it is of the superior type.

Glancing over your letter, I note that you intimate that my supposed bias or prejudice against intellectualism might result from my having "been made to feel at a disadvantage" by the intellectual types. This assumption is without foundation. I understand that a certain class of the intelligentsia delight in lancing less sophisticated individuals with their supposedly lacerating wit, but I can assure you that none of them ever tried that on me. Any one who deliberately starts out to bait me needs something besides intellectual superiority. I have tried to make it plain that I have no indiscriminate prejudice against true intellectuals, and it is true that I regard even the would-be intellectuals with tolerance, or at most only amusement. I have been rather disgusted with some of them, but the feeling never amounted to actual enmity. In fact, I've rather liked all I ever met, though some of them didn't like me. My habits and opinions seemed to shock most of them to their quivering souls—I am speaking here of the intelligentsia, or baby-intellectuals, as they might be called. Even if I had any real enemies among that class, I'd hardly be so indiscriminate as to declare war on all of them. As a matter of fact, all my personal enemies are members of the working class, or the professions. I'm hardly so emotionally unstable as to condemn a whole class just because I dislike certain of its members. I don't dislike farmers indiscriminately merely because one of them shot at me from a mesquite thicket once; I don't dislike oil field workers merely because one knifed me once; I don't indiscriminately hate business men merely because some of them have gypped me occasionally. Then I certainly don't condemn the intelligentsia, among whom I have not one single enemy, who have never attempted my life, nor even ventured to insult me verbally.

I look on some of them as rattle-brained, and on certain others as feather-weights, but my record is largely tolerant. If I haven't seemed so, it's probably due to an unfortunate aggressiveness of expression rising, perhaps, from the rough environments among which I have spent so much of my time. I can not remember ever being even slightly angered by one of them, not even when one young genius held me up in the pages of a certain publication of national circulation as a horrible example of the "twisted thinking and brutal psychology of the South." Or something like that. Evidently the "Southern heritage of violence" that he denounced so strenuously caused him some qualms, for at the end of the article he expressed his desire to apologize if he had misquoted me, or presented a false picture. He needn't have bothered to tack that on; I was merely amused, though he did misquote a statement of mine, lending a social significance to a comment I intended only as a biological observation. But that didn't upset me either; I'm a fiction writer, not a sociologist. But the point is that I have no such indiscriminate prejudice against intellectuals as you seem to think I have. I merely refuse to burn incense to every human being who calls himself an artist or an intellectual. I could parade under that flag if I wanted to be hypocritical, for, scant claim as I have to either title, I've seen persons laying claim to both honors, who deserved the terms of artist and intellectual as little a I deserve them.

This answer to your letter has been delayed considerably, partly because of an accident that proved non-fatal to me only by the merest chance. Three other young men and I were returning from Brownwood late in the night of December 29th, at which time it was raining, with a heavy fog on, making ordinary driving extremely difficult. We passed through a small town about fifteen miles from Cross Plains, where a steel flag pole was planted in concrete in the middle of the street. The pole was painted grey and was practically invisible. None of us saw it until we had hit it, head-on. Naturally the car was wrecked. The fellow on the seat beside me, a Tennessean, was thrown through the windshield, head and shoulders, and struck his belly terrifically against the dash-board, and a piece of glass gouged out most of his eyebrow and a piece of scalp larger than a dollar, and left it hanging over his eye by a shred of flesh. Of the men sitting behind, one was practically unhurt, but the other suffered a badly wrenched and almost broken leg, and some veins and tendons were evidently ruptured. As for me, I was driven against the wheel with such terrific force that I crumpled it with my breast-bone and my head was driven down against a jagged shard of glass with a force that would have fractured or dislocated a more fragile jaw than mine, and a gash two and a half inches long was ripped along the under part of my jaw, laying the bone bare the full length of the cut. I also received a deep cut—to the bone—across the middle knuckle of my left hand, and the flesh inside the joint of my right thumb was literally mangled. My knees caved in the solid steel instrument-panel, which naturally bruised and tore them considerably. But the worst hurt was to my breast. The arch of my breast was flattened and for hours it was only with the most extreme pain that I could draw a breath at all. Well, the instant I recovered from the blow—which was almost instantly—I shut off the engine and leaped out to see what damage had been done to the car, and though I don't remember my remarks, my friends say my profanity was fervent and eloquent when I saw the crumpled bumper, the ruined radiator and the other damages. I didn't know I was cut until, during my remarks, I happened to put my hand to my jaw and felt the bare bone through the gaping wound. At about that time the other boys piled out, and the man who had gone through the windshield, evidently having been numbed by the blow, suddenly was made aware of his plight by his awakening sensations. He was bleeding like a butchered steer, and was really a ghastly spectacle, with that great flap of flesh hanging down over his eye, and the contour of the skull, covered only by a layer of membrane, showing beneath. But he was suffering most from the terrible blow of being hurled against the dash-board. He was suffering internal pain, and apparently unable to straighten up. He was convinced that he was dying, and indeed I thought it quite likely, and he was making considerable noise about it; indeed I was so taken up with his injuries that I didn't even know the other fellow was hurt—of old Texas stock, and stoicism being part of his instincts, he didn't even mention the agony he was enduring with his leg, so I didn't even know he was hurt until the next day. I don't reckon I was making much noise about my injuries, either, because he didn't know I was hurt, until the next day, either. But the fact is I didn't think much about them at the time. It was about midnight, and a small town; we made an effort to get a doctor, but they were all out on calls, and not even a drug store open. But a young fellow offered to take us anywhere we wanted to go, and the man whose head was laid open wanted to go to the nearest hospital, which was in a town about twenty miles from there. I tried to persuade him to come on to Cross Plains and let my father bandage him, which wouldn't cost him anything, but like many people he had something of a hospital complex; so I told him and the fellow with the hurt leg to go on to the hospital, and I'd see about getting my car towed home. So they went, but it was useless trying to get anybody to see about the car; everything was closed, so I phoned my father, at Cross Plains, and he came over after me and the other fellow, who, as I said, wasn't hurt. When we got home he put five stitches in my jaw, and one in my thumb, which is the first time I was ever sewed up, though I've been ripped open before. I'm rather fat-jowled, and the gash on my jaw presented a rather ghastly appearance, gaping widely and the white of the bone showing through. The other fellow who was cut had fourteen stitches taken in his head, and it left a rather horrible scar, which, however, may become less obvious as time goes on. He had accident insurance, which was lucky, though I offered to pay his hospital bill, which he refused. A funny thing happened while my father was sewing me up; the watchman was holding his flashlight for my father to work by, and a young drug-clerk was standing watching. In the midst of the job he asked me if I was getting sick, to which I honestly replied that I never felt healthier in my life, and presently he pulled out in considerable of a hurry. I asked my father what was the matter with him, and he said the young man got sick at the sight of blood and raw flesh. Can you beat that? I'd heard that there were people who got sick at the sight of blood, but I'd never seen one before. I'd always wondered how it felt to be sewed up like a piece of cloth, but a gash like mine was appears to offer no particular problem. I imagine other wounds might require a local anesthetic. I was forced to lead a very quiet life for a few days, because my knees and ribs got so sore I could scarcely move, and the bandages on my hands prevented me from doing much with them. Indeed we were all lucky to come out of the wreck alive and no worse injured than we were. People who have seen the wheel I wrecked with my breastbone have repeatedly expressed wonder that it didn't kill me, or at least cave in most of my ribs. It was a heavy steel frame covered with very hard rubberish material; I bent the frame almost double, rim, spokes and all, and broke great pieces of the rubber off, in many places leaving the frame work bare. Indeed, it has only been a week or so since the soreness has entirely gone out of my breast bone and ribs. I was not only thrown against the wheel with all my weight and the velocity of the car, but the man behind me, a bigger man than I am, was hurled on my back—the car is a coach, with movable front seats— driving me forward with his weight against mine. That was one of the cases which sometimes do occur—when sheer muscular ruggedness meant more than intellectual development. Of course, it was only chance that kept a piece of glass from severing my jugular; yet even there my bodily build saved me; if I did not have a short, thick neck, if my neck had been an inch longer, the glass shard that struck my jawbone would have been driven in below the bone, and cut my throat. And what saved me from death or frightful injury on the wheel was simply an unusually powerful set of ribs, backed and braced by heavy muscles specially developed. A body stronger than the average may not be required by our modern civilization; but in that affair, as in others I have encountered, a powerful frame saved my life. There were no broken bones, though it is possible that some of my ribs were slightly cracked, yet this even is not certain; my breast has resumed its normal arch, and the cuts healed quickly; I have a rather large scar on my jaw, but as I never had any beauty to be marred, that doesn't amount to anything.[23]

Well, my ramblings seem to be endless. Thanks very much for the picture of your house, which goes into my permanent files. Thanks also for the opportunity of reading "The Thing on the Doorstep" which I enjoyed very much indeed. Your mastery of the weird theme is evident there, as in all your stories. I have also very much enjoyed the poetic beauty of your stories which have been appearing in "The Fantasy Fan".[24] I've also been considerably amused by the controversy raging there, apparently precipitated by this Ackerman gentleman—I believe that's the name.[25] It's always been a strange thing to me why some people think they have to attack fiction they don't care for personally. If it was an article on government or sociology, dealing with some vital national problem, it might be different. But it seems rather absurd to me for one to attack a fiction story that has no connection with everyday problems at all. If Ackerman doesn't like Smith's stories, why, no law compels him to read them.

Thanks for the article on cats. Bebe, the cat I rescued from the post-oak grove, is dead, and so is the Persian's son. Cats, particularly male cats, seem to be very short-lived in this country. I hated to lose Bebe, for I really thought a great deal of him. I tried to treat him when he fell sick, but without success. He and the other cat both died of a disease known generally as cat-cholera, a complaint of the bowels. That, and diphtheria are the main diseases that kill cats in this country, though fits and rabies are fairly common, also. One reason cats are unpopular in many families, especially those with small children, is their habit of carrying diphtheria germs. They not only die of the disease themselves, but spread it among human beings, having come in contact with a person suffering from diphtheria. As I said, rabies is common among cats, and the ordinary bite of a cat is more likely to become infected than that of a dog, as I well know, having been bitten more than once by both animals. It need not be concluded that, because I am not able to give felines undivided worship that I dislike cats. Any idea that a man is superior because he likes cats, or inferior because he likes dogs, is too fantastic to be considered, but I uphold the sincerity of a liking for cats, just as I uphold the sincerity of a liking for dogs. All my life I have been fond of animals, whatever their breed.

With best wishes, and hoping to see many of your stories soon, I am,

Cordially,

REH

Notes

1. HPL had undertaken his now customary post-Christmas visit to the New York City area (26 December–9 January).

2. See letter 19, n. 12.

3. Ellsworth Torrey (1830–?) was born in Connecticut and spent a number of years at sea. When he was almost fifty, he secured backing from a Boston bank and settled

near Tascosa in the Texas Panhandle, where he raised first sheep and then cattle. Once established, he brought his family and freighted in fine furnishings from Boston. In other versions of the legend REH relates here, Torrey's objection was not to having fed Billy and his gang, but to their rudeness to Mrs. Torrey and failure to acknowledge the hospitality. Torrey left Texas in 1881 and presumably returned to New England.

4. John George Adair (1823–1885) was an Irish businessman and landowner. Although he acquired considerable wealth and built a castle, he was not a member of the aristocracy, but the son of a farmer. He became notorious in Ireland as "Black Jack" Adair when, following a dispute with his tenants over hunting rights, he evicted over forty families, almost 250 people, from their homes on the estate he had purchased near Derryveagh, County Donegal, in 1861. In 1866 he opened an office of his brokerage firm in New York City, and it was there he met and married Cornelia Wadsworth Ritchie. In 1874 the couple went on a buffalo hunt, and he became so enamored of the West that he established an office of his brokerage firm in Denver and decided to go into the cattle business. In Colorado he met Charles Goodnight, who told him about land in the Palo Duro Canyon of Texas, and the two went into partnership to create the JA Ranch there. According to *The Handbook of Texas,* "Adair's conventional, and sometimes arrogant, British mannerisms were received poorly by the cowboys; even Goodnight later admitted that his partner's overbearing attitude was irritating."

5. Charles Goodnight (1836–1929), pioneering American cattleman and rancher. Following the Civil War, he began herding Texas Longhorn cattle toward railheads for shipment east, and in 1866 with Oliver Loving established the Goodnight-Loving Trail from Texas through New Mexico into Colorado. It was later extended to Wyoming. When Loving died in Fort Sumner, New Mexico, of wounds suffered in a Comanche attack, Goodnight honored his pledge to his partner and returned his body to Weatherford, Texas, for burial. This episode was among the inspirations for Larry McMurtry's *Lonesome Dove.* Goodnight is also credited with the invention of the chuckwagon, the mobile kitchen that accompanied cattle drives.

6. William Matthew Tilghman (1854–1924) was a lawman and gunslinger in the American Old West. He was shot by Wiley Lynn, a corrupt Prohibition agent.

7. I.e., Clyde Barrow.

8. Judge Samuel Seabury's probe of official corruption in New York City had uncovered widespread graft, perjury, and other malfeasances among members of the police department's vice squad.

9. A raid on this prison, located on the island of the same name (later named Roosevelt Island) in the East River of New York City, by Corrections Commissioner Austin MacCormick, on 25 January 1934, had found that four gang leaders were ruling the prison through graft, corruption, and vice.

10. In November 1933, Maryland Governor Albert Ritchie sent state militia to arrest the ringleaders of a mob that lynched a black man who had confessed to an attack on a white woman in Princess Anne county. The four accused lynchers were briefly held at an armory in Salisbury, where a mob of about 2000 gathered to demand their release. When the state attorney general and militia commander decided to transfer the prisoners to Baltimore, their vehicle and the trucks carrying the prisoners were at-

tacked by the mob with rocks and clubs. One man was attacked and his car overturned when the mob thought he was the attorney general.

11. On 26 November 1933, a crowd of 5000, gathered to protest a speech at Ford Hall in Boston in support of the Hitler government, attempted to surge past police to enter the lecture hall and were dispersed by club-wielding and mounted officers.

12. On 16 February 1934, Communists broke up a meeting called by Socialists and trade unions to protest the suppression of unions in Austria, at Madison Square Garden. The Associated Press report used terms like "free-for-all fight," "bedlam," and "incessant fighting" to describe the proceedings.

13. Striking coal mine workers in Pennsylvania had rioted in late July and early August 1933, leading President Franklin D. Roosevelt to call for a moratorium on strikes, to allow his recovery efforts to work.

14. REH refers to *The Scarecrow* (1908) by Percy Mackaye, adapted from Nathaniel Hawthorne's story "Feathertop," a play about witchcraft and the Devil; a radio play based on Poe's "Metzengerstein"; and *The Sunken Bell* (*Die versunkene Glock*, 1897) by Gerhart Hauptmann.

15. Irvin Shrewsbury Cobb (1876–1944), American journalist and author of more than 60 books and 300 short stories, best known for his humorous tales set in Kentucky, such as *Back Home* (1912), which was in REH's library. His short story "Fishhead" was cited as "banefully effective" by HPL in "Supernatural Horror in Literature."

16. AE is the pseudonym of the Irish poet and essayist George William Russell (1867–1935).

17. The character Dr. Fu Manchu was invented by Sax Rohmer, the pseudonym of British writer Arthur Sarsfield Ward (1883–1959).

18. Alexander Humphreys Woollcott (1887–1943) was a critic and commentator for the *New Yorker* magazine and member of the Algonquin Round Table. His *The Early Bookworm* ran on CBS Radio from 1929 to 1933, and *The Town Crier* on the same network (1933–38).

19. Following the enactment of a "Law for the Prevention of Hereditarily Diseased Offspring" in Nazi Germany, July 1933, a number of articles appeared in U.S. newspapers and magazines on the subject of eugenics. Most noted that the U.S. was, in fact, the first country to enact forced sterilization laws, with Indiana being the first, in 1907; by 1935, 27 states had such laws, with California leading in the number of forced sterilizations. There were many "noted scientists" among the supporters of eugenics laws.

20. In response to growing numbers of transient unemployed persons moving around the state, in 1933 Texas created twelve "transient bureaus" to provide food, clothing, shelter, and work on relief projects for the estimated 25,000 to 30,000 transients. A law against hitchhiking and "riding the rods" (catching rides on freight trains) went into effect 1 January 1934.

21. Glenn Scobey "Pop" Warner (1871–1954), American football coach for Iowa State University, the University of Pittsburgh, Stanford University, and other colleges. James Ewell Brown ("Jeb") Stuart (1833–1864), Confederate general who fought at Gettysburg and other battles.

22. No information has been located about this cousin. Hester Ervin Howard's sister, Christina, married a physician whose name is given in the 1880 census only as "L. Thomas." Two children were enumerated in 1880, a daughter with the initials "J. W." and a son "C. E." By 1900, Christina was running a boarding house in Abilene under the last name "Cobb," and was reported to have had five children, three still living. Only one child, Lucile Cobb, six years old, was living with her at the time. (Her sister Hester was also living with her.) This is the only family connection named "Thomas" unearthed to date.

23. The accident occurred in Rising Star, at the intersection of what was then Texas Highway 206 (now Texas 36) and US Highway 283/Texas 23 (now US 183). The three men in the car with REH were Dave Lee (the "Tennessean"), Lindsey Tyson, and Bill Calhoun. In a letter to L. Sprague de Camp (18 February 1977), Lindsey Tyson wrote: "We [Dave Lee and Tyson] were both in the car you spoke of that was involved in the wreck in Rising Star[,] Texas. It was a misty night when we were returning home from Brownwood. What we hit was a flag pole located in the middle of the Street and did not have a light on it. We had been to Brownwood to see the Golden Glove tournament. It was not because of Bob's driving, none of us saw the thing before we hit it, we were traveling slowly and none of us were seriously injured." No contemporary newspaper accounts of this accident have been located.

24. "The Other Gods" (October 1933); "Polaris" (February 1934).

25. Forrest J Ackerman had precipitated a controversy when, in a column in the *Fantasy Fan* called "The Boiling Point," he violently attacked CAS's "The Dweller in the Gulf" (published in *Wonder Stories*, March 1933, as "The Dweller in Martian Depths") as being unworthy of being published in a science fiction magazine. HPL, RHB, and many others sent heated replies rebutting Ackerman's contentions.

[96]   [nonextant postcard by HPL]

[97]   [TMS]

[c. January 1934]

Dear HPL:

I deeply appreciate your sympathetic expressions in regard to my wreck. All parties made rapid and uneventful recoveries, and feel lucky it wasn't worse. The town where the accident occurred helped me pay for having my car repaired, and the flagpole has been removed—though one of their own citizens had to wreck himself on it before that was done. He was hurt worse than I was. Strange; that pole stood there for years without doing any damage, but as soon as one car was wrecked against it, another shortly followed.

I hope you get to take that Florida trip. I read your article in Fantasy Fan with great interest, and noted the mistake you mention. I was sure that it was a misprint, and in reading it I substituted "no", for "an".[1]

I'm glad my recent lengthy letter didn't prove too boresome or rambling. After presenting arguments in a letter I always hesitate about sending it, for fear my clumsiness of expression might give offense, or fail to convey the impression I intended, because of an imperfect vocabulary that leads to a lack of clarity.

The Southwest is being swept by heavy floods, with terrific thunder and lightning. Just a few hours ago lightning struck a house in an adjacent block, tearing a great hole in the roof and practically wrecking the room beneath. I felt a distinct shock myself at the instant of the stroke. These heavy rains follow the warmest winter I ever remember.

With best wishes,

Cordially,

R.E.H.

Notes

1. The reference is to a letter by HPL that appeared in the *Fantasy Fan* (March 1934) as follows: "It requires an especial morbidity to enjoy any authentic word-depiction, whether it is conventionally 'pleasant' or not."

[98] [nonextant letter by HPL]

[99] [TLS]

[24 March 1934]

Dear HPL:

Here's a little item which might interest you, about a cat that killed a rattler.[1] Snake-killing cats are not at all uncommon. I've known more than one myself. Knew a big white tom once whose owner swore subsisted on snakes, particularly rattlers, almost altogether, though that was an exaggeration. Used to own one myself that was not only a great hunter, but a fisher as well, catching crawfish, frogs and occasionally a small catfish. He generally brought them to the front porch and displayed them proudly with much meowing, before devouring. Cats in this country hunt a great deal in the woods for rabbits.

Some time ago I sent you a clipping concerning the doings of the Oglesby boys, bank-and-train-robbers.[2] (Another one of those boys recently came to the end of his trail in Oklahoma; pardoned from a Texas prison, he went to Oklahoma, killed an officer, was captured and sentenced to the chair.) Here's a clipping that may mean the end of the career of another local outlaw, and one of the most dangerous men this part of the country ever developed—Dick Yarbrough.[3] Dick used to be a prize-fighter—a tall young fellow, with a magnificent body. I remember him in particular as the only man who ever gave me a black eye. It was the end of the fourth and last round, and we were slugging over near the ropes. I had one eye on the timekeeper, because I was far outclassed, had taken pretty much of a beating, and in addition was completely winded. As the time-keeper struck the bell, I instinctively dropped my hands too quick, before the bell actually sounded. Dick naturally drove his right through my lowered guard and knocked me back into the ropes, skinning my face and blackening my eye, just as the bell sounded. It was my own fault; I should have kept up my hands.

Dick used to say they'd never take him alive, but apparently he and his partners made no resistance when arrested. One of the other boys—Giles by name—used to hang around this town, but I didn't know him personally. It seems to me that he is the one Dick and his pal, a kid called Pee-Wee, broke out of jail, but I'm not sure. At any rate it was a most spectacular break, though ultimately futile.[4]

I notice there is a move in the legislature to vote a thousand dollar reward for Clyde Barrow.[5] That's far too small. Nobody wants to risk his life against Barrow for a mere thousand dollars. A man can get five times that amount by killing a bank robber. The man that killed Pee-Wee, Yarbrough's pal, about a year ago, got five thousand dollars. Pee-Wee and a friend were trying to rob a bank in a town to the southwest of this place. Citizens mowed down both of them, and collected for them—five thousand a piece.[6] Think of that—five thousand for a pull of a trigger. More than the average man makes in four years. This Pee-Wee, incidentally, was one of the most deadly gunmen I ever knew; a kid of about eighteen or nineteen, small, well-dressed, quiet, with curious opaque blue eyes that had no more expression than the eyes of a rattler; nor was there any expression in his broad, immobile face and thin lips. The psychology of a killer is a curious thing. Notice they haven't caught Dillinger yet; by the way, the man who put the cuffs on him in Arizona was a West Texan.[7]

Cordially,

R E H.

Notes

1. A United Press item published in newspapers on 10 May 1934, dateline Los Angeles, reported: "A two-year-old Persian cat named Popeye received the admiration of humans and animals alike for its feat of killing a four-foot diamond-back rattlesnake which crept into the yard where the cat was sunning itself. Grasping the snake by the back of its neck, like a mongoose, Popeye shook the reptile until it was lifeless. When its 30-year-old mistress, Betty Welch came into the yard, the cat purred contentedly."

2. The clipping was undoubtedly the one discussed in REH's letter to HPL, 2 November 1932 (see letter 73, n. 5).

3. R. G. Yarbrough and three associates, including L. R. Giles, were captured by police in Clovis, New Mexico, on 16 March 1934, charged with killing Deputy Marshal R. J. Hammers, who surprised them during an attempted bank robbery in Clearwater, Kansas, early in the morning of 14 March.

4. Yarbrough had been given a two-year sentence for helping Giles escape from the jail in Breckenridge, Texas, in 1932. He had only recently completed his sentence when he was arrested for the murder of Deputy Marshal Hammers. "Peewee" McMinn, see n. 6.

5. The Texas legislature voted on 16 February 1934 to offer a $1000 reward for the capture of Clyde Barrow, after deleting the words "dead or alive" following a lengthy debate.

6. Herschell C. (Peewee) McMinn, of Eastland County, Texas, was killed by a posse when he and another Eastland County man, Archibald Harten, robbed the Security bank of Wingate. McMinn later died of his wounds at a sanitarium in Ballinger; Harten died outside the bank. The Texas State Bankers Association had offered a $5000 reward for any dead bank robbers.

7. John Dillinger was captured, along with members of his gang, in Tucson, Arizona, on 26 January 1934. Transferred to a jail in Lake County, Indiana, he escaped on 3 March and remained at liberty until he was killed by FBI agents in Chicago on 22 July. Contemporary news accounts consulted do not mention whether any of the Tucson officers involved in Dillinger's arrest were from West Texas.

[100]

Out on Prospect Terrace
April 3, 1934

Dear Ar-I-Ech:—

As I said on the postcard, I was tremendously sorry to hear of your accident. It is surely a wonder that you and your companions came out alive, and one can't blame the windshield-crasher for thinking his time had come. You certainly showed the most distinguished fortitude—and your father evidently exercised no ordinary skill in his surgical ministrations. I'm glad you've come out of it so well—but the whole ordeal must have been appalling. I've never been through anything as bad as that, but imagination can at least give a suggestion of what it was. It seems to me that a flagpole situated like the one you encountered is a definite and reprehensible menace to traffic. If a town wants to have a pole in the centre of a square, it ought to see that it possesses high visibility—white paint, and clear all-night lighting. Traffic menaces of this kind are, however, slow to be eliminated. We have one here—at the end of the street I was born in. This highway—Angell St.— extends half way down the central precipice of the town and comes to a dead end in the rear of the First Baptist churchyard—forcing right angle turns into Benefit St. at the foot of a slope of dizzying steepness. While warning lights are provided, strange drivers are often confused—and come to grief against the wooden fence of the churchyard—through which they crash over a high stone embankment to the grassy sward below. Also—a car under imperfect control often makes the crash even when the driver knows the region. Obviously, this peril should be abolished through the purchase of certain parts of the churchyard (in which there are no graves) by the city, and the establishment of easy curves into the two streets—Waterman and Thomas—leading down to the foot of the hill. But like other needed improvements, this will be postponed indefinitely under a democratic form of government.

Well, anyhow, thank nature and your father's medical skill, that you've come out of it as well as you have! I don't blame the drug-clerk for flinching a bit at the sight of the drastic emergency surgery. Not many people of normal sensitiveness and imagination could remain unmoved at the sight of such a mangled state of the human form—though of course surgeons and nurses have to train their emotions to stand such things. Repetition of such sights— as in an hospital, at a battle-front, or in the course of medical practice, gives one a protective resistance. Many very high-grade persons are abnormally and unconquerably sensitive in such matters. I know an old gentleman of the keenest ability and strength in ordinary matters who faints at mention of blood in an emphatic way—or at any picture representating the mangled human form. He has always been so. And our fellow-weirdist Frank Belknap Long Jr. is forced to leave the table in haste when blood or slaughter is too vividly brought into the conversation. This of course represents a somewhat non-typical extreme, but a psychologist finds no difficulty in understanding it. I am not as hypersensitive as all this, but don't know how I would react to mangling or large-scale bleeding in *another*. Profuse bleeding in *myself* does not sicken me, as proved by my reaction to a severe bicycle accident (the cause of my slightly crooked nose) in 1913. Callousness in such matters is no universal virtue, though it is a convenient quality for persons of active and uncertain life to develop. And of course, it *has* to be developed in doctors, nurses, soldiers, and persons in kindred occupations. Those who cannot acquire it simply have to drop out of such careers. Well—in any case, I hope it will be a long time before any accident of yours affords another occasion for the quailing of the sensitive!

Your supplementary note duly arrived, and I was greatly interested by the text and enclosures. Those rattler-killing cats are surely an intrepid breed— reminding one of the mongooses of India, whose inroads on the cobras make them in such demand. Cats can certainly be hunters and fishermen of rare quality. I have a feline-loving friend in Haverhill[1] whose chief cat bears the appellation of "The Killer", while in Florida young Barlow's white cat brings home all sorts of strange game. Fishing cats have always had considerable charm for artists—probably you have heard of the *Rue Chat qui Pèche* in Paris . . . no doubt named after some bygone shop sign depicting a cat fishing in a pond or brook with graceful paw.

The arrest of your former townsman surely must have aroused curious memories. Incidentally—I have a friend—an old Presbyterian clergyman—in Clovis, N.M. where he was finally apprehended.[2] It is a tremendous pity to see so much youthful energy and stamina sidetracked into anti-social channels; and one wishes economic and governmental conditions could be coördinated in such a way as to salvage it. Perhaps a majority of these reckless beasts of prey might have been valuable and constructive citizens if started in the right direction in childhood.

This is the first day of 1934 that I've been able to do any considerable amount of reading and writing outdoors—I'm now on Prospect Terrace, a small park half-way up the great hill (about midway between Barnes St., where I used to live, and College St., where I live now) and commanding a magnificent view of the outspread roofs and spires and towers and domes of the westward-stretching lower town. The winter has been of atrocious severity—all local records for cold having been broken. The mercury sank to -17° on Feby. 9th. It was devilishly cold, too, around New Year's, when I was visiting Long in N.Y. Only the shelter of the all-extensive subway system enabled me to get about at all. I think I told you about that trip, did I not? . . . of how I met Howard Wandrei, Donald's young weird-artist brother, Harré the weird anthologist, Desmond Hall of *Astounding Stories*, and the one and only *A. Merritt* of "Moon-Pool" fame. It is now quite likely that I shall be able to get down to Florida soon to visit Barlow—stopping en route for a week at Long's. I certainly hope I am—for after the past winter I'm just about ready for a good thawing-out! I shall of course stop in Charleston—and hope I can get at least a week in St. Augustine. Alas that there is no longer any Whitehead to visit in Dunedin! Doubtless Price has told you of his move from New Orleans to Pawhuska, Okla., where he is now partner in a garage business. He was lucky to get this financial anchorage aside from his writing, for cheap editors were hounding him into a career of hack-scribbling utterly unworthy of his powers. He appears to be having rather a good time among the Osages, and I trust he may linger long enough to get some important work done. No doubt he'll find an opportunity before long to pay you a visit in his intrepid and indestructible Juggernaut. Oh, by the way—if I get down to Florida there's a possibility of my meeting Edmond Hamilton and Jack Williamson, who will be returning northward from Key West about a month hence. That would be highly interesting. Hamilton has great talent despite his hack junk, and Williamson shows definite freshness and promise.

By the way—I greatly enjoyed your "Shadows in the Moonlight" in the new W.T. You weave a haunting magic around that ruin with the moon-wakening statues—and the primal, pre-human phrase in the parrot's mouth is the master stroke! The wide popularity you are achieving is certainly well-deserved. At present you come close to forming the star of the W T outfit! The present issue, I think, is far above the average—with your tale, the splendid Burks reprint, the powerful Smith yarn with self-drawn illustration, and the strikingly potent, original, and distinctive "Black Thirst".[3] Unfortunately not many issues come up to this standard. I am extremely glad to see Smith's drawings used at last—a thing for which I've been rooting for 11 years! Some of them may be a bit stiff, but there is an imaginative power which extends far down beneath the surface. I liked particularly the one last month—illustrating "The Charnel God".[4] Despite the woodenness of the human figure (always Smith's weakest point), the funeral effect is subtly and inescapably haunting. That cyclopean, hieroglyphed hall of columns . . . . those nameless, gliding corpse-bearers. . . . . I assuredly wish I could draw like that. Have you ever seen Smith's drawings to any extent—the grotesque, hybrid heads and abhorrent, non-terrestrial vegetation? If not, and if you'd like to, I'd be delighted to lend you such of them as are in my possession. They are at present going the rounds of some interested connoisseurs.

Regarding our controversy—it is only natural that many mutual misunderstandings as to opinions and meanings should occur in any debate involving *values* rather than facts. In an argument about mere facts—whether one thing or another is true—it is relatively easy for each participant to make his position clear; for all speak the common language of logic. Differences can become very quickly narrowed down to definite points—such as the validity of certain evidence, or the accuracy or rationality of certain deductions from that evidence. In the matter of *values,* however, every phase of discussion becomes infinitely more complex and confusing. It is no longer a question of deciding whether something definitely is or isn't so, but a problem of justifying or discrediting a given set of working assumptions or systematic preferences whose essential basis is some person's or group's view of the universe rather than some readily demonstrable fact or condition in the universe. Thus it is one thing to say "good-will is *different from* hate", but quite another thing to say "good-will is *better than* hate". In that little phrase "better than" lies a whole abyss of distinction and increased complexity and indirectness. The *difference* between good will and hate is very clear scientifically. These instincts are seen to be diverse in excitation, manner of operation, and effect—modern research shewing the one to be a product of hormones from such glands as the gonads and the pineal, while the other comes almost exclusively from adrenal hormones. So far all is clear—there could be no possible difficulty in discussing the fact that good-will and hate are *different.* But when the question of *preferability* comes in, we are all at sea! One man says that good will is *better than* hate—but he no longer has any easy standards of reference in the external world to justify his assertion. His opponent asks, "how do you know it is *better?*"—or sometimes, "what do you mean by *'better'?*"—and no instant or simple reply is possible. What the upholder of the preference will bring up in his behalf depends upon his temperament and opinions. If he is religious, he will say that good will is "better" because it is 'commanded by the ruling powers of the cosmos' (he doesn't say *how he knows* what these "powers" command, or whether any such "powers" exist as conscious and volitional forces!). If consistently humanitarian, he will say that it is "better" because it promotes the collective survival and endurable existence of the race of mankind (he doesn't prove that the survival and comfort of man are important or desired ends in the cosmic economy). But any one of these statements (unlike the definite and final evidence which establishes a pure *fact*) is merely the start of a long line of speculation and argument. Nothing is proved at the outset; and in order to reach even a rough working basis (i.e., justification) for an opinion, one must go over a complex and prodigious amount of ground—examining all that is known of the movements and processes of the cosmos, and seeing whether any moderately constant trends or indications of *direction* exist . . . . and if so, what relation to such the phenomena in question possess. It is no wonder that the more conservative thinkers give this complex and indirect question of *values* a completely separate classification from the simple and direct question of fact-determining. *Values,* they say, are the subject of *philosophy* as distinguished from *science*. *Facts* are the subject of *science* alone. That, of course, is why philosophy is so much more complex and abstract and attenuated than sheer science. Fundamentally, both are one—for all values, in order to be valid, must have an underlying reason* based on facts. But in practice the methods of value-seeking are so sharply differentiated (by reason of their greater complexity) from those of simple fact-seeking that the conventional distinction betwixt philosophy and science is amply warranted. And so, as we may see, it is no wonder that now and then a pair of disputants get tangled up in their disposal of deep questions of preferential judgment—questions of "better" and "worse", "superior" and "inferior", "ampler" and "poorer", "advanced" and "primitive", and so on. Not only are many permanently insolvable impasses certain, but wide misapprehension as to the other fellow's meaning are to be repeatedly expected. No wonder it takes a long session of debate, with many chances for misconceptions to come to light and be disposed of, for any average set of arguers on values to know just where all hands stand. One man says art is more important than science, another man says science is more important than art. Christians say their way of life is the best—but Moslems and Buddhists and Nazi racialists each say the same for their own respective ways! Who shall decide amongst such claims? Or is any decision logically possible? Such are the brain-taxing problems with which philosophy has to deal . . . and into this arduous category, of course, fall all our primary topics—evolvedness versus unevolvedness, freedom versus order, civilisation versus barbarism, and so on. No actual agreement, of course, is ever necessarily to be hoped for—and we will be lucky if either ever gets more than an approximate idea of what the other is driving at. But each exchange of views generally more or less clarifies a few points, so that debate is nearly always broadening and profitable. Now and then some connexion betwixt a value and an actual cosmic condition or direction comes to light,

---

*even if no more than the natural workability resulting from long custom.

which seems to lend either one position or the other at least the rudiments of a solid basis in logic . . . . but then again, there may be debates in which no such ground for quasi-anchorage comes to light.

Another frequent source of misunderstanding in long and complicated arguments is the difficulty of maintaining a well-proportioned and always-visible *scale of emphases*. By that I mean that discussion often tends to be presented in such a way that each participant finds it hard to see which things in the other's argument are vital and basic, and which are merely illustrative and supplementary. A common result of this difficulty is the condition whereby one debater seizes on some chance word or essentially trivial or subsidiary concrete example in the other's exposition (usually something which happens to catch his eye through sheer accident or individual bias), and turns his whole larger framework of which that point forms a part, and completely overlooking these other points which really constitute the nucleus and decisive factors of the case. There are very few long debates which do not get held up at certain stages by this difficulty—a difficulty generally occurring in about equal proportions on both sides. Fortunately such sidetrackings usually become visible and receive rectification before the debate is over—so that they merely retard rather than defeat a conclusion. They always have to be allowed for, and there is no use in regretting their occurrence too deeply. When one of them comes to light, the only thing to do is to recognise it frankly and go back for a fresh and better perspective on the phases of the argument concerned.

Well—getting around to our especial debate—since so much of it concerns *values* rather than *facts,* there is certainly no need for either participant to seek to alter the other's opinions. The most each can sensibly hope to do is to make his own position clear—removing misconceptions as to what he believes, distinguishing main issues from minor side-issues, and bringing forward enough significant facts to show that his belief is no mere personal caprice or hasty outgrowth of imperfect evidence, but the mature product of a long and careful examination of all the available and genuinely relevant evidence.

Accordingly I will try to be more concise than in former letters—concentrating on major points and resisting the temptation to explore the many byways leading off from the theme. In some cases I may content myself with stating a belief in the validity of a certain distinction or valuation without expounding in full my reason for such a belief . . . . this not to evade argument (for I'll gladly take up any such point in detail later, if it interests you), but to avoid the possible complication of ideas involved in such an excursion. It is best to get the *main argument* straight—i.e., to find out just what each party *really does* believe concerning the primary matters at issue—before studying in detail the many separate factors which cause each one to believe what he does.

First of all—my observation of some time ago, that you seem to "refuse to accept the basic standards of human development", was *not* designed to imply that you deny *all values*—or at least the possibility of a system of working values. Indeed, my simultaneous recognition of certain intense preferences of yours is testimony to the fact that I have never thought of your views as implying a total qualitative chaos. As a matter of fact, my observation was completely limited and literal in every way—meaning not an iota more than the actual words implied . . . . i.e., that your position includes a repudiation of the *basic* (not necessarily any other) scale of human (and by that I really meant *all organic*) valuation whose criterion is *degree of removal from the state of inorganic unconsciousness or amoebal simplicity.* I did not say that you repudiate *all* scales of valuation. For example, I even objected to what, in your arguments, I considered an *overemphasis* on the preferred values of certain conventional or secondary scales (= liberty, courage, justice, &c.). My point was that you allowed your preference for these conventional or secondary values to obscure your recognition of the *primary* organic value-scale . . . . i.e., that based on the *absolute* principle of *complexity of organisation* as measured by *degree of conscious comprehension of environmental objects and general ideas.* To put the matter more concretely, and without the formal language necessary to a general statement: I believed that you attached so much importance to matters of preference *not* based on general evolution—i.e., courage, fairness, freedom, etc. (which of course have no relation to height in the organic scale)—that you tended to undervalue or even disregard the fundamental quality-considerations which *do* arise from the steady march of matter away from the amoebally simple toward the complex and conscious . . . . i.e., thought and taste and the natural uses to which these are put in man's quest of an endurable and satisfying existence. It was my idea that you considered a savage or courageous bulldog or prize-fighter or tiger more intrinsically important than a highly evolved human philosopher who might not happen to be courageous . . . . forgetting that, no matter how much you may *like* courage, it is after all not essentially a product of high development in the organic scale; whereas the power of complex thought most emphatically is such a product. That is, I thought you were so strongly influenced by certain personal likings for things which might or might not be high in the organic scale, that you had come virtually to deny the existence of any *basic organic* scale. I didn't think you denied the one whereby we call a fish "higher" than a moneron,[5] a lizard "higher" than a fish, a horse "higher" than a lizard, an ape "higher" than a horse, a man "higher" than an ape, and so on. You did certainly give signs that your *personal likes* were entirely disregardful of this scale, hence I drew the perhaps hasty inference that you excluded it altogether from consideration.

Well—as to this basic scale—whatever we may think of the *importance* of its distinctions, the fact remains that the distinctions *do exist,* and in the most absolute sense. It is true that in a purposeless and directionless cosmos we cannot rightly call any one object or force more "important" than another. But it is equally true that we cannot deny the *vast and systematic differences* between certain different groups of objects and forces . . . . differences based on degree of complexity of structure and function (i.e., whether made up of the simplest and least organised units of matter and energy—loosely grouped molecules not greatly differentiated in physico-chemical function from single molecules—or made up of extremely complex patterns of the basic units, with a collective behaviour utterly unlike that of any component unit, and involving types and shades of energy-transformation unknown in simpler arrangements), and forming a complete series of steps *away from the unorganised state of blind gravity, cohesion, inertia, single electrons, etc., toward an intricately organised state whose most advanced* (i.e., farthest developed in the direction of the original differentiation) *examples possess the capacity* (= consciousness) *to retain, correlate, and voluntarily respond to the organic modifications* (= sense-impressions) *produced by environmental stimuli.* This is a series of steps we must recognise as *absolute even in a cosmic sense,* since it involves fixed types of arrangement of the basic matter-and-energy units of the cosmos. True, the fact that the cosmos is a blind drift from nowhere to nowhere makes it impossible for us to speak of the *absolute importance* of anything. We realise that even the most complex life forms—a Shakespeare, Beethoven, Einstein, Newton, Plato, or Lucretius—are merely accidental and mechanical outgrowths of an impersonal, unconscious, and eternal flux of alternate building-up and breaking-down; and that every stream of increasingly complex organisation (what we call evolution or upward development, and of which the growth of animal life on this infinitesimal planet is a single negligible example) will eventually reverse itself and become a stream of decreasingly complex organisation (i.e., devolution, decay, disintegration), extending even to the dispersal of solid matter into separate electrons and protons. We see instances of this devolution at work all over the visible universe—and even in some of the rocks of our own planet . . . radio-activity is based upon it. But in spite of all this, the absoluteness of the *differences* between different stages of the evolutionary scale cannot help suggesting to us a *quasi-absolute* standard of quality and importance. We know that the complex forms are the seat of energy-transformations much more extensive and influential than any occurring in the simpler forms; so that, even when realising that these transformations are merely parts of a larger blind flux, we cannot help feeling that the intricate instruments which effect them are more "important" than the simpler instruments whereby lesser energy-transformations are effected. Hence our persistent instinctive belief that dogs are "higher" than worms, and that men are "higher" than dogs. It really must be admitted as a matter of common sense that this evolutionary scale has a right to be regarded as quasi-absolute which no other scale—moral or otherwise—possesses. Other scales are based on mere human preference, or upon mere practical utility in promoting the survival of human groups, whereas this scale rests on actual fundamental differences in mode of organisation from the elemental units of the cosmos. We may *like* bulldogs better than men, but we can't lightly dismiss the actual fact that men represent a vastly greater degree of differentiation from the primary units of matter and energy than do bulldogs. To call a bulldog "higher" than Xenophanes, Aristotle, Bacon, Milton, Keats, or Santayana would be to strain our natural sense of proportion and probability to a rather grotesque extent. And by that same token, there is something equally grotesque in any effort to place physical strength and achievement on a par with the strength and achievement involving more evolved forms of organic energy. Even though you may value physical strength and courage above all else in an emotional way, I think you can see what I mean when I say that certain other human phenomena are "higher" in the sense of representing a greater differentiation from the blind drift of unorganised electrons.

So much, then, for the absolute organic groundwork. But I think it must be clear to you that certain supplementary valuations are almost impossible to escape. For example—since we are forced to recognise the quasi-absolute "superiority" of men over apes, we cannot avoid attributing a corresponding "superiority" to *the typical manifestations of man's evolutionary differentiation from the ape.* That is, we deem the *fruits of man's capacity* to be somehow more "important" than the more limited fruits of simian capacity; so that we think less of a man who—even if he is *able* to exercise the most evolved human faculties—fails to *utilise reasonably* the qualities which differentiate him from the ape. This variety of valuation may seem confusing, since it bases its standard of human "superiority" not only upon a man's *capacity* but upon *the use he makes of that capacity;* yet it is very natural and deep-seated. "By their fruits shall ye know them". One man may be actually biologically or evolutionarily inferior to another; yet if he exercises his most evolved functions to the limit, while the other lets his capacities lie idle and lives like a primitive ape in spite of them, it is clear that he is the "superior" man so far as his status in the human group—or even absolutely, as an energy-transformer—is concerned.

A little more reflection ought also to explain the system of values whereby we instinctively classify various human activities (as distinct from the men who perform them) along a scale descending from what we call "important" to what we call "trivial". Of course, the element of *absoluteness* grows less, the further off we get from the dependable yardstick of biological status as manifest in a specific organism. But despite the increased latitude for caprice and personal emotion, there exists a good deal of basis for an approximate unanimity of feeling as to what constitutes "high" or "worthy" human activity and what constitutes "trivial" or "primitive" or "low and animal-like" human activity. Roughly, "important" human goals and pursuits are those with which the *most complexly evolved* (= "highest") human qualities are concerned, and vice versa. This does not mean that the primitive matters of security and food and warmth are lacking in importance, since of course these are largely prerequisite to anything else. Perhaps I am phrasing the matter rather clumsily, after all. What I should say is that this criterion of "importance" versus "triviality" is something we do not begin to apply until the matter of material bases has been considered. Its real application is to the goals and pursuits which men choose *after* they have found a means of survival. We call these goals and pursuits "important" if they embody and provide for man's "higher" qualities (taste, intellectual curiosity, sense of order, intelligent civic and economic projects, art, drama, museums, literature, public works, etc. etc.), and "trivial" if they embody and provide only for the "lower" human qualities (physical sense-gratification, play of primitive instinct and immature, undeveloped emotion, etc.—as embodied in overemphasised sports, low-grade writing, acting, or iconography aimed at childish and undeveloped personalities, etc.) which do not involve man's greatest differentiation from other organisms in the direction of complexity. It may seem strange and unacceptable to you, at present, to have a distinction drawn between the human effort which seeks to measure the universe, or crystallise a phase of beauty, or evolve a more harmonious social order, and that which seeks to apply science to the mutual slugging of two sullen giants—but that is something which must be left to time and to your instinctive *sense of proportion*. If what I have somewhat clumsily tried to outline above is not sufficient to indicate why, to most people, a given amount of mental energy put into a serious matter of politics, science, art, or socially motivated engineering is *intrinsically "better" employed* than *the same quantitative amount of mental energy* put into a prize-fight or street brawl or football game (yes, or sedentary bridge or chess game either!) . . . things which basically mean nothing and lead nowhere as judged by the standards of maximum differentiation from unorganised matter and force . . ., then I greatly doubt whether I could in any way make this point clear at the present stage of the debate. Probably my attempts at distinction-drawing seem very forced and artificial—hence all I can say is that they rest on evidence, connexions, and proportion-factors which seem extremely important and virtually conclusive not only to me but to millions of others.

However—in order to forestall possible misunderstanding, let me make it clear that this reference to the *comparative triviality* of certain things *does not in the least form a condemnation of them*. If I speak of certain sports as *essentially minor matter*, I mean no more than that. They have their place. All I am criticising is the system of values which, contrary to nature and proportion, seeks to represent them as of equal status with the really significant major activities of the human spirit. Pugilistic and baseball heroics may be admirable enough in their respective fields. The only mistake is in comparing them to the real titans of human activity—the great discoverers, colonisers, statesmen, artists, scientists, engineers, and leaders of all sorts who extend the frontiers of human comprehension and experience.

About your idea that I exalted formal artistic activity above all other forms of human effort—I don't see quite what I could have said to create it . . . though perhaps I did cite art as a very *typical* aspect of human aspiration at its best. If I did choose formal aesthetics as an illustration, it was perhaps because of its emphatic position as an *end in itself.* Other forms of human activity of equal status are so connected with the mechanics of mere survival that we cannot fully appreciate the *intrinsically rewarding* quality in them. They go toward the patching and fuelling of the necessary social machine, but do not so clearly and visibly illustrate the reasons why that machine is worth saving and running. Hence when it comes to selecting some activity as a type of *what high-grade men live for,* it is natural to pick something which is *exclusively a reward* instead of something which forms part of the struggle to keep alive. The things *which make existence worth enduring* for the well-evolved are the various experiences whereby man's mental, emotional, and imaginative needs are most amply satisfied—whereby, as we phrase it, his personality is the most enriched and expanded. And of the sources of such experiences, none are more typical than the arts and the pure sciences. While of course other forms of effort are just as necessary to keep a civilisation going, it is also true that no civilisation is worth keeping going unless it can supply artistic and intellectual nourishment to its more evolved members. Incidentally—I would not at any time have thought of disputing the fact that the efficient management of a farm—or a factory, or a business, or a government—requires a high degree of intelligence and scientific skill. I would not even dispute that such survival-activities have a concomitant aesthetic quality about them, whereby the successful performer derives a certain amount of intrinsic reward—the glow of an act of symmetrical arrangement well executed—in addition to the purely material fruits. It is simply that pure art and science more emphatically and conveniently illustrate the principle of reward—of a *purpose* in organised human life.

Regarding my objections to an *overemphasis* of ethics—I thought I stated quite plainly that these involved not the slightest depreciation of ethics per se. On the contrary, no one intrinsically values ethics—which, aside from their utilitarian social bearings, are a branch of aesthetics—more than I do. I regard a ruthless, unscrupulous, and unmoral man as essentially vulgar—and, if his amorality be anti-social, as a fit subject for restraint and punishment. All I was driving at was that morals pertain to a *different and less basic* scale of values than does sheer evolutionary status, and that one must not let the ethical bearings of a given organism blind one to its absolute evolutionary bearings. Thus if a certain person or group or type represents a very high degree of purely intellectual achievement, it is erroneous and puerile to deny its importance merely because it may fall short in another field. Take the case of an individual like poor Oscar Wilde, who as a thinker and artist was important, but as a liver of life was a disgusting mess. No person of sense wishes to excuse the low status of his ethics, but on the other hand no person of sense thinks the less of him *as an abstract cultural force* merely because he was such a miserable failure as a man. A telescope may be ugly and battered and repulsive-looking, but that does not count if its optical qualities are notable and unimpaired.[6] The idea is to be on guard against letting a judgment formed on one scale of values interfere with such parallel judgments of the same object as may be formed on other scales of values. Ethics are one thing, but not everything—and as I have pointed out, are certainly not as closely connected with an *absolute* criterion as is the matter of evolutionary status. They are indeed important in the formation of any social fabric, nor do I wish to belittle the balanced regard which they receive from well-proportioned thinkers. What I attacked was merely the prevalent habit—very common where the religious tradition holds or has lately held sway—of letting ethical criteria loom larger than all others. The typical reaction of the average citizen to the "liar-thief-coward" charge—as opposed to the "fool-clod-ape" charge—so aptly cited by you—is a characteristic popular residuum of this moralistic prejudice. However—there is nothing especially absurd about this prejudice except when it goes to the extent of interfering with one's really serious judgments of individuals, institutions, and general trends . . . . . and of course this point has nothing to do with an individual's choice of personal associates, in which ethical factors must necessarily bulk to a very large extent.

Incidentally, I don't recall saying that a high ethical code can exist only in a long-settled and thoroughly civilised region. If I mentioned anything resembling this, it was merely to suggest that only under civilisation can the *fruits* of ethics be reaped. Under barbarism the best of standards and intentions tend to be wasted through the reign of physical force and the absence of any regulating medium. Not that honour and benevolence are necessarily less, but that their operation is more often defeated. There is always a stultifying *callousness* where human life and the integrity of the human form are lightly regarded. Just how this fits into formal, codified ethics I'm not enough of a philosopher to say; but I do know that there's something definitely *immature and incomplete*, even if not definitely *"wrong"*, about a social order where promiscuous ripping and tearing is the natural court of first resort, and is regarded as a mere everyday incident. Undoubtedly there are normal stages of social development where such a code of tooth and claw is inevitable—and therefore not blameworthy. But to exalt such a code as an *ideal* is certainly an error.

Regarding the "ethics" of the lower animals—this is really a purely academic question. What the bulk of organic creation does is simply to react to external stimuli in a fixed way—conditioned by the nature of each organism as determined by fortuitous evolution. There is no such thing as conscious choice of conduct. Each species is merely a machine which behaves in a certain way when certain buttons are pushed. Reflexes can be conditioned, but they are just as automatic for all that. Whether we like or dislike the typical reflexes of a certain species is wholly irrelevant. There is no more reason to call a lower animal (or a primitive man) "good" or "bad", "decent" or "evil" than there is to apply these terms to a volcano or wind or river or sandstorm. All are primitive automatic forces—though of course poetic early man personified and attributed complex human motives to all the phenomena of nature. To our remote forebears, volcanoes and winds and rivers and sandstorms—and all the lower animals—*did* have human motives and ethical consciousness! The lower animal's real motivation is simply one of responding to very elementary stimuli in a fixed way. It does what nature tells it to—even though such dictated performances are often quite complex. In other words, it does what it wants so far as it thinks it is able to. Just how much we like this conduct-pattern, or how we compare it with human conduct-patterns, may be of interest but can scarcely be of significance. As for human patterns—they are basically of the same sort, except that in the more evolved types the responses to external stimuli are vastly more indirect and complicated by the influence of internal subjective stimuli based on memory, rhythm-craving, symbolism, and association. Naturally some human conduct-patterns differ considerably from many lower-animal conduct patterns, but this difference is certainly no greater than that existing among the conduct-patterns of different lower species. One can't establish a grand division of conduct-types and range man on one side and all other animals on the other. Considering the known habits of all the animal forms inhabiting the earth, it sounds pretty radical to assert that man is the most "brutal" of them all. Whether his added degree of consciousness makes him able to inflict more injury than he could if he lacked such consciousness, is a little beside the point. Both man and the lower animals have the same motivation—to gratify their natural urges as far as possible—and each furthers that end by using all the forces at command. What results, depends wholly on the nature of the forces available.

I never heard it stated that "courage, kindliness, and honesty are the exclusive possessions of the human race". Indeed, the qualities one associates especially with mankind are those which concern another side of organic evolution—the side involving perception, coördination, rhythm-sense, idea-association, etc. "Courage" is simply an organic condition based on neural insensitiveness and lack of imagination except in a few cases* where the primitive sort is parallelled by a complex form in which a strong set of special motives so far overshadows the normal perceptions and reflexes of self-preservation that the latter are neutralised. The lower the organism, the less perception and imagination—hence the greater natural "courage"—it will tend to have, although of course there are species specialising in flight. But

---

*not necessarily persons of formal cultivation—merely persons of an exceptional natural type, found in all classes.

the only sort of courage which can be called mainly human is the rare form involving full perceptions and weighed motives. Even so, the form displayed by average humans is probably more often the lower than the higher. As for "kindliness"—this is simply a negative result of lethargy and indifference in the average animal—including the human. Naturally an organism doesn't bother to be hostile unless it has something to gain thereby. Whether the human being has more or less than the bulk of other species (which vary in this respect over an enormous range) it would be almost impossible to say. Certain types of human have imaginative qualities which cause them to cherish social ends; but on the other hand, ants and bees are far more social. On the whole, I don't think that mankind as such has ever laid claim to especial kindliness. As for "honesty"—that is simply the lack of a dual policy—or rather, the lack of an assumed policy to cover a real one. I never heard mankind boast of its superior honesty as a species. On the contrary, all animals, save certain (not all) strongly imaginative men, are as dishonest as they know how to be—the lower ones being less successful in dissimulation because they have less brains. In mankind, "honesty" is essentially an aesthetic or decorative quality—a mark of pride. Honest men, primarily, are those who appreciate the rhythm of a single purpose—plus those who wish to emphasise a power and competence lifting them above the need of strategy.*

So—although the *aesthetic or modelling instinct* of mankind may cause certain ethical qualities like "courage", "kindliness", and "honesty" to be *highly esteemed and cultivated* under the dictation of the imagination, and to be more or less achieved in the case of certain individuals or groups strongly influenced by specific traditions; it would be extravagant to regard these things as *basic organic traits* of homo sapiens. It is not on these things, but upon the intellect and imagination which tend to substitute complex associative motives for many of the primitive urges, and which create whole new spheres of enriched consciousness and experience for the individual, that man's claim to superior status is founded. To be plain, man does not boast of being *morally better* than other animals; but simply of being *more complex* and therefore open to richer consciousness and experience, and intrinsically higher in the scale of structural removal from the simple cell—than are his non-human ancestors and cousins.

One more point—I assume you now realise that what I say of man's definite net superiority *in the cerebral evolutionary scale* does not necessarily involve a claim that *every phase of difference* between man and *his non-human forbears marks an absolute* IMPROVEMENT. In view of the vast number of separate features of any

---

*Of course, much apparent human honesty is simply the result of stupidity and fear. But *aesthetic honesty* must not be thought of as confined to formal aesthetes. The basic urge of pride and rhythm occurs in many types vastly remote from conscious or formal aestheticism.

organism's structure, and of the independent chain of evolutionary accidents lying behind each separate feature, any such claim of a simultaneous parallel advance would be absurd. Man is "superior" to other animals not because he is physically stronger (he can't best the ox and elephant), not because his senses are keener (the dog has a better smeller), and not because he has fewer modes of derangement (as you say, leprosy and syphilis are indeed purely human). He is "superior" simply because a certain local part of his anatomy—the convolutions of nervous tissue in his skull—has happened to undergo a greater development toward complexity and the increased consciousness and imagination which go with complexity. A small change if you look at it externally or try to measure it with a ruler, yet an infinitely vast change when reckoned in terms of actual subjective relationship to the universe. *It is this, and this only, that we praise in mankind.* We do not exalt every phase of human anatomy and physiology as an absolute standard. The phrase "purely human" has no absolute significance except in connexion with the one feature of men which *really has* undergone a more complex upbuilding than any other type of matter and energy known to us in the cosmos. It is the human *mind*—not the human nose or ear or shin-bone—that is great. How could you have fancied I thought otherwise? Did you think I claimed that a man could out-lunge a rhinoceros, outrace a deer, out-roar a lion, or out-tear a wolf?

Mentality—the complex condition of organic matter involving perception, association, reason, imagination, and such other consciousness-factors as produce an extensive, sensitive, retainable, and correlatable response to environmental stimuli—is certainly the most complex (and therefore "advanced") form of matter-and-energy organisation in all time and space of which we have any knowledge. Its status is quasi-absolute in a sense that no other object's or principle's status is; and it might not be going too far to say that *nothing else in our ken is of any real significance.* Only a feeble imagination can fail to realise the *cyclopean, unbridgeable gulf* between the conscious mind of man, with all its perceptions and analyses of its surroundings, and anything else within the radius of our cosmic vision. Whether other complex developments of matter and energy in other abysses of time and space equal or surpass or dwarf to negligibility the human mentality visible to us, it is not likely that we shall ever know. All our feeble terrestrial debating can do is to observe, classify, and justly appraise the one small sample of organic consciousness which actually is before us. It takes the ignorance and effrontery of the religionist to read into the material consciousness precisely like the one which we perceive as a product of certain chance local evolutionary influences operating on a certain form of matter!

April 7

The foregoing instalment was ended by the dusk following a glorious sunset. Since then there has been no day mild enough to invite outdoor writing—hence I continue from my accustomed western window . . . . which overlooks a sunset vista of old roofs and steeples not inferior in picturesqueness, even if vastly less in scope, to that obtained from the Terrace.[7] As I look back over Tuesday's arguments I am inclined to fear that I did not keep my initial promise of brevity and abstinence from bypath-and-foundation-exploration—yet after all what can one do where issues as complex and elusive as those involving *values* are concerned? Issues of that sort simply cannot be clarified in a few words—and any attempt to do so leads merely to confusion and fresh misunderstandings. However—in the pages to come I can perhaps manage to ramble a little less, since I recall expatiating in a former letter (to which, if it is still in existence, I'll refer you when the time comes) on the principal value-question that looms ahead.

In the matter of *freedom* I fancy we differ more in mere taste than in basic theory. I am as ready as you to place a very high valuation on reasonable latitude of action—my difference being that I do not resent such slight curtailments as are necessary to secure other and in some cases more important boons. As for *leisure*—of course I realise that the added leisure inevitably connected with any stable regime of machine economy is *not yet here*. We are unlucky enough to live in a transitional age—with the old order in chaos and the new not yet evolved. But that such general leisure *will eventually exist* there can hardly be any question. There is no longer work enough in any fully mechanised nation to keep all the population employed save by spreading it out through very short hours—and the population will not indefinitely tolerate a regime that leaves a large share without earning power. Whether by evolution or revolution, the short hours are coming sooner or later. It is as nearly inevitable as anything well can be. You are right in pointing out the difficulty of bringing agriculture into the new order, but it will have to be done somehow. Personally, I don't think the *restriction* of agricultural production is a good permanent policy. Certainly, the rewards of agriculture must be increased; but I feel that this increase ought to be effected in some way other than one which lessens the possible resources of the nation. Governmental direction is a necessity in any case, for without it there is probably no possible way to raise agricultural prices. Let the individualists talk as they will, there *must* be governmental price-fixing—and also, I think, governmental purchasing of surpluses for use in collective enterprises. For there is no question but that, in the end, the government will have to take over most of the basic manufacturing industries for largely profitless operation. Machinery has sounded the death-knell of the economic order which we have known. Ultimately I believe that farming will be done coöperatively, on a larger scale. As you point out, present conditions force a few men to work inordinately long hours in order to make a living—yet other men are unable to get any work at all. Agriculture will have to be given such a place in the new order that its rewards will justify the employment of many more men to do the same amount of work—the same principle as that necessary in other industries. But remember that this relief can never come through pioneering individualism. Nothing but the concerted scientific action of a government *which also has power over the urban and industrial areas forming the chief markets* can ever work out the needed adjustment.

Returning to the freedom question—it seems to me that your comparison of a man in prison to one working at a salaried job for the usual number of hours is a rather exaggerated one. There are plenty of differences—as most will be very ready to admit. I don't see many salaried men applying for berths in gaol! The average salaried man has about as much free time as the business man who employs him and with the wages of normal times he has usually been able to have a fairly good time in life. This of course does not apply to the so-called depressed classes—but even they have been the objects of much serious philanthropic planning which will later bear fruit when industry is governmentally controlled. That the amount of time and energy demanded of a man (either employer or employed) by industry is excessive—that he ought to have more time for his own interests and the free expression of his personality—is universally conceded by modern sociologists . . . . but the only way this can possibly be secured is through governmental control. Under individualism a man may call himself free, but if he does not comply with the terms of industry the freedom will be a foodless and shelterless one. And no pioneering revival can provide a cure for this.

Incidentally—no argument of mine in this line should be taken as a reflection upon any special profession which *does* happen to give greater leisure to the few able to follow it. I have no grudge against commercial writing, except that I hate to see it stifling anybody who could do notable work if freed from its demands. In your case I merely wish that the economic order should provide some source of income making less demands on your time and energy, and leaving you free to develop to the full the remarkable powers of dramatic vision, imagination, and expression manifest in your stories and letters. It seems unfortunate that such potentially magnificent material is still unwritten . . . . the epics of the Southwest, the annals of other days, and fantasies of forgotten civilisations . . . . . though perhaps it *will* all be written some day, when economic conditions are different. With your youth, you will live to see days far different from the present.

I thought I took pains to emphasise my appreciation of the difference between your freedom-worship and that of the self-conscious "intelligentsia". The reason I mentioned the latter at all was merely because they form, today, the most vociferous protesters against all curtailment of indiscriminate licence. I can surely understand the preference of anybody for a rural, uncrowded environment—though it seems to me that such can be found in our existing civilisation. It is not necessary to revert to bloodthirsty barbarism to secure a setting free from the friction of urban life. New England is full of villages and farms where one can be extremely independent—and yet our people don't carve one another up over trifles. I myself much prefer a *village* to a *city* environment—indeed, the environment of my youth was really half rural, since the old home was so close to what was then the edge of the compact district that a walk of a couple of blocks brought one to the ancient fields and woods and farmsteads of bygone centuries. I would never be at ease in a really metropolitan retention of the village atmosphere. I think I told you that the venerable precipice on which I live still retains in many places the grassy lanes, rambling walled gardens, and overtaken farmhouses of a simpler and earlier age. Right now I am looking out over as quiet an old garden as any village of 1500 could produce . . . . . with the valiant but orderly Mr. Osterberg drowsily perched on his favourite fence. Only the distant towers of the lower town suggest the urban.

Regarding the frontier—I hope I have by this time made it plain that I do not disparage it as a logical and necessary outgrowth of its time and place. Not for a moment have I ever confused it with the violence and chaos of *decadence* (very different thing, involving a *complete lapse of standards* instead of a seriously regarded and rigidly enforced code of primitive standards), or compared it to the alien gangster-activities of contemporary megalopolis. (Incidentally, I assume you realise that such gangsterism is not a native product of our civilisation, but a product of the lawless instincts of foreigners living among us but not of us.) I don't suppose my idea of the frontier is even half correct as yet, since my sources of really first-hand information are so recent and limited . . . indeed, if it were not for your own vividly dramatic letters I should be all at sea. Thus all my observations are largely tentative. I don't try to criticise—I merely suggest a few conditions forming what seems to me a rational minimum for endurable living, without attempting to judge how completely the frontier world met them. When I speak of *endurable living,* I mean living as judged by any normally varied population. You surely realise that you cannot prove a certain state of society to be a paradise merely because it completely satisfies *one special type of adventurous individual.* Adventurous men can enter a region and thrive on a programme of tension and hostility and shooting, but that does not mean that all their children can tolerate such a gory and unfruitful arena. To maintain a *general population* with the normal varieties of human taste, a region must not be fitted for one special type alone. What could an orderly-minded boy demanding opportunities for self-development do in a region where all his energies must be dedicated to the savage knife-and-gun guarding of a meagre heritage? Where is he going to get the schools and libraries and galleries and museums and colleges and other opportunities that most mature minds demand—these things, and the chance to utilise them without having to be on guard against the bullets of thugs who want to steal his cattle and outlaws who don't like the tone of his conversation in public places. You may say that such "poor sissies" had better go away to the effete east where people are "soft" enough to insist on law and order and to value the development of man's highest faculties—and yet in the end I fear you'll find such "poor sissies" in the majority. For most men had rather develop than claw and shoot. In the end, no normally balanced population of civilised Caucasian heritage will be willing to tolerate an environment which denies them the security and facilities for development—hence the frontier can be permanent only so far as it can meet such reasonable demands. If the normally varied children of the original adventurers cannot work out a compromise with the few who wish for a prolongation of the primitive struggle, then it is difficult to see how that primitive few can be satisfied save by duplicating the course of their adventurous ancestors and faring forth in search of other untamed regions. One can't expect the conquest of the wilderness to be a continuous process on the same spot. Of course you will say that you don't expect the frontier to be permanent—that you merely regret that you didn't live when it fully existed—but certainly, there must be a subconscious cherishing of a permanent frontier ideal behind your repeated attacks on all the attributes of settled civilisation. For my part, I don't resent the frontier when it is necessary. I can even see that it favours many valuable human qualities. I merely think that when advantages and drawbacks are compared, settled (not necessarily *urban*) civilisation can show the *most* advantages. Not that the frontier lacks advantages, or that settled civilisation lacks disadvantages—but merely that the latter enables a maturely evolved personality to get incomparably more out of life in the long run.

What you say of the opportunities for advancement on the frontier are doubtless true—yet kindred opportunities are not lacking in many forms of settled civilisation. Early New England, with its exceptionally orderly history, can produce as many examples of the rise of vigorous characters from obscurity as can the sanguinary west. Our history from 1630 to 1760 is worth studying. You may say that this era of advancement has closed—but were you not saying that the west's also has? My point is that, admitting the evils of over-urbanised civilisation, the terroristic frontier is not the only alternative. Colonisation and settlement—a kind of pioneering, one may say—is possible under a regime of civilised order. Early New Englanders rose no less quickly because they referred their differences to well-constituted and universally respected courts, and provided educational advantages to their children. They had all the opportunities without the waste of energies and callousing of sensibilities inherent in the maintenance of pistol "justice" and murderous tension. And kindred combinations of opportunity and orderliness existed all the way down the Atlantic coast. As for occasional severity toward heretics—this was mild as compared with the frontier's attitude toward heretics to its code . . . . as when a man refused to feed outlaws.

But let me pause to avoid misapprehension. In pointing to the east's orderly settlement, I am *not* thereby attacking the conditions of the west's set-

tlement. The regions themselves—their facilities and demands, and their inevitable circumstances of colonisation—determined the course of events in
each. Each set of colonists, given the other's conditions, would have done
just as the other set did. I am merely trying to show that there *are* cases when
all the opportunities of the frontier can be encountered under civilisation.
And by the way—don't let it be thought that I am trying to idealise the early
New Englanders. It was simply their good fortune to carry over the European
concept of law and order, and to be able to enforce it *among themselves*. Admittedly, their conduct toward the Indians was ruthless and inexcusable . . . . .
nothing can condone the wholesale slaughter of Narragansetts in the Great
Swamp Fight of 1675 . . . . a slaughter going far beyond the necessities of self-
defence and legitimate expansion.

    Another thing—it occurs to me that we are both making the mistake of
drawing too sharp a line betwixt the frontier and settled civilisation. In many
respects there might be approaches of the one to the other—fusions of good
qualities and eliminations of bad ones on either side. A vast lot of the things
you resent in civilisation are not proper attributes of civilisation at all, but
products of a decadence as bitterly opposed by urbanites as by yourself. Conversely, I can well imagine that many dyed-in-the-wool frontiersmen may agree
with me in deploring callousness toward human life and the quick resort to
brutal murderousness in trivial disputes. I am probably unconsciously doing
the frontier an injustice when I seem to imply that it does not basically repudiate the crudely sanguinary tactics which inevitable circumstances have occasionally forced upon it. Let it not for a moment be thought that I would have
anything but admiration for a spacious-minded region of large-scale agriculture
and stock-raising operating under proper protection and legislation, and with a
normal regard for human life, bodily integrity, and the providing of civilised
opportunities for development . . . . . schools, libraries, and so on. *I dare say
large slices of the old frontiers are like that.* Indeed, my friend in Clovis, N.M. seems
to reflect a very civilised yet vigorous frontier milieu in his letters. Don't let my
ignorance be mistaken for prejudice. What I oppose *isn't the frontier, but merely
certain human callousnesses, wherever they occur.* Indeed, I resent them *far more* in urban people—who have no excuse for entertaining them—than in those upon
whom they have been forced by historic circumstance.

    As to any obscurity in my supposition that your regard for the frontier is
based on a *moralistic attitude*—here is what I meant. You praise the frontier
because it emphasises certain *moral qualities*—qualities of *character* like courage,
resourcefulness, honesty, fairness, and so on—*at the same time ignoring its unfavourable effect on other phases of human development* . . . its absence of good educational facilities, etc. That would seem to argue *that you value moral qualities more
than you value a general development of the personality.* Is my meaning now clearer? I
don't see any inconsistency in my assumption, for your tolerance toward outlaws and other killers would imply only that you don't regard their form of

anti-social activity as gravely unethical. Every different individual has his own moral code—but some hold theirs lightly, some with philosophical relativity, and some very zealously . . . . . whatever that code may happen to be. I am a sort of middle-grounder—personally following the ethics of my heritage, and preferring others who do; but endeavouring not to let moral bias blind me to values which have nothing to do with morals. I would resent—physically if necessary—any imputation on my own honour; and yet I would not exaggerate the position of honour in the general scheme of things, or imagine that it can serve as a substitute for other essential phases of human personality.

As you see, the gist of my whole objection to excessively primitive conditions is *that they do not give human personality a chance to develop fully, and to exercise the whole of its fruitful potentialities.* My charge is that a regime of callous struggle and violence—all for mere survival and material gain—gives no maturely developed personality an adequate reason for existence. No average person of adult emotions can get the most out of life in a region where there is not enough security to allow schools, libraries, museums, and the atmosphere and conversation-opportunities which go with such things, to flourish.

Such is my position—and it applies as much to the debate on *barbarism* as to that on the *frontier.* Now I am perfectly aware that you will attack this position, seeking to undermine the *values* on which it is based. You will say that, because a special minority of born adventurers can get perfect satisfaction from a roving life of physical incident, no person would need more than such a life if his tastes were not "corrupted" by civilisation. You would set a seal of perfect approval on a social order satisfying only to this rare adventurous type, and call it just as intrinsically good as a social order able to satisfy the emotionally maturer types who demand security and chances to develop the more evolved parts of their personality. Indeed, you would deny that a man demanding full development is emotionally maturer than one content with hazardous adventure—basing your denial on a denial of the superiority of the qualities whose development the first man demands. In your opinion, the struggle for material gain—including both the physical combat and the exercise of shrewdness and judgment necessary to success on the frontier—involves just as high a type of human development as the struggle for personality-unfoldment typified by man's enlargement of his mental horizon and area of appreciative sensitiveness. You think a crude, narrow, ignorant man of few vistas and sensitivenesses, but of great physical strength, native keenness of judgment, acquisitive ability, courage, and honesty, represents just as perfect and worthy a development of the human raw material as does a man of balanced vision, trained sense of proportion, enlightened information, developed taste, and awakened sensitivenesses, possessing in addition many of the courageous and honourable qualities of the other type. You think this so keenly that you even *prefer* a social order which caters to Type A rather than to Type B. You would rather that Type B did not exist, so that there would be no need of a civilisation fulfilling his needs. You would prefer that nothing be known of the world and universe beyond the savage's or barbarian's narrow ken; that no rhythmic eloquence ever fall from human lips, nor any painting, sculpture, music, and architecture ever flow from the human imagination; that no force of nature be harnessed in man's service, and that no enlightened sociology free man from the slavery of the priest-king and strive to bring out his fullest potentialities in a rationally organised society. You would rather see three-fourths of man's personality—the ¾ involving these instincts highest in the scale of evolution—forever drugged to sleep and uselessness by ignorance, violence, and the material struggle. And you would call the resultant quarter-man a whole man—and claim that a society framed to fit him is better than one framed to fit a really whole man. You would do this because you refuse to recognise that any one type of human activity is "higher" than any other; because you think that a group of shrewd, honest, courageous fighters struggling for material survival form just as admirable and just as happy a social fabric as a group of orderly and enlightened men exercising rational perceptions and enjoying vistas and imaginative experiences which involve the highest evolutionary elements, incalculably enrich the emotional life, and depend wholly on the broadened perspective and enlarged sensitivenesses made possible by normal security and decent cultivation.

Well—what can one reply to all this? You sneer at human development—and as Dean Milman said (or rather, *quoted* from Paley) in his preface to Gibbon, "Who can refute a sneer?"[8] I shan't try to refute a sneer at the validity of human development and the need for a culture catering to the developed man. I don't need to. As I admitted at the outset, no question of values can be settled with really definite logic. So I will merely refer back to my first argument on the subject of *basic standards of human development* (cf. sheets V, 2 to VII, 2) in order to explain why *I* (and countless millions of others) *believe* (be it rightly or wrongly) that a man with full intellectual and aesthetic cultivation is (other things being equal) a tremendously more intrinsically important entity than a man lacking such cultivation, and that no social order is worthy of tolerance as a permanent goal or ideal unless it lives up to the possibilities of the human race by providing for the acquisition of the cultivation by such of its members as can assimilate it.

That is all I can say. *I think* that reason—plain common sense—is on my side. I can't *see* any evidence to the contrary. Perhaps that is because I am ignorant—but these are my beliefs, and I think my earlier remarks on values (whether foolish or not) will prove that I do not hold them hastily, unreflectively, or capriciously. If I err, I do so honestly and through no fault of my own. I have tried to look at every side of the question—including what you say of the loss of unrestraint which sometimes comes as the price of development—but I can't see it any way but this. It seems flamingly obvious to me that a mature and enlightened civilisation is so *infinitely and incalculably* superior (in a basically intrinsic way, and not merely as my personal taste views it) to a state of barbarism or frontierism which represses the highest side of human activity, that *nothing* which is lost in its acquisition can possibly be compared with what is gained. Laugh if you will—but before ridiculing my assumption that the fruits of civilisation are necessarily worthy more than the licence of barbarism read over my argument on development-values again. You will at least see that I have *considered* the point—that I realise the need of justifying a quasi-absolute preference before basing any important opinion on it.

But possibly I have missed the point. You may concede the *theoretical* superiority of a full personality, but insist that this means nothing in a purpose-less cosmos. You may contend that the only valid standard (apart from the moral code which makes you exalt courage, fairness, and honesty) is the hedonistic one, and *that one social order is as good as another, provided it satisfies the bulk of its members as well as any could.* That is, (to illustrate by an extreme example) you would think a savage culture of sadistic torturers and marble-players just as *good* (even though not as *"high"*) as a nation of philosophers *provided the members wanted nothing more than they had.* You belong to the school of thought (to which, incidentally, I myself belonged at one period—for my beliefs constantly change as new evidence presents itself) which believes that pleasure or richness of experience is *purely a balance between desire and fulfilment,* so that a cat basking comfortably in the sun *is just as happy and rich in experience* as a scientist verifying a discovery, or poet capturing a mood, or philosopher grasping a value-concept. By that theory, a barbaric or pioneer culture would surely be the hedonistic peer of any provided it satisfied the primitive (in the case of barbarism) or exceptional (in the case of frontierism) emotions of those composing it. I wish it were so—for the sake of my tiger friend in the garden below, who has now gone over to the shed roof looking for his black and white friend Mr. Randall. I'd like to think that the delectable furry gentlemen of the Kappa Alpha Tau[9] led as rich lives as anybody else! But as earlier letters have shown you, I am no longer able to adhere to that view. I now believe—after the maturest sort of reflection—*that the satisfaction of a richly stored and sensitively developed human consciousness is intrinsically and quantitatively greater than that of any unawakened or half-awakened primitive consciousness can be.* Despite the greater pain-quota provided by increased world-contacts and sensitiveness, I believe that cultivation raises the appreciation-quota or pleasure-quota to a much higher degree. An enlightened and artistic man or group *can have a vastly better time, intrinsically,* than a barbaric man or group. And all this apart from the question (V, 2–VII, 2) of higher evolutionary status. I realise that in your opinion the intellectual strategy and goal-fulfilment of a pioneer struggle for subsistence and wealth affords as great a real reward as the development of broadened vision and sensitive taste—but I honestly can't agree. When I think of the *enormous* bulk of *keen, active pleasure* which a developed taste and vision adds to one's life—no matter how much pleasure one may have thought one had before—I simply cannot believe that anybody would be just as well off without it. Certainly, the process of acquisition is not offset by any corresponding loss. The gain is net—and enormous.

But in case you tend to shelve this as "just another *value* question", let me refer you back to a former letter (unfortunately I can't recall *which* one) in which I went into this matter quite exhaustively. You may remember when I tried to demonstrate that a rich cerebral life must indubitably involve a much greater amount of metabolic cell activity—of a pleasurable sort—than a meagre subsistence-struggle varied by primitive relaxations. I tried to point out that this principle furnished almost a quantitative yardstick wherewith to measure pleasure in terms of energy-transformation. Possibly the matter produced no impression on you then; but if you'll go back to it now—in the light of the present argument—I think it may take on a more illuminating aspect. You'll probably disagree with my view—but you will at least appreciate that I have considered the point with minute care. In short, *I can't see any way in which an alert civilisation is not infinitely more rewarding than any form of primitive or semi-primitive life could possibly be.*

I'm not denying that pioneering appeals vastly to certain very superior types of men, but I'm merely claiming that these types are exceptional. We can't generalise too extensively from their reactions and satisfactions. And I don't think even these men would feel quite at ease if there were no civilised world to send them literature and to be in readiness in case they might some day wish to return to it. As for barbarians—though most of the old northern tribes never really knew any other existence, I think many facets of their history furnish significant evidence of the essential incompleteness of their lives. They were too high-grade organisms for the institutions they had, and most of them were moving rapidly toward civilisation. Of the psychological abnormalities caused by their barren lives, anthropologists like Briffault have revealed much. We all know of their moodiness (what a psychiatrist would call schizophrenia or manic-depressive aberration), their berserk outbreaks, and their tragic sottishness in quest of artificial oblivion. All these things cannot be offset by their occasionally childish exuberance.

Nor is this all. Modern biology and anthropology strikingly corroborate from a wholly independent angle the point that barbaric or primitive life is *essentially and absolutely unsuited to the emotions of average normal adults of the white race* .... that it is, inherently and unmistakably, *immature and juvenile*. This comes through what Haeckel[10] called the *first and basic law of all biogeny*—namely, that in outstanding essentials, *the history of any life-series is repeated in the development of the individual from egg to senility.* As he put it, *ontogeny* repeats *phylogeny*. The human embryo before birth duplicates virtually all the basic forms which man's ancestry has included—being at one period, for example, *gilled*—like the fishes far back in our heritage. Well—the parallelism keeps up after birth as well as before; the development of the individual's endocrine glands (which determine desires, tastes, and personality) repeating with remarkable precision the corresponding development of the race-stock's endocrine glands from a low mammal stage (stage of man at birth) to successive later stages including those of the quadrupeds (Dr. Hrdlicka of the Smithsonian Institution[11] has extensively investigated the reactions of babies at the stage where quadrupedal instincts are likely to crop out), the higher apes (prehensile qualities in infants are strikingly developed), the human sub-races (flat nose, rudimentary chin), the evolved savage races (cruelty, anti-social narcissism, etc.), the barbaric races (love of wild life—hunting and fishing—irresponsible irritability—continued cruelty gradually evolving into mere callousness—pugnacity—gang or tribal spirit and loyalties—social consciousness still repudiating external society but concentrating on single natural leaders—hero-worship—wanton destructiveness—contempt for refinement—reliance on violence as a deciding element—imitativeness—mechanical constructiveness—the running-away impulse, etc. etc. etc.), the young-mature races (artistic and emotional fervour of adolescence—sentimental worship of ethical values—patriotic zeal—religious mania), the settled civilised races (normal social, constructive, peaceful, orderly instincts—intellectual curiosity—sense of disciplined form—craving for security), and finally the decadent races (vacillation, timidity, senile caprice, return of infantile characteristics, etc.). This is a significant cycle universally recognised—and the present point of it is that *we always find the typical emotions and perspectives and habits of barbaric or otherwise late-primitive society exactly and strikingly reproduced in the pre-adolescent boy of about 10 or 11 or 12.* The implications are unmistakable. Barbarism is what satisfied the race when its natural emotional development was what a 10-year-old boy's is now; hence the only white human beings it can continue to satisfy fully and in large quantities are 10-year-old boys. It is the small boy who naturally turns to physical violence as a vindicator and decider, who is callous regarding the infliction of injury, who magnifies physical courage and exalts outlaw leaders, and who in short duplicates all that barbarians and primitives felt in their day. Of course, something of the 10-year-old boy—or the barbarian or pioneer if you will—survives in nearly all of us . . . but most of us have too little of it to be *permanently satisfied* with a social order aimed to suit the needs of that stage of emotional (note that emotional, mental, and physical development are wholly separate things—a boy may be *intellectually* precocious yet *emotionally* infantile, and at the same time *physically* average. Any one of these lines of development may shoot ahead or stay normal, or lag behind, independently of any other) development. We can't get away from the fact that primitivism is essentially *immature*—not generally suitable, by the laws of nature, for the average adults of our race. This is a matter of strong *objective* evidence, biological and anthropological, and has nothing to do with anybody's prejudice or preference one way or the other.

But remember, this is not a condemnation of the frontier. No one supposes that the pioneers chose their life—and determined its details—because they were emotional holdovers from small-boyhood. On the contrary, as I have clearly emphasised before, pioneer life was the natural result of the effort of intelligent, resourceful, courageous, and capable men to cope with a given set of natural, social, economic, and industrial conditions; and in view of those conditions the result cannot be regarded as other than successful and admirable. It is impossible, I think, in view of all evidence, to believe that their leaders did not strive *toward law and order*—envisaging law and order as an indispensable condition of the ultimate empire they were building. My whole attitude will be misrepresented if it is thought that I have other than a sincere admiration for, and a great interest in, the pioneers themselves. Also, don't fancy that I am *belittling* your own taste in the matter even when I *criticise* it on the basis of the value-scheme I have taken such pains to expound. It is, as I've said before, my opinion that you believe as you do mainly because you have not given the *external* evidence a thorough and minute analysis in the light of all the complex factors (some of which I've sought to suggest) that have a vital bearing on it. I don't expect you to agree to all I'm propounding—but I think you may at least concede that I have strong reasons for believing as I do. Let me add that the most significant phase of the controversy seems to me that concerning actual *barbarism* rather than pioneering. The two phases are of course inextricably intertwined, but the principles at stake appear most clearly when we range general barbarism against general civilisation.

Your description of many of the causes of typical pioneer folkways interested me greatly. Boundary or resource disputes are certainly among the most ancient causes of animosity . . . . I suppose you recall that the very word *rival* comes from the Latin word *rivalis* (in turn from *rivus,* a brook), which signifies a man who uses a boundary brook in common with his neighbour. I certainly don't criticise the pioneers for defending their boundaries forcibly in the absence of any court authority competent to render an impartial and effective verdict based on the proper records. Regarding the treatment of open-gate-leavers—one may only hope that the element of deliberate malice was well proved before the administering of the extreme penalty. I certainly agree with you as to the unwisdom and unfairness of hastily judging a differently-environed group—but you can easily see how hard it must have been in pioneer days for an eastern traveller to realise the difference of the conditions prevailing in the west. It is easy to comprehend the differences existing in foreign lands among alien peoples, but hard to perceive equally great differences in a region where the people and language and *hereditary* traditions are one's own. In the case of the Boston cattle-magnate you will have to admit that the idea of committing what forms a grave crime according to the race's general code—i.e., giving aid and comfort to a robber and fugitive from justice—was enough to give anybody a sizeable psychological wrench. A more adaptable or broad-visioned man would doubtless have met the situation more tactfully and comprehendingly—but vision and flexibility are not given to all! What really *was* inexcusably pusillanimous was his cringing when faced with the outlaw's pistol. Even when up against a wild beast, a sincere upholder of principle does not need to cringe. It is better to perish defiant and unbroken, even when helpless, than to disgrace one's cause with ignominious crudity and bounderism . . . as much so by the standards of the east as by those of the west. It involved such a lack of any sense of proportion that he could nowhere have gained such sympathy. He surely got what was coming to him—and his penalizer amply earned that vacation with pay!

I note especially what you say of laws hastily passed without a study of the peculiar local conditions dangerously affected by them; and agree that they ought to be forestalled if possible, and largely nullified in practice if unavoidably passed. Certainly, nothing will more gravely weaken an innate respect for the law, than laws which no sensible person can respect. That is one of the many reasons why I believe all legislative and other government power will have to be confined to highly trained, intelligent, and deeply informed officials, as determined by stiff examinations, if (in this age of complexly inter–locked interests and issues dependent on involved technology) we are to escape a lapse into utter chaos. The cases you cite are quite typical.

As to the question of violence attending free expression of opinion—I don't gather quite how drastically the principle works in every-day practice. Just how excusable violence at expressed opinion is, would seem to me to depend greatly on the degree of real offensiveness of the opinion—for certainly, nothing is more wastefully and criminally immature than a resort to fatal weapons over what a well-balanced adult would recognise as essentially trivial. It was the grotesque and repulsive wastefulness and disproportionateness inherent in the later days of duelling—when men used measures over *trifles* which properly pertained only to the avenging of deep, inexpiable wrongs—which brought the duel into its ultimate disrepute in non-Continental countries. The logical response to *trivial* disrespect is reciprocal disrespect in kind—nothing pays off a casual slight so well as a still more cutting reply which deflates the offender at the same time that it refutes the offence. Even if one have not the spontaneity to meet a slight appropriately and devastatingly, there are firm attitudes and remarks which show one's unbroken repudiation as well as wit. However—this is of course merely a matter of custom. Though in settled civilised regions a too ready resort to fisticuffs is considered stupid and clownish, the exact degree of derogation needed to excite them may well be left to local tastes. Of course, they are called for in *all* regions when the degree of derogation passes certain limits. In the present age, it seems certain that *deadly weapons* for such reprisals are inexcusable under any circumstances except after due notice, and in return for a *vitally grave* wrong. How necessary they may have been to the every-day maintenance of self-respect or community respect in the irritable elder world of the pioneer, I am not historian enough to say. By the way—I hope that the custom of

752 ❖ *A Means to Freedom*

shooting or challenging the utterers of dissenting opinion did not extend to expressions of honest, impersonal views where no affront to anyone was intended. If everyone who differed with anyone else on any question was forced to back up his opinion with a revolver or knife, the result must necessarily have been a denial of the right of free speech as drastic as anything the Nazis have contemplated! Honest thought and enlightened opinion can never exist where men are not free to communicate their sincere views on the various vital topics of the world. It is such an unhampered exchange of opinion which makes human company agreeable, and raises us from the condition of narrow bigots to that of broadly enlightened citizens and well-proportioned thinkers. Fancy Millikan and Compton settling their differences over the nature of the cosmic rays with a pair of bowie-knives!

As for my mention of the frontier's social order as "inefficient in achieving goals"—I did not seek to imply that the inefficiency was *avoidable*. I merely called attention to the fact that a tremendous amount of waste and diverted energy is involved in any regime where guerilla warfare and wholesale massacre are called in to take the place of that protective regulation which the law is normally able to afford. I didn't say that the law *could* have afforded proper regulation in frontier days—indeed, I feel certain it could not have, and believe the frontiersmen did the best they could. I merely regretted that such cruel waste *had* to exist, and suggested that the regime involving it was scarcely one to wish back again if anything better has been attained or seems reasonably possible of early attainment. The specific problems you cite are immensely interesting as glimpses of a stirring phase of empire-building—indeed, all your pictures of southwestern life seem to me to form genuine literature. As for solutions—in the case of the two herds at the water-hole, fairness and reason would of course suggest that *half* of each be watered, so that the degree of gain and loss sustained by each of the equally-situated outfits might be equal. That, undoubtedly, is what the law would dictate if able to be invoked and enforced. In the absence of law, it would depend on the herdsmen in question. If thoroughly imbued with a sense of fairness, they would probably agree on a half-and-half programme themselves. If not—and I suppose only a few sensitive men would be—they would probably start a general massacre killing off vast numbers and perhaps leaving both herds without guardians. That would be a natural and perhaps inevitable result of the situation without the law—but it would scarcely be an ideal one. In the case of the fenced spring, law-abiding men would surely seek a verdict from some impartial umpire, perhaps proposing a bargain whereby the spring-owner would sell water at some rate (perhaps consisting of future concessions of some sort) agreed upon, and dependent on the amount of stock he might have to lose through the lessening of his own supply. But I'm not saying that this could be enforced in the absence of a legal background. It is the inability of the pioneers to achieve such a background that one laments. In the case of the unbranded calf, it seems to me that men of sense would have rationally tried to settle the issue of ownership—and if there was nothing to decide this, acknowledge the animal as *joint property*—giving it a special brand and equally dividing the ultimate proceeds of its sale. That they could seldom do so is what one laments—even though one realises that the condition was inevitable.

As for *modern* western violence—I suppose, as I have said in other letters, that it is an inevitable legacy of the old pioneer days—a result of that dulling of the sense of the importance of human life which the ancient conditions could not help breeding. It is of course deplorable, both in civilians and in policemen—but how can policemen be expected to use forbearance in a region where citizens commonly resort to firearms and knives instead of invoking the proper legal processes or discussing matters with rational compromises? What I am driving at is that *the habit of regarding weapon fights lightly, and of using weapons on slight provocation,* is bound to affect policemen's psychology in such a way that they will show an equally careless ruthlessness in their own actions. The only remedy is to build up a higher standard of human forbearance—to outlaw the free use of weapons and restore the Anglo-Saxon's original heritage of law, order, and rational adjustment. That is what I meant when I said that the *real* need of Texas in meeting the evils outlined by you and in the *Gladewater Journal* is not *less* civilisation but *more.* If the citizens would outlaw violence as it is outlawed in the older Anglo-Saxon regions, there would be an infinitely better chance of improving the police. As you know, none of the extremes you have described could occur in Rhode Island or in England. The London police carry no firearms, and are instructed never to use their sticks except under extreme provocation. As a result, they are extremely popular as a class among every element in the community. In the eastern U.S. the police are armed, but no law-abiding person ever sees one of their revolvers in use. And policemen are nearly as popular here as in England. They tend to be genial and helpful—almost universally so outside New York, and more or less so even there. To my mind, this condition is simply one phase of the general law-abidingness of the regions in question. I hardly need point out again that the criminal of today—in the east—is in 80% of all instances a foreigner. The bookings at the Providence station-houses read like mixed censuses of Naples, Sicily, Poland, the Cape Verde Islands, and the St. Roch slums of Quebec. These are not fruits of any civilisation of ours, and do not change the hereditary good will subsisting between the police and the native population. However, one may of course make no prophecies of the future. What I *call* the east is the old American East of the past. It may be that a slow decadence is setting in—both here and all over the heretofore civilised world. We can't tell as yet. Certainly the utterly ruthless and standardless gangs of foreign killers are an insidious menace which may eventually lower the hitherto high local standard of law-abidingness and respect for human life. Even now some complain of a growing tendency of young romantics to side with the criminals instead of with the police when the two clash. When I was a boy we used to play detective and policeman, but now I hear that many of the modern boys play gangster instead. That's surely a hopeful sign! But so far promiscuous violence and ready resort to firearms is still unheard-of among respectable native Americans in this part of the world. All that kind of thing is what we associate with the turbulent foreigners. Incidentally—you of course realise that all the displays of violence in the northeast which you mention are foreign phenomena. Anti-Nazi mobs consist of hysterical Jews urged on by radicals, and all radical groups are of central or southeastern European origin. However—don't let it be thought that the east views these things with complacency. They are not tamely accepted as parts of the local tradition, and their great infrequency and abortiveness shows how generally discouraged and well-controlled they are. But of course all regions have their sporadic riots—old London, Boston, and Providence being no exceptions. This vague and infrequent milling of the ignorant and desperate is hardly to be confused with a tradition of lawlessness whereby all the community holds life lightly and resorts to force readily. The difference is tremendous. The oppression of certain unskilled labouring elements by exploiting mine-and-mill-owners is an evil which no impartial observer denies. All agree that it is to be fought without ceasing, and few doubt but that the social and economic developments of the future will tend to end it. I freely agree that the ruthlessness of the powerful elements responsible for such conditions is every inch as crude as the violence of barbarism or the frontier. Naturally, civilisation does not wholly abolish evil and oppression. What does? It merely restricts the area of lawlessness—but that restriction is generally extensive enough to allow for the growth of a whole expanded life which could not exist without it. That much is clear gain, and later one hopes that (in spite of occasional lapses toward decadence) the area of control may be extended to cover the whole of society and reduce avoidable injury and suffering to a vastly smaller minimum.

As to the state of civilisation in Germany—of course what I said about the crudity of cultural youth as an explanation was only a guess. Who can really do more than guess? Since my former letter Spengler's "Hour of Decision" has appeared,[12] and it is interesting to note this philosopher's doubts of the future. He is, as a result, getting in a bit bad with the Nazis—though his book has not been censored.

Getting at last to the question of barbarism—really a more basic issue than the frontier—I trust that some phases of the discussion have already been disposed of in the value-demonstrations connected with the frontier argument. In outlining many of those demonstrations I really had this matter of barbarism primarily in mind. Thus I won't have to repeat my point that barbarism's prime flaw is its failure to bring out the highest parts of the human personality—that it is essentially keyed to the emotions of small boys and unsuited to white adults at the present historic stage. I won't have to repeat that it could never satisfy the natural aspirations of high-grade men. Coming directly to your points—I do not deny that civilised life includes much suffering (slums, mines, etc.), but I *do* deny that the *proportion* of the suffering is even nearly as great as the proportion of suffering under barbarism. Nor is oppression of this sort peculiar to civilisation. You forget that the barbarians had large quotas of slaves and serfs whose lot must have been at least not less miserable than that of the underprivileged today. As to the number of depression-sufferers—of course it isn't "insignificant" *in relation to our modern norm*. But none the less it is probably vastly less than the proportional number of sufferers in a state of barbarism. Critics of different social systems too often make the mistake of comparing a certain class in one to a *wholly different* class in another. Thus you say that the lot of a *civilised peasant or plebeian or yeoman* is probably inferior to that of a *primitive northern freeman*. Well—what if it is? The barbarian *freeman* was the equivalent of a *gentleman** or even *petty nobleman* in the civilised world. If you want the equivalent of a civilised *peasant*, look to the barbarian's *serfs and slaves!*† But it was not alone the serf or slave who suffered. The whole race did. With all the higher and wider powers of the personality left undeveloped (I refer to *real* barbarians—of course the Britons and some others were well on the road to real civilisation), with every hardship of nature inflicted, and with the menace of inhuman cruelty (cf. Gallic sacrifice, treatment of captives, etc.) and constant slaughter (frequency of war and private armed quarrels) constantly hanging over, there was certainly little enough for the barbarian to live for. One does not wonder at his savagely perverted psychology and his constant efforts to seek oblivion in swinish drunkenness. As to the toll of disease and accident as opposed to the corresponding toll in civilisation—I don't think statistics would favour the barbarian. Granting that their physique was hardened to a degree above the modern level, the hellish mangling of their constant needless warfare remains. They were constantly cutting one another to pieces‡ for trivial and capricious reasons, yet lacked the art to patch themselves up as modern man manages to do. Of their basic *unhappiness* there can be no doubt. Nothing in their lives rewarded what they had to suffer. Sombreness is in all their folklore, and you know from Tacitus[13] how they languished in sloth and gluttony between their fits of ill-motivated butchering. They were innate sadists, and their quarels when coarsened by liquor were frequent and sanguinary. Just what redeeming feature life held for them is doubtful. If the pleasure of constant butchery sustained them, it does as much for many madmen today

---

*whether you'd call a Saxon *ceorl* (before the Conquest) a yeoman or gentleman is a toss-up. But an *eorl* was certainly a noble

†The actual slaves of the Germans were classed as beasts or live-stock!

‡All the modern accident figures you cite certainly cannot approach the shocking total which the barbarians' needless wars and trivial quarrels ran up.

. . . . but I fancy a modern had better think twice before deciding that their savage blood-lust and blind courage and childish fits of exaltation formed any boon to be wished for. What high-grade man could endure the thought of such a bestial wallowing if he knew of any other way of life? If such *latitude of choice* (between equally repulsive courses) as the freemen possessed formed any transcendent boon sufficient to redeem the squalor and emptiness and savagery of their common lot, it surely can seem so only in the eyes of a special worshipper of the freedom-ideal! Of course this picture is an especially emphatic one, but it is needed to correct the idealisation we are prone to make of our blood-ancestors. It is, however, merely the *stage of development* which is open to criticism. The *race itself* certainly had every quality necessary to future greatness, while even the *institutions* were of a *nature* (i.e., basic *tendency or direction* as distinguished from *stage of unfoldment*) promising the most enduring and salutary sort of future civilisation. It involves no disparagement of our remote forbears to point out that the firmness, courage, self-discipline, independence, and political genius of their later and civilised years had a far less pleasing and rewarding aspect during that period of incubation. It's no insult to a fine rooster to say that he was a pretty crude and messy proposition when he was only a bit of yolk and albumen inside an egg! As you say, the northern tribes during the Roman period were for the most part advanced beyond the grossest depths of barbarism—yet their policy of alternate drunkenness and monotonous manslaughter certainly seems to present little worthy of emulation. I don't doubt but that their pride and self-discipline and ethical ideas in certain fields gave them an intermittent psychological life of a sort—they had their bards, and some of their ideas and folklore display a strong sense of drama, and of the poetry in life. But the point is that this was only an embryonic or nascent psychological life—merely a promising forerunner of what the race would later evolve. To say that it was *better* than the higher life which came after, and that it formed an adequate compensation for the murderous horror of average barbarian life, is to strain matters rather arduously! What fully reflective modern would admit that the really pathological blood-frenzy and sadistic glee of Regner Lodbrog (of the "Pugnavimus Ensibus" ballad)[14] or of the Saxons who butchered the whole Britanno-Roman garrison at Anderida (Pevensey), or of the Danes who slaughtered all the Peterborough monks and unspeakably mangled King Aella (severing his ribs from his spine, drawing his lungs out, and throwing salt into his wounds—an act of insanity or constitutional degeneracy which merits only hanging or the madhouse), or of Harold Harefoot, who had 600 men maimed, blinded, hamstrung, scalped, and disembowelled, form *a source of joy and motive for living superior to the mental and artistic experience of normal, decent, civilised man?* What modern policeman or mine-owner or even gangster ever did *things like these?* God! Those ravening beasts weren't fit to live, and one shudders a bit at the thought of being descended from them. In some ways, we have gone farther (psychologically) since their day than they had gone since the days of the prognathous semi-ape. Who can complain of the routine, human ruthlessness of the ordinary *Roman* armies when confronted with hydrophobiac degeneracy like *this?* Did P. Ostorius Scapula or Cn. Julius Agricola or M. Julius Frontinus ever tear out an enemy's lungs from his breast?[15] Faugh! Taine sums up the northern barbarian character when he says: "Torture and carnage, greed of danger, fury of destruction, obstinate and frenzied bravery of an over-strong temperament, the unchaining of butcherly instincts—such traits meet us at every step."[16] However, the Celts were not quite so bad as the Teutons in some ways. The pre-Roman Britons had pulled quite a way out of sheer barbarism—having dealings with the Phoenicians, Greeks, Egyptians, and others, and leaving many artifacts of splendid workmanship—but I suppose they were getting too civilised to suit a barbaric taste.

This reminds me that I picked up a copy of the late Arthur Weigall's "Wanderings in Roman Britain" last January, and was tremendously interested in some of his points. He performed a vast amount of archaeological and historical research in the field of Britanno-Roman history, and seems to have demonstrated beyond a doubt (a) that the native Britons of the Roman period were thoroughly Romanised and Latin-speaking from the 2nd century on, (b) that their blood was extensively mingled with that of the legionaries (largely Gauls and Germans by blood) stationed at various points and later settling down as civilians after their discharge (scores of lately exhumed Roman gravestones with marriages and births recorded tell a significant tale), and (c) that the bulk of the conquered Britanno-Roman population was not driven out or exterminated, but was first enslaved and then absorbed by the conquering Saxons; so that we probably have as much Britanno-Roman as Saxon blood in our veins today. This means that I, personally, undoubtedly possess unknown blood-ancestors who wore the toga, spoke Latin, had names like L. Julius Civilis or M. Valerius Fronto or C. Aurelius Candidus, lived in Roman towns or centrally heated villas with running water, frequented Roman baths and temples and amphitheatres, and gloried in the designation of CIVIS. ROMANUS! Alala! S.P.Q.R.! Not that I believe in hereditary memory, but it certainly gives me a thrill to consider the likelihood of a real blood link with the mighty civilisation of which I have always felt myself to be spiritually a part. Ave Roma Immortalis! *Racially*, it doesn't mean much; since the Britons and legionaries were both about as Nordic in origin as the Saxons.

April 8

Mehercule, but how this epistle grows! But I guess I'm getting to loose ends now, so that I shan't have to bore you with any more long harangues. Trust you've lived through the preceding without lapsing into a weary coma!

About the details of personal freedom—I didn't mean to take an extremist's position in any way when I said that it is mental and aesthetic freedom which matters *most*. It is not to be thought that this opinion implies the desirability of incarcerating everybody in cells! On the contrary, I would not think of denying that a certain amount of physical freedom forms a definite and irreducible minimum. My real point is that I don't believe there is any danger of a serious or permanent attack on that minimum. The only drastic regulation needed in this nation is an *economic* one, and I feel sure that the force of the Anglo-Saxon tradition will prevent even the consideration of restrictive measures like those of the bolsheviks and Nazis. A few temporary measures of excessive regulation may be tried out from time to time—like the anti–highway walking law to which you so justly object—but it is virtually certain that such will soon suffer repeal or become forgotten dead letters. However—I frankly dodge the prediction of anything outside the Anglo-Saxon world. It is possible that you are right in foreseeing cultural harm in some of the continental dictatorships. Italian fascism has certain *principles* which clash with free thought and expression, but I believe they are not really enforced. Nazism, on the other hand, really will do some harm if not quietly modified pretty soon; for there is systematic discouragement of certain types of research and opinion and art, plus a persistent propaganda in favour of definitely false scientific opinions. And of course Russian culture is all shot to hell.

Returning to American conditions—the problem of degree of freedom is very complex, and can't be sized up in any offhand formula. Some restrictive measures are absolutely necessary. For example—while I agree that a ban on firearms might work harm in Texas, I believe you will agree that a perfect freedom of firearms in a criminal centre like New York would mean an immense strengthening of the sinister underworld—a strengthening far overbalancing any added defence facilities the law-abiding people might gain. There is no question but that the existing Sullivan Law has enormously reduced the murderous activity of gangsters without working any harm on the general population. Persons with a special need of carrying arms are almost never denied a legal permit to do so after a thorough examination of the circumstances. As for labour legislation—I don't think the right of striking would ever be challenged except under a socialised programme of government employment—and then only in an emergency. The right to *choose work*, on the other hand, is a ticklish proposition—involving the deepest essence of our new economic alignment . . . . the predicament caused by intensive mechanisation. The truth is that today—and in all future time—*there are not and never will be jobs enough to go around naturally.* No man can be sure of the power to earn a living except through the intervention of the government—and if the government is to guarantee jobs (or equivalent unemployment insurance), it will undoubtedly feel that the recipients ought to take such jobs as are most necessary of performance, rather than insist on having a certain type of congenial job provided. There is certainly a good deal of fairness in this principle—especially since, under a programme of spread work, no job will be as confining and irksome as at present. Whatever a man is asked to do, it won't mean the sinking of his whole time in it. A stated quota of hours will be asked of him—but outside of these hours he will be his own man . . . . just the same, whatever his job is. However—even conceding the fairness of the principle, I doubt if non-voluntary work-assignment would ever be more than a reserve or last-resort policy. To a very great extent—until a very marked overcrowding of some industries and a dangerous desertion of others might be noted—everybody would presumably be encouraged to pick his own job. In the matter of thumb-printing, etc.—I fancy that petty and capricious inter-state legislation will be replaced by some rational federal policy. Much is to be said for the universal and impartial finger-printing of every individual in the country. It can't do any honest man any harm, and it can do a lot of good in a thousand different ways. About the child-labour amendment—I think Lowell is unduly excited about it.[17] Perhaps it could have been better drawn, but even as it is it will probably do some good and no harm. It is inconceivable that the government would so interpret it as to interfere with commonly accepted rights. By checking up, I think you'll find that the anti-amendment hue and cry, like the anti-NRA and anti-stockbroking and other anti-administration hues and cries, comes to a suspiciously large extent from the callous old lais-sez-faire capitalist element that wants to wreck the New Deal and defeat the permanence of any of its principles. They use the language of liberty and in-dividualism—but they are not the people who are trying to see that every-body shall get a chance to earn a decent living.

A good antidote for undue fear of curtailed human freedom is a consid-eration of how little anybody has to gain by it. After all, it wouldn't especially profit anybody to regulate the motions of the population beyond certain lim-its—so that I fancy such regulation will never be attempted. Nobody would think it worth while to override popular resistance.

As for that Macfadden editorial on the constitution—all one may ask is whether or not our revered Sacred Cow of 1789, written before any of our present economic and social conditions were even dreamed of, interferes with the stern and necessary task of creating an economic order capable of giving every man a chance to earn his living. If it does not interfere with that task, then let it alone. It has its valuable points as well as many irrelevant and obso-lete points. But if it *does* interfere with that task—a task undoubtedly demand-ing some governmental checks on business unforeseen in 1789—then the only thing to do is to ignore or amend it. It is more important to restore earn-ing power to the people than to follow out literally some now irrelevant pre-cepts written 145 years ago in a vanished world. If a constitution is to be of any use, it must have some reference to the conditions of the age. To amend the hoary document in certain necessary places would not mean the destruc-tion of the basic spirit in which it was conceived.

Government certainly has a devil of a struggle ahead of it. Every move ahead in the direction of a more equitable and humane order will undoubt-

edly be fought tooth and nail by the blindly selfish interests of the old decaying order, so that each change will have to come slowly. Moreover—there are
always the well-meant protests of individualists who resent the regulation
needed to restore opportunity to the whole population. These latter don't
seem to realise that governmental oversight doesn't *destroy* opportunity, but
rather *restores* an opportunity previously destroyed by other forces. A laissez-
faire policy means merely a hidden control by great industrial and financial
interests. To fight this *natural result of technical "freedom"* it is worth while to
yield a bit of the technical article. That is the only way we can hope to get a
bit of the freedom which is real . . . . . freedom to live and think outside the
shadow of imminent want and suffering, and outside the prison of paralysing
overwork. But what a job! After the new system is won, then will come the
squabbling and indecision. Only the restriction of office to trained men will
ensure any successful regime.

More loose ends . . . I think I disposed of the Corbett-Michelangelo bout
on sheet VII, 2 . . . . that is, the valuational principle involved.

Regarding the late Houdini—I didn't say I *blamed* him, but I said I was
sorry that so phenomenal a mind was sidetracked from more richly rewarding
fields to a type of activity essentially meagre and sterile. As to the values concerned—the reference on VII, 2 is applicable. The question of relative pleasure—whether Houdini would have got more from life if dedicated to tasks
worthy of his brain—brings up the reference on XVIII, 1 and 2, which in
turn refers back to a former letter of mine and introduces the idea of measuring actual richness of experience by the amount of cerebral metabolism concerned. Of course, once Houdini had fallen through chance circumstance into
the cheap preference he had, it might have been impossible for him to enjoy a
transfer of activity to a profounder and intrinsically rewarding field. But that
would have proved nothing. The condition of emotional resistance would
have been due to the biassing influence of whatever early and unidentified
circumstances caused the formation of the original cheap taste. The time for
steering toward a fruitful and adequate life would have been early childhood,
before any casual or freakish taste could have had a chance to crystallise. The
same thing, I would say, was true of your artist-acrobat cousin—whose un-
timely fatal accident was surely lamentable. It would be rash to assume that he
could not have enjoyed a serious painter's career more richly than an acrobat's if steered from the beginning—although, on the other hand, there are
some individuals with twists so incredible that there is no accounting for their
actions and tastes. Of course I realise that you'll attack the theories and values
I apply in these cases—but I cite such things merely in order to show what *I*
believe. The privilege of disagreement is always yours. About yourself and
biology and literature—that may or may not be in a class with the preceding.
Literature is no such cheap performance (VII, 1 & 2) as showmanship or acrobatics, and evidence seems to indicate that you have a tremendously power-

ful natural literary gift. Still, of course, I say this without having sampled your biological aptitude. Naturally, with a fully-formed taste and almost-adult age, you did the wisest thing in choosing what you felt best adapted to.

You've certainly had some interesting things on the radio. Sorry I missed that Mackaye playlet and Hauptmann's "Sunken Bell", though the dramatisation of Poe's "Metzengerstein" (one of my favourite yarns for 35 years) might have been a shock to a lover of the original tale. Most radio and cinema versions of classics constitute a combination of high treason and murder in the first degree—I'll never get over the cinematic mess that bore the name (about the only bond of kinship to the book!) of "Frankenstein".[18] Wish I could have heard Gandhi as a curiosity! Æ (George Russell) is a really great poet. He has spoken more than once in Providence. My aunt hasn't used her radio very much of late, because she found it disturbed the hypersensitive old lady (a somewhat fussy high-school teacher) downstairs. There's a case of urban restrictedness out of which you could doubtless weave a sermon—Ariovistus and Arminius and Hengist and Horsa probably played their radios full blast all night despite what any Roman or Gaul or Briton might think about it! And these spring nights some of the Kappa Alpha Tau boys aren't overly considerate of the hyperaesthetic in the timing and timbre of their serenades!

Well—since beginning this letter I've heard again from Sultan Malik— who is pulling up stakes in Pawhuska and will probably be rolling around to Cross Plains before long. I envy him his opportunity to call at the palace of Conan the Cimmerian—he'll be the first fellow W T scribe you'll have met, will he not? I'm sure you'll both have a tremendously enjoyable session.

Looks as though I'd be getting on my jaunt in about a week. I never started out for such a distance with so little cash in addition to 'bus fare—but I'll cut down on the eats. 15¢—plate of beans and coffee—will do me for dinner any day. I may have to curtail my St. Augustine stop—but I *will* get at least 3 or 4 days in good old *Charleston*. What a town! Next to old Providence, I think it's about the most fascinating place on earth. I'll drop you any new cards I find on sale. De Land, where I'll be visiting Barlow, is nothing at all historically. That's the trouble with Florida—St. Augustine and Key West are the only places (except perhaps Pensacola in the northwestern part, which I haven't seen) with any real background. I want to get a glimpse of Savannah either going or coming—my 1931 inspection was all too brief. I shall pause at least a day or two (on the return) in Richmond, and will pray Yuggoth for the cash to get to Williamsburg . . . . the old Virginia capital now under restoration to its colonial condition. When I last saw it—1930—the Raleigh Tavern had just been restored (new structure on original foundations), but the old Capitol and Governor's Palace were not even begun. The original foundations of the Capitol were dug out—but on the site of the Palace stood a comparatively new high-school. Now the school is torn down, and both Capitol and Palace are rebuilt—in the exact style of the originals according to old prints and descriptions. I'll send you postcards of the reproductions if any are printed. They represent the best type of public buildings of Queen Anne's day.

Quite an amusing debate is going on over the original German title of our old friend von Junzt's "Nameless Cults". You'll recall that I got the rendering *Unaussprechlichen Kulten* from young Derleth—who ought to know, being one of a compact German-American community. Price, however, was not satisfied with the translation, and finally decided that *Unnenbaren Kulten* was much more exact. Wright is now trying to decide what he'll do. *Unnenbaren* is probably more exact—but *Unaussprechlichen* has such a sinister, mouth-filling rhythm that it seems almost a pity to let it go if it can be found in any way usable. I think I told you that a coming story in W.T., which I ghost-wrote for a client, will revolve to a very great extent around a certain ritual in the hellish Black Book.

. . . .

Yr most obt Servt

E'ch-Pi-El

Notes

1. Charles W. Smith (1852–1948), editor of the amateur journal the *Tryout*.

2. Eugene B. Kuntz, D.D. (1865–1944), whose slim volume of poetry, *Thoughts and Pictures* (1932), HPL edited and revised. It was "cooperatively published by H. P. Lovecraft and C. W. Smith."

3. The April 1934 *WT* included "Bells of Oceana" by Arthur J. Burks (reprinted from the December 1927 issue), CAS's "The Death of Malygris," and C. L. Moore's "Black Thirst."

4. CAS's "The Charnel God" appeared in *WT,* March 1934, illustrated by himself.

5. An organism that typically reproduces by asexual budding or fission and whose nutritional mode is absorption, photosynthesis, or chemosynthesis.

6. HPL refers to his own battered and dented telescope.

7. HPL refers to Prospect Terrace, off Congdon Street, where a spectacular view of downtown Providence and points west can be obtained.

8. H. H. Milman (1791–1868), "Preface" to his edition of Gibbon's *History of the Decline and Fall of the Roman Empire* (Paris: Baudry's European Library, 1840). Milman was referring to Gibbon's attitude to Christianity. The comment is a direct quotation from *The Principles of Moral and Political Philosophy* (1785) by British theologian William Paley (1743–1805), Book 5, ch. 9, also referring to Gibbon on Christianity but not mentioning him by name.

9. Because 66 College Street was on Brown University's fraternity row, HPL devised the Greek name K.A.T. (standing for *Kompsōn Ailurōn Taxis,* or "Band of elegant [or well-dressed] cats") for the array of cats at adjacent boarding house. Peter Randall was "president" of the fraternity.

10. For Ernst Haeckel, see letter 60, n. 1. HPL refers to Haeckel's treatise *Anthropogenie* (1874), translated as *The Evolution of Man* (1879).

11. Ales Hrdlicka (1869–1943), Czech anthropologist who became the first curator of

physical anthropology of the U.S. National Museum (later the Smithsonian Institution) in 1903. See his *Children Who Run on All Fours and Other Animal-like Behaviors in the Human Child* (1931).

12. Oswald Spengler, *The Hour of Decision* (1934), a translation by Charles Francis Atkinson of *Die Jahre der Entscheidung* (1933), a book whose criticism of anti-Semitism and Nazism caused it to be banned in Germany.

13. Roman historian Cornelius Tacitus (56?–115? C.E.) wrote of the German barbarians in his *Germania* (98 C.E.).

14. The ballad "Pugnavimus Ensibus" was translated by HPL as "Regner Lodbrog's Epicedium" (1914; *AT* 90–92).

15. P. Ostorius Scapula was governor of Britain (47–52 C.E.). Cn. Julius Agricola (40–93 C.E.) was instrumental in subduing the British tribes in the later first century C.E. His biography (*Agricola*) was written by his son-in-law, Tacitus. Sextus (not Marcus) Julius Frontinus (30–104 C.E.) was governor of Britain (74–78 c.e.) and subdued the Silures.

16. Hippolyte Taine (1828–1893), celebrated French historian and literary critic. The quotation is from *Histoire de la littérature anglaise* (1863), tr. by H. Van Laun as *History of English Literature* (1871), ch. 1, sec. 2.

17. An amendment to the U.S. Constitution to outlaw child labor had been adopted by Congress in 1924, but was never passed by a sufficient number of state legislatures to be enacted (by 1950, only 24 states had ratified it). In early 1934 A. Lawrence Lowell (1856–1943), former president of Harvard (1909–33), issued statements opposing the amendment. The Roosevelt administration did pass a Public Contracts Act in 1936 that set the minimum age for employment of boys at sixteen and of girls at eighteen for firms doing business with the federal government.

18. *Frankenstein* (Universal, 1931), directed by James Whale, produced by Carl Laemmle, Jr.; starring Colin Clive, Mae Clarke, John Boles, and Boris Karloff.

[101]   [ANS][1]

[Postmarked Charleston, S.C.,
25 April 1934]

Greetings from my favourite town! Had a pleasant week in N Y with Long & others, leaving at midnight Sunday & spending Monday morning in Washington . . . where I intensively explored the old Georgetown section. Richmond in the afternoon, & Raleigh, N.C. in the evening. Reached Charleston Tuesday at dawn. Am stopping at the Y M C A & doing the ancient town as usual. Virtually nothing has changed since my last visit—1931. It is fully summer here—rich green vegetation, hot days, straw hats, & all. In Washington & Richmond it is merely springlike—with delicate young foliage. And in N.Y. it is still wintry, with bare boughs. There is a vast kick in passing from winter to summer in a few hours. Shall move on to Savannah May 1st—& be in De Land May 2nd, unless plans change. Trust all is flourishing in Cross Plains, & that no ill effects of your accident remain. I'll wager you & Price had a great visit—a card from him in Juarez, Mexico, came the other day. My temporary address for a fortnight or so will be c/o R. H. BARLOW, BOX 88, DE LAND, FLORIDA.

All good wishes—

—H P L

Notes

1. Front: St. Phillips Gateway, Charleston, S. C.

[102]   [ANS][1]

[No postmark; enclosed with letter?
c. May 1934]

Hail, Conan! "Queen of the Black Coast" is certainly great—a prose poem if ever there was one. It easily tops the May issue. Hope you can conveniently grant the request of our young friend Ar-E'ch-Bei.[2] ¶ Still having a great time here, though today is beastly cold. Hopes of Havana run very low—but I shall get a week in St. Augustine anyhow. ¶ Let me thank you (before I know what I'm thanking you *for*) for the package which my aunt says has arrived from you at #66. I shall open it with eagerness when I get home.

You ought to see the four *cats* here. They would cause you to rival me in affection for the species!

Regards—

E'ch-Pi-El.

Notes

1. Front: A Cocoanut Tree, Florida.
2. RHB had asked about obtaining Hugh Rankin's illustrations for REH's stories. REH replied that he was "sort of a fiend about Rankin's drawings myself," and was making a collection of the illustrations of his stories from *WT*. The ultimate fate of these illustrations is unknown. See *CL2*, letter 266, p 212f, and letter 268, p 215.

[103]   [TLS]

[May 1934]

Dear HPL:

Glad you're having such a good time in Florida. I'm sure that Mr. Barlow is a delightful host. Hope you get to take that trip to Havana. If so, look out for the revolutionists! From what I've heard, the Cubans are blood-brothers to our Mexican neighbors in that pastime.

Thanks very much for the kind things you said about my "Queen of the Black Coast". I have a three-part Conan serial starting in September, "The People of the Black Circle". And thanks for the pictures and the folder from Savannah. Georgia is a state that interests me very much, though my conception of it is extremely vague.

The package I sent to Providence contains a large and extremely venom-ous spider called in these parts (erroneously I think) a vinegarone.[1] I hope it didn't come to pieces on the way, as I'm nothing of a taxidermist. This par-ticular specimen took up its abode in the back yard, just outside the bathroom window. I recognized its hole, drowned it out, captured it, asphyxiated it with gas, and placed the carcass in a sealed bottle of alcohol. I thought you might like to add it to your collection of curiosa. I'll try to get you a tarantula at the first opportunity. They are much scarcer in this country than they used to be. They were almost as common as grasshoppers when I was a kid. Maybe they'll come back with the other varmints. Not long ago I surprized an arma-dillo just a block or so off the main business part of town, one night.

As you can well imagine, I deeply enjoyed Price's visit.[2] My only regret was that he was unable to stay longer. He is delightful and I feel that he is destined to become one of our foremost writers. He is a great admirer of yours, and feels (as I do) that you are just about supreme in your line.

Speaking of cats, there was an addition of three to the feline community while Price was here, and since then a fourth kitten has wandered in from somewhere and been adopted by the old cat—I say old to distinguish her from her brood; she's really a young cat, with the maternal instinct very highly developed. Any stray kitten which comes along is allowed to tug at her fecund teats with her own progeny. Modest and retiring almost to the point of timid-ity, she is valiant in defending both her natural off-spring and her adopted children, and is in addition a mouser of no mean ability. To the best of my knowledge this is her second brood; at least it is the second brood she has had since taking up her abode here, and she was scarcely mature when she came. Her first litter consisted of two she-kittens (indeed she seems unable to produce anything but females; the last three were sows too); one of these was given away, and the other concluded her brief career just a few days ago. I was awakened one morning by cries of feline agony just outside my window and found her lying on her side, unable to arise, panting and shaken with convulsions, and evidently in great pain. Possibly she had been poisoned. The only thing I could do for her was to put her out of her agony with an auto-matic pistol, as I'd want done to me if I were in a similar plight.

Hope your journeys continue pleasant.

Cordially,

R E H

Notes

1. The common name for the whip scorpion, *Mastigoproctus giganteus*. As whip scorpions are not venomous, it is possible that the specimen referred to was of another species.
2. E. Hoffmann Price and his then-wife, Wanda, visited REH from 8 to 11 April 1934.

[104]   [nonextant letter by HPL]

[105]   [TLS]

[c. late May or early June 1934]

Dear HPL:

Glad you're finding your stay in Florida so enjoyable. Glad you liked "Queen of the Black Coast". The fans seem to have liked the verse headings of the chapters. Thanks for the kind things you said about the Kull stories, but I doubt if I'll ever be able to write another. The three stories I wrote about that character seemed almost to write themselves, without any planning on my part; there was no conscious effort on my part to work them up. They simply grew up, unsummoned, full grown in my mind and flowed out on paper from my finger tips. To sit down and consciously try to write another story on that order would be to produce something the artificiality of which would be apparent.[1]

Yes, I hope the spider didn't fall apart on the way to Providence. I've been looking for a tarantula, and a good sized scorpion. I mashed one of the latter in the kitchen sink the other day, but it wasn't big enough to suit me. "Stinging-lizards" as we call them, are always more or less plentiful in Texas, but some years they are bigger and more numerous than in others. I remember two or three years ago they almost amounted to a plague. They are vicious fighters, and some people suffer greatly from their stings. I remember about that time my father treated several people for stings, and one fellow particularly, who was stung on the hand. They phoned my father to come and see the man, and he'd hardly started when they called again, urging him to hurry, said the fellow was having spasms, and getting blue spots all over him. He quickly recovered, however, under proper medical attention. But scorpion stings don't effect everybody that way, for shortly thereafter I was stung by a bigger lizard and in a more sensitive place, and no such symptoms were observable. I was sitting in a rocking chair, studying rather late one night, with pencil and paper on the floor beside me, and from time to time I'd reach down and pick up the writing material to make notes, becoming so accustomed to this movement that I wouldn't pause in my reading, nor look where I was reaching. Presently, groping for my pencil, I was aware of a sharp stinging pain in my finger, near the nail, and so quickly does the mind work, that in the instant in which I jerked back my hand and looked down, possibilities flashed through my mind of a splinter on the floor, a wasp and a tarantula. I saw a large scorpion running across the floor with his armed tail curled over his back in the militant attitude these creatures assume when roused. I set my heel on him and looking at my hand, was convinced that scorpions have a natural instinct for inflicting injury at the most vulnerable point. Somehow, I forget how, the skin next to my finger nail had been torn to the quick, and in this raw, sensitive laceration the scorpion had thrust his barb to its fullest extent. There was a stinging sensation, accompanied by a slight numbness of the wrist and forearm, scarcely any swelling of the wounded part, but a curious tingling in the elbow. These sensations endured, with a gradual cessation, for about fifteen minutes, and then disappeared, and I felt no nausea at any time. The only treatment given it was a little antiseptic I put on the stung place to keep it from getting infected.

No, I had not heard of Mr. Barlow's pursuit of reptiles for book-binding. Their hides ought to make good material. Rattlesnake skin belts used to be very popular in the Southwest, and you can still buy them in the old Buckhorn at San Antonio.

Yes, I did indeed enjoy Price's visit here, and my only regret was he was unable to stay longer. I hope to meet him again some time. Yes, he's the only Weird Tale writer I've ever met—not only that, he's the only professional writer of any sort I ever met. He is writing some oil fields stories, and was much interested in the spudders of this locality—shallow wells, drilled by a small portable machine frequently run by an ordinary farm tractor. They are funny looking things to anybody used to standard rigs. I remember how surprized I was when they first began to be brought into this country. While he was here the weather was marred only by the tag end of a sandstorm, but that wasn't a Texas product, but one that started in Nebraska and dumped the sweepings of Kansas and Oklahoma into the Panhandle. By the way, Price was stopped at the Red River crossing by men with guns in their hands, looking for the famous outlaw Clyde Barrow, who was working in those parts at that time. As I told him, it was fortunate that his car was loaded with objects that evidenced his innocence, for Barrow was about his size, and was, like him accompanied by a blond young lady: Bonnie Parker. As you might have read in the paper, Bonnie was with Clyde when he met his finish at the hands of the ex-Rangers, in Louisiana. Bullets from machine rifles, ripping through him, riddled her, plastered the interior of the car with blood, brains and bits of Barrow's skull. 167 slugs were poured into the automobile of the outlaws.[2]

I was much interested in your narration of the Barlow felines. A desire to display their prey seems to be a fairly common trait among cats, and I am unable to decide whether it is merely an expression of vanity, or a rather pathetic effort to show that they are industrious and earning their keep. The young she-cat I mentioned in my last letter is at present reclining in her favorite spot in the grass by the back step, just outside my window, with her brood—natural and adopted—snoozing about her. She talks more to her kittens than any cat I ever saw. Ordinarily silent, I frequently hear her discoursing at great lengths to her offspring. The sounds she produces are midway between purr and mew, and contain many variations of tone and inflection; honestly, it's almost like an intelligible language! She is very peaceable, under ordinary circumstances, even timid, and will even allow another cat to appropriate her food. But any hint of threat toward her kittens transforms her, and when she does fight, she displays more implacable determination than I ever saw in any cat, of either sex. She fights silently, with steel-spring quickness, yet with a coolness that is almost impersonal; nine out of ten cat-fights are more noise than bloodshed, with interludes of spitting and yowling. Not with her; she goes straight for the vitals of her enemy without prelimi-nary threats, and slashes and tears with cold ferocity and without pause until her enemy is hors de combat or has fled beyond the boundaries of her abode. There's no compromise with her; she fights to the finish. She has a way of fighting that reminds me of Jack Dempsey—rearing on her hind legs and striking right and left with the fury and intent to destroy behind each blow.

Very little of interest is happening in Texas these days; not much interest is yet being evinced in the governor's race, since none of the candidates is connected with the big outside interests whose control we voters have been fighting against so bitterly for years. Locally, we had a beer election,[3] and the county went wet by a big majority. I've lapped up quite a bit since then; it's good simply as a beverage, being too weak for a real drink. Not that I always demand a heavy kick. My hard drinking days are over—have been over for some years. I did get on an awful bust around Saint Patrick's Day over at San Angelo, but that wasn't on beer.

Well, good luck, and I hope you get to make that Havana cruise.

Cordially,

REH

Notes

1. In addition to the three stories featuring Kull that appeared in *WT*, REH wrote seven complete and three incomplete tales with this character. According to his semi-autobiographical novel *Post Oaks and Sand Roughs,* the writing of "The Shadow King-dom" took nearly a year, and several drafts.
2. Clyde Barrow and Bonnie Parker were ambushed and killed by a posse led by Texas Ranger Frank Hamer in Bienville Parish, Louisiana, 23 May 1934.
3. An election to vote on legalizing the sale of beer with 3.2% alcoholic content was held in Cross Plains on 30 June 1934.

[106]   [TLS]

[c. July 1934]

Dear HPL:
[inserted]: I started writing this months ago.

Thank you again for your expressions of sympathy in regard to my slight accident. Yes, all parties concerned are fully recovered, and my scar doesn't amount to much, after all, thanks to my father's really remarkable ability in such matters. As for my own stamina, if any, it's true that my flesh always heals quickly and easily (or always has, so far) but I wouldn't want to try to create an impression of any particular or unusual ruggedness on my part. But it is true that, in this particular episode, my nervous system didn't suffer as much as I myself would have expected, or indeed, as much as the nerves of the other fellows who were hurt, apparently. Both required sedatives to get them asleep later (though in the case of one of them this was caused by the intense pain) whereas I, who was hurt worse than either, having had my wounds sewed up immediately went to bed and slept as soundly and heartily as I ever did in my life. This remark isn't made with any intention of creating an impression of undue stamina or anything on my part, nor am I criticising the other boys. But for some reason or other, neither the jolt of the wreck nor the pain of my hurts particularly upset my nerves. One thing I might mention—my heart has been in rotten shape for months now, and for some time before the wreck I'd been forced to keep it braced up with digitalis. I've often been warned that a heavy blow over the heart might well mean my finish, but that terrific smash against my breast didn't affect the old organ at all. I think it was because my ribs resisted the impact. If they had been broken and smashed in against my heart, very probably it would have stopped.

I was much interested in your remarks about people who couldn't stand the sight of blood, particularly the old gentleman who faints at merely hearing blood mentioned. That is indeed a strange complex, or whatever is the scientific name for it, and I am unable to understand it. Do people of this type have the same feelings in regard to the blood of fowls and animals, or is it only human blood which affects them? If I had ever had any such qualms, my work in the oil-fields booms would have rid me of them. I remember when working in the drug-store that almost every day or night somebody was brought in streaming blood from mangled limbs or wounds of one nature or another. But I never was upset by the sight of blood, either my own or somebody else's. Indeed, when I think of the vast amount of blood I've seen spilled in the ordinary course of a short and uneventful life, it seems strange to realize that there are environments wherein the mere sight of blood is such an unusual and extraordinary occurrence as to upset grown men.

Thanks for the kind things you said about my "Shadows in the Moonlight". (My original title was "Iron Shadows in the Moon".) I'm afraid I can't claim originality in regard to the parrot and his repetition of the god's invocation. I got the idea from a poem of Noyes', entitled, I believe, "The Parrot". As I remember, it goes something like this:

> "When the king and his folk lay dead,
> And the murderous horde was gone,
> He gnawed through his cage and fled
> To the sheltering woods alone.

But after an endless age,
He was taken by man once more;
And swung in a sturdier cage
By a white-washed ale-house door.

Through the long hot afternoon,
From his place by the blistered wall,
He whistled a dark old tune,
And called as a ghost might call:

"Farlo, merillo, geray!"
And the wondering people heard
The voice of the dead that day
Talking again in a bird."

The poem ends on what seems to me a powerful and shuddersome note.

"And once, oh dreadful and wild,
In the blaze of the noonday sun,
It shrieked like a frightened child
That into the dark has gone."[1]

I don't know whether I've quoted it correctly or not. But shucks, you've probably read it anyway. Noyes is one of my favorites. I like the music of drums and wind-harps that throbs through so much of his poetry.

As for values, I tried to make it clear in my last letter that I did not deny the existence of what you call basic values. If I failed, then there is not much use in merely repeating what I said, because in my efforts to make my position clear I just about exhausted the possibilities of my limited vocabulary. I notice, with a feeling of considerable despair and futility, that you have resurrected the ghost of the old, thread-bare mental-physical argument which I thought finally settled months and months ago. How you can still accuse me of exalting physical strength above mental development is a mystery I can not solve. You say it probably seems "strange and unaccountable" to me "to have a distinction drawn between the human effort which seeks to measure the universe . . . . . and that which seeks to apply science to the mutual slugging of two sullen giants" and hint that this is because of my extreme youth, and an immature sense of proportion . . . . . well, admittedly twenty-eight is not particularly a ripe age (though I hardly see what I'm to do about it) but it is at least rather more mature than the ten years of age with which you apparently credit me. I can not remember the time when I was so puerile that I was not able to tell the difference (or at least that there *was* a difference) between "measuring the universe" and boxing. Perhaps this fantastic accusation was brought forth by my remarks on Jim Corbett. I tried, heaven knows, to make it plain that I quite realized the difference between Corbett and Michel Angelo. What I was trying to illustrate was that Corbett himself was superior to the general run of men. Apparently, if I mention an unusually intelligent athlete, and remark that his development places him above that of an ape, you decide that I am worshipping physical strength, and am exalting him above "the real titans of human activity". Obviously, it was not Corbett's physical development at all that caused my remark, but his mental equipment.

This debate, I thought, rose from a misunderstanding of positions. I thought you placed an exaggerated value on the formal expressions of art, and you accused me of exalting physical strength above mental development. I discovered my mistake and accepted your explanations as to your position, but apparently you refuse to accept mine, as shown by your repeated accusations of my "exalting the physical" after I've explained my position as lucidly as I know how.

These seem to be the main points on which you attack me:

.1. You accuse me of exalting physical strength above everything else.

.2. You accuse me of exalting ethics above evolutionary development.

.3. You accuse me of repudiating the standards of basic development.

I have tried the best I know how to make it plain that I do none of these things. But you apparently take the position that if I fail to agree with you on every point, I repudiate the whole system of human standards. There's no use in my offering elaborate and pains-taking explanations if you refuse to accept them. I will not attempt to. I will simply limit myself to plain and unadorned statements of unrefutable fact.

.1. I do not exalt physical strength above everything else.

.2. I do not exalt ethics beyond the point that any normal, intelligent man does.

.3. I do not repudiate, or fail to recognize the standards of basic development.

These are simple statements of fact, and when I've made them, my responsibility ends. It's up to you whether you accept them and recognize the true facts of the matter, or prefer to cling to a misconception. It can't affect me one way or the other, for facts are not dependent either upon acceptance or rejection.

As for my personal preferences, which you have attacked so bitterly throughout our correspondence, I am not aware that they need either defense or apology. My expressions of preferences are merely statements of facts, which can not be refuted or successfully attacked. You certainly can not expect me to renounce them, because they don't chance to fall within your particular set of personal preferences. My tastes and interests may not coincide with the preferences which you evidently feel an intelligent man ought to have, but I hardly know what we are to do about it. If we were living under your ideal intellectual-ruled government, you could doubtless have me burned at the stake as a heretic. But since we haven't reached that enviable stage of civilization, it looks like you'll just have to classify me as another of the imperfections and crudities allowed to exist under a democratic form of government, and let it go at that.

I greatly admire the eloquence with which you narrate the arguments you expected me to present in the debate on values. If you have already made up your mind that I hold all these views, and would reply with all these arguments (most of which never occurred to me in my life) then it's useless for me to point out that most of your assumptions are erroneous. As for your accusation that I hate human development, etc., that's absurd. I don't wish to seem offensive, but that's the only term that fits it. You say I sneer at "human development". I have disagreed with you on a few points, and expressed personal preferences that differ from yours. Apparently you consider that this implies a sneer at "human development."

In regard to our debate about freedom, I don't see how you so completely misread my illustration about the man in prison and the man outside. I didn't compare a man in prison with one working for a salary. I don't remember even saying anything at all about a man working at a salary. If you'll glance over that paragraph again, you'll see your mistake.

As for modern economic trends: I have told you that I was heartily in accord with the Roosevelt administration. You say that "no pioneering revival" can iron out the present difficulties. I certainly never said anything that could suggest that I was such a drooling imbecile that I thought a "pioneering revival" was possible. We might as well be reasonable in these debates. There's no use ascribing to me views I never expressed and that only a congenital idiot would express.

In your criticism of my preference for my native region, you say that "it is not necessary to revert to bloodthirsty barbarism to secure a setting free from the friction of urban life." Well, who ever said it was? I merely expressed a preference for country rather than city life. You say that "people don't carve one another up over trifles" in rural New England. Well, what of it? What's that got to do with the matter? You surely don't imagine that the rural people of the west devote their time to slashing and hacking each other for amusement, do you?

Concerning my personal feelings for the frontier—you have left no possibility of argument there. I have been at pains to make it clear that my wish that I had lived then was merely personal, and that I have never advocated anything so fantastic as "the perpetuation of frontier conditions". But now you tell me bluntly that this is not so, that I do advocate such perpetuation. What reply can I make in the teeth of a flat contradiction like that?

Aside from this point: you intimate that if I am not satisfied with the growth of "civilization" in my region I had better "fare forth" and find some other frontier. I would greatly appreciate it if you could tell me just where I'd find a duplicate of the old Southwestern frontier.

You say you would not object to "a spacious minded region of large-scale agriculture and stock-raising under proper protection, and with a normal regard for human life." And from your remarks about New Mexico, I gather that you consider Texas is not a "spacious-minded" region, "with a normal regard for human life." Your remarks imply an accusation that all Texans are outlaws and criminals. I'll return to this point later.

No, your attack on my "moralistic attitude" is not clear, neither is it logical; for in your debate on values you accuse me of overemphasizing ethics, and now you accuse me of under-emphasizing ethics.

Concerning modern conditions in the Southwest—you have repeatedly attacked me because you thought I was too strongly influenced by the conditions and standards of my particular environment. And now you turn around and do the same thing yourself. You condemn the whole state of Texas because, you say, the citizens are not "orderly." Not orderly, that is, according to your conception of the term, as conceived from the conditions and necessities of your particular environment. We have our standards of order, but because they do not correspond exactly with yours, always, you condemn six million people as criminals and outlaws. You use the conditions and standards of your special environment as a criterion for passing judgment on other localities, regardless of the different problems that exist there. In a word, you accept the conditions of your particular environment as an absolute standard, demanding that the rest of the country shall conform to it. This statement will surprize and puzzle, and doubtless exasperate you. You will say that your standard of order *should* be accepted universally; that it represents the normal conception of a civilized community, and therefore is absolute. And that precisely confirms what I have just said.

As for the problems I mentioned which sometimes caused violence on the frontier—from your remarks on what "fair-minded men" would have done, it is evident that you consider the only obstacle in the way of their "rational" solutions was the depravity of the men concerned. So it's useless for me to try to point out the physical difficulties of the solutions you suggested.

Concerning Billy the Kid and the Boston capitalist who didn't want to feed him—Torrey didn't have to be imbued with a special gift of second-sight to know that hospitality was the custom of the west. That was the first thing any stranger found out. Don't you understand that the unwritten code didn't demand that you feed a thief *because* he was a thief? It was the custom to feed and shelter *any* man who came along, without asking him any questions. You didn't subject a man to a third-degree to find out his business before asking him to light and sit. Don't you realize that this hospitality was a necessity in the west, without which settlement and development would have been impossible? There *had* to be a tradition of the sort, in a country where there were no hotels, inns, taverns or the like. And didn't I make it plain that no harm came to this fat Boston capitalist? If he didn't like the Kid's joke—which was all it amounted to—why didn't he put up a fight? He was a full-grown man, with a gun at his hip, and, if he was like most of his breed, he had a gang of gunmen within call. Billy was up there in that country stealing cattle, it is true. But for whom was he stealing them? For some brutal, bloody-handed Texan? Not at all. For Mr. Patrick Coghlin, a cultured British gentleman who had a big ranch down on the Tularosa. He commissioned Billy to go steal cattle up in Texas—and when his housekeeper and her husband overheard that bargain, he had them both murdered to keep them from testifying in court.

That happened in New Mexico, which brings me back to the question of the relative lawlessness of that state and of Texas. Yes, New Mexico's crime rating is lower than that of Texas. Why not? There are 423,317 people in New Mexico, mostly of Latin-American or Anglo-Saxon descent. Most of the state consists of farming land and scenery. The natives own the farming land and not even Wall Street capital has devised a way to exploit scenery. In Texas there are about six million people, of every race and nationality under the sun. We have sea-ports, gigantic oil fields, mines, whole-sale production they nothing about, problems they don't even know exist. The position of New Mexico is merely similar to what Texas would have been, if allowed to develop gradually and in her own way, by the efforts of her own citizens. But that we were not allowed to do. You compare New Mexico and Texas to the latter's extreme disadvantage (according to your way of looking at it.) How do you account for the difference in crime and violence of the two states? New Mexico has just as much of a frontier tradition as Texas. I know, of course, how you account for it. You have a conviction that the native people of Texas are a peculiarly vicious and bloodthirsty breed. Why do you think the New Mexicans are different from us? Don't you realize that the state was first settled by Texans, and that a large number of its present citizens were born and raised in Texas? Do you suppose that some special alchemy of the soil or air changed them from bloody outlaws to peaceful citizens when they crossed the state line? I'll tell you why there is a difference: New Mexico has never been exploited by Eastern capital as Texas has. No other western state, not even California, has been exploited to such an extent. Because no other state on this continent possesses such natural resources, such opportunities for great wealth. I have told you this before, but you refused to accept my statement, maintaining that our turbulence and unrest was the result of a pioneer tradition, and the innate viciousness of our citizens.

All right. We'll see. I enclose a clipping showing how crime is distributed over the United States. As these are not my figures, but statistics, you can hardly keep from recognizing their veracity. (Please return this clipping for my files.)

You will notice that Texas ranks higher than any other western state in homicides. But on the whole, the other western states rank low. Idaho and Montana, for instance, are at the very bottom of the list, with Vermont. If the pioneer tradition is the sole cause of homicide and crime, why do these states, which have a pioneer tradition fully equal to that of Texas, rank even lower in homicide than your own state? Simply because the pioneer tradition is *not* the sole cause, nor even a strong contributing cause to crime. If you know anything about the economic conditions of the western states, you will notice *that the homicide record of each state has a direct relation with the extent to which that state is exploited by Eastern capital.* Texas heads the list with homicides as with exploitation of natural resources. Of course, you'll deny that there is any connection between these things, because that proves what I've said all along—that nine-tenths of the crime, turbulence and unrest in Texas is the direct or indirect result of inconsiderate or corrupt exploitation of the state and its people by, or at the instigation of interests from the long-settled regions.

You'll deny that, but then, how will you explain the small homicide percentage of Montana, Idaho, Utah, and Oregon? Do you actually think that these states are inhabited by a breed of people different than, and superior to, the people of Texas? Don't you realize that most of them were first settled and developed by Texans? If you'd trouble to look up the histories of these states, you'd find that their early periods were as violent and bloody as that of Texas. Some of the bloodiest feuds ever fought on this continent took place in New Mexico, and the others. And what caused most of these feuds? Natural results of pioneering? Scarcely. The same thing that caused so much hell in Texas about the same time—the exploitation of the cattle business by big Eastern and British beef syndicates. All over the west feuds and wars and fights were going on, with the big cattle trusts on one side and the small ranchers and squatters driven to frantic desperation by the threat of utter ruin, on the other. When the syndicates shifted their big interests to South America, the cattlemen of the western states were practically ruined. But, as there was nothing left to exploit, in most of the states, the natives were left alone, to develop along their natural lines as they might. But in Texas it was different. Cattle wasn't our only resource. We had oil, gas, water-ways, sulphur, huge-scale production of agriculture, timber, fruit—a hundred natural resources unknown in the more purely cattle-raising states. Capital with its ruthless practises came to stay. And with it came all the riff-raff that follows in the wake of whole-sale exploitation. A few corrupt politicians sold us out, and we've been fighting for our rights ever since. And by God, we're still fighting, and we'll keep it up until the state of Texas is again owned by Texans.

Naturally all this exploitation led to a certain amount of turbulence and unrest. When a state is being torn to pieces by rival forces, amidst a constant clashing of interests, you can't expect it to present the same tranquil appearance that a rural New England countryside would. And it is bitterly unfair to condemn its people as criminals because it doesn't. You've got it backwards when you assume that the ruthlessness of the police is a result of the lawlessness of the common people. The common people are sometimes driven to desperation by the brutality of the police, who are merely carrying out instructions of corrupt officials, in turn doing the bidding of big business. (Though since we booted out the Sterling administration,[2] which was openly controlled by Eastern capital, I haven't heard much about police brutality.) I return to my first assertion which can not be refuted: whole-sale theft and exploitation of the natural resources of the state by unscrupulous and alien interests cause the majority of the crimes committed in the state, directly or indirectly. If we ever kick these powers out of the state and take it over, and are allowed to run it as we, the true citizens, wish it run, you'll see a state second to none on the continent for peacefulness and crime control.

As another item to clinch what I have said: crime is most rampant in the cities and sections most influenced by outside interests, and is least where the population, native population I mean, is in full charge. The Great Plains are inhabited almost exclusively by Texans of the old stock, employed in unexploitable agriculture, and the crime list there is the smallest in the entire state.

Incidentally, you'll notice Texas is only seventh in the homicide list, being lower than North Carolina, Florida, and Virginia—all eastern states. How do you explain that? And Texas is away down the line on the robbery list, being far surpassed by Illinois, South Carolina, Florida, Indiana and Ohio, all civilized states boasting a high type of culture.

Aside from crimes, you denounce us because some of our citizens—you think—are a bit too quick with their firsts or with some weapon, when oppressed or insulted. Well, it would be strange if a section as big as Texas, with a history so vital and unique, didn't develop a few characteristics of its own.

From some of your remarks I gather that you object to what I said about some of the native boys resenting epithets applied to them by certain drillers, back in the wildcat days. I am curious to know what you would recommend in such cases. Let us glance at a case: A young Texan who is just learning to dress tool is struggling with an unfamiliar job when the driller enters. He is from some other state, and perhaps has been working in Mexico, China or South America, where he is accustomed to using rough methods with the natives. He glares at the youth and bellows: "Why in the hell haven't you got that job done, you dumb hunk of chicken manure?" (Expurgated.) "Well," begins the youth, embarrassed, "I —" "Shut up!" roars the gentleman from the civilized section. "Don't you talk back to me, you G— d— lousy bastard! Trouble with you, you're just a damned, lazy, egg-sucking son of a slut that hasn't got brains enough to pull your foot out of dung!"

What is the accepted civilized reaction in such a case? Is the youth required to rise with his hat in his hand, thank his opponent, and perhaps present the seat of his pants to be kicked? Or, if he is allowed to resent these quips, should he rise with a calling card in his hand and challenge the man to a duel? Don't you know he'd have had a Stillson wrench bent over his head if he'd made that archaic gesture? I'll tell you what did happen. The youth rose, but he had neither a calling card nor his hat in his hand. He had a rock, and he knocked the driller so cold that they had to use a pulmotor to bring him to. Nor have I ever heard that he was troubled by the thought that people of the civilized regions might condemn him as a barbarian for resorting to "deadly weapons" to resent this "trivial slight."

Incidentally, don't get the idea that all drillers had to be knocked in the head, or even many of them. But a few thought they could bluster and bully the men working for them, and they had to have it taken out of them. And it was.

As for barbarians, I think your use of the word "degeneracy" in condemning the actions you object to amongst the Germans, is hardly correct. My dictionary defines "degeneracy" as "The state of being degraded or of growing worse than formerly." This could hardly be applied to the German barbarians, who were climbing up the ladder of evolution rather than down.

You seem to be somewhat shocked by the fact that the Danes cut the blood-eagle[3] on King Aella. Well, what did you expect? Didn't he put old Ragnar Lodbrog to death in an equally savage manner? What do you think Ragnar's sons *should* have done?

You inquire what modern, even what modern gangster ever committed anything like the blood-eagle. Easy enough. It hasn't been more than three years at the most, since I read an account in the newspapers of a gangster's body found under the wharves of a certain eastern city after his rivals had finished with him. His head had been nearly severed from his body, apparently by a razor, his nose, ears and tongue had been cut off, and his heart had been cut out of his breast—other mutilations were hinted at. Most of this slicing, the police believed, had been done before the victim was killed. One doubts if the Danish blood-eagle was any more ingenious than the "light chair" of the modern police. You strap your victim to that chair, with his head tilted up and fastened so he can't move it. Then you lower a very powerful electric light to within an inch or so of his eyes—and leave him there. A few hours of this and he is a raving maniac, due to spend the rest of his life in a padded cell. Nor would it seem that it would be any picnick to be trussed up for fifty or sixty hours at a stretch in a strait-jacket of a modern prison, or to be subjected to the water-cross which rips out the linings of a man's guts. How do you know the Romans didn't use the blood-eagle? They wrote their own history, and left out what suited them. Anyway, they had crucifixion and red hot irons and other persuaders, and their descendants, your Fascist friends, are not lacking in similar ingenuity—their famous "nut-cracker" for instance, which crushes the testicles of the victim to a purple pulp.

I read with interest your rhapsodies over the Romans, and am puzzled, as I have been in the past, as to how you can idealize one people of a former age to such a degree and at the same time so bitterly attack me for my interest in another. But I suppose it's in keeping with your peculiar intolerance for interests differing from your own.

I was deeply interested in your remarks concerning the Roman occupation of Britain. That gives me another reason to be thankful that there is so little English blood in my veins, and that what is there is more Danish than Briton or Saxon. If I thought I had a drop of Roman blood in my veins, I'd be glad to take a knife and let it out. My pride in my distant ancestors is not based on the fact that they were conquered by the Romans, but on the fact that they whipped the socks off those big-shot racketeers of antiquity.

All the above was written months ago. Since then we have exchanged cards and letters during your Florida trip. I do not know whether you have returned to Providence yet or not, but if not, this letter will be waiting for you on your return. I'm glad you got to take that trip, and sorry you didn't get to go to Cuba. Personally, I've never cared much about the idea of going to Cuba, but believe I'd enjoy a trip to Haiti.

I haven't done any travelling to speak of this year. Most of my time has been spent at home, working. I did have an enjoyable time Saint Patrick's day, though I didn't go any place particularly. I went to Brownwood Saint Patrick's Eve and Truett Vinson and I celebrated in our small way. I wish you could know Vinson—a fine, upstanding man a few months older than myself, six feet two in his socks, about 185 pounds with no fat on him, shoulders broader than a barn door, and all man. I knocked him down once when we were both drunk, but nobody ever floored him when he was sober. He's an accountant for a big whole-sale company and a stock-raiser for himself. Keen witted, with a natural knack for finances. Once an ardent Socialist, but too strongly individualistic for that, as I often told him. Well educated and very well read.

We saw a fight card that night—Saint Patrick's Eve—fair, though I've seen better, and next morning I drove out to Lake Brownwood and spent some time in watching the rising wind kicking up the white caps in an almost Gulf-like manner, and in musing over the miracle of that great body of water where in times past I suffered of thirst, trudging along roads over which seventy feet of liquid blue now roll. You people who live in generously watered countries can not realize how much water means to dwellers in the dry lands. The South wind was rising to a gale, lashing the waves to foam, and clouds were drifting down from the north, spilling over the rim of the Caprock hundreds of miles away, which I knew presaged a storm of some sort. A rising cloud bank in the north west and a strong wind from the south east always means rough weather. Vinson was off work at noon and we went after a mare of his he'd left with a horseman to be bred. As you may know 90% percent of the nation's polo horses come from Texas and the country around and below Brownwood is especially famed for such animals. There are a number of men who make their living by raising and training horses for the Eastern market. Once a year they take a load of mounts to New York, and usually their profits are large. Frequently they bring back stallions which have been injured in some way which ruins them as polo-mounts or race horses, but does not affect their breeding capacities. Such a stallion it was which had served Vinson's mare—a magnificent brute, who numbered among his ancestors winners of the Kentucky Derby and the Grand Prix. There were some other fine animals at this farm—notably a splendid racing mare, for which her owner was demanding $2000, and which was easily worth it. Her earning power is much greater than that, probably. The expected storm broke in the middle of the afternoon—one of the worst sandstorms I ever saw. We had purchased our whiskey and intended to celebrate Saint Patrick's in a fitting manner, after seeing a whimsical movie called "The Invisible Man" from a story by Wells, I believe,[4] but the sandstorm was followed by a biting blizzard, with driving sleet and lightning and thunder, so we postponed the merry-making. Next morning broke clear and cold, though, and we spent the morning hauling a load of hay to Vinson's ranch, some miles east of Brownwood, among the sleet-frosted hills, and feeding his cattle which had suffered from the cold wave. After dinner we set out for San Angelo, which lies 105 miles west of Brownwood, amidst rich and limitless Plains, where 85% of the nation's mohair is produced, which is to say 85% of the world's supply. It is a prosperous town, wide and spacious like most new western cities, with free and easy ways. At that time Callahan County was still dry, and Brown County is always dry. So to us thirsty hill-billies this lush city of the smiling plains was a veritable oasis in the desert. We saw a movie and leg-show, and then plunged into the occupation of liquoring up properly, according to the usual traditions of hillmen in a rich plains town. Vinson didn't hit the bottle with his usual vigor. And after all, I didn't drink a great deal, myself, six or seven bottles of lager, bock and ale, and perhaps half a pint of whiskey, not enough of either to induce a real bat; but whether it was mixing the drinks, or the fact that a long time had passed since I had indulged, anyway, the fact remains that I got on a roaring drunk, the biggest I'd been on in years. In fact, it had been years since I'd been soused. On the way back to Brownwood I enlivened our progress by bellowing "Wearin' of the Green", "The Shan Van Vocht", "The Risin' of the Moon" and other belligerent Gaelic chants in a voice that has been compared to a fog horn, and criticizing English policies in the same voice—which caused no conflicts, since most people in West Texas are either Germans or Scotch-Irish. We hit Brownwood some time before midnight and I couldn't have hit the floor with a Stetson hat, though I could still walk in a straight line, as I triumphantly demonstrated. My legs seldom get out of control, regardless of how my head is swimming. Altogether, my activities of those three days remain a high spot in my life. It was a most enjoyable drunk. The only thing that would have made it even more perfect would have been that we were able to pick up a couple of warm dames. There's nothing to make a drunk a success like a dame with ball-bearing hips and a broad mind.

Last month Vinson had his vacation and he spent a week with me. We had a most enjoyable time. I had an unbroken case of Sterling bock all ready when he arrived, but much to my regret he had a slightly corroded gut and had to go easy on his imbibing. He got to Cross Plains on Monday and in search of a show, we went to Ballinger that afternoon. Ballinger lies about seventy miles southwest of Cross Plains, an old town that has a romantic and sometimes violent past. The county is dry but the town is wet and the citizenry favors Rheingold—Sterling bock is Cross Plains' favorite drink, and still farther west they go in for Blatz' Old Heidelberg in a big way, from Midland clear to El Paso. Discussing plans for amusement we decided to take a small swing westward the next day, so returned to Cross Plains early and got to bed before midnight. I must admit that my appetite had been so whetted by the Ballinger Rheingold that upon our return I plunged into my private stock of Sterling bock (a headier drink than Rheingold) and contrived to demolish so much of it that I was well soused when I retired. We were up early the next morning and on our way, and I can not remember a more enjoyable day than that one, spent in whirling across the wind-whipped, sun-baked plains in the direction I love best to go—southwestward. It was hot, as usual, dry, the crops burning up under a savage sun and a fierce hot wind. But alcoholically speaking, the farther west we went, the wetter it got. From the time we left the Callahan divide until we hit the spurs of the Rocky Mountains it was plains, plains, plains, hundreds of miles them, interspersed, in some places, by rolling, desolate sand dunes much like pictures of the Sahara, except for a sparse growth of grease wood and stunted chaparral, and by dry basins, covered with dully gleaming salt deposits, that once were lakes. Throughout our whole trip we crossed only one county where it was impossible to get beer, and that was the one adjoining Callahan. And how good the cold beverage tasted, in that dry heat! It dries a man out, dries up his sweat pores. Ordinarily I perspire like a work horse, but I hardly sweated a drop after we left the hills until we got back. We crossed the Pecos in the middle of the afternoon, 300 miles from Cross Plains, near the town of Pecos. We halted only long enough to down some beer, and then turned up along the river to Carlsbad, New Mexico, ninety miles away. A vast, empty land it is, on both sides of the line, the awesome desolation and monotony broken only by clumps of steel oil rigs, or fringes of green marking irrigation ditches where the salty Pecos feeds a thirst-maddened realm.

Carlsbad was reached well before sun-down—a beautiful little town, with broad streets over which giant cottonwoods, planted by the first settlers, form lofty green arches. In the residential sections concrete irrigation channels parallel the sidewalks. When a citizen wishes to water his lawn, he simply opens the flood gates. Water, brought from dams built on the Pecos, is the reason for the town's existence. Behind it at a distance of a few miles roll the barren desolate foothills of the Rockies, and from its feet the desert stretches gigantically away. New Mexico is dry, as far as water is concerned, but wet in regards to alcohol. Saloons are barred, as such, but drug stores and cafes sell hard liquor by the bottle. My joy at discovering 6% beer (Coors' Golden Beer, made in Golden, Colorado) almost caused me to forgive the inordinately high prices of everything and the abominable sales tax levied in New Mexico. I laid in a goodly stock, naturally. I would like to have spent a few days in Carlsbad, but our time was limited. We were up early, and proved the barbarism of my taste by guzzling beer with my breakfast—remembering our discussion concerning the relative superiority of New Mexico, touched on earlier in this letter, I was at some pains to note the number of Texans residing in that section of New Mexico. The word "Texas" appeared on many business establishments, "The Texas This," "The Texas That" etc., and the number of Texans seemed large. For instance: the barber who cut my hair was one of three in a shop; the other two were both from Texas. He himself was from Little Rock, Arkansas, and seemed more familiar with happenings in Central Texas than he was of those in New Mexico. He spoke with longing of the melons of Parker County, with which sentiments I quite agreed. I was born in that county, which raises the finest melons that are raised on this continent and supplies the markets of the nation regularly. Though I understand the drouth ruined the crop this year. I asked him how many Texans lived in Carlsbad, and he was unable to reply exactly, but said each business house in the city averaged at least two Texans, proprietors or helpers. So you see your idea of our western neighbors being a race different than, and superior to ourselves does not stand up to the harsh test of actual facts. We did not spend much time in Carlsbad. Pausing only long enough for Vinson to buy a bottle of whiskey, and for me to tank up on gin and 6% beer, we sped on to the Cavern, twenty-six miles west of the town of Carlsbad.

I can not describe the fantastic wonders of that great cavern. You must see it yourself to appreciate it. It lies high up among the mountains, and I never saw skies so blue and clear as those that arch titanically above those winding trails up which the traveller must labor to reach the entrance of the Cavern. They are of a peculiarly deep hue beggaring attempts at description. The entrance of the Cavern is gigantic, but it is dwarfed by the dimensions of the interior. One descends seemingly endlessly by winding ramps, for some seven hundred feet. We entered at ten thirty o'clock, and emerged about four. The English language is too weak to describe the Cavern. The pictures do not give a good idea; for one thing they exaggerate the colors; the coloring is really subdued, somber rather than sparkling. But they do not give a proper idea of the size, of the intricate patterns carved in the limestone throughout the millenniums. The largest stalagmite in the world is in that cave—I forget

the exact dimensions, but the diameter, I believe, is 16 feet, and, since it requires a century to build one cubic inch of stalagmite or stalactites, scientists
have set its age at sixty million years. In the Cavern natural laws seem suspended; it is Nature gone mad in a riot of fantasy. Hundreds of feet above
arched the great stone roof, smoky in the mist that eternally rises. Huge stalactites hung from the roof in every conceivable shape, in shafts, in domes, in
translucent sheets, like tapestries of ice. Water dripped, building gigantic columns through the ages, pools of water gleamed green and weird here and
there. It was like a descent of damned souls into hell as we wound down the
sweeping ramps, over four hundred of us (and 178 of them were from Texas,
the rest a scattering from twenty-one different states and Canada). The crowd
was strangely hushed—not strangely, either, for the place was awe-inspiring,
and a man felt his insignificance and unimportance. We moved through a
wonderland of fantastic giants whose immemorial antiquity was appalling to
contemplate. God, what a story you could write after such an exploration! I
thought of you repeatedly, and repeatedly voiced my wish that you were with
us to our companion. *Anything* seemed possible in that monstrous twilight
underworld, seven hundred and fifty feet below the earth. If some animate
monster had risen horrifically from among the dimness of the columns and
spread his taloned anthropomorphic hands above the throng, I do not believe
that anyone would have been particularly surprised.

We ate lunch in "The Big Room", the biggest cavern-chamber in the
world, measuring in some places over a thousand feet across. The lunch was a
gyp, and the beer was not cold enough, but I had no kick coming. I was getting my money's worth, and so was Vinson. The rest of the stay was taken up
with seeing The Big Room. We passed a small green, transparent pool called
the Wishing Well on the solid rock bottom of which shimmered copper and
silver coins cast in by wishers. But I believe it's a fake, because I threw in a
penny and wished for a bottle of beer, and none was forthcoming. Oh, it's *big*
that Cavern. You could lose Mammoth Cave in one corner of it. Only thirty-
two miles have been explored so far, and how far it extends in various ways,
nobody knows yet. Below the caves we traversed lies yet another system of
caverns into which tourists are not admitted. At one place we stood looking
down into a titanic hole three hundred feet deep, and above us the roof towered two hundred and fifty feet. Another place we crossed on a narrow
bridge, with sheer space yawning hundreds of feet below us. But I was most
greatly impressed on our return trip, which we took by a route differing from
that by which we entered. I find my vocabulary failing me. But wait, I had
forgotten something else. The ultimate limit of our exploration was a hill
overlooking a vast chamber filled with columns fantastic as a dope-dream,
which in turn opened into another, a great black mouth that was only a hint
of what lay beyond. On that stony hill we halted and sat down, over four
hundred of us, at the request of our guide. As we had advanced, lights had

been flashed on ahead of us, and turned out behind us, each great chamber being well wired and lighted. Darkness had marched before us and slunk behind us, but each chamber we traversed glowed with radiance. Now all lights were turned off, and, seven hundred and fifty feet under rock, it was such a darkness as can hardly be imagined. It was almost tangible. It remained thus for half a minute, then, half a mile away, the lights flashed on in a distant chamber. But before then, far away, four melodious voices were lifted in "Rock of Ages". Chamber by chamber the lights approached us, until the whole cavern was aflare, and the voices faded eerily away in the distance. Incidentally, a huge stalagmite, shaped in bewilderingly intricate patterns rose on the side of the hill, known as "The Rock of Ages". The chambers and columns are most all named, such as "The King's Chamber", "The Queen's Chamber", the "Queen's Bell-cord" which is a curious stalactite eight feet long and no bigger around than a man's finger, etc., "The Crystal Dome", and so on.

But it was not the curious columns which inspired so much awe in me. It was on our return, when we toiled up and up for hundreds of feet up narrow ladder-like stairs and tortuous ramps that twisted upon themselves like the trail of a serpent. Part way up I paused to stare and wonder. The impact upon my senses was almost overwhelming. It was like nothing so much as a nightmare encountered in waking life. The vaulted roof towered a hundred and fifty feet above me; two hundred feet below me the floor of the cavern; far below and behind me toiled the lines of travellers, trailing away and away like tiny files of insects, back and back to an opening from which they had emerged from the deeper chambers of the cavern. Above and beyond me rose the tortuous ramps, laden with their slowly moving occupants; some had reached the crest of the gigantic wall up which we were laboring and were moving along it in single file before making the final turn; etched against the brooding grey of the mist-veiled roof they did not look like humans. They looked like creatures of nightmare—like inhabitants of a subterranean hell. But it was not the heights and the dimensions which seemed so overwhelming—not the weird columns perched on the heights, nor the weird horned shadow cast by a curious shaft-like formation gigantically upon the smoky wall; it was all these things combined, but more than all it was the silence, the weird misty coloring, the utterly *alien* appearance of everything. It was nightmarish and in a way, terrible; I have dimly glimpsed such scenes in monstrous nightmares; I had not thought ever to see them in waking life. The weird lofty ceiling, with its sullen mist fascinated me. Looking upward I forgot the narrow, slanting ramp on which I was walking, stumbled, and wavered for an instant on the edge with a fall of two hundred feet imminent. I managed to catch myself. Those ramps really should be railed.

Oh, I could talk all day, and still impart only a very little of the wonders of the subterranean world. It was so big; one does not get the impression of being in a cave always; sometimes one feels as if it were really a gigantic canyon, and the lofty rock ceiling merely a curiously colored sky. There are hills in that cave that would be considered good sized hills in the world above. But you should see it for yourself, and I hope you will some day .

Oh, yes, I forgot; as we emerged into the only part where daylight strikes, the great chamber directly under the opening, a shaft of marvelous, gleaming, almost frosty blue slanted down like a radiant sword; only the beam of the burning New Mexican sun, transformed into a miracle of glittering color, giant in volume, as is everything in that country, transforming the cavern into a vast pagan shrine. You must see it, some day, and let its alien wonders flow into the literature of the nation through your magic pen. The stories you could produce after revelling in those wonders!

Coming out of the Cavern we paused only long enough to imbibe some bottled refreshments and then hit out for El Paso, 170 miles to the southwest. We passed no towns on that lap, scarcely any filling stations or ranches—it is a vast, empty realm, a big country, a man's country. Twenty, thirty, fifty miles the road would stretch ahead of us without a turn or bend. It led around the foot of Signal Peak, towering nearly ten thousand feet into the sky, and visible for seventy-five miles across the desert. It is the southern extremity of the Guadalupe Range, which extends far up into New Mexico. But Signal Peak is in Texas, the highest point in the State; indeed, the highest point anywhere from the Atlantic ocean to the higher peaks of the Rockies. It is only a foothill of the Rockies, but it would dwarf the best the Appalachians could offer. It is more impressive in that it rises almost sheer out of the rolling plains. It is known on the maps by another name, but the natives call it Signal Peak. It was still in sight when we crossed the Salt Lakes, broad expanses of salt that caused a bloody feud between whites and Mexicans back in the '80's known as the Salt War. Pipe lines running to El Paso are elevated and cross the salt beds on low trestles.

We had flats and were delayed, and didn't get to El Paso until about ten o'clock that night. Next morning we were up and exploring, for it was the first time either of us had ever been there. I like El Paso; big, wide streets, the people moving with a leisurely air—it is in Texas, but hardly of Texas, separated as it is from the rest of the state by mountain ranges and uninhabited deserts. The spirit of western independence is highly developed there.

Apparently they don't give much of a damn what goes on in Austin. For instance, Texas, as a state, is still dry, as far as hard liquor is concerned. Only the sale of 3.2 beer is legal. But El Paso is wide open. They sell you anything you want across the bar. With one exception; I found no 6% beer, though I might have if I'd looked long enough. El Paso lies in the midst of an irrigated belt, overshadowed by the bare and desolate Franklyn mountains on both sides of the river. We went over into Juarez, in search of a bullfight, but they weren't having one that day. I was disappointed in Juarez; from tales I'd heard, I had an idea it was somewhat more elaborate than it really was. But it was just as dirty and lousy as any border town I ever saw—more so than Piedras Negras, for instance, and swarming with the usual pimps and touts. We drove around awhile, made a brief exploration of what is politely known as "the red light district", and of course imbibed some. I tanked up on tequila and beer; Vinson stuck to beer, and we both found it disappointing— Moctezuma 6.5% and not ripe enough to suit my taste. We came back across the river and located a likely saloon and did our heavy drinking there. Schlitz 4.5%, big McGintys[5] of it, and drawn by an old time bartender that knew his business, which means a lot. I tanked up on it and on Baccardi rum, and Vinson did his part manfully as far as the beer was concerned, and then we went to a show and saw pictures of the Baer-Carnera fight and it was the weirdest battle ever waged for the heavyweight crown, as I said the night I heard it over the radio.[6] Well, after the show we primed ourselves at "The Aztec Bar" and headed east, along a different road than we came in; a road running between alfalfa fields and irrigation ditches and lined with giant cottonwoods. And I could kick myself in the trousers for what I missed in El Paso, because when we stopped in Madeira Valley—a long, beautiful valley between barren mountain ranges, but rendered a garden by the life-giving water—a kid sold me a bottle of ABC beer, made in California and the best beer I ever drank in my life. Every joint in El Paso handled it, and I'd been passing it up in my ignorance. And Madeira Valley is as far east as I found it. One sees lots of commodities in El Paso from the West Coast, not found anywhere else in Texas—indeed the town is more a part of the extreme west than it is of Texas.

We spent the night at Van Horn, a little old town built on a flat with the Van Horn, Eagle and Davis Mountains towering about it at distances from five to thirty miles; next day we whirled on through historical old Fort Stockton, paused only long enough to have a flat fixed and to admire Comanche Spring, which flows 65,000,000 gallons of water a day and makes human life possible in the vicinity, and then we rushed on, crossed the Pecos at a place where once stood the oil town of Girvin but of which now there is no slightest trace, stopped at San Angelo long enough to see a movie, and then on home, arriving at Cross Plains about 10:30 that night. The speedometer showed 1137 miles for four days travelling.

Some days have passed since I wrote the above, and I learn that San Antonio is as wide open as El Paso. Perhaps Vinson and I will investigate the matter. It would be like a breath out of the past to see the old Buckhorn as I saw it when a child. (When I was a child, I mean; there was never anything infantile about the saloon, from its first beginning.)

I have spoken to you about Price's visit and expressed the pleasure I derived from it. My only regret was that he was unable to stay longer. I wish he could have remained for several weeks, and that I had been able to show him something of the state. He is a marvelous conversationalist. I could to him talk for hours on end. I was much interested, incidentally, by his comments on fencing, and would like to watch him demonstrate his mastery of the art with some foeman worthy of his steel. I used to wish that I could learn to fence, but the opportunity never presented itself, fencing masters not being very commonly met with in West Texas. A friend and I, several years ago, decided to try to learn the art by practice, and being unable to obtain foils, we used a pair of army swords. It was my misfortune, however, to run him through the right hand in the very first bout and thereafter he could never be persuaded to fence again. I doubt, though, if fencing could ever have interested me like boxing, since it is, apparently, founded on finesse, and gives little opportunity for the exercise of ruggedness and sheer physical power.

Price and I discussed another science of mayhem, the French savate, or foot-fighting. He had not, as I remember, ever seen it demonstrated, nor have I, though I have talked with a pugilist from the American navy (a battle-marked slugger with scars on him from implements ranging from post oak clubs wielded by Texas ridge-runners to knives in Chinese ports) who once fell victim to this vicious art, in a sort of international ring exhibition. In a battle between a savate artist and an English or American boxer, the advantage would seem to rest with which ever man got in the first blow. Foot fighting of any kind is particularly vicious and crippling, whether enacted with the developed science of a French apache, or the instinctive ferocity of a backwoodsman. A kick in the crotch or groin will disable the toughest, and hobnails applied to a fallen man may leave ghastly results. The only time I was ever knocked off my feet from a blow delivered by a human being my downfall resulted from a kick, rather than a punch. My cousin planted his heel just below my belt and I went down as if I had been struck with a piledriver. The sheer force of the blow knocked me down, but the intense pain of it prevented me from rising. As I went down, blinded with pain, I grabbed and threw the first thing that came to my clutching hand. I didn't know what it was; I was simply following my instinct. It happened to be a long-handled gourd dipper, and it shattered to pieces on the wall as my cousin ducked. I felt as if my whole pelvis were caved in; almost paralyzed with the pain of it, I couldn't get up and commit the whole-hearted mayhem on my attacker I desired; I could only lay there and curse him, while he stood out of my reach and laughed like a jackass eating prickly pears. It's comical to think about it now, years later. But I got even with him not long after that, when I caught him off guard and jovially deluged him with the scalding contents of a red-hot coffee pot. I'll never forget his maddened howl, and the convulsive effort he made to brain me with a mesquite log. I was laughing so I just managed to duck it. An inch lower and the post oak ridge country would have been deprived of its pioneer writer.

I seemed to have wandered far afield as is my habit. But there's not much else to say, except that Price came up fully to my expectations, that I hope to meet him again some day, and that I feel certain of his ultimate success in the literary line. Big success, I mean.

But it's time I drew this lengthy missive to a close. Glancing back over it, in regard to our debate, I have but little to add. Considering your criticism of my "moralistic attitude", I find it clear enough, upon reflection, and probably consistent with your views in general, though I feel it is a bit illogical.

You condemn me vigorously for criticising things that violate my particular code of ethics, but you are equally vigorous in condemning anything that violates *your* particular code of ethics.

For instance, you accuse me of placing too much emphasis on the purely human conceptions of "honesty, justice and fairness"; but at the same time you strenuously denounce a whole geographical section because its conception of "order" does not always agree exactly with yours. "Honesty, justice and fairness" are no more questions of man-made ethics than "order" is. Your conception or code of ethics would seem to be quite as arbitrary as you accuse mine of being.

I know, of course, by what reasoning you will condemn my attitude and justify your own. You will say that your particular conception of ethics represents the necessities and requirements of civilization. All your arguments, apparently, are based on your conception of the unqualified superiority of "civilization" as represented by your region; a region which, it would seem, you consider all other regions must copy precisely before they can be considered properly civilized.

Consistent with this conviction, your hostility toward the Southwest is only natural. If you accept the necessities, requirements and conditions of your own region as a criterion by which to judge all other regions, it is natural that you would condemn all traditions, habits and customs that differ from those of New England, and refuse to recognize the existence of problems which do not exist there.

You may retort that whole-sale butchery and violence are wrong, judged by any standard. But your belief that conditions are so wholly sanguinary in the Southwest (your apparent belief, that is) is the result of a distorted and exaggerated conception which I fear can be corrected only by first hand experience. You once advised me to spend a year in a civilized city. I think you would find it an equally enlightening experience to travel in the Southwest. You would find, I believe, that when people have customs and habits and ways of thinking that differ from those of the older, more thickly-settled sections, it is not always the result of viciousness and stupidity.

I naturally enjoyed re-reading your and Price's story in the current Weird Tales. As I wrote to Mr. Wright, it is much more than a story; it is a philosophical masterpiece. I hope you are even now working on a sequel.

My Costigan stories, which used to appear in Fight Stories and Action Stories, and one of which you read in Magic Carpet, in an altered guise, are now running in the new sport magazine, Jack Dempsey's Fight Magazine.[7] I am particularly gratified to have been given a niche in Dempsey's publication for he was one of my boyhood heroes, and I still entertain a deep admiration for him. The editor asked me for the series before the names of the publication and publishers were divulged, and it was not until I saw the first copy of the magazine that I learned that Dempsey was connected with it. He was a great champion; possibly the greatest of all, though I have always believed that Jim Jeffries deserved that title by a shade. But that is only my own opinion, and it wavers sometimes, when I reflect upon the tigerish ferocity and blinding speed possessed by Dempsey in his prime. Action Stories is running a series of humorous westerns, concerning the mythical exploits of one Breckenridge Elkins; Price read some of these stories and seemed to like them very much. He advised me to try the smooth-paper market with this character and I think I will, if I ever get around to it. At present I'm trying to crash a new western market.

Well, best wishes, and many sales.

Cordially,

REH

Notes

1. Alfred Noyes (1880–1959), British poet. The poem appears in Noyes's *Dick Turpin's Ride and Other Poems* (1927) and also in his *Collected Poems* (Edinburgh: William Blackwood & Sons, 1927), Vol. 4, pp. 247–48.

2. Ross Sterling served one term as governor of Texas, 1931–33. He was defeated for re-election by Miriam "Ma" Ferguson in the 1932 election. See letter 65.

3. The blood eagle reportedly was a method of torture and execution sometimes mentioned in Norse literature. It was performed by cutting the ribs of the victim by the spine, breaking the ribs so they resembled blood-stained wings, pulling out the lungs, and sprinkling salt in the wound.

4. *The Invisible Man* (Universal, 1933), directed by James Whale, produced by Carl Laemmle, Jr.; starring Claude Rains.

5. "McGinty" was a term used in El Paso for a large-capacity glass, 20 or 21 ounces. (In 1934, most members of the El Paso Cafe Owners Association reduced the size of their McGinties to 16 ounces, but at least two were reported to be continuing to serve the larger glasses.) The term is probably related to the McGinty Club, a turn-of-the-century El Paso social and civic club, though the club itself had ceased any organized activities by about 1905.

6. On 14 June 1934 at Madison Square Garden, Max Baer defeated Primo Carnera by a technical knockout, after having sent Carnera to the mat ten times.

7. American boxer Jack Dempsey (1895–1983) was editor of *Jack Dempsey's Fight Magazine* in name only; the real editor was William Kofoed.

[107]

66 College St.,
Providence, R.I.,
July 27, 1934.

Dear R E H: —

As you know from my card, I duly reached home again and found the spider in excellent condition. This monster now adorns my museum shelf in company with the Florida snake and other exotic bits—including the rattles for which I am indebted to you. I'd certainly rather see him there—safe in a bottle—than crawling around my quarters!

My trip, it is needless to say, was enjoyable down to the bottom line. Since I probably described St. Augustine in detail in 1931, I needn't cover the ground again—except to repeat how potent an imaginative spell lies around those ancient houses and that centuried, brooding fort. Here is a place that was over fifty years old when the first Pilgrim landed in Plymouth! On this occasion I saw an added feature of great interest—an old Indian graveyard just unearthed at the site of the primitive native village north of the town. The skeletons lie side by side, with feet toward the east, and will be permanently preserved in their original positions. The excavation work has been very careful—each skeleton and the earth around it being protected by a low wall of cement. Eventually a large museum building will be erected over the unearthed area. The aspect of the find—which was made only a few weeks before I saw it—is very weird indeed. From the posture of the bodies it is plain that they were buried under the auspices of Franciscan priests—probably around the year 1600.

In Richmond I stopped at an hotel only 2 doors from the site of the house where Poe grew up. In Washington I did three things I had never done before—saw the *interior* of the capitol, ascended the Washington monument, and inspected the furnished interior of the Custis-Lee plantation house—Arlington mansion—on the heights across the river. I had explored this house before it was furnished, but its equipment just as it was when inhabited gives it a double charm. In Philadelphia I visited the pleasant brick cottage where Poe lived from 1842 to 1844—restored and opened as a museum only a few months ago. This 3-story edifice is in the rear of a larger house at 530 N. 7th St. Around it is a small garden, now restored as it used to be. The cottage has lasted well, and no structural alterations have ever been made. It was built around 1800, and the small-paned windows, tasteful mantels, and panelled doors, all bespeak the quiet architectural grace of that period. There are only 2 rooms to a floor, and all are furnished just as during Poe's tenancy; though only a desk and chair are actual Poe reliques. Eastward on the ground floor is the parlour with its attractive fireplace, pianoforte, sofa, and book-closet—the latter filled with such volumes as one would be likely to have in the '40's. Across a narrow hall is the kitchen, where the family also ate. On the second floor is Poe's bedroom, with a neat black slate mantel; while across the hall is a smaller study. On the low-ceiled third floor are the rooms of Poe's invalid wife and aunt, with modest fireplaces and small casement windows. Everything is neatly kept—curtains, flowers, plants, pictures, china, and linen—just as it was in Poe's time. In the large adjoining house, which has a connecting door, is one of the finest Poe collections in existence. Here are copies of magazines with the first appearance of most of the tales and poems, and other associative items too numerous to record. Of all the many Poe houses still standing, none (save perhaps the Fordham cottage) come to life more vividly as a typical home than this unpretentious structure.

Well—I arrived home on July 10th to confront an appalling stock of accumulated work . . . . . so much that I haven't had time even to complete the unpacking of my valise! I was surely glad to see the rolling hills, great elms, stone walls, quaint streets, and white steeples of my native region once more, and have done my work in scenic outdoor spots as far as possible. There has been no rain since my arrival, and the weather is for the most part warm. I found my aunt in excellent health—going everywhere without a cane—and at the boarding-house across the back garden there is an exquisite coal-black kitten—just getting vigorous and playful—which I borrow very frequently. Next week—August 2-3-4—I expect my friend James F. Morton (curator of the Paterson N.J. Museum) as a guest—an event which will mean a vast lot of interesting conversation and spirited argument.

I am glad indeed to hear that you and the other smashup-survivors are fully recovered—and hope the cardiac trouble will also disappear before long. It surely was lucky that your ribs got the brunt of the impact! As to varying degrees of sensitiveness at the sight or mention of blood—of course, actual fainting represents a pathological extreme . . . . as does also, perhaps, Long's acute nausea. One does not very often come across cases as acute as these. It is, however, perfectly normal for persons of active imagination to experience more moderate reactions of unpleasantness—faintness, nausea, or psychological horror—at the sight or very vivid description of phenomena involving the violation or mutilation of the human form, including the shedding of blood in large quantities. The blood of lower animals, if known to be such, would not cause such sharp sensations as a general thing; although very finely-organised persons would probably find it difficult to tolerate the habitual sight of it except through special training. All violation or mutilation of the higher organic beings is essentially repulsive to persons of advanced evolution, though they can conquer this repulsion when circumstances make it necessary or advisable—as in hunting, war, surgery, or kindred pursuits. The circumstance is hardly remarkable, since in a normal environment the sight of blood or mutilation is very rare, and associated altogether with the gravest and saddest disasters. Habit and will-power, of course, build up a resistance; so that those whose special positions require them to confront blood and mutilation—as in an hospital—sooner or later become able to face these things without flinching or indeed thinking much about the matter. The same thing, naturally, is true in the oil fields, where tragic accidents are still unfortunately common. I think my own sensitiveness to blood would be below rather than above the average—for although I've never seen a sanguinary accident to another, one which happened to myself left me unmoved. Actual mutilation of the human (or any higher animal) form, however, would probably repel me strongly. It is probable, I think, that no highly developed person could very comfortably endure the sight of blood or mutilation unless distracted at the time by some *other* emotion such as rage, fear, anxiety, determination to help, and so on. That is, until habituated by custom. Some can never become accustomed to sanguinary sights, as they discover in the early stages of hospital or medical-college experience. Others are abnormally callous—like my friend Harry Brobst, whose description of a case at his hospital had even Price, with all his varied experience, pretty well fed up.

Too bad Wright shortened the very effective title "Iron Shadows in the Moon"—he has a damnable tendency to reduce anything original and striking to something more approaching the commonplace. But it was a great story, for all that—and so was "Queen of the Black Coast". Still another fine item is "The Garden of Fear", which I've just read in *Marvel Tales*. I really can't understand Wright's rejection of that item. That Noyes poem about the parrot was new to me, and I am indeed glad to form its acquaintance. But I have an idea that this parrot's span of survival was not as immense as that implied in your story—or am I wrong? When I planned to use the idea I meant to employ some unknown talking bird other than a parrot, so that its life could last infinitely beyond any parrot's allotted term.

As to our debate—I'm sorry if any of my arguments seemed vague, contradictory, or disregardful of the text which they answered. Considering the haste with which most of them have had to be written, I suppose that many a 'boner' must have slipped past my critical eye. I won't endeavour to protract the discussion to further excessive lengths, but will merely note a few points bearing on specific objections raised by you, or correcting certain misapprehensions I seem to have created.

First—as to values, if I seemed to resurrect a dead argument concerning mental versus physical attainments, it was merely because a large number of expressions and enthusiasms and ironies in your text appeared to qualify to some extent the formal opinions previously outlined. Also—I thought that somewhere in one of your letters you had said that all kinds of *perfection*, whether in sculpture or pugilism, were essentially equal. It was from memory—over several months—that I covered this point, and it is quite possible that my recollection was at fault. I can't find the passage I recalled now. Pray accept my apologies if I did ponderously attack something that never was written!

Second—as to my ideals of government, you certainly have me wrong. You say you do not hate human development, and yet you sneer at my ideal of a government restricted to men who are properly trained for the job and who know what they are doing! Moreover, you say that if my ideal of government were in force, I would—or could—have you burned at the stake because of your tastes and interests. Now that is *precisely the opposite* of anything which my kind of government would ever do, want to do, or permit to be done! The *absolute first* requisite of any mature or genuine civilisation is *complete intellectual and artistic freedom;* so that no restriction whatever would be placed upon any sort of individual thought or tastes. An opinion changed by force is an opinion not really changed at all. No real civilisation wishes to change anyone's opinion except through rational arguments designed to make the holders of error see the error of what they have been holding. Do not judge the sort of fascism I advocate by any form now existing. Every different civilisation needs a different form adapted to its own temperament; and the Italian, Turkish, and German forms represented by Mussolini, Mustapha Kemal,[1] and Hitler are not for us. I would be the last to endorse any of these restrictive systems as applied to Anglo-Saxons.

Third—as to what you regard as my mistake in saying that you overemphasise *ethics* as a basic value, let me see if I can explain my meaning. I had been at some pains to show that *degree of evolution*—in the sense of *removal from the amoebal stage,* or *extent of utilisation of the consciousness-and-comprehension forces inherent in organic matter*—formed about as close an approach to an "absolute" standard of human quality as can be conceived of. I presented certain facts and perspectives which appeared to sustain this position, and tried to take care not to utter any snap judgments or unqualified assertions. In reply, you seemed to pass over this matter entirely, and to subscribe to a system of human values based on such local surface characteristics as "courage", "fairness", and so on—qualities of a certain pragmatic value in human relationships, but certainly not indicative of the extent of the organism's removal from the primordial protoplasmic stage. It seemed to me—whether rightly or not—that your ultimate working criterion of human worth lay in these ethical traits instead of in the basic qualitative development which distinguishes a man from a lizard, and a Pythagoras from a cotton-picking nigger. Because this was my impression, I expressed a belief that you overemphasised ethics. Of course, I may well have been wrong through a mis-reading of your argument. Let it be noted that this phase of the argument had nothing to do with the relative merits of different forms of social organisation—civilisation, barbarism, and so on. It dealt solely with the innate, intrinsic quality of the isolated human individual, as if each one were alone in a void. The social argument forms the *next* step—for *after* we have decided what intrinsic human quality is, we must decide what form of society is best suited to bring out the most in the race. When it comes to the consideration of *human society* as such, then no one could be more solicitous about ethics than I—indeed, I thought I said so before. I would never have thought of saying that you overemphasise ethics *as a factor in life*. I merely said that you overemphasise them *as an intrinsic measure of individual human evolution*. That would have applied just as much to the phase of ethics which *I* had occasion to stress elsewhere (*order,* etc.), as to the phase which *you* happened to stress. To call *orderliness* a basic index of individual human worth would be just as erroneous as to give that distinction to *courage, honesty, fairness,* or any other ethical quality. Certainly, I would never have thought of calling any *one* sort of ethical qualities any more or less erroneous than any *other* sort in this connexion. It was simply that I don't think ethics belongs at all in that particular field of judgment. I certainly hope that you did not think I was trying to use the ethical quality of orderliness *as an index of degree of removal from protoplasmic primitiveness*. That would be belying my deepest beliefs just as thoroughly as a similar use of justice or courage would be! When I extolled orderliness, it was as an attribute of society calculated to give intrinsic human quality its best chance to develop to the full. I also recognise that honesty, fairness, and courage are highly necessary in any society devoted to this end . . . the only end worth pursuing. The fact is, I value fairness, courage, and honesty well-nigh as much as you do—not less so because I place orderliness on a par with them. It was merely a matter of chance that *they,* instead of *orderliness,* happened to be the aspects of ethics mentioned during the course of my argument that *ethics as a whole* has no place in the measuring of *absolute human quality*. I would have objected just as violently had orderliness been the aspect mentioned. This, I hope, clears up your misconception about my favouring one side of ethics at the expense of another. Of course, I value orderliness more than you do, and give it a more important place in the ethical scale; but that is merely a difference of opinion. As you see, I am not trying to claim that orderliness is any different in essence from any other phase of ethics, or that it has any far-reaching implications which others lack. I am merely insisting that—along with honesty and the other elements you stress—it is very highly important as a means of bringing out the greatest qualities in the human organism; and that, therefore, no society can be really mature or desirable without a very large quota of it—no matter how much honesty and courage and justice may be present. Remember that I am not trying to say that a desirable society can be founded on order alone, without honesty and justice and the like. I am merely saying that a desirable society cannot be founded on honesty and justice and courage alone, without orderliness. *All* are necessary. I seemed, in my argument with you, to be favouring *order* unduly; but that was only because, in this case, *order* happened to be the quality which needed defending. In an argument with an immoralist who would consider order the sole needed quality and depreciate honesty and fairness and courage, I would find myself defending the latter things just as staunchly as you do. Do you see my point now? I am asserting nothing more than *that order is of* EQUAL *importance with honesty, justice, and courage in the constitution of human society*. And that is all I have ever asserted. As factors in society I don't think you overvalue honesty and courage; I merely think you undervalue order.

Fourth—if any paragraph of mine seemed to imply that I consider the state of Texas, as a unit, more barbaric than any other unit, it can have been only through a slip of the pen obscuring and belying my actual intended meaning. Certainly, no such idea ever entered my head; for no one realises more keenly than I how little arbitrary boundary-lines mean. I merely mentioned that—judging from scraps of information received—some parts of the southwest (whether within or outside Texas was immaterial—indeed, I had no way of knowing how these parts were locally distributed) pursued a life less sanguinary than the type you have described as prevailing in certain regions. It happened that the source of information in question was a clergyman in Clovis, New Mexico—not at all far from the Texas line, if I read the maps aright—but it would never have occurred to me to make the inference that New Mexico as a whole has one kind of life while Texas as a whole has another! If I seemed to do so, it was certainly a mistake of the most flagrant sort. Actually, I realised that the scene of this mode of life might just as well have been in Texas as in any other state—that indeed such a life probably *does* exist in dozens of places in Texas. I realised, too, that the less fortunate conditions you have described undoubtedly flourish in any number of places outside Texas. So complete and unreserved was my realisation of all this, that it never occurred to me to take specific steps against misinterpretation. Perhaps I applied place-names carelessly now and then—using the word "Texas" as a sort of abstraction to signify conditions which you have described chiefly in connexion with certain parts of Texas—and if so, I apologise most profoundly for the confusion.

Fifth—you err when you attribute to me any hostility toward the southwest or toward pioneering in general. I have repeatedly expressed my admiration for the struggles of those who overcame a difficult environment and opened up new sections to civilisation, and I have specifically recognised that their violent methods were necessary adjuncts of the existing conditions. I certainly do not think they could have done otherwise. My only objection is to the survival of a tradition of violence *when it is no longer necessary*. I blame only those who *voluntarily* choose bloodshed and personal vengeance *when the facilities for orderly regulation and crime-punishment are available*. It is important that this distinction be made clear, lest I be accused of enmity toward a chapter of American life which in truth I highly respect.

Sixth—as to the specific problems which you brought up, I did not claim that my solutions would in every case be possible. Rather would I say that these solutions are the kind of thing which ought to be *tried*. If the elements on the other side are given a chance to coöperate in such solutions and then refuse, it is naturally quite all right to go ahead in as forceful a way as possible. Nothing else could be done. As to the question of hospitality and the Bostonian—I merely said that it might be hard for an outsider to understand any code which involved harbouring one who ought to be delivered to the legal authorities. A criminal is outside the system of obligations prevailing among honest men, because he has broken the rules of that system himself. To anyone not initiated in a special local code, the only thing to do with a criminal is to withhold aid and comfort from him and deliver him to the authorities when possible. He can be fed after he is captured—before that he has no right to food. This, of course, is merely the basic theory. In practice, there can be dozens of exceptions. I don't doubt but that the local code was fully justified, and that any person of really alert and flexible mind would have realised it. My point was merely that all minds are not alert and flexible. Another thing—don't fancy that I blame the absentee capitalists behind western outlawry any less than I blame the outlaws themselves. All were equally culpable, and I regret the escape of the capitalists from the noose just as much as I regret the similar escape of any of the actual killers who may have chanced to survive.

Seventh—as to the connexion of outside exploitation with survivals of homicidal violence, I certainly believe you are right. You make the point very clear, and I'd hesitate to say you are wrong in your explanation of the violence and brutality prevailing among the police. My theory was only a working hypothesis based on one grouping of apparent evidence—and you seem to furnish another body of evidence which explains the given condition even better. Regarding homicide rates—the table you enclose is highly interesting. I would explain the high rates in N.C., Florida, and Virginia by calling attention to two things: first, the large and turbulent negro population; and second, the lawless "poor white" element which is as distinct as the negro from the civilised inhabitants of the given region. These elements swell the figures when we reckon things by states, but they do not give any clue to the mode and standards of life prevailing in Richmond and Raleigh and Jacksonville or the long and thickly settled farming districts where the bulk of the responsible population reside. By the same token, of course, I have never been so naive as to fancy that the west's high statistical homicide-record meant a reign of terror in the streets of Houston or Tucson or San Antonio. I realise that the bulk of all homicides and violence pertains to an underworld not truly representative of a region's best population. In New England, for example, there is much violence among the Italian and Slavic immigrants; but we consider ourselves civilised because this violence does not touch the dominant and long-seated population except occasionally. As for robbery—the Italian gangsterism of Chicago undoubtedly explains Illinois's high place on the list—just as the negro undoubtedly explains South Carolina's and Florida's. Indiana gets the overflow of Chicagoism, and Ohio has a foreign gangsterism of its own. The absolute connexion of crime and violence with foreigners, negroes, and retrogressive backwater elements in the older parts of the country is apparent in all tables where any attempt to classify the origin of the criminals is made. Another point—it may be that I have had a totally wrong idea of the extent to which violence figures in the southwest. Remember that I have repeatedly called attention to my ignorance in this matter—pointing out that your accounts are really my only substantial source. Before receiving these accounts, I had thought the wild western way of life entirely vanished. Now it is quite possible that in speaking of violent and sanguinary incidents of recent date you have been citing phenomena which are dramatic and interesting rather than typical, or which pertain only to certain limited sections and economic zones. If so, it is only my combined stupidity and total unfamiliarity with the whole southwest which has caused me to regard the condoning of violence as a general regional characteristic apart from Mexicans, oil-workers, and other special classes. No one would be readier or gladder than I to admit such a mistake; for my object in all arguments is *not to make any preconceived opinion of mine seem right,* but merely *to discover and establish the truth, whatever the truth may be.* In one point I can see that I erred through sheer ignorance. I spoke in a general way of the inadvisability of translating a verbal quarrel at once into blows—but of course I did not envisage anything like the abuse of oil-drillers as now quoted by you. I thought you were referring to an altogether different stratum of life and speech. Assuredly, with the violent verbal provocation you describe, the only fitting reply *is* one expressed in muscle rather than acoustics! You can hardly think that I would regard such language as that of the drillers as a "trivial slight"!

Eighth—regarding the very interesting printed matter, of course I have never claimed that the long-settled regions are wholly free from violence and crime. Murders, brawls, police abuses, etc. exist everywhere. They are parts of human nature. The significant thing is the *frequency or infrequency* with which they occur, and *the degree of tolerance or disapproval shown toward them by public opinion.* The Tombs and Cleveland police incidents you cite are probably correctly reported—but does that alter the fact that, in general, no respectable person ever runs afoul of the law or is persecuted by it? You read certain incidents, culled over periods of time from regions representing a population of 50 or 75 millions, yet how typical can these be of the actual daily life of any given individual in the regions concerned? These things are rarities which make news. In truth, not one person in a hundred thousand ever comes into contact with them or anything like them. I've never been arrested. Nobody I know has ever been arrested. And certainly the people I happen to know are no exceptional group in the community. The fact remains that in these parts the law is a protection and not a menace, as attested by the experience of the overwhelming majority. A few criminals now and then among the police means no more than a few criminals now and then among the medical profession or among the clergy. We don't say that all doctors and clergymen are corrupt merely because abusers of privilege have been found among doctors and clergymen. And it is the same with the police. Against all the flagrant cases that can be found in the massed newspaper items of a year, we can scale the simple pragmatic fact that in the east hardly any average person has ever had any contact with the seamy side of the law, and that the policeman is a distinctly popular figure among all classes of honest society. Even the cases of brutality sometimes reported usually have as their victims definite underworld characters whose real guilt in a thousand ways is enough to make them deserve all that they get and more. Extreme sympathy with criminals is almost always misplaced. Even the much-discussed point of clubbing women has two sides. Cases of this generally concern riots where hostile radicals deliberately place tough-lunged viragoes in strategic points in order to handicap police handling. In cases like these, the artificial laws of chivalry—based on totally different conditions—simply have to be suspended to a greater or lesser extent . . . . just as in the case of military procedure, when some nation like Russia throws a female regiment into the battle line. In the recent war, when the famed women's "Battalion of Death" went into action with rifles and artillery,[2] one could hardly expect the Germans or Austrians to cease firing and lift their hats to the ladies while the latter mowed them down with bullets! By the way—that Barrow-Parker ballad is quite a bit of folklore, which will probably take its place among kindred chants of the border.

Ninth—turning to barbarians, I used the word *degeneracy* advisedly in referring to inhuman mutilators. In psychology, degeneracy signifies *the deterioration or perversion of an instinct from its proper function;* and all wanton cruelty or delight in human suffering and mutilation comes under that head. No normal human being could either desire or tolerate the cruelties practiced by certain barbarians and savages, and all modern anthropologists agree that abnormal psychology—sadism, etc.—is rampant among primitive races because of their disordered and maladjusted lives. The notion of the "noble savage"—or of savagery and barbarism as a wholesome norm of any sort—was long ago exploded. Actually, savages and barbarians are the most neurotic, abnormal, and complex-ridden sort of persons conceivable. Briffault and Calverton[3] can tell things enough to break up most cases of barbarism-worship! It hardly surprises me to learn that isolated cases of fiendish mutilation have occurred among modern gangsters. It is in keeping with their duplication of barbarism in other ways. I merely had never heard of such a case as that which you cite, since I'm not especially interested in crime and don't read crime news closely. As to Rome and other civilised nations of antiquity—they were callous as compared with the best modern nations, but they did not equal the barbarians in steady and calculated brutality. Sporadic outbreaks of brutality occurred under evil rulers; but the national ideal was always opposed to brutal extremes, and great humanity prevailed over long periods. It is not a matter of historic concealment—indeed, the very *wish* to conceal brutality would imply a higher standard than that of the barbarians who gloried in violations and mutilations which no normal man could even read of without sickening.

Tenth—as to 'my conception of the unqualified superiority of civilisation as represented by my region', let me call attention to the fact that I have (a) not only given a clear definition, apart from all regions, of what I consider a praiseworthy civilisation, but (b) have specifically stated that I do *not* consider my own region more civilised than dozens of others I could name. I have said that I regard civilisation as *something which brings out a maximum of man's innate capacities, and increases the distance of his life from the dull, vegetative, unorganised life of the amoebal moneron.* I have also said that I consider western Europe—especially France and Great Britain—as the most civilised part of the globe. France, Great Britain, Italy and Germany—all have developed certain sides of civilisation to a tremendous extent, so that it is hard to strike averages and declare any one of them a really greater culture than the other. I do not think that any part of America has achieved a degree of civilisation equalling western Europe's, and I do not even give my own region first place in comparing types of American civilisation. Instead, going by such evidence as I have received and digested, I would tend to award that distinction to Charleston and the South Carolina low country. I don't favour or oppose any region as a region. I merely recognise and respect certain qualities in life, and rejoice when I find them anywhere. Very often the same region will combine the qualities I respect with those I detest in the most paradoxical fashion. What I admire is human development away from the unicellular stage—development of all the powers latent within man, and encouragement of such conditions as give them scope. What I detest is human degradation or retardation in any form—violence, ugliness, ignorance, sensuality, brutality, cruelty, abnormality, filth, cloddishness, rapacity, egotism, encroachment, violations of physical or spiritual integrity, and everything that goes with a dull acquiescence in the animal patterns of the lower part of creation. Any civilisation or way of life which encourages what I respect and combats what I detest gains my endorsement, in whatsoever part of the world it may lie; and vice versa. And I may add that I have tried to found my likes and dislikes on actual cosmic evidence and not on mere caprice. I know how hard it is to talk of external standards in dealing with human preferences, and would scarcely care to call my criteria infallible ones. On the other hand, I think the long biological, psychological, and philosophical explanations of these *proximate* or *pseudo-absolute* standards which I have made in former letters will convince you that they are not superficial, capriciously-adopted pieces of guesswork and prejudice. You may consider them *wrong*, but you can hardly consider them as *lightly or arbitrarily held.* That is, when I say I believe this set of standards to be profoundly more valid than some other set, it is not merely a question of mood and taste. I have thought about the other sets and tried to see what relation they have to any phase of human existence and differentiation, and in some cases have tried to believe in them. My reason for believing as I do is that all the evidence I can pick up seems, to my mind, to point that way. Thus when I say that civilisation is superior to barbarism, I am doing more than uttering a personal preference for civilised as distinguished from barbaric life. I am maintaining that civilisation utilises vast reservoirs of human capacity which barbarism leaves undeveloped; and that the effect of this utilisation is to make mankind an infinitely higher and more important being, as measured in distance from the condition of primitive slime, than he would otherwise be. I am maintaining that it is the *natural* condition for any animal as highly developed biologically as man is; that the most superior types (biologically measured) of mankind *can never be satisfied as a whole till they attain it*, and that the free exercise of the faculties liberated by it gives an infinitely richer and finer range of enjoyment to any well-organised person than the narrow range of crude animal sensations (some of which civilisation admittedly diminishes) exercised by the brutish barbarian. I am furthermore maintaining that the standard of human quality expressed in *degree of removal from amoebal simplicity* is *not* an arbitrary or superficial one, to be lightly discarded for any other, but a well-nigh absolute thing founded on the only traces of progressive organisation to be found in the cosmos. And remember that I do not maintain any of these things merely because they appeal personally to me. I maintain each of those points *because I believe there is evidence for it*. When I say that I think degree of removal from the amoeba (either in physical organisation or in habits of thought and imagination) forms a qualitative standard more valid than any other standard, I am expressing *an inference from evidence* exactly similar in kind to that whereby I think that light travels 186,000 miles per second, or that the sun is 866,500 miles in diameter and 93,000,000 miles away. My inference may be wrong, *but it is an inference and not a guess or mere preference*. It cannot be said that I prefer one set of standards to another *without definite reasons which seem valid to me*. I believe that there are *certain real and specific reasons* for considering civilisation as different from barbarism in a direction intrinsically favourable to man's degree of importance, enjoyment, symmetry, and completeness in the cosmic flux; a direction to which we may logically apply the term "upward" (as based on the only scale of progressive organisation in the cosmos), and which we cannot help endorsing if we are friends rather than enemies of mankind. I believe that no corresponding reasons exist to indicate any similar advantages on the part of barbarism as distinguished from civilisation. This is not caprice. It is not merely that I like civilisation while another likes barbarism. It is that I have, or think I have, strong and concrete reasons for considering civilisation intrinsically favourable to human welfare and development whilst barbarism is intrinsically hostile to man and wasteful of his most important qualities . . . . . both "welfare" and "important qualities" being in turn defined according to what seems to be sound objective evidence.

Here I am quite content to leave the controversy. My evidence may be erroneous or incomplete, or I may have drawn fallacious deductions from it. I may be wrong in any one or more of a dozen different ways. But this is what I think, and I have tried not to think anything which is not suggested by the testimony of the actual phenomena of the universe as objectively studied and impersonally interpreted.

July 28

Your wanderings of last March and afterward, though brief, were certainly piquant, varied, and in one instance titanically impressive! I can imagine how odd Lake Brownwood must look to you, for I have seen parallel phenomena in my own district. Many an ancient valley and village of western Rhode Island lies beneath the waters of the great Scituate Reservoir. Once in a while the reverse phenomenon occurs, and an old reservoir is abandoned and allowed to subside into the small pond it originally was. A case of this has just occurred in northwestern R.I., at the so-called Ponnegansett Reservoir, and has resulted in a discovery of considerable importance—a prehistoric Indian dugout, the largest ever found in the U.S., which lay sunken and imbedded in the weeds at the lake's bottom. Why it was never discovered in the remote past, no one knows; but for the last hundred years it was under vast depths of water. The lowering of the level to shallowness a month ago brought the treasure to light—it was found by a bunch of small boys, and now reposes in the museum of the R.I. Historical Society, only a few doors from 66 College St. It is in very fair shape, though eaten away at one side. It must antedate the coming of the white men, since it shows no influence of their craftsmanship. It evidently belonged to the Nipmucs—northern allies of the Narragansetts.

Your friend Vinson seems to be interesting indeed, and an ideal companion for your favourite type of jaunt. You surely saw a piquant variety of scenes, and it must have been interesting to explore El Paso for the first time. I trust you'll be able to arrange for more trips before winter sets in—or even after it sets in if your direction is comfortably southward.

But of course the high spot was the Carlsbad Cavern. Ædepol! but how I envy you! As I told you, I vastly appreciated the cards and folder—but the description in your letter is the most fascinatingly vivid of all. My clergyman friend in Clovis N.M. has described the caverns to me, and I've read a good many articles on them; but I'm hanged if anything has made them seem as real and as stupendous as the almost lyrical account which you furnish. What a nether world of supernal marvels those linked abysses of fantastic blackness must be! It really takes one's breath away to read about them. My trivial experiences—in the Endless Caverns in Virginia and the Lookout Mountain caves in Chattanooga, Tenn.—sink to nothingness beside the thing you have sampled![4] The "Big Room" must be a virtual realisation of the subterrene inner worlds of fiction-writers—and the manipulation of the lights doubtless enhanced its sinister magic. They turned off the lights once in the Endless Caverns—also in Lookout Mountain—but the distant-light effect you describe was not to be duplicated elsewhere. And yet I suppose the real climax was that system of ramps. Your description fairly makes my mouth water, and I can poignantly understand the nightmare effect you mention. I, too, have seen such things in dreams—but unfortunately lack the reality so far.[5] No use talking—I'll have to get down there some time. Some summer I must try to blow myself to a round of western travel!

Price's visit must surely have been an event. He is the most versatile chap I've ever struck—and could have matched that fencing lecture with one on Arabic, mathematics, Oriental rugs, or what not . . . . . each as ample and scholarly as its fellows. His remarks about foot-fighting must have been interesting. I have heard of this art—which in France seems to be a science somewhat different from the hobnailed brutalities of Maine and Michigan lumberjacks. Price, by the way, is now visiting Clark Ashton Smith again, if he carried out the design mentioned in his latest card. He forms quite a connecting link in the group—being, I believe, the only outside weirdist ever met in person either by you or by the Seneschal of Averoigne. Glad you liked the Silver Key sequel—which somehow disappointed me in print. Collaboration tends to hold my imagination in check, and thus to handicap my inventiveness to a great extent. I need an absolutely free hand in composition.

Glad to hear of your new markets—I didn't know that Dempsey was entering the magazine world! I must get a look at some of this Breckenridge Elkins material; for as you know, I've always advised you to utilise your extensive knowledge of the west—past and present—in literature. Hope you'll take Sultan Malik's suggestion and try Breckenridge on some more ambitious markets! Meanwhile I expect to enjoy the announced "Devil in Iron" in the coming W.T. By the way—have you heard of a new magazine called *Terror Tales,* issued by the publishers of *Dime Mystery?* I suppose it's just another pulp, but any potential market is doubtless worth a glance.[6]

I've just written an article on interplanetary fiction at the request of Crawford—of Marvel Tales—though it has come out so long that I doubt if he'll want to print it, after all.[7] I try to outline—roughly—the things that could be done to drag this sort of story out of its present appalling rut of banality and conventionality and incidentally, I venture a few remarks on weird fiction in general.

As soon as I get some more prints, I'm going to show you a photograph of the Cthulhu bas-relief which Barlow made for me. I think you'll agree that it's tremendously clever. I guess I mentioned that he also made an elephant-god statuette for old Bill Lumley—the eccentric weird fan in Buffalo, whose verse you may have noticed in the F F.

Hope I can get my programme reasonably under control for Morton's visit next week—I thought I was cleaning things up, but a beastly new order (troublesome but ill-paying) has just blown in, which shoots the schedule all to hell! Novel to revise and prologue to write—and must be ready Septr. 1st. Hades!

Europe seems to be stewing around as ominously as it was 20 years ago. I certainly hope it won't explode! Poor old Austria—once the head of the Holy Roman Empire! It's hard to say what is best for the place, but every faction seems to use the damndest tactics—massacre on the one hand, assassination on the other. It looks as if the bulk of the people wanted to go Nazi, but that Italian influence resists the change. If Germany took Austria into the Reich there would certainly be a problem for diplomats to solve. With so many Tyrolean boundary problems in the air, a Hitler-Mussolini international line would be a sort of powder magazine!

Wandrei is home in St. Paul for the nonce, and may or may not take a far western trip. His weird-artist brother is still in N.Y. I guess I told you that Barlow has an idea of publishing Howard Wandrei's marvellous drawings in the form of 11 x 14 photographic reproductions—done by an expert professional with colour-filters and all the necessary gadgets. As you know, Howard W. also writes, both under his own name and under pseudonyms. He is the author of "The God Box" in the April *Astounding*.

Had a shower or two this morning—first rain I've seen, except for a sprinkle in Richmond July 1st, since the deluge season in De Land ended June 15th. Lawns and trees are getting a bit parched—and of course the agricultural crops are finding the drought a problem all over the country.

With all good wishes—

Yours most cordially—

H P L

Notes

1. Mustafa Kemal Atatürk (1881–1938), army officer, revolutionary statesman, founder of the Republic of Turkey, and its first president.

2. In 1917, hoping to inspire their soldiers to continue fighting in World War I, the Russian government created a number of all-female combat units, including the 1st Russian Women's Battalion of Death. In all, about 5,000 Russian women served in the battalions, which suffered heavy casualties.

3. HPL refers to V. F. Calverton (1900–1940), American sociologist who examined both modern and ancient culture from a Marxist perspective. HPL probably refers to Calverton's anthology *The Making of Man: An Outline of Anthropology* (1931).

4. HPL visited the Endless Caverns in the summer of 1928, the Lookout Mountain caves in the summer of 1932.

5. In "The Shadow out of Time," written shortly after this letter, the ancient city discovered underground in the modern era featured inclined planes as a means by which the Great Race navigated from tier to tier in lieu of stairways.

6. *Terror Tales* (1934–41) was a weird menace pulp, hence not a suitable market for HPL.

7. "Some Notes on Interplanetary Fiction." It did not appear in any of William L. Crawford's magazines.

[108]   [TLS]

[c. September–October 1934]

Dear HPL:

Thanks very much for the post-cards. Nantucket must be a fascinating place. I'm sure you had an enjoyable time there. I've seen the name of Nantucket mentioned in old tales of whalers and clipper ship sailors. It must have bred a hardy race of men in the early days.

I sent you a couple of magazines under separate cover, which you've doubtless got by this time. The paragraphs marked with a pencil in "Gent From Bear Creek" are not mine. The enthusiasm of the editor prompted him to insert them. They doubtless help the story. The phenomenon of an outlaw looting a section under the guise of an officer of the law was not unknown in the early West—as witness Henry Plummer, and some others. In some cases there was a legal aspect about their appointment to office; honest men were too busy working to vote, so the lawless element—which always works together better than the honest element—got together and elected, or caused to be appointed, one of their own gang. These sort of conditions led to a peculiar state of affairs in Caldwell, Kansas, back in the early '80's. The city marshal stood in with the toughs, but, to placate the honest elements, always appointed some man for his deputy who was not on the inside, and who sincerely tried to establish law and order. These deputies were quickly killed, if not with the aid, at least with the permission of the marshal. Then one day he hired a stranger from New Mexico, and presented him as a burnt offering to the wild gang. But that stranger happened to be Hendry Brown, a former partner of Billy the Kid, one of the warriors of the Bloody Lincoln County War, and one of the deadliest gunmen that ever wore leather. The way they generally trapped the deputy was to start a commotion in a saloon. Ordinarily the deputy ran in and saw one drunk—apparently—standing in the center of the saloon and shooting at the ceiling, while a large gang looked on from the bar. When the deputy started to arrest the drunk, the lights suddenly went out, and when they were lit again, there was a deputy with several lead slugs through him. But Brown was wise. When the commotion started he didn't rush in blindly, turn his back on the gang at the bar and collar the drunk. Your real gunman was always a man of keen perceptions and a high order of intelligence. It was not merely physical superiority that made such men as Billy the Kid, John Wesley Hardin, John Ringgo and Hendry Brown super-warriors. It was their razor-edged intelligence, their unerring judgment of human nature, and their natural knowledge of human psychology. Well, that night in Caldwell Brown entered the saloon with his long easy stride, unhurried, unruffled. He seemed to be watching the pseudo-drunk staggering about in the center of the saloon; in reality he was watching the crowd, and the three desperadoes who crouched back among their fellows with their hands on their guns. Without warning and quick as a striking rattler he wheeled and his guns were out and roaring death before the slower-thinking outlaws realized that the new deputy knew their play. They were down, riddled, dead on the floor without a chance to fire a shot in return. With the methodical air of a man who does his job thoroughly, Brown stretched the "drunk" on the floor with the barrel of his six-shooter and dragged him off to jail. That was the beginning of a new era in Caldwell. The gang who had hired Brown for a sheep for the shearing, found they'd picked up a rattlesnake. Single handed he fought the mob to a stand-still and while he was marshal of Caldwell—for he deposed the reigning official and took over his job—law and order was respected—by everybody except Brown. He was like a blood-mad wolf at times; he did not limit his activities to the hoodlums; he killed anyone who displeased him—and he was very easy to displease. Without flinching he would face roaring guns and terrific odds and shoot his way to victory, and he would as quickly put a bullet through the heart of some wretch who accidentally jostled him on the street. In that respect he was infinitely worse than Billy the Kid.

The incident in the Steve Costigan story,[1] of the referee encouraging one of the fighters, and becoming embroiled in a fight with the other, was taken from real life. I saw a very similar episode take place in one of the fiercest, bloodiest fight cards ever staged in a fight club noted for its bloody goes, the Brownwood A.C. I'll never forget that card. It started with a k.o. that a big dinge from the West Coast plastered on one of the local niggers. That put the crowd in a good humor, which was altered somewhat by a substitute being put on—a big, green high school kid thrown in to meet a rangy, man-killing slugger from the Comanche country. The kid couldn't have been over sixteen or seventeen; maybe not that old. It was his first professional fight, and he didn't expect to win. It takes plenty of sand to crawl into a ring knowing you're in for a bloody beating. And he staged as fine an exhibition of pure courage as I ever saw. Outclassed in every way except guts he was knocked all over the ring and stayed with it, trying to last the limit; if he finished on his feet the moral victory was his. But when the last round came it looked like he was finished; floored repeatedly, his face and breast a mass of blood, he staggered up from a vicious knock down at last with glassy eyes and buckling legs and swayed drunkenly, unable to fight back, and too inexperienced to know what to do or to do the only thing that could do to save him. His seconds were kids like himself and too green or excited to help him. One more punch and he was done, and the crowd held its breath in expectation; but I didn't want to see the kid on the floor; I wanted him to finish his first fight on his feet, for he'd given me a glimpse of courage as high as any I ever saw. I took advantage of the momentary quiet to yell for him to clinch and hang on, in a voice nobody ever called weak. He heard; he should have, for I was right at the ringside. He didn't know who was shouting, or care; it was just a voice from the outer darkness reaching his battered and befogged mind with advice he desperately needed. Without trying to guard or strike, either of which would have been fatal, he plunged forward blindly, threw his arms around his opponent and hung desperately on. And by the time the referee had wrestled him loose, the gong sounded, and the kid stumbled out of the ring under his own power, instead of going out feet-first as the crowd had expected.

That was a good start, and next came a couple of Brown County lads with unusual names for fighters: Kidd R. Talley and Presley Van Zandt! They didn't have much science but they were rough and willing, and the ring was fairly swimming in blood when the referee at last called it a draw and the gory and groggy battlers were helped through the ropes. Then came on a couple of really classy lads: Bobby Burns, the Memphis Southpaw, and Doc Kitchen, the Azle Ghost. They were at each other like wildcats; a real grudge fight, that was; no fake stuff about it. There was an old hate between them, and they fought like savages, mean, fierce and dirty; cursing, butting, elbowing, spitting in each others' faces, thumbing, heeling—hell, they just about exhausted their bag of tricks, and all the time they were flailing away with fury and science. The crowd was on edge by this time, in a frothing frenzy; nothing like a grudge fight to bring out the wolf in a crowd. A couple of battlers can nearly kill each other, and so long as it's an impersonal, business-like affair (as of course most fights are) the crowd whoops and yells and laughs and has a good time. But let the fans sense a personal antipathy between the fighters, and it's like an electric spark that sets off a powder-train of passion. You can feel it sweep over the crowd; chins jut out as jaw-muscles clench and knot; eyes blaze; hands become fists; legs jam hard against the floor; the roar of the throng grows deeper, tinged with a blood-thirsty note; and an ordinary, mild, good-natured fan becomes a tense, quivering, ferociously-eager wolf-pack figure, snarling for his favorite to make the kill he craves to see. If you want to study human nature in the raw, go to the ring-side. Not that I was studying it much that night; I vaguely remember standing up in a slightly red haze and bellowing for Kitchen to hang Burns's guts on the ring-ropes and smear his brains over the canvas, while some fellow beside me was urging Burns to do the same thing to Kitchen. (Neither of us had ever seen either one of them before.) I never saw a fiercer fight, nor a greater exhibition of stamina and ruggedness. After ten savage rounds they went to their corners; Burns ironically offered his hand to Kitchen as they passed each other and Kitchen struck it aside. The referee (Kid Dula, once a fighter himself and the greatest middleweight Texas ever produced; he'd have been a champion if he could have let women and liquor alone) the referee, after consulting the judges' slips, called them to the center of the ring again and lifted both their hands in token that the fight was a draw—a good decision. Instantly they jerked their hands away and began slugging like hell. Dula stopped several clouts as he endeavored to separate them; he could only hold one at a time, and while he was holding one, the other was enthusiastically knocking hell out of the fellow who was helpless; officers and others stormed into the ring, grabbed the maddened fighters, threw them and sat on them . . . . . .

At last the ring was cleared, but feelings were running high. Dula, a hotheaded Irishman, was slightly on edge, and the crowd was roaring almost continually with that peculiar note of wrath which rouses a corresponding feeling in almost any man's breast. The main eventers were Duke Tramel of Ft. Worth, and Charlie Light, an Irishman from Indianapolis—the most peculiarly-built man I ever saw in a ring: short, stocky, with enormous legs, rather short, thick arms, a body like a barrel, an abnormally short, abnormally huge neck, dead-white skin, colorless blond hair, flattened nose, eyes that seemed to bulge out with an air of constant astonishment, a mouth that curved down at the corners, while the thin under-lip thrust out—picture a human frog and you've got him. The resemblance was really startling. Nothing peculiar about Tramel; just a compact, strongly built middle-weight, with a battered, immobile face, peculiarly cold, inexorable eyes, and bristly blond hair. An old-timer, long past his prime, but still packing a murderous punch. He and Dula, the referee, had met several times in bloody ring battles, in their prime, and indeed it had been Tramel who had finished the Kid's ring career in that very ring by a thundering knock out. So naturally they were old friends. The kid began to talk to Tramel in the first round (as I had the referee in the story doing) and Light objected. Technically he was right in his objections, but actually no harm was being done. But he was high-tempered and intensely jealous of his rights. Hell, that's all right. I like to see these young fighting cocks ruffling up to each other. He appealed to the judges to make Dula shut up, which angered Dula; and of course the Kid redoubled his conversation after that, and gave Tramel advice between rounds; which really wasn't ethical. But he was mad. Along about the third or fourth round, I don't remember exactly, Light stopped and asked Dula if he was a referee or a second, and Dula responded with a stinging open-handed slap in Light's face. Light didn't hit back—probably afraid he'd be suspended for slugging a referee—but Dula was frothing by that time, and followed Light back across the ring. I don't know just what passed between them, but the first thing I knew, they were fighting like hell along the ropes. Dula, fighting with his bare hands, of course, against Light's gloved maulers, forced his man into a neutral corner with a barrage to his belly and seemed to be having the best of the milling when the ring was again invaded by the promoter, officers, fans and the like, who fell on Dula and wrestled him to the floor, while others grabbed Light.

. . . hell, it was a rough night. The promoter jerked Dula and refereed the go himself, and Light pounded out a well-earned decision over the ancient Tramel. It was funny to watch the sympathies of the crowd shift; they cheered Tramel when the fighters first entered the ring; later booed Light because he objected to Dula's talking; but booed Dula for slapping Light; and thereafter cheered Light to the echo and booed Dula—their fellow-townsman, with a few impartial boos for Tramel thrown in, though he was in no way to blame.

But anyway, there's where I got the first part of the Costigan yarn.

Cordially,

REH.

P.S. I'll answer your last letter as soon as I can devote to it the time and care it deserves.

Notes

1. "Sluggers of the Beach," *Jack Dempsey's Fight Magazine* (August 1934).

[109]   [nonextant letter by HPL]

[110]   [TLS]

[c. December 1934]

Dear HPL:

I read your account of your trip down the Atlantic sea-board, and later to Nantucket, with great interest. I'm sure you must have had a fascinating time. In case I have not thanked you for the pictures you sent me from the latter place, let me take this opportunity to do so. I was particularly interested in the sketch and description of the Poe cottage in Philadelphia, and was reminded of a discussion Price and I had concerning Poe.[1] Price, if I remember rightly, considers Poe over-rated.

Concerning our debate: as I told you at the beginning of our correspondence, I have had no experience in argument. I've always been too busy trying to make a living to devote much time to debate. It is quite possible that at times I have offended you by my clumsiness in presenting my side of the argument; if so, I am very sorry. It has never been my intention to seem to be attacking any of your interests, or criticising you for any of your views. In every case I was merely defending myself, or trying to explain my own viewpoint. I am quite ready to drop the debate, and will only note briefly a few points in closing my side of the argument.

Concerning values: there was never any real use in most of these arguments, anyway. In practically every instance the debate began the same way. I expressed a personal preference that did not coincide with yours, and you attacked me for it, apparently assuming that a mere personal preference for something that you did not consider "superior" implied a criticism of *your* taste, and a repudiation of "basic values"! I have tried to make it clear that I was not criticising your taste when I expressed a preference that differed from yours; and I certainly never "repudiated basic values" merely because I happened to like something that wasn't of the superior order, or was indifferent to something that was. It was just my nature to like or dislike the thing, and I was merely expressing my feelings in the matter, merely stating a fact as material as if I had said I had bow legs. Would you consider I was criticizing your straight limbs, or repudiating the values of symmetry, because I said I was bow-legged? Would you consider it logical and reasonable to attack me, and accuse me of being an enemy to humanity, because I had bow legs? Well, it would be just as sensible to attack me because of my bow-legs as it is to attack me because of my private interests and personal tastes. You attack me because you say my private tastes don't coincide with evolutionary standards. Well, I can't help that. A chance set of circumstances, working through heredity and environment over which I had no control, caused me to find my deepest satisfaction in a certain set of ideals, aspirations, interests and pursuits; just as chance circumstances of environment and heredity caused you to possess a temperament which happens to find its deepest satisfaction in another set of ideals, aspirations, interests and pursuits. The things you do satisfy your temperament; the things I do satisfy mine, to an equal degree. The fact that your set of interests happen to coincide with those things considered superior in the evolutionary scale, and mine don't, always, is beside the point. My interests, pursuits, ideals and tastes are just as important and vital to me as yours are to you; you have told me that I don't really enjoy these "inferior" pursuits, that I just "think" I do! Do you really think that I am such a moron that I don't know what I want, or what I don't want?

In the matter of ideals of government, I do not remember ever having sneered at your theories, or at anything else you ever did or said. I merely expressed a doubt in the working of it, when put to a practical test. You accuse me of "hating human development" because I mistrust Fascism. Well, there can't be much tolerance about a system whose advocates denounce as "enemies of humanity" anyone who disagrees with them. According to that, you consider as "enemies of humanity" every man and woman in the world who is not a Fascist.

I do not condemn the reforms you say would be possible under Fascism. I simply do not believe they would exist under a Fascist government. Of course you can draw glowing pictures of a Fascist Utopia. But you can not prove that Fascism is anything but a sordid, retrogressive despotism, which crushes the individual liberty and strangles the intellectual life of every country it inflicts with its slimy presence. The Fascist movement in this country is nothing new; it is merely presented under a new name; it is the same old gang that in bygone days were called Tories, or Federalists, or Black-Republicans, or Hoover-Republicans—the same gang that are now ham-stringing the administration and yelling "Communism!" every time Roosevelt tries to free the country a little from their monopolistic clutch. I know it is the fad now to sneer at Democracy; but Democracy is not to blame for the troubles of the world. The men who are most to blame are the very men who now would "save" the country under the new name of Nazis, or Fascists. The last really Democratic president we had was Andrew Jackson. For nearly a hundred years this nation has not been a Democracy at all; it's been a capitalistic oligarchy parading as a Democracy; except on the fringes of the frontier, where Democratic conditions really existed up to within the last generation. And Fascism is nothing but a new fad-name for industrial tyranny. It's the final step of entrenched special privilege-holders, which would peon the people beneath them beyond all hope. The Fascist movement in America is nothing but a move on the part of the money-barons to establish themselves more firmly than ever, to stamp out the last vestige of freedom in the people beneath them.

Of course, you say that the type of Fascism you advocate is without despotism and persecution of intellectual freedom; you might as well say you advocate a cobra without its venom, a skunk without its stench, or a leper without his scabs.

As for tolerance, you haven't given me much reason to suppose that any government you would advocate would tolerate any independent thinking on the part of its citizens. Throughout our debate you have attributed to me the worst possible motives for my beliefs and tastes. Every time, when I have expressed an opinion that differed from yours, or even a personal taste, you have condemned it as sentimentalistic, romantic, a result of prejudice or distorted thinking; and denounced me as an enemy of development and enlightenment! Just as in this case, when you call me an enemy to humanity, and therefore imply that I am a villian of the deepest dye, because I happen to be a Democrat instead of a Fascist. Judging from your arguments, in our debate, you would, if you were a dictator, for instance, consider any expression of difference of opinion as an attack on civilization, and a threat to progress and enlightenment. You would therefore consider it your duty to humanity to sternly crush out and suppress any and all ideas, ideals or opinions that differed from yours. This would not be a display of personal vanity on your part, or conscious despotism. I don't believe you would enjoy imprisoning, deporting and hanging people who disagreed with you, because it is evident that you are naturally a kind-hearted man. But you would simply consider that you were protecting and defending civilization from vandals who were trying to over-throw it. And I have no reason to suppose that you would not carry this procedure on to include private tastes that have nothing to do with government; you have attacked me so bitterly for my private tastes. You have not only accused me of being a foe to mankind because of my political beliefs, but have intimated the same thing—at least it seemed so to me—because of my personal preferences. You profess to be a friend of civilization, which you consider should be preserved at all costs; therefore, you would consider it your duty to squelch an enemy of civilization if you had to hang him to do it. And if you consider that it is being an enemy to civilization to have private tastes that differ from your private tastes, the implication is obvious. If you were dictator, in the sort of government you advocate, I see no reason to suppose you would not imprison, deport or hang me because I like the Goths and dislike the Romans; because I wish I had lived in 19th Century Texas instead of wishing I had lived in 18th Century England; because I enjoy a prizefight more than I do an art-lecture; and because I like dogs better than I do cats. Why not? You have denounced me for all these things in terms that lead me to suppose that you consider them evidences of enmity to human development.

Concerning my mistake regarding your attitude toward the Southwest, it seemed to me that your criticisms of the conditions I had mentioned here rose from a hostility, not toward pioneering conditions (for you had said you had no prejudice against the pioneers) but toward modern Texas; obviously I misunderstood your attitude, and I am sorry if I seemed to do you an injustice.

Concerning the problems which I mentioned as often causing war-fare and bloodshed in the old West, you still miss the point, which is that frequently range-wars and feuds and fights were the result, not of deliberate aggression on either side, but simply because of economic, climatic and even geographical conditions beyond the scope of human control. I will admit that it is probably difficult, even impossible, for a dweller in an old, long-settled, industrial district to understand that statement, and I will not try to enlarge upon it. When you travel in the West, you'll see what I mean, and realize that often enough wars and feuds were not caused by wanton encroachment on either side, but simply by inexorable natural conditions. You can hardly pick out a western feud and say definitely that one side was "right" and the other "wrong". In almost every case right and wrong were about evenly balanced; and usually the moral question was beside the point, any way.

Concerning crime, I do not doubt that the negro population of the old Southern states is largely responsible for the crimes there. But don't forget that Texas, too, has a large negro population, and that there is also a big Mexican population, and larger yet, a portion of the population composed of the descendants of those very "poor whites" which you say commit so much crime in the states further east. Texas has, too, a large foreign white population—more so, I believe, than most of the southern states: Germans, Italians, Poles, Bohemians, Russians, Scandinavians, French-Canadians, Jews, Syrians,

Chinese, Japs, Cubans, Hawaiians, Irish, Scotch, Welsh, English, French, Greeks, Dutch, Belgians, Austrians.

Concerning the clippings about the police, etc., I didn't present them in an effort to show these things were typical. Why should I? I know nothing about conditions in those parts except as I read them in newspapers and books and magazines and newsreels, and hear over the radio. I merely enclosed those clippings as proof that all the violence and rough stuff wasn't exclusively confined to the state of Texas. I didn't suppose that you, or any of your friends had ever been arrested. As far as that goes, I've never been arrested either.

As for my "extreme sympathy with criminals" as you call it, all I ever asked was that the police themselves should obey the law they are supposed to uphold. It is indeed ironic that I should be accused of "sympathizing with criminals" merely because I object to criminal practices among the men whose duty it is to uphold the law. Whether criminality is common or rare among the police is beside the point; I am merely replying to your charge that I "sympathize with criminals."

Your comparison with the Russian "Battalion of Death" in regard to the clubbing of the woman in the courtroom is pretty far-fetched.[2] That woman was not going "into action with rifles and artillery". Even according to the cop who knocked her in the head, her only offense was that she "called him names"! Even that was denied by the witnesses. Well, suppose she did call him "names"? Do you consider that sufficient provocation for three or four men to knock a woman down with clubs, beat and kick her? I've had some pretty uncomplimentary titles applied to me by irritated members of the weaker sex, but I never considered it incumbent upon me to resent it by the use of physical violence. You have condemned the practice of men resenting slights from other men, physically. How do you figure that it's barbaric and brutal for a man to attack another man, his equal in size and strength, but reasonable and proper for a man to knock down a woman with a club in return for a similar provocation?

You say that chivalry is artificial. Chivalry is nothing more nor less than the custom, or instinct that accords certain special privileges to the physically weaker sex. The practice is not limited to human beings alone. Most animals observe a certain law in that respect. A normal male animal does not take advantage of his superior strength to abuse a female of his species. Is that artificial? When a male dog refrains from employing his fangs on a she-dog who has snarled or snapped at him, is he acting in an artificial manner? If you consider it artificial, and therefore unnatural for men to show more respect and consideration for women than they ordinarily show to other men, just what course of behavior would you consider natural?

Concerning barbarism and civilization, at the very beginning of that controversy, I told you that undoubtedly a form of civilization, even a decaying form, was better for humanity as a whole than barbarism. I never claimed that you, for instance, would be better satisfied as a barbarian than as a civilized man. I never claimed that most men would be. I merely said that I had rather have been a Goth than a Roman. And so I had. You started out to prove that I wouldn't—which you have not done. You have offered proof that you, and that most men would be happier as a member of a civilization. I never disputed that. All I said was that if I had lived in those times, I would have preferred to be a Goth, rather than a Roman. You have accused me of romanticism, of ignorance of the true conditions of those times, of idealizing the Goths, but you have not proved that there is any foundations to those accusations. You might as well deny that I'm bow-legged and offer as proof the fact that most men are straight-legged; and therefore assert that I'd be happier with my bow-legs stuck in boots made for straight-legged men, instead of wearing my own.

That's all that I've ever argued; the fact that it was logical and reasonable for me to like the things that satisfy me, and shun the things that bore, irk or dissatisfy me—just as you do. I've never claimed that you would be happier if you adopted my pursuits and interests; I've never claimed that the average man ought to do the things I do; like the things I like and avoid the things I dislike. All I ever did was simply to state my preferences, without criticizing those who had other preferences. But you have tried to prove that it's inexcusable for me to have the tastes that I have, and to do the things that satisfy my particular temperament. At least that's the way it's seemed to me.

You say you have proofs and evidences to show that you are right in your inferences, but you have no proof to show my tastes are sentimental, illogical, romantic and naive as you have charged. You've told me that I didn't really enjoy the things I said I enjoyed; that I just *thought* I did. And you have rather contemptuously dismissed my deepest interests and most powerful aspirations and most vital motives as mere romantic whims. You seem to feel that any preference that differs from yours is bound to be the result either of stupidity or ignorance.

Let me use a concrete example: you have repeatedly condemned my wish that I had lived on the early frontier, as a mere romantic gesture. If you didn't use those exact words, the implication was unmistakable. At the same time you said that you wished you had lived in 18th Century England, or in 19th Century New England. What "evidence" have you to offer that it's logical for you to wish you'd lived in New England a hundred years ago, and illogical for me to wish I'd lived in Texas a hundred years ago? But you instantly accused me of idealizing the frontier, of being ignorant of conditions. Let me point out to you that I was born in a region that had suffered Indian raids less than thirty years before my birth, and range-wars less than ten; a region of whose population a large percent still consisted of the original settlers. That from my very birth I have listened to first-hand narrations and descriptions of the pioneering era by the people who made that era. That as a child I had at least a child's part in the last great pioneering movement of the southwest—the settlement and development of the Great Plains and the Lower Rio Grande regions. That my entire life has been spent among pioneers and their children and grandchildren. Is there, in the name of common sense, any intelligent reason why I should "idealize" the recent past of the country I was born and raised in, or why I should have a romantic and erroneous conception of it? If I'm not capable of having a realistic conception of the frontier of thirty, forty or fifty years ago, then who is, outside of the people who lived then? The whole trouble with your viewpoint is that the idea of a man really wanting to have lived on a raw frontier is so unusual and unfamiliar to you, that you refuse to credit it. So you put my feeling toward the frontier on the same level as that of some dreamy, romantically-minded—and very immature—youth who has never been in a setting more primitive than New York or Boston or Chicago, but who has absorbed a vast, vague, glamorous misconception of illusions from reading sensational Wild West hokum. There's nothing really scandalous or romantic or incredible about a westerner expressing the wish that he had lived when land was cheap and cattle plenty and the range was open and men bulked bigger than the dollar. It merely seems outrageous to you because it's so alien to the interests and aspirations with which you have always been familiar. I'm not the only Texan who has expressed such a wish. I've repeatedly heard that wish expressed by other men—and men who had never read a Wild West story in their lives, hard-headed business men, ranchers and farmers, who were about as romantically inclined as a horse-pistol.

Not that what they wanted or didn't want affected me any. When I want a thing I don't care whether anybody else wants it or not. I wish I had lived in Texas a hundred years ago, and what somebody else wants or doesn't want, has nothing to do with it. In trying to prove that I didn't really want to live on the early frontier, but just *thought* I wanted to, you presented what I reckon you'd call evidence and proof; but it was just an enumeration of the things you'd consider drawbacks. Well, what of it? I never claimed you'd be happier on the frontier than you would have been in 18th Century England or early New England. I'd never think of dismissing your wish to have lived in those places as a romantic whim. I don't wish I'd have lived in either place; I'd much prefer even this modern life to either; but I don't doubt your sincerity in saying you wish you'd lived then, and there. I'm sure you'd have found perfect satisfaction in either place. On the other hand, my wish to have lived in 19th Century Texas is just as sincere. When you tell me that I wouldn't have been more satisfied then, than now, you're merely expressing your own preference. Undoubtedly you would have found life on the frontier unbearable. But I'm quite sure you'd find life unbearable in modern West Texas. But are you going to say that a preference for living there, instead of in some long-settled section, is a mere romantic whim? And that the million odd people who do live there are being romanticists and sentimentalists because they don't instantly migrate to New York, or Richmond, or Boston?

But I'm dragging this summing-up much further than I intended. I would not have inflicted its boresome reiteration on you at all, but for the fact that I felt your repeated accusations that I was an enemy to human development were too unjust to go entirely unanswered. I realize that I live in a sphere or on a plane totally different from the one in which you move. There is hardly any common plane at all upon which our ideas can meet, and therefore misunderstandings are bound to be common in any sort of debate between us. I realize that to you most of my aims and interests and tastes seem outlandish, naive, and perhaps puerile. Some of yours are equally meaningless to me, but I do not question the fact that they are vital and real to you, and I would not think of attacking, or criticizing you for having them. I have tried to show why my interests are important and real and vital to me, and that is all—the only motive behind my side of the debate. Perhaps I have failed. If so, it does not really matter. My particular interests, occupations, ideals and aspirations satisfy my particular temperament. If my temperament is "inferior" according to your standard, I can not help it. I did not select it; I was born with it, just as I was born with my particular shape of body; in order to be comfortable I have to wear clothes cut to fit my frame, not somebody else's. And if I am to get any satisfaction at all out of life, I must follow the pursuits that satisfy my particular temperament. And that is precisely what I intend doing.

Glad you found my remarks concerning my small travels in the early summer of some interest. I hope you'll decide to turn west some day in your travels. I believe you'd find much to interest you, particularly west of the Pecos River where the country changes so subtly that it can scarcely be defined in words, yet so definitely that it impresses one vividly. The world seems suddenly to expand—the horizons roll back illimitably. What has been a dreary and monotonous waste suddenly takes on the somber grandeur and magnificence of a primal desert. Man seems small and insignificant, his works mere scratches ignored by the slumbering titan and soon to be forgotten—and yet there a man is conscious of an individuality, a dignity, and a vitalness not to be realized or experienced or recognized in any city or swarming bee-hive of humanity. I am sorry my ancestors stopped in the hill-countries and the timbered lands; I wish they had pushed on to the westernmost extremities of the region. I would like to have been born and raised in that Trans-Pecos desert. We saw the ruins of the old stage-coach stand near the foot of the Guadalupes, on which spot, undoubtedly, Bigfoot Wallace rested many a time while driving the stage between San Antonio and El Paso.

But my remarks concerning the Carlsbad Cavern were wretchedly inadequate. No written words of mine could approach the marvel of that gigantic spectacle. As I told my friend Vinson, you might be able to describe it as it should be described, but there is no other man in the world that could do it. I hope some day you'll explore it and write down your impressions on the spot.

Yes, I enjoyed Price's visit immensely. He showed me his collection of Oriental rugs, which was my first close-up glimpse of such things, and gave me a great deal of interesting information concerning them and the art of their manufacture. Concerning *savate*, I don't know whether the foot-fighting of the lumberjacks is a heritage from France, passed along by French-Canadian woods-runners or not. Where men fight without rules they use their feet as naturally as they do their hands. That holds good in the oil fields, and was equally true of the backwoods fighters before the oil field workers came. I remember when I was a kid I seldom saw a blow struck with the clenched fist in a fight. Men wrestled, gouged, kicked, bit, clawed—don't think that finger nails and teeth are effeminate weapons. An experienced rough-and-tumble fighter can almost rip a man's face off with his nails, and tear off a nose or ear with his teeth. I notice girls wearing their finger tails trimmed to points. But long before any such style as that attacked the feminine members of the population I saw male bullies wearing their nails trimmed sharp as an aid to flesh ripping. But rough-and-tumble can't be much more savage than scientific *savate*, the purpose of which is to disable your opponent by a kick in the groin or the crotch. I saw a newsreel of a friendly exhibition match, in which the fighters naturally didn't kick each other in the accustomed spot, but aimed for the jaw and the back of the neck. They were limber as chorus girls. Which reminds me of the old song: "Oh, the French they are a funny race, they fight with their feet, etc."

Yes, Dempsey was made editor of the new fight magazine, though I imagine his activities are limited largely to writing a monthly editorial, and that may be written by his ghost writer. It's not surprizing to find him in the magazine racket. He's been many things and done many things in the course of his life. Nature was not generous with Dempsey; she gave him a fair mind, not an unusual one; chance placed him in a condition of extreme poverty, with consumptive parents; he never had a chance to acquire an education. He didn't even start life with a good body; he was a weakly, sickly youngster; but his people were poor and it was work or die. And he couldn't pick his work. He had to take what came. And what came was back-breaking, soul-crushing work of the roughest, hardest kind. But nature gave William Harrison Dempsey one gift that burned with as strong a flame in his sickly, undernourished body as in any man that ever trod this earth. And that was an unconquerable and invincible determination. He worked in mines and on farms and on road-building jobs when most youngsters were in grammar school. He gave most of his money to his parents, and he roamed over the country as a working-hobo. Many men stronger and hardier than Dempsey have died under such conditions. Dempsey did not die because he would not die. And when nature can not kill, she builds. Under the terrible slugging he endured as a child and a boy, he developed and grew strong; the work that killed other youths gave him a body the magnificent strength and ruggedness of which has never been surpassed. He went into prize-fighting because it was so much easier than the work he was doing, and because it pointed a way out of the muck in which he was writhing with thousands of his miserable kind, who lacked his strength and resolution. In this life a man does what he can and must, not always what he will. Jack London and Jim Tully wrote their way up out of the abyss; Jack Dempsey fought his way up. All men can not be writers and scholars.

He was a mine worker and a farm laborer, a lumberjack, a hobo, a bouncer, a roaming pugilist. As a fighter, he began at the very bottom, as he had begun life. Sometimes he starved. Once he went three or four days—and fought a desperate battle at the end of that time—subsisting on turnips stolen from a farmer's field. He had nobody to teach him anything about boxing. He knew nothing of the game. He had only the primitive resolution that had saved him from being ground to small bits in the wheels of the system that had ground up so many, and the iron body that had been forged under the merciless hammers of circumstances. The punishment he took in the ring is appalling to think on. But he had been steeled to punishment. Any man who climbs up out of the abyss knows how to endure and suffer without flinching.

He became champion in spite of hell and high water. He made millions for himself and for others. During his reign the prize-fighting profession reached a height it will never reach again. He set a new style in fighting and in the literature of fighting men. Just as Corbett popularized scientific boxing and placed the game on a higher level, so Dempsey popularized the rushing, desperate style of fighting, the swift onslaught and unfaltering attack. In his tours of Europe he interested the Continentals in boxing. His bust was placed in a German hall of fame, and he was directly responsible for the enthusiasm for boxing that rose in Germany and is still burning strongly. Up to his time the Continentals had fought in the orthodox British style, and had been easy prey for the Britons. But their admiration for Dempsey caused them to abandon the English style for the crouching, slashing American method, with the result that British domination of European boxing came suddenly to an end. Up to his time, in literature, the hero was usually a clever, "gentleman" type who won his fights by speed and science against a hairy slugger. But Dempsey made the slugger popular. It is not the Sailor Costigans alone, the wood-pulp heroes who emulate the terrific punch and iron man style of Dempsey. I have recognized him again and again in the more sophisticated type of stories that touched on fights and fighting men. His personality has impressed itself on things foreign to the ring itself, and Europeans and Asiatics who don't know who the president of America is, are in no doubt concerning the identity of Jack Dempsey. He is a successful man, measured by whatever standards, and he deserves his success. Nature dealt with him grudgingly, but he made the best of what she gave him in manful fashion. If all men did as well with their gifts as Dempsey has done with his, this would be a better world in which to live.

Glad you liked "The Garden of Fear" in Marvel Tales. I wrote that especially for Crawford when he asked me for a contribution. I hope he'll be able to continue the publication. And I'm looking forward to your article on interplanetary fiction.

I've been trying to break into Terror Tales, but so far no luck. It's strictly a formula magazine. It's hard for me to write straight formula stuff and make it convincing. My latest sales to Weird Tales have been a two-part Conan serial: "Beyond the Black River"—a frontier story; and a novelet dealing with Mississippi negroes, etc. "The Moon of Zambebwei", which I understand will be changed to "The Grisly Horror." In the Conan story I've attempted a new style and setting entirely—abandoned the exotic settings of lost cities, decaying civilizations, golden domes, marble palaces, silk-clad dancing girls, etc., and thrown my story against a back-ground of forests and rivers, log cabins, frontier outposts, buckskin-clad settlers, and painted tribesmen. Some day I'm going to try my hand at a longer yarn of the same style, a serial of four or five parts.

I'd like very much to see that photograph you mentioned—Barlow's bas-relief of Cthulhu. I was glad to see an issue of the Fantasy Fan dedicated to you.[3] Of course, I've been reading and enjoying your stories, poems and articles appearing in that magazine.

Yes, you're right about Europe being a stewing caldron. I don't believe any of them really want war, but their combined stupidity and cowardice will eventually result in an explosion. They remind me of a gang of barroom bullies, each trying to yell louder and wave more guns than all the others simply because at heart he's shaking in fear that the others will start rough-housing him. I'm not surprized at the massacre of helpless people, the torturing and abuse of women and children. It's what I expect of cultured Europeans. It's what I'll expect of the people of this country when they get sufficiently imbued with European culture and civilization. It didn't surprize me when Dollfuss murdered the helpless women and children of his enemies. That's the "superior European" style. It didn't surprize me when his enemies assassinated him; that too was in keeping with the best traditions of European culture. Reading in one of the biggest capitalistic dailies of the state—which is above all charges of "radical"—I noted the outrages committed on women by the Fascists of Germany and Austria. That too is characteristic, both of the Fascist movement and of the European character.

At any rate, Dollfuss is in hell which is one advantage to the world at large, though the men who shot him and let him bleed to death like the hog he was were no better than him.[4] I have no interests and no preferences either way in that European mess. I am as indifferent to their squabbles and massacres as I would be to the wars of that many naked Indians beyond the border. Except as it affects the United States, I'm not even interested. Europe, to me, is nothing but a rat-den where teeming, crowded rodents, jammed together in an unendurable mass, squeal and gnash and murder each other. And some of our "best minds" prattle of European superiority and urge us to copy their ways!

The "superiority" of the European character was vividly demonstrated when King Alexander was transported to the infernal regions on the hot end of a bullet.[5] Reading the account I was minded of nothing so much as a herd of bawling, mad, senseless cattle milling and goring each other brainlessly. The assassin, according to the papers, walked through a cordon of policemen with his weapon in his hand, shooting down the cop that tried to stop him. Why in hell didn't some other cop shoot him? Apparently they stood like so many wooden soldiers—awaiting orders! One man like Tom Hickman, Wolf Gonzales, Bob Goss[6] or a score of others I could mention would have been worth more than all the French police. That chauffeur that socked the murderer on the jaw—futilely of course, it being hard to find a Frenchman that can really hit—and the officer who cut the man down with his saber showed some presence of mind. But then what did the police do? Fired blindly into the crowd and mowed down a number of innocent bystanders, while the murderer, lying on the sidewalk, added his fusillade to the general merriment. Hell, he was down; why didn't somebody bash his brains out with a gun butt, at least? And then, by heaven, they let that Frenchman, whatever his name was, bleed to death on the way to first-aid simply because nobody had brains enough to put a tourniquet around his arm![7] And those are the people who claim to be so far superior to those Americans!

I'm strikingly reminded of a case which occurred in San Antonio a week or so ago, when a special policeman, gone insane or maddened by marijuana, opened fire on a crowd in a cafe, without warning. But before he had time to do more than wound one man in the arm, somebody wrenched the gun out of his hands and somebody smashed him on the jaw and knocked him stiff. Then came the cops and lugged their erring brother off to the hoosegow without any more disturbance. And somebody jerked off his belt and slung a tourniquet around the wounded man's arm, and rushed him to a place where he could get first aid. Judging from cases I've read of, if that had happened in Europe, the madman would have emptied his gun into the crowd without hindrance, while they milled wildly, scuppering a large number of them—and then the trained European police would have arrived with their eyes shut and their trigger fingers working at random and slaughtered several more, after which there would have been wholesale arrests and clubbings, with special attention given to old men, cripples, women and children, and some nation would have sent an ultimatum to some other nation, and sabers would have rattled loudly in their scabbards. Superiority!

One of the main troubles of America now is the fact that there are so many Americans who meekly accept the European's assertion that Europeans are superior to Americans, and who try to copy European ways and ideas.

Now England, with Japan looming the offing, is howling for an Anglo-American alliance. I am opposed to it. We'd get gypped, just as we always do when we have dealings with those slippery Europeans. If we had sense enough to build up our army, navy and air-forces we'd need no alliance with anybody.

As for war, that will come when international capital is ready. I do not believe, and have never believed, that Mussolini, Hitler and the other European strong-arm, he-man dictators are anything but figure-heads and tools for international capitalism. The same crowd that recently approached Smedley Butler with a proposition to overthrow the government and set up a Fascist dictatorship;[8] the same gang that would have made Hoover dictator if they had dared. The same gang that is now opposing everything Roosevelt tries to accomplish.

Well, I noticed Alabama University got the invitation to the Rose Bowl. I was a bit surprized. I figured Stanford would do like they did last year, and try to pick a set-up, like Colgate, Columbia, or Princeton. Alabama has gone to the Rose Bowl[9] three times—twice won, once tied. I hope they kick the guts out of Stanford. I have a warm spot for the state of Alabama, though I've never been there. But my people had a hand in its conquest and settlement. The Henrys from South Carolina and the Walsers from Georgia came into the Black Warrior River country before Alabama was even a state, and fought Indians, British, Spaniards, and swamp panthers and helped build the commonwealth, until the early 1840's when it began to get too densely settled for them, and they moved on into Mississippi, into the Big Black River country, immortalized by the legends of John Henry, the negro Hercules. The next move was in the early 1850's and took them into Arkansas.

I was fairly well pleased with the recent football season, in which Southwestern teams demolished most of their important intersectional rivals to the astonishment of various sportswriters of the metropolitan sections, the smug complacency of some of these gentlemen being stupendous. But outside of these games, the game which caused me more unholy glee than any other was Yale's unexpected defeat of Princeton.[10] I passed up the first part of the T.C.U.–Texas game to listen to that broadcast. I always had a high regard for Princeton, though I know nothing about the university, but I admired its traditions of mellow culture and the like. But its attitude this year in regard to its football team was nauseating. With a fairly strong—though highly overrated team—it picked set-ups, and when urged to meet somebody like Minnesota, or some other equally powerful team, the objection seemed to be (emanating, I will admit, not from the team but from the alumni and student body) that it would be lowering the dignity of Princeton to meet any of the universities mentioned—the idea seemed to be that Princetonians considered students in Minnesota, Ohio State, California, etc., not quite their social equals! With unconcealed glee I listened to Yale kick their guts all over the gridiron.

It looks like the drouth, which has been parching the Midwest and Southwest for months, is finally broken up. Grass looks good and there's some stock-water. I hope it rains enough to fill up Lake Brownwood. The rice-farmers on the lower reaches of the Colorado bought ten thousand dollars worth of water from Brown County—and got several hundred thousand dollars worth. They paid their money, the Brownwood people opened the gate, and the water rushed into Pecan Bayou, flowing in turn into the Colorado, and eventually arriving—in part—among the rice-farms 480 miles to the south. But when they figured they'd let out the proper amount of water and tried to close the gate, they couldn't.[11] Something busted about it; more faulty work on the part of the Eastern company which built the dam, they made a lousy mess of the whole thing from start to finish. So Lake Brownwood emptied itself except for the water in the river channels. Where the water stood there is a thick deposit of rich black soil that washed down from the valleys. That shows where the soil of Texas is going; erosion is wearing it away, laying bare the naked rocks, depreciating the value of the land year by year. Texas is a sloping state, practically the whole state is like a mountainside, and every year, millions of dollars worth of soil washes into the Gulf. Terracing helps a little, but more than terracing of individual fields is necessary. If they'd spend a fraction of the money they waste on wars in building up and preserving natural resources, this might eventually get to be a decent age in which to live. God knows it isn't now.

I'm enclosing a few clippings which you may find of some interest, and some verses, please return the verses at your leisure. I'm still hoping to find a publisher for them some time. I'm looking forward to seeing more of your work in print. Hope you write a lot for Weird Tales this coming year.

The recent elections were certainly a triumph for Roosevelt, in most of the cases;[12] I wish I could be as equally well satisfied with our Texas elections. One thing gratifies me; the man who was elected governor[13] had to pretend that he was opposed to the big interests before he could get elected. Most of the folks who voted for him did so because of an illusion that he was fighting these interests. The time is past in Texas when a man can come out openly and declare himself for alien corporations. From now on a candidate's task will lie in fooling the people into believing that he's opposed to the systematic looters. And when the people finally learn to distinguish lies from truth, we'll begin to get somewhere in our state government.

I notice the big boys are singing jubilation because of Sinclair's defeat in California.[14] Well, I didn't believe he'd be elected because I didn't believe the campaigns against him, or the elections, would be run on the level. I guess there went Tom Mooney's last chance of freedom—a filthy blot on the whole nation.[15] I read, with contempt and amazement, Moley's naive dissertation on that subject.[16] He piously rejoiced that Sinclair was defeated, and then added that it would well if the incoming administration would free Mooney, because, as he naively remarked, it would increase the confidence of the people in the conservative element! Not a word about the damnable injustice of keeping an innocent man in prison; not a word about decent fairness and justice; he advocated turning Mooney loose, simply as a means of fooling the people into thinking that a capitalistic super-machine means to deal fairly with them. I always thought Moley was a jackass, but I thought he did at least possess the subtleness and shrewdness of time-serving hypocrisy. But he hasn't even that.

I reckon you folks in New England are beginning to feel winter-time. I'm going to try to make it to South Texas later in the winter, but don't know whether I'll be able to or not. I hate winter, mainly because of the extra amount of clothes one has to wear. Speaking of clothes, I recently made the biggest concession in the way of wearing apparel I ever made in my life, when I consented to wear one of these damned narrow-brimmed hats. My mother has been insisting that I take to wearing one of the things for some time, and when she bought one for me, I told her I'd wear it to please her. I detest the things. I never wore anything before but a cap or a broad-brimmed sombrero. I go bare-headed most of the time. I know nearly all men wear them, but that doesn't make me like them any better. I've always resented their invasion of the Southwest; I knew the old ways were fading when I first saw them making their appearance, years ago. I don't know why people in this country ever adopted them. They serve no practical purpose in this region. They won't stay on in a sand-storm, they don't shade one from the sun, and I believe a man could have a sun-stroke wearing one. They're all right in cities where there's no wind, or sun or anything else natural, but for an open country the only head-gear is a broad-brimmed Stetson. And now I'm wearing one of the accursed things on dress occasions. Along with coats and vests that winter makes necessary. Well, anyway, it's going to have to get a damn sight colder than it has been before I go to wearing underwear and socks. I hope we have a mild winter, but since that is the weather-men's predictions, I have my doubts.

With best wishes.

Cordially,
REH

Notes

1. "Homes and Shrines of Poe."

2. On 27 May 1934, police clearing a New York courtroom at the order of a magistrate pushed Mrs. James Lechay out the door; when her husband protested, according

to witnesses, another officer hit her in the face and, as general pandemonium broke out, officers allegedly kicked the woman while she lay on the ground. It was also alleged that other officers took her husband outside and beat his head against a wall. The Associated Press report did state that the patrolman "asserted the woman called him names, although other witnesses deny this."

3. The *Fantasy Fan* 2, No. 2 (October 1934) was dedicated to HPL.

4. Engelbert Dollfuss (1892–1934), chancellor of Austria (1932–34), became an autocratic leader who ruthlessly suppressed all political parties and abolished the legislature. He was assassinated on 25 July 1934 by the Nazis.

5. King Alexander I of Yugoslavia (1888–1934) was a dictator who, while on a state visit to France, was assassinated on 9 October 1934 by an agent of Croatian separatists.

6. Texas Rangers Thomas R. Hickman (1886–1962), Manuel T. Gonzaullas ("Lonewolf") (1891–1977), and Robert G. Goss (1898–1978).

7. French foreign minister Louis Barthou was fatally wounded in the attack on Alexander, dying hours later in a hospital of blood loss.

8. Smedley Butler (1881–1940) was a Major General in the U.S. Marine Corps and, at the time of his death, the most decorated Marine in U.S. history. In 1934, he informed the U.S. Congress that a group of wealthy industrialists had plotted a military coup—"the Business Plot"—to overthrow the government of Franklin D. Roosevelt.

9. On 30 November 1934, Alabama accepted an invitation to play Stanford in the Rose Bowl game on New Year's Day. On New Year's Day 1934, Columbia University had defeated heavily favored Stanford, 7–0.

10. Yale defeated Princeton 7–0 on 17 November 1934.

11. On 27 June 1934, a sluice gate was opened in the Pecan Bayou dam above Brownwood in order to let out 14,000 acre-feet of water sold to the Gulf Coast Water Company for use by rice farms in Matagorda and Wharton counties. When workers attempted to close the gate on 4 July, they discovered it had slipped off its track and could not be closed. By the time the gate was forced shut on 16 July more than 50,000 acre-feet of water had been lost from Lake Brownwood, lowering the lake level about 19 feet.

12. In the congressional elections of 1934, Franklin D. Roosevelt increased his Democratic majority in the House by a count of 318–99 (11 representatives belonged to other parties), and in the Senate by a count of 69–27.

13. James V. Allred was elected to the Texas governorship in 1934. See REH's comments in his letter of 2 November 1932, where he refers to Allred as "our candidate for attorney general," and says "now he's sinking the gaffs in the looters."

14. Author and journalist Upton Sinclair (1878–1968), running on the EPIC (End Poverty in California) ticket, was defeated in his campaign for governor of California. He was vigorously opposed by business interests.

15. Tom Mooney (1882–1942) was a socialist labor activist who was convicted in 1917 for the 1916 bombing of the Preparedness Day parade in San Francisco, which killed ten people. His death sentence was later commuted to life imprisonment; he was then pardoned by Governor Culbert Levy Olson of California, the successor to Governor Frank F. Merriam, who had defeated Sinclair in the election of 1934. The

evidence leading to Mooney's conviction was widely suspected of being weak or fabricated.

16. Raymond Moley, editor of the magazine *Today,* was an original member of Franklin Roosevelt's "brain trust" who broke with him in mid-1933 and became a Republican opponent of the New Deal. His open letter to California governor Frank Merriam appeared in the 22 November 1934 issue of his magazine.

[111]   [nonextant letter by HPL, c. Dec. 1934 or Jan. 1935]

1935

Dear HPL:

I have finally found time to answer your (as always) interesting letter. In regard to our controversy, I am sorry if I have misunderstood any of your statements or attitudes, or seemed to be doing you an injustice. I'm pretty thick-headed in many ways, and find considerable difficulty in following the intricate workings of a mentality as complex and highly developed as yours. I appreciate the time and trouble you've taken in argument and explanation, and the interest you've shown. Of course you understand that that works both ways. I wouldn't have devoted as much time to our argument if I hadn't had a very high regard for your intellect and admiration for your abilities. In fact, this is the first and only debate I ever carried on by correspondence, and the longest debate I ever engaged in in any fashion. I must admit that I do not value the average man's opinion highly enough either to try to correct his misconceptions or to defend my beliefs against his attacks.

I have already expressed my own standpoint to the best of my ability and will only remark that I am not aware that I possess any "violent emotion in a direction contrary to the truth" and I certainly have never written any "essays" "full of emotion" against any sound or sincere type of expression.

As to your ideal of government, it seems sensible and logical enough and I have no criticisms to offer; my belief that it would fail within a few generations, of its avowed purpose, is not a criticism, it simply rises from my belief that all forms of government prove failures ultimately; doubtless some form of government similar to the one you advocate will be adopted before many years.

I am sorry if I attributed to you a lack of tolerance which does not exist. The fault was largely my own stupidity in misunderstanding your intentions, and an unfamiliarity with the style of argument which is apparently characteristic of the intellectual class in the older parts of the country. The charges you made against me were so unexpected and unusual that I was bewildered and confused. My friends and acquaintances range from judges and Ph.D's to small-time gamblers and hoboes, and we all have our own ideas and disagree on many different points. But never before was I ever accused of being "an enemy to humanity"; nor did I ever hear a native Texan bring that accusation against his opponent in any debate. We say: "I think you are wrong or mistaken to think this." But we do not say: "You are an enemy to humanity and truth if you think this." If any one of us adopted this attitude, he would be considered an intolerant fanatic. So you can see how easy it was for me to make the mistake I did. You say you have never tried to suppress or silence me; I will admit that's over my head. I don't see how anyone *could* suppress or silence me, even if he wanted to. Accusing a man of anarchistic and criminal tendencies almost every time he expresses an opinion or a preference seems a rather strange way of "encouraging him to describe his beliefs." It seems to me that it would have the opposite effect on the average man. But of course I understand that my conception of your attitude was entirely wrong; I freely admit that the fault was mine; and I repeat that I am extremely sorry if I did you an injustice.

As for my alleged "anti-human" tendencies, it is true that I have criticised certain phases of modern civilization, impersonally, and entirely apart from my own particular preferances. I do not believe our civilization is perfect and I reserve the right (just as you do) to criticise the phases which observation, experience, comparison, and common sense lead me to believe are objectionable. I believe the modern system contains many shams and hypocrisies which move in the exact opposite from the ideals and standards they are supposed to represent. I believe civilization breeds certain objectionable characteristics and things of itself, where are not merely hangovers from barbarism. I believe that our modern civilization has passed its peak already (except in the mechanical way) and is receding from, rather than advancing toward a higher plane of life. I believe many modern trends are retrogressive rather than progressive. I believe these things, not because of any prejudicial enmity to civilization or anything else, but simply because all evidence seems to indicate that they are true. I do not consider that I am "an enemy to humanity" because I believe these things, nor do I concede to any man the right to so consider me. To make that charge against anyone who criticises any phase of modern civilization is too extreme. Many of our scholars and writers have attacked certain phases much more violently than I ever did. For instance Professor B. Schidloff, the noted anthropologist, says in the introduction to one of his most profound books: *"No thinking person who forms his own opinion on the modern times doubts any longer that civilization is equivalent to moral degeneracy."*[1] If I'd said that I bet you'd have instantly accused me of enmity to progress and enlightenment. But are you going to say that Schidloff is "an enemy to humanity"? Of course not. And neither am I.

As for love of Truth, it never occurred to me to doubt that you were motivated by a desire to establish truth. I supposed it was a fact that everybody took for granted, that the aim of every intelligent man was Truth. I knew it was your aim, and it did not occur to me to make the formal statement that my aims were similar. I did not suppose it was necessary.

It was because I recognized your devotion to facts and realities, that I inflicted so much data and statistics regarding the frontier and the modern West, upon you. I thought you wanted to know the facts, even if they chanced to conflict with some of your theories. I wasn't trying to force any of my personal opinions on you, I was merely presenting facts—just as if I had told you that Guadalupe Peak was higher than the Alleghanies. If some of these facts contradict popular beliefs held in the older districts, I really cannot help it. A misconception, however popular, is still a misconception. If I have bored or offended you by my persistence in debating points concerning my own region, past and present, I am sorry. My only purpose was to remove some apparent errors in your conceptions of the country and people and entirely devoid of any offensive intent.

I have but one thing to add, in this connection. Concerning crime in the Southwest, I once told you that a big percent of the crime was committed by people from other states. I am afraid you dismissed this statement as a mere fabrication, invented to support a prejudice. But recently the State Legislature appointed a committee to investigate crime in Texas, and after an exhaustive investigation they reported *that 90% of the habitual criminals in the state were natives of other sections entirely*.[2] They named New York, Miami and Chicago as the three principal centers that supplied these characters. Please note that this is not simply my opinion. It is the authentic and documented report of the committee appointed by the Legislature.

Concerning police methods: you say that you do not advocate indiscriminate torturing of suspects and prisoners; you admit that police abuses *do* exist; you say there is plenty of room for improvement, and that "standards should be vastly raised". All this is so similar to my views that I don't understand why you keep charging me with "sympathizing with criminals". The only difference in our views seems to be that I believe that corruption, brutality and crookedness among the police is more widespread than you seem to believe, considering the country as a whole, and not merely your section or mine. (I have never questioned your assertions in regard to the high standards of the New England police.) I believe this not because I am an enemy of the law, or a friend of criminals, but because all evidence seems to indicate that it is the truth. You can't reasonably accuse a man of being a sympathizer of criminals merely because he criticises what he believes corrupt or wrong in the process of law-enforcement, or is unable to believe that all cops wear haloes. Lawyers, judges, writers and others have all uttered criticisms more sharp than any I ever made. I once heard an internationally famous man-hunter say: "There are two people I never try to reason with—an hysterical woman and a beef-headed cop." Now that was a much sharper and more indiscriminate criticism than I ever offered—and he wasn't referring to the cops of any one section, either. But are you going to say that this man, a Federal detective, who had spent the best years of his life running down crooks—are you going to say that he was a sympathizer of criminals? Of course he wasn't. And neither am I. I detest and despise an habitual criminal. And if you'll pardon me for saying so, I have an idea that between the two of us, my first-hand experience with criminal types is the wider. I've been personally acquainted with gunmen, crooked gamblers, bootleggers, dope-fiends and peddlers, bad-check experts, thieves, rustlers, smugglers and what not, and there's no reason under the sun why I should have any illusions regarding them.

Regarding the clubbing of women, I am not surprized to learn that the practise is a common one; sadism seems to flourish in all decaying civilizations.

And so we wind up the long debate, in which, as it dealt with so many indisputable facts on both sides, I cannot see that either of us was either victor or vanquished; it has proved very stimulating to me, and given me many new slants on things; the fact that has impressed me more than any other is the gigantic and apparently unbridgable gulf which still exists between the East and the West.

I hope you enjoyed your trip to see Long in New York. I learn with interest that Long is now a Communist. But I suspected it when I read his story in Weird Tales some months ago—the one about the dictator and the ape.[3]

I read with interest your remarks on the European situation—into which new tangles have entered since I wrote you, of course. I didn't know that the belief that dictators were tools of capitalism was so widespread that opponents of the belief referred to it as a "legend". I reached that conclusion some time ago—a conclusion I see no reason to abandon. As regards American and English interest in the Pacific, I can not agree with you that America and England are "one except in name." Nor is that belief generally shared in the West. It is obvious that a wider difference separates the people of the West from the English than is the case with the Anglo-Saxons of the East Coast. To most of us, an Englishman is simply another foreigner; and a distinct anti-British feeling exists in some quarters.

I am opposed to an alliance with England in the Pacific, or anywhere else. I don't care to have my head shot off protecting Australia, and I'm quite sure that the average Englishman wouldn't care to spill his blood defending Hawaii or California. Let each nation defend its own. We're big enough, and strong enough; all we need is preparation. We'd have that if enough of our leaders and people realized the necessity. Incidentally, are the Japs buying up all the scrap iron in your parts? A lot of old pipes, collars, bits, drill-stems, etc., have been bought in this country. When they start shooting it back at us, I hope they'll mold that junk into smoother shapes. I'd hate to get shot in the neck with an old anvil or something similar. Tons and tons of old iron have been secured from the surrounding oil-fields.[4]

The pacifist movement seems to be growing all over the country. I understand quite a movement is on to persuade the youth of the nation to sign pledges never to enlist in a war of aggression, or bear arms except to defend the country from invasion. Don't they realize that the best way to defend one's own country from invasion is to invade the other fellow's country? That in case of a war—regardless of the reason—this country *would* be invaded, if the other nation was able to do so? I believe that peace should be maintained as long as possible; I don't want some fat capitalist to be allowed to drag the nation into a war simply to fill his moneybags. But I wouldn't sign any such pledge as I mentioned. Once a war starts, it doesn't matter much who started it. I don't think any man would be justified in standing aside with empty hands, while his native state was overrun, his property destroyed and his friends and relatives shot down, even if the war was started by ruthless capitalists, for their own profit. Whoever started it, it's *his* war after it's started.

Last summer I encountered an extreme pacifist attitude in a friend of mine, a man who took his Ph.D. degree at Columbia University, and remained there as an instructor. He returned to Texas on a visit last summer, and I had quite a stimulating conversation with him. I did not debate the point I mentioned above, because I saw it would be useless. But I can not agree with him. Among other things, he said that submission, without resistance, to the rule of a foreign or alien nation, was preferable to war—a sentiment I never before heard a Westerner voice. Well—his folks were living comfortably and quietly in Germany during the '60's and '70's. If they'd lived in the South of the United States during the war and the reconstruction, he'd know that there is no hell more abominable than living in a defeated land under the arrogant heel of the winners—and arrogance which would be increased a thousand times if the defeated simply accepted the yoke without resistance. The Civil War did not end at Appomattox or at Palo Alto; it didn't end until 1875 in Texas, though we kicked that bastard E. J. Davis out of the capitol in 1873.

I could fill a book with incidents to prove my point. I could tell of the so-called Lee-Peacock feud; of the Union League; of the Fort McKavett war; of Bob Lee, Ben Bickerstaff and Cullen Baker, and others who even to this day are known as bloody outlaws. There was old man Fisher, up in Red River County, where I used to live. The Union Leaguers tore out his finger nails and toe nails and cut out his tongue. I am at present going with a young lady[5] whose people lived in Alabama during and after the war. Federal soldiers tortured her grandfather and his brother to make them tell where they had their money hidden. The brother was stubborn; the blue-coats burned out his eyes with a red hot iron. He died from the effect of the torture. There was John Wesley Hardin. Wrestling with a big nigger as a boy of fourteen, he accidentally scratched the coon's face with his finger nails. The nigger came at him with a club to beat his brains out. John shot him. The Federals put a price on his head and hunted him up and down the land until he became an outlaw in good earnest. There was John's cousin, Simp Dixon, a boy of eighteen or nineteen. A blue-coat officer wanted a fine horse he had. So a warrant of arrest was sworn out, charging Simp with having stolen the horses. When the squad went to arrest Simp, he wasn't at home. They murdered Mrs. Dixon and her daughters, and burned down the Dixon cabin. Then they returned to their post and placed a big price on Simp's head. Poor Simp wasn't appreciative of the efforts being made to refine and civilize him. He was crude enough to go on the war-path and kill a large number of his enemies before they trapped and killed him. His enemies wrote his story, and so today Simp Dixon is known in the civilized regions as a fiendish outlaw.

There was Bob Lee. Lived in the big thicket country, near Red River. Served through the war under old Bedford Forrest, and was honored and respected in his community. He made the mistake of carrying gold pieces in his pockets. The Union Leaguers thought he had money; kidnapped him and made him write a ransom note in his own blood, found he couldn't raise the money, and made him sign a note. When he got away he refused to pay the note—who wouldn't?—and tried to get redress in the courts. The court was dominated by Federal bayonets and threw the case out. A few days later a Union Leaguer walked into a blacksmith shop where Lee was and shot him in the back of the head without warning. A physician who lived nearby took Lee in and kept him there, until he recovered. A Union Leaguer shot the physician in the back. Lee took to the thickets and lived there until 1869, in a hut hidden deep in a big thicket, and camouflaged with black oilcloth. Altogether he and his men killed about fifty Union Leaguers. A neighbor and supposed friend finally betrayed him to the soldiers and helped murder him. A nephew of the murderer was a friend of Lee's. Learning of his uncle's perfidy, he rode all night, called the murderer out in the dawn, and shot him down on his own doorstep.

And so on. A man must believe what his conscience dictates, and if he believes in pacifism, so be it. But I'd rather be shot down in a battle than live under the heel of an arrogant alien despotism.

Alabama took Stanford in grand style,[6] maintaining its record of having never been defeated on the West Coast. I don't know just what year my people moved into the state of Alabama, but it was long ago. My great-grandfather, Squire James Henry, was born in South Carolina in 1811, and he was a small boy when they went into Alabama, so you see it was pretty far back, anyway. The Henrys and a family named Walser from Georgia settled in what is now the counties of Bibb and Tuscaloosa, near the Black Warrior river. James Henry married a Walser woman and most of their children were born in Alabama. In 1847 they moved to Choctaw County, Mississippi, and settled near the upper reaches of the Big Black River, immortalized in the legends of John Henry, the mythical black giant. Both the Henrys and the Walsers made the move. The Walsers remained in Mississippi until a year or so after the Civil War, and then moved to Texas and settled on what was then the western frontier. But the Henrys moved to southwestern Arkansas in 1856. Squire Henry was a typical pioneer. When the country about him began to settle up and grow tame, he grew restless and moved on. He was a man of great natural abilities, and managed to acquire considerable education. In his old age he had what was probably the most extensive private library in southern Arkansas, and would have been considered a well-read man, even in this day and age. In hewing homes out of the wilderness, he hewed out a fortune for himself that was considered large in those days. He had not even the proverbial shoe-string to start on, in the beginning, but he was well fixed financially even before he left Alabama. But he had recognized what few today realize; that the ever westward-receding frontier offered unparalleled resources, and that any man of guts and intelligence had the best chance in the world of building a successful career, or making a fortune. And he proved his belief by following the frontier until he was too old to follow it. His last venture was to the Texas frontier. Having been forced to retire from the Confederate Army in 1862 because of a wound, he took his slaves and went to Texas where he raised cotton until the end of the war, hiding the bales so cleverly that even the carpet-baggers couldn't find them. Then he hauled them to Jefferson by ox-wagon and sold them at a tidy price—he was the only Southerner I ever heard of who had more money at the close of the Civil War than he had at the beginning. But he earned it, by three years of hard work, constantly threatened on one hand by a revolt of the slaves, and on the other by Indian attack. The Comanches overran the frontier during the Civil War, just as they did during the Texas Revolution.

I'm sorry to hear about the cold weather in the East. This has been a very mild winter. I haven't had to don underwear, and have worn an overcoat only once. It was about four or five above zero then. No other cold snap has approached those figures. But the fruit trees are budding out, and I'm afraid a late freeze will ruin them. Some good rains have helped things a lot, and I understand some sixty feet of water is now standing in the Brownwood Lake. I sympathize with your grandfather in his dam troubles[7]—it's pure hell to stand helplessly and watch the elements destroy one's labor and hopes. In the case of the Brownwood Lake, though, the fault was in poor planning and construction. The imported engineers were too all-wise to listen to advice from the natives. And the natives had to pay for their ignorance and arrogance. Not long ago I noticed a map of Texas, put out by a certain large corporation in the Mid-West—a big, expensive wall-map. It was supposed to be the height of accuracy. Glancing at it I discovered that they had left Brownwood some ten miles to the south of the Pecan Bayou; in reality it runs through the edge of the town. According to that map the Bayou then turned east and ran into the Leon River; in reality it turns south and runs into the Colorado. It is the most important stream in a large stretch of country, and there seems to be no reason why a map-maker should make such a mistake. Moreover, to flow as it was depicted on that map, it would have to flow directly uphill for quite a long distance, up over the Callahan Divide, one of the most important geographical features in the state. The company that put out that map has made millions of dollars in Texas; yet their map-makers weren't sufficiently familiar with the state to correctly place a good-sized river, or to be aware of the existence of a watershed several hundred miles in extent. Of course the mistake was trivial, in so far as it was merely an error on a map; but when the same, or similar mistakes are made in regard to the planning of dams and the like, it is a different matter.

When I woke up this morning a dust storm was on; the rising sun, unseen behind the veil of dust, turned that veil to gold. A glowing golden fog seemed to fill the sky; a phenomenon not often seen, since most sandstorms begin after sun-up and subside before the next sunrise. Sunsets are lurid rather than golden. The wind has ceased now, in the late afternoon, and light clouds have followed the dust. It's getting colder, and will probably turn into a blizzard or a rain, or both. I always dread springs, because of the possibility of destructive storms. But last spring was a dream of soft, clear weather that never even threatened. There was not even a menacing looking cloud throughout the whole of the year of 1934—the first year in all my life I ever knew such a thing to happen. Nor could it be explained by the fact of the drouth. Some of the most destructive hurricanes the state has ever seen have come during drouthy years. In fact, drouthy years are more likely to be stormy than are rainy years. I certainly appreciated the tranquil weather. It's a relief to lie down at night knowing you won't be blown into the next state before morning. The last bad storm this part of the country has seen was the summer before last. It missed Callahan County but tore things up in Brown. I was in Brownwood just a few hours before it struck. It was an unnaturally hot, still day. The air seemed dead, oppressive. A peculiar whitish haze hung over everything in this section of the state. Atmospheric conditions produced a peculiar sluggishness and drowsiness. It was almost impossible to keep awake. I believed a storm was brewing, and after I returned to Cross Plains, I kept watching the sky. I could not believe that the storm would strike there, however, because the clouds all lay to the east. To the west the sky was clear. In this country storms generally come from the west, northwest or southwest. When a northeaster does come, though, it comes with devastating fury and swiftness. And it was a northeaster that hit Brownwood. I felt that a storm had passed somewhere to the east of the Cross Plains country, because shortly before sun-down, I saw the clouds rolling and churning far off to the southeast, as if all the wind in the world was swelling their bellies, and then a little later a crest rose above the solid mass, towering toward the middle-arch of the sky, turned gold by the sunset, and curiously curled at the ends—exactly as if the long fleece of some mythical sheep had bee combed out in long curving fans. Only a terrific wind could produce such an effect, and the sight, with the knowledge of what must be going on there, was extremely impressive.

The hurricane had struck a strip of farming country just east of Brownwood, and its edge had ripped through the town itself. It was of terrific intensity, but narrow in expanse and the destruction to life and property was not as great as it might have been. Four people were killed, a woman, a man and two children; or perhaps it was three children instead of a man.[8] I do not exactly remember. I do know that either two or three children were killed. I remember discussing the storm with the banker with whom I do business in Brownwood. He had seen the bodies. Their fate had been grotesque and horrible. One was crushed by the falling timbers of a house, but the other three had been killed in a different manner. Apparently they had not been struck by flying timbers or hurled against anything hard enough to kill them; but their heads had been blasted; above the ears there was no skull at all. It was as if their heads had *exploded* from a terrific pressure inside. That was the theory; the center of a cyclone is a vacuum, and it was believed that the sudden removal of the normal air-pressure on the outside had caused their skulls to burst apart—a theory supported by the experience of my friend Pink Tyson who was once in the dead center of a small cyclone. He said his eardrums seemed to be expanding outward, as if his head were about to burst from some pressure from within. The bodies were utterly bloodless when discovered. Whatever caused the blasting of their heads, the terrific suction of the tornado had sucked every drop of blood from their bodies through the ghastly wounds. That might form the theme of a horror-story—"Vampires of the Storm" perhaps—unseen fiends lurking in clouds and winds to devour human victims.

Passing through the storm-torn area not long later I saw evidence of the whims of the storm—mesquite trees uprooted and torn to shreds, and perhaps a few feet away other trees standing untouched; the whims of a tornado are unpredictable; it is a perversion of the elements, Nature gone mad and running amuck blindly.

Some days have elapsed since the above was written, during which time another cool snap has swept over the country. You possibly read of the snows and storms that raged in the mid-west. Texas got its share of violent weather in the shape of the worst sand-storm I've seen in at least ten years (though prior to that time similar storms were common enough) which combining the features of a sand-storm and a blizzard, jerked the weather from 75 to 20 degrees in a few hours. However it got no colder, and I did not find it necessary to put on either underwear or an overcoat. The spell was short in duration, but if it doesn't rain I'm afraid this spring will be one sand-storm after another.

I note your remarks concerning apparel, and heartily agree with you about dressing lightly. I hate coats, partly because they are uncomfortable to a man of my build. I have a thick, very short neck—I wear a 17 size collar—thick chest and shoulders, with heavy masses of muscles about my shoulder-blades and arm-pits, and find it almost impossible to get a coat that fits me properly. I am forced to have my clothes tailor-made and even then the coat collar invariably saws at the back of my neck until I'm ready to bite people. I go in my shirt sleeves—and them rolled above my elbows—most of the time; when an outer garment is necessary I prefer a light sweater.

I had a very quiet Christmas. One pleasant feature was an unusually fine turkey which a friend gave me. I drove him to the county-seat, a distance of only thirty miles, to arrange bail for his brother, as he had no means of transportation himself, and he seemed to think he was obligated to do something in return. He offered me a turkey, and when I refused to accept it for so trivial an accomodation, he brought it over that night, walking more than a mile and carrying it, and practically forced it on me. And I believe it was the fattest, finest turkey I ever set tooth in.

I didn't even have anything to drink Christmas, but a few weeks later I more than made up for it. In fact I got on the biggest bat I was ever on in my life. It sneaked up on me, too, so to speak, for when I started out I had no intention of anything more than a mild souse. It was the first time I'd been lit for about eleven months. But my jags are few and very far between. A friend and I started out for a county-seat in a county to the south of here, and I took on a fair cargo of beer before we left Cross Plains. On the way we destroyed about a pint of hill-country rot-gut, and when we got to our destination we fell in with some friends and got a pint of bottled-in-bond which three of us lapped up in short order, I drinking most of it. Then we got a couple more pints, which quickly followed the others, and from that point my recollections are very hazy. I know that we were all soused to the hilt, and that one of the party, a six-foot-one, 220 pound giant, went on such a tear as not even the hill-country often witnesses. He smashed all the glassware he could get his hands on, he shot the panels out of the doors, cracked a few windows, threw a few slugs through the light bulbs, and altogether, shot up the place pretty thoroughly. He was on the damndest roaring tear I ever saw. I have a vague recollection of coming to grips with him, but how or why I don't remember. I do know that during the melee I heaved him bodily off his feet, but before I could throw him, just as I got him on my shoulders, all the liquor got in my legs and they buckled, and we came down on the floor together with a crash that must have shaken the roof, and nearly shattered my knee. I limped for a month. And from the way I felt the next day, somebody must have tried to stave in my ribs with a gun-butt some time or other during the revel.

I always maintained that a drunken man knew what he was doing, if he was able to stand and walk, admitting that he probably didn't give a hang, still I believed he was aware of his actions. I based that belief on my own experiences, up to the time of the bat just described. I must admit I'm wrong. I don't have the slightest recollection of many of the things I've been told I did after the third or fourth pint. They say that the aforesaid giant and I, after the smoke cleared away, sallied forth to visit a young lady, that we got into the wrong front yard, and that I got sick. And that my companion, when the family who owned the yard objected, invited the entire clan to come out of the house and get the hell beat out of them. I don't remember anything about it, nor was I aware of what was going on, or what I was doing at the time. I don't remember my bellicose friend kicking down anybody's front door—as they say he did, but whose or why or when I haven't the slightest idea—and I don't remember the young lady whom we had started to visit in the first place coming out and making peace and getting us started back to the place we'd come from. They say I was walking straight, without a stagger, was speaking plainly and apparently intelligently, didn't seem to be unusually drunk. But the plain fact was that I was drunker than I ever was in my life, that I was utterly without knowledge of what I was doing, and that I can't remember at all, the incidents just enumerated. I was, in fact, unconscious, yet I was walking, moving about, laughing, taking part in the conversation and in every way acting like a man in full possession of his faculties. There's something for psychologists to explain.

Thanks for the kind things you said about my verses. And thanks, too, for the splendid picture of Cthulhu. Do you wish it to be returned? Barlow seems to be a very versatile young fellow.

Hoping that I haven't bored you too much by this rambling missive, and hoping that you had an enjoyable time in New York—as I'm sure you did have—I am, as always,

Cordially,
REH.

P.S. Not long ago, Wright accepted a 73,000 word serial novel, tentatively scheduled for some time in 1936. A Conan yarn, "The Hour of the Dragon." Wright says it's my best Conan story so far, and I agree with him. I hope you like the yarn.

Notes

1. REH refers to Berthold Schidlof, *Venus Oceanica: The Sexual Life of South Sea Natives* [with *Erotic Rituals of Australian Aboriginals* by Doctor H. Basedow; *Ethnopornographia* by Doctor W. E. Roth], ed. R[onald] Burton (New York: Oceanica Research Press, 1935), p. 37. This is a translation of his *Das Sexualleben der Australier und Ozeanier* (1908).] The quotation is from Schidlof's introduction.

2. REH is quoting out of context. In the "Reports and Recommendations of the Senate Committee Investigating Crime" (*Journal of the State of Texas,* 44th Legislature, 8 January 1935), in the section on "Bookies," is stated: "We quote from a very distinguished citizen of Texas, the following: 'Ninety percent of these racketeers have come from Miami, Chicago and Los Angeles. When our liquor laws were liberalized they took the liberty that was extended to Texas citizens as a license to come into our State, collect money that was due legitimate business and take it back home with

them.'" The report includes no statements regarding habitual criminals and their places of origin.

3. REH refers to FBL's story "The Beast-Helper" (*WT*, August 1934).

4. A November 1934 Associated Press report stated that "Shipments of scrap metal from Texas ports to Japan in October were nearly three times as large as in October, 1933. Figures compiled [in Galveston] showed that shipments in October, 1934, amounted to 20,473,231 pounds, as compared with 7,993,870 in October of last year." Scrap iron was used in the making of steel for ships and munitions. During World War II it was widely believed that the munitions being used to fight American soldiers had been manufactured from American scrap iron, as expressed in e. e. cummings's 1944 poem, "plato told," in which he refers to "a nipponized piece of the old sixth avenue el."

5. Novalyne Price.

6. Alabama defeated Stanford 29–13 in the 1935 Rose Bowl.

7. HPL's grandfather Whipple V. Phillips had organized the Owyhee Land & Irrigation Co. to dam the Snake River in Idaho and to construct a suitable irrigation system, but met with failure through two successive burstings of the uncompleted dam.

8. On 11 May 1933, a tornado swept through Brownwood and two small communities to the east. Newspaper accounts reported one woman and two children killed, with seven others hurt, some seriously. The dead and injured were all from two families whose homes were destroyed.

[113]   [nonextant letter by HPL, spring 1935]

[114]   [TLS]

[c. May 1935]

Dear HPL:

The reason I haven't answered your letter sooner is that I was forced to spend a month in East Texas, on account of an operation performed on my mother, during which time I wasn't able to write any, and since then I've been trying to catch up with my work and rebuild my bank account a little. My expenses, naturally, were great. It was necessary to remove my mother's gall-bladder, and reduce adhesions resulting from an old appendicitis operation, and she had a very bad time of it. She seems to be recovering gradually; but the process is very slow and at times discouraging. After coming home from the hospital she developed an abscess in the wound, which is still draining slightly. The operation was done in Temple, and after she had spent a month in the hospital, she came home in my car, in which my father and I fixed a bed out of blankets and cushions and quilts. Temple is about a hundred and ninety-odd miles from Cross Plains, in the prairie country, and we'd hardly gotten into the hill country, perhaps thirty-five miles from Temple, when the clutch broke all to pieces and left us stranded on a country road, five miles from the nearest town, and a storm coming up. I found a farmer with an ancient Ford who pushed us to the next town, a little village called Copperas Cove, and we got my mother into the one hotel the place boasted just before the storm broke, with the usual terrific thunder and lightning, rain and hail that is common with hill-country storms. We had a new clutch put in and started on after the rain, in the middle of the afternoon, through the barren and thinly-settled hills that lie between Copperas Cove and Lampasas, where my mother spent her girlhood. I had had some work done on the car in Temple, by a dumb Bohemian, who, unknown to me, had left some parts out of the differential. We just got to Lampasas before the differential broke all to pieces. We spent the night there, in an old rock hotel built in 1870, when it was as much fort as hotel, and got the car fixed. We got home the next day without further mishap. But you can imagine the licking my pocket-book took, with all that car trouble. Getting the differential fixed alone cost me twenty-six dollars.

The drouth is apparently over in the Southwest which is a great relief. It looks like we're going to raise a good grain crop. Those rains in April and May certainly changed the aspect of the country. Before them the whole country was a dry, barren, bleak, dust-tortured, heat-lashed expanse without a sprig of green to break the savage monotony, and gaunt, ribby cattle staggering along like ghosts. Now the whole land is a green carpet with luscious grass covering the hills and plains, and pools and rivers and creeks brimming where sixty days ago the bare stones of the beds showed gaunt and dust-covered. The rich green foliage reaches almost tropical luxuriance, and red and yellow wild flowers make a carpet of color gleaming vividly against the green background. On the rolling prairies especially the rises seem to have been smeared with gold that gleams almost dazzlingly when the sun strikes them. Nothing is so beautiful as a field of blue-bonnets, stretching away and away under the mesquite trees, but these Indian daisies and yellow flowers approach them in beauty. The blue-bonnets were not so vivid this year; they come earlier, and the drouth baked them and the dust-storms whipped them to shreds. You may possibly have read in the papers of the dust-storms that assailed the west this year. I never saw anything like them. They were not like the sand storms that used to be so common. They were far more devastating in their total effect. But general rains seem to have conquered them

Lake Brownwood is brimming full, and its tributaries look like rivers near their mouths. I hear the fishermen are pulling some fine catches out of Pecan Bayou and the Jim Ned River. But my friend Pink Tyson, who is a fisherman of fishermen, tells me that the streams are in a fair way to be ruined by these infernal carp they have imported from Europe. I never in my life ate fish that tasted better—or even as good—as our native catfish. But somebody with European tastes had to import carp from Europe where they are very popular, I understand. Naturally would be, as they live on carrion and taste similar. hey don't eat live prey like catfish, I'm told, but subsist (being European by origin) on dead things exclusively, with the exception of the eggs of other fish. That too is a European characteristic. And like most things imported from Europe, they have a carrion taste. I suppose that recommends them highly to European gourmets. I have often heard of the disgust of the old-time settlers of this country with the taste of Englishmen who came out here as immigrants or sportsmen in the '70's and '80's, and who, after shooting rabbits, used to hang them up and let them reach a stage approaching putre-faction before eating them.

Your letter was forwarded to me at Temple, and somehow got lost or de-stroyed, so I'll have to try to answer it by memory.

As for the question of British and Americans, and the proposed Anglo-American alliance, your pro-British sympathies are doubtless natural, but there's no reason why I should share them. I have no prejudice whatever against an individual Englishman, any more than I have any prejudice against any individual of any race whatsoever. But there's no reason in the world why I should share your worship of the British Empire, or should wish to rush forward and risk my life in defense of that empire. All that my people ever got from the British was abuse and oppression, and I speak not only for my race, but for my family. Every branch of my family that came to America came to escape British tyranny. The last branch that came, the Henrys, were prosperous and peaceful landholders in West Ireland, and they were dispos-sessed, falsely accused, imprisoned and banished in misery and poverty, merely in order to enable a fat bastard of a British plutocrat to grab their lands and belongings. And you tell me that it's my duty to fight for the Em-pire that exiled my ancestors! For that's what an Anglo-American pact would amount to—America pulling England's chestnuts out of the fire for her. Ac-cording to this view, I suppose that if you knocked a man down, broke his leg, stamped in his guts, kicked out his teeth and threw him into the road to starve, you'd expect his sons and his grandsons to love, honor and admire you, and rush with dutiful joy to your defense when you had a squabble with some of your other neighbors. I doubt if there are enough Tories in America to drag this country into the position of a catspaw for Great Britain. How-ever, if you feel that it's the sacred duty of Americans not only of English descent, but also of Irish, German, Jewish, and Italian ancestry to fight for the Empire, there's nothing to prevent you stepping over into Canada and joining the British army.

As for police atrocities, I assure you that I am quite aware as to what is the definition of the term "sadism". And I am also aware that it is the only term to be applied to the action of four or five brawny men knocking a woman down with clubs, beating and stamping on her and kicking her, and later dragging her into the street and repeating the process merely because she was suspected of having spoken impertinently to one of them. To claim that her fault constituted an assault on civilization, law, order, progress, art, literature and culture, that had to be overcome with loaded clubs and boot heels, is slicing the bologna entirely too thick. Your enthusiastic defense of such actions certainly is an ironic contrast to your vivid denunciations of western "brutality". Brutality!

You asked me something about the contrast between East and West Texas, I believe, as near as I can remember, or perhaps it was something about the natural causes which make Texas distinctly different from the other states of the South.

Well, the causes are mostly geographical. Texas is a sort of cross-roads for the continent. The woodland country of East Texas lies on the western slope of the Mississippi Basin, and is merely a continuation of the conditions existing in the older Southern States. For a hundred miles after you crossed the Sabine, I do not believe you could tell any difference, particularly, between that region and the regions adjacent to the Mississippi River. (Excepting for the oil fields, of course.) You would find lumber camps, clusters of nigger huts, piney woods, stump-dotted fields, swamps, cotton fields, moss-hung live-oaks, etc., just about like it is further east, in Louisiana, Arkansas and Mississippi, and, from what I hear, Alabama. A country of big land-holders, swarms of niggers, and miserable tenant farmers of both colors. Coming further west, you'd come into the broad prairie belt that runs from Red River southwestward almost to the coastal plain. There you'd find fewer big landholders, more independent farmers, more people enjoying prosperity, less huge fortunes in the hands of a few, and many, many more foreigners— Bohemians, Germans and Swedes in solid, compact and surprizingly prosperous communities. The most of the cities of Texas lie in or adjacent to that prairie belt, which is, I feel, merely a continuation of that great Central Western prairie belt which composes the most productive farming region on this continent, extending from Canada almost to the Gulf. I was born on the western edge of that prairie belt, and can testify that it is one of the richest regions in the whole state. It was there, and on the coast, also, that the cattle industry got its growth. Before the land was cultivated the grass grew stirrup high, affording one of the finest grazing-lands in the world. Still further west, and to the north, lies the hill country where I have lived for the last half of my life. This is a country of small stockmen, with a few large ranches, and farmers working medium sized farms. The percentage of tenant farmers is high, but there are also many men who own their own farms. The population is overwhelmingly old American, the few foreigners mainly Germans. To the southwest of the prairie belt lies an even more rugged hill country, where farming is comparatively unimportant, except in strips, and big ranches are the rule. There is a large foreign population there, mainly Germans. The coastal plain, stretching from San Antonio to the Gulf, is heterogeneous of population and occupation. In the west, along the mouth of the Rio Grande, citrus fruit raising's the main occupation, and the finest oranges in the world are grown there. In the valley itself the people are mostly Americans of old Texas stock, or Middle-West Germans, and Scandinavians. A little further to the east is a country of vast ranches, with a dominantly Irish population. And from there to the mouth of the Sabine, far to the east, the country presents many phases of industry, occupation and population—Poles, Germans, Italians, Irish, Americans, Mexicans, negroes—cattle-raisers, rice-planters, cotton-planters and fishermen, etc. North of the hill country in which I live, and west of it, begin the great plains which stretch up into the Panhandle—"The Bread-Basket of the Nation" as it is called. The population on the plains is mostly Anglo-Saxon—or rather Scotch-Irish—of old Texas stock, and it is a country of vast farms and ranches, mostly lived on and worked by the men who own them. As the Grand Prairie is a continuation of the Mid-West prairie in the eastern regions, so the Panhandle is a continuation of the western plains of the Mid-Western states. The Trans-Pecos, through which runs a spur of the Rocky Mountains, is geographically a part of the Far West and the Mountain States. Agriculture is possible only through irrigation. It is still a cattle country and always will be, probably.

You can see, from this brief description, how natural it was for Texas to develop on her own lines, differently than the older Southern States, except in the east, where conditions were duplicated. The first men to come into Texas as settlers were farmers. They learned stock raising from the Spaniards. (Cortez was the first to introduce European cattle onto this continent.) Cattle raising, however, did not reach its full importance until after the Civil War, when the railroads were pushing westward into and across Kansas. The few cattle brought into Texas by the first settlers, work-oxen and milk cows, were scrubby, stunted mostly; it was the longhorn cattle, brought from Africa originally by way of Spain and the West Indies which formed the herds of the first American ranchers.

Concerning our wars with Mexico, I understand that there is a feeling in the older states that all the settlers who came to Texas came with the fixed intention of starting trouble, overthrowing the Mexican government and dragging Texas into the union by force. That's not so. There were of course some men like Houston who came or were sent by the United States government to stir up trouble and eventually persuade the colonists to revolt and join the union. But a large majority of the settlers were like Austin—men who were content to live as peaceable Mexican citizens, and who were finally driven into revolt because of the outrages of the government under the adventurer Santa Ana.

I quote from the Texas Declaration of Independence.

"The Mexican Government, by its colonization laws, invited and induced the Anglo-American population to colonize its wilderness, under the pledged faith of a written Constitution, that they should continue to enjoy that constitutional liberty and republican government to which they had been habituated in the land of their birth, the United States of America. In this expectation they have been cruelly disappointed, inasmuch as the Mexican Nation has acquiesced in the late changes made in the Government by Gen. Antonio Lopez de Santa Ana, who, having overturned the Constitution of his country, now offers us the cruel alternative, either to abandon our homes, acquired by so many privations, or submit to the most intolerable of all tyrannys, the combined despotism of the sword and the priesthood.

"It hath sacrificed our welfare to the State of Coahuila, by which our interests have been continually depressed, through a jealous and partial course of legislation, carried on at a far-distant seat of government, by a hostile majority, in an unknown tongue, and this, too, notwithstanding we have petitioned in the humblest terms for the establishment of a separate State Government, and have, in accordance with the provisions of the National Constitution, presented to the General Congress a Republican Constitution, which was, without just cause, contemptuously rejected.

"It incarcerated in a dungeon, for a long time, one of our citizens, for no other cause but a zealous endeavor to procure the acceptance of our Constitution and the establishment of a State Government.

"It has failed and refused to secure, on a firm basis, the right of trial by jury. . . . .

"It has failed to establish any public system of education. . . . .

"It has suffered the military commandants . . . . to exercise arbitrary acts of oppression . . . . . . rendering the military superior to the civil power.

"It has dissolved by force of arms the State Congress of Coahuila and Texas . . . . . . depriving us of the fundamental political right of representation.

"It has demanded the surrender of a number of our citizens, and ordered military detachments to seize and carry them into the interior for trial, in contempt of the civil authorities, and in defiance of the laws and the Constitution.

"It has made piratical attacks upon our commerce by commissioning foreign desperadoes, and authorizing them to seize our vessels and convey the property of our citizens to far-distant ports for confiscation.

"It denies us the right of worshipping the Almighty according to the dictates of our own consciences, by the support of a national religion calculated to promote the temporal interests of its human functionaries rather than the glory of the true and living God.

"It has demanded us to deliver up our arms, which are essential to our defense, the rightful property of freemen, and formidable only to tyrannical Governments.

"It has invaded our country, both by sea and by land, with intent to lay waste our territory, and drive us from our homes; and has now a large mercenary army advancing, to carry on against us a war of extermination.

"It has, through its emissaries, incited the merciless savage, with the tomahawk and scalping knife, to massacre the inhabitants of our defenseless frontiers.

"It has been, during the whole time of our connection with it, the contemptible sport and victim of successive military revolutions, and hath continually exhibited every characteristic of a weak, corrupt, and tyrannical Government."

The man mentioned in the third paragraph as having been imprisoned was Stephen F. Austin, who was thrown into a dungeon merely because he went to Mexico City to ask Santa Ana to allow Texas to have a State Government separate from Coahuila.

I suppose some of the distorted ideas concerning early Texas and the Mexican Wars are hangovers from the deliberate lies circulated by the abolitionists and others in the '40's and '50's. As you possibly know there was much sympathy in the East, especially in New England, for the Mexicans during both the Texas Revolution and the Mexican War. When Santa Ana, after being defeated and captured at San Jacinto, went east, he received a tremendous ovation. "Santa Ana," emotionally exclaimed the Woonsocket Patriot, among others (though they spelled his name wrong) "How can we style him a tyrant, who opposed the efforts of rebels and used them with deserved severity!" They didn't seem to realize that some of the "rebels" who suffered from his "deserved severity" were New Englanders. William Linn, who died in the Alamo, was from Massachusetts; Stephen F. Austin was of New England stock, and so were some of the others. Santa Ana "opposed the efforts of rebels" in a way that evidently brought joy to the hearts of the gentlemen of the Patriot and their colleagues, for he always made a practise of murdering his prisoners, and mutilating their bodies. After the fall of the Alamo this was carried out in a manner to suit the most ultra-civilized taste, even the super-civilized tastes of the gentlemen of the Patriot. The tongue of Travis was cut out, for instance, and his head hacked off, and the bodies of Crockett and Bowie tossed by the bayonets of the peons until they were mangled beyond recognition. The bodies were then burned, not for purposes of sanitation, but in contempt. However (judging from what you tell me of the ultra-civilized viewpoint of "chivalry") the gentlemen of the Patriot would have been shocked and disappointed had they known that Santa Ana not only refused to allow the women survivors of the Alamo to be harmed, but treated them with courtesy and kindness.

One is forced to believe that if these super-civilized gentlemen had known this, they would have administered a sharp rebuke to Santa Ana for his "sentimentalistic" behavior, in allowing himself to be swayed by the "artificial" convention of chivalry. Butler at New Orleans doubtless was more to their liking.

But if Santa Ana was uncivilized enough to spare the women and children who fell into his hands, he was "unsentimentalistic" enough in other ways. No civilized general, not even one of the Patriot's writers, could have been more deft in breaking promises, ignoring truces and butchering the helpless men he captured. Probably the super-gentlemen of the Patriot would have enjoyed Goliad more than the Alamo, for at Goliad there was little fighting but much cold-blooded slaughter. The Mexicans, finding that the Texans wished to be shot in the breast, so as not to have their features mutilated, facing the enemy unblindfolded, took pleasure in blindfolding them and shooting them in the back of the head. And some of these men were from the same region as the gentlemen of the Patriot.

I find the smug and self-righteous attitude of the "Patriot's" gentlemen in striking contrast to men like James W. Parker, who lived in that period. It was less than a month after San Jacinto that James Parker wrote his red chapter into Texas history. He lived, with others of his kin, at old Fort Parker, near the Navasota River. Early in the morning five hundred Comanches appeared before the fort, led by a Mexican agent who had been stirring up the tribes against the white people—one of the noble defenders of civilization whom the gentlemen of the Patriot praised in such unrestrained terms. He was not known to be an Indian agent by the people of the fort. Waving a white flag, he disarmed suspicion and by his wiles got the gate opened. The rest was red massacre. The braves swarmed through like a steel-tipped wave before the Texans could prepare their defense. What followed should have pleased the gentlemen of the Patriot even more than Santa Ana's massacres did, for the ideas of the Comanches regarding chivalry approximated those of a European general's, or a modern intellectual's. Women and children as well as men were cut down, scalped and mutilated and in that holocaust Fort Parker perished. Some few were taken captive by the Indians, among them Cynthia Ann Parker and her brother, John. Cynthia Ann grew up among the Comanches, married Peta Nocona and bore him a son, Quanah, who became the last war-chief of the Comanches and led the painted hordes against the barriers of Adobe Walls when the long rifles of the buffalo hunters raked the red riders out of their saddles and littered the prairie with their gaudily-painted bodies. But Quanah's head was not one of the many which decorated the palisades in token of a white man's victory, and he came to live at last in a white man's house, on the Comanche Reservation, and to exercise almost dictatorial power in his tribe. But it is not of Quanah I would speak, nor of Cynthia Ann's brother who grew up like a naked, painted brave, who carried off a Mexican girl in a wild raid over the Border, and who was by her persuaded to quit the tipi and the war-trail and return with her to the settlements and take up the white man's ways and life. Nor would I speak of Mrs. Kellogg, captured from Fort Parker, traded to the Keechies, sold by them to the Delawares for a hundred and fifty dollars, and by them sold back to Sam Houston. Nor is it my intention to speak of Mrs. Plummer, who gave birth to a baby during her captivity, and who saw her Indian master tie a lariat to the baby when it was six months old and drag it back and forth through a cactus bed until it was torn to pieces, and who was at last ransomed by William Donoho, a Santa Fe trader, or Comanchero, in the Rocky Mountains. It is of Jim Parker I would speak, and I can not tell his story better than in his own words. Visualize that scene for an instant: the Fort has fallen; a thick column of smoke rises and wavers against the morning sky. A little band of fugitives huddle together amongst the thickets near the bank of a sullen creek winding through almost impenetrable brush. They are unarmed, half-naked, some wounded, all dazed by the suddenness of the disaster. Their brains are still sick from the sights they have seen, the cries that tortured their ears. Faintly they still hear the bestial, exultant yells of the Comanches. They have seen their relatives butchered before their eyes, shot, speared, their scalps torn from their still living heads. On all sides the wilderness stretches, scarcely marked by the brief occupation of humanity. It is hundreds of miles to the nearest settlement, and every foot of the way is beset with hardships and perils. Let James W. Parker tell his own story.[1]

"We were truly a forlorn set, many of us barefooted and bareheaded, a relentless foe on the one hand and on the other a trackless and uninhabited wilderness, infested with reptiles and wild beasts. We were entirely destitute of food, with no means of procuring it. Added to this the agonizing grief for the death and capture of our dear relatives and the expectation of meeting at any moment a like fate, utter despair almost seized us.

"I took one of my children on my shoulder and led the other. The grown person followed my example. Our mournful party, consisting of eighteen persons, left for Fort Houston. Our journey led through thickly tangled briars and underbrush. My wife was in bad health; Mrs. Frost was in deep distress for the loss of her husband and son, and all were bitterly mourning the loss of loved ones; and all being barefooted except my wife and Mrs. Frost, our progress was very slow. Many of the children had nothing on but their shirts, and their sufferings from briars tearing their little legs and feet were almost beyond human endurance.

"We traveled until three o'clock in the morning, when the women and children were worn out with hunger and fatigue. We then lay down on the grass and slept until daylight, when we resumed our perilous journey. The briars tore the legs and feet of the children until they could have been tracked by the blood that flowed from their wounds. At dark of the second day after leaving the fort, the children, and especially the women who were nursing infants, began to suffer intensely from hunger, but alas, we had not a morsel of food! But providentially at the moment a polecat came near us. I immediately pursued him and caught him just as he jumped into the river. The only way I could kill him was by holding him under the water until he drowned. Fortunately, we had the means of striking a fire, and we soon had it cooked and equally divided among the women and children, the share of each being small indeed. This was all we had to eat until the fourth day, when we were lucky enough to catch another polecat and two small terrapins, which we also cooked and divided, giving the women and children the larger share. On the evening of the fifth day I found that the women and children were so exhausted that it would be impossible for them to travel much further. After holding a consultation it was agreed that I should hurry on to Fort Houston for aid, leaving Dr. Dwight in charge of the women and children. Early the next morning I started for the fort, about thirty-five miles distant, which I reach[ed] early in the afternoon. I have often looked back and wondered how I was able to accomplish this extraordinary feat. I had not eaten a mouthful for six days, having always given my share of the polecats and terrapins to the women and children; and yet I walked thirty-five miles in about eight hours. But the thought of the suffering women and children I had left behind inspired me with strength and perseverance, and above all, God in his bountiful providence upheld me in that trying hour.

"The first person I met on reaching Fort Houston was the generous and brave Captain Carter. He soon had five horses saddled and other means of conveyance, and he and Jeremiah Courtney went with me to meet our little band of starving, bleeding women and children. We met them just at dark, and placing the women and children on the horses, we reached Captain Carter's hospitable home about midnight. Every preparation had been made to receive the mournful company of sufferers. The hungry, weary women and children, with their bleeding feet, were tenderly cared for. The following day, May 25, my son-in-law, Mr. Plummer, reached Fort Houston. He had been given up for lost. After so many years, I look back over that scene of unparalleled suffering with inexpressible horror, yet with devout thanksgiving and praises to God for His merciful support and protection."

Evidently James W. Parker did not know that "chivalry" is supposed to be an artificial pose, by our intellectuals. It was strong enough in him to drag his starved and bleeding body thirty-five miles through briar thickets I doubt if the average modern could walk thirty-five yards through, in something like eight hours, after having already walked for days, and having eaten nothing in six days. What inspired him to do this—a love of art, or some of the other cultural impulses which our intellectuals seem to consider constitute the only "realities" in the universe? Scarcely. He says: "The thought of the suffering women and children I had left behind me inspired me with strength and perseverance." Doubtless this seems inexplicable and a bit ridiculous to that school of moderns which sneer at "chivalry" as artificial, and at self-sacrifice and heroism as mere romantic poses; but it is to men like Parker that these very persons owe the ease, security and leisure which they employ so well in striving to tear down everything that men like Parker built with their sweat and blood.

I remember another man, or rather a mere boy, who did not realize that "chivalry" and the masculine protective attitude are "artificial" either. He was only a backwoods kid, born and raised on the Texas frontier. I doubt if he could read or write. I don't even remember his name. Most of his people had been murdered by the Comanches, but the remnant clung doggedly to their tiny log cabin, their pitiful field of corn, shadowed by trees that the axe had never touched, and from which painted death struck again and again. It struck suddenly, one day, and littered the rude yard with corpses. The boy and his sister gained the shelter of the cabin; but the boy had a flint-tipped arrow through his body. He could not draw it out. He knew he was dying. But his only thought was to save his sister. She bolted the door and stood staring at him with wide, numbed eyes, incapable of thought or action. She was only a child. Great beads of sweat stood out on his forehead as he dragged the muzzle-loaded rifle from the wall and thrust the muzzle through a knot hole. The Indians saw it, and they kept to cover. He was only a boy, but he was of the old Texas breed, which was more deadly than a wounded panther at bay; and he had killed and killed again. They knew him, those lean, painted, furtive figures slinking through the live-oaks. They did not know whether he was wounded or not. They did know that as long as he lived they would not rush the cabin, for the price they must pay for his scalp and the scalp of his sister would be too high for their liking. He knew they were waiting to hear his death-groans, and he grinned, a ghastly, savage grin of pain. He knew he was dying; he could not withdraw the barbed shaft, and if he could have, it would only have hastened his death. He made his sister lie down on the floor out of range of possible shafts finding cracks between the logs. And he lay on his bunk, grasping his rifle, and choking back the groans that rose involuntarily to his lips, and which would have told the lurking braves that he was dying. The slow hours dragged and the sun dipped behind the trees, but the starlight glinted on the barrel thrust from the knot-hole, and it did not waver. No sound came from the woods but the dismal hoot of an owl, the far wavering cry of a wolf. But the shadows were full of phantoms, gliding from tree to tree, with red eyes and glinting weapons. In the cabin the boy fought his lone, grim fight with death. What agony he endured no man can guess, save dimly. Thrust a thorn through your foot; tear your hand on a sharp stone; and try to guess the pain a man must suffer with a jagged flint point and a yard of wooden shaft through his body. But no sound escaped his lips. Blood dripped slowly on the puncheon floor; blood oozed from the corners of his livid lips; he clenched his teeth and made no sound, not even in the delirium that shook him did a single moan escape him. His will-power rose above human weakness; above pain and fear and suffering and delirium, above death itself. Not even his sister knew when he died. But the sun came up at last, a sick, red sun staggering above the trees, and splashed crimson on a rifle barrel that jutted from a knot hole. And the trees about the cabin were empty, the slayers were gone; only the scalped and mangled dead in the clearing stared with sightless eyes up at the rising sun. And on the rude bunk the boy's body crouched stiffly over the cocked rifle, and his sister rose numbly from the floor to stare vacantly at it. He had won his fight; he had died without a moan to betray his plight to the skulking devils among the trees.

The Comanches had no better claim to Central Texas than the whites had. They swept down from the north, driving the Lipans and the Spaniards before them, about the time the Americans began to drift in from the east. They proposed a Comanche-American alliance to take the land from the Mexicans, whom they despised. The Texans refused, telling them plainly they meant, not only to free themselves from the Mexicans, but also to harry the Comanches from the land. There was no treachery, trickery in the dealings of the Texans with the Comanches. It was open, declared war from the beginning, and the Comanches, who destroyed the Tonkawas, drove out the Lipans and Apaches, repeatedly defeated the Utes and Pawnees, terrorized the Mexicans, defeated Spanish armies and on occasion almost destroyed Latin-American civilization north of the Rio Grande, found themselves at last at grips with a foe grimmer than themselves. It was war to the knife, bloody, merciless, ceaseless, but with the Comanches always driven northward and westward, driven even from the reservations the United States Government tried to give them, until at last they crossed Red River for the last time, and Texas was free for ever of the red menace that once swept victoriously from the Canadian to the Rio Grande. But it took a long time. As late as 1873 all the counties west of Fort Worth were exempt from taxes, because of the continued devastation of Comanche raids. Some were absorbed by the native population of Mexico; others live to this day in the Wichita Mountains Reservation in Oklahoma.

The cat population now numbers twelve. There is Mubsy, the matriarch, and her grown kittens, Nip and Tuck, and her latest brood, three of them; Nip's two kittens; Tuck's two kittens; Greedy, who wandered in from nowhere, was raised with, and suckled with Nip and Tuck, and is the paternal parent of all but Tuck's kittens; and a kitten who toddled in from nowhere and was given a place with the others. Mubsy's latest brood are about two months old; Nip's are a few weeks younger, and Tuck's still younger than Nip's. The stray kitten is somewhere between the ages of Nip's and Tuck's. When we got back from Temple Mubsy was nearly starved, on account of her idiotic way of letting the other cats take her food away from her. Her kittens were stunted, weak, with bodies too small for their heads; she'd been too poorly fed to give them the proper nourishment. They were scrawny and miserable, too much so to play. They could not walk except for a few feet, when they would fall down and drag themselves along by their fore-paws. But I fed her up, separately from the other cats, got her fat again, and likewise gorged the kittens on carefully warmed milk, and now you ought to see them. They're round as butter-balls and every time I go out to the barn they come squalling and meowing to fall all over my feet. Nip had her kittens in another barn, amongst the cotton-seed, and I had the devil of a time making her leave them where I put them, which was in the barn with Mubsy's brood. Their eyes are in poor shape, and are continually gummed together, but I wash them at morning and evening with a boric acid solution and they're getting much better. Nip finally decided to leave her kittens with the others, partly because I allow her and Mubsy to drink milk there when I feed the kittens. Tuck observed this, and brought her kittens to the barn herself, from the garage where she had them—for she returned to the very place where she and her sisters were born, to have her kittens. Nip suckles all impartially, with the possible exception of the stray kitten, who however, seems quite capable of taking care of itself, and which I'm trying to teach to stand on its hind-legs and drink milk squirted from the cow's teat into its mouth. I haven't had a cat that did that since Bebe. I've named none of the kittens so far, except one of Mubsy's, who has a black smudge on its chin which makes it look as though it had a black beard, so I named it Captain Teach. One of Tuck's kittens is white and will probably be called Blanco, and another I suppose will be La Cucaracha. Greedy is a small cat, but his name suits, and he is undoubtedly the most lecherous little bastard I ever saw in my life. He doesn't prowl around like most tom cats, but with three she-cats on the place he doesn't need to. He attempted intercourse with Tuck the day before she had her brood, and got a bat on the ear as a result.

We have plenty of milk for them, because our cow came in fresh recently, but with a bull calf, to my disgust. I'd hoped for a heifer. The cow, Delhi, otherwise called the Begum, is a fine milch-cow, Guernsey with a touch of Brahma, or Holy Cow of India, which gives her more poise and a better temper than a Jersey cow generally possesses. She was bred with a registered Jersey bull, and I hoped much for the result, if it had happened to be a heifer. But a mixed-breed milk bull is no good; all you can do is can him, so we gave him away. That is to say, you can't make any money out of him, because everybody wants to breed their cows to a pure-bred registered animal. Price was much interested in Delhi's Indian blood, and found her milk much to his liking. Indeed, her milk does taste better than any I ever drank, and tests out a very high percentage of butter fat; almost the maximum. On good grass she gives about four gallons a day, and in a dry lot, when well fed, she gives two to three gallons, enough for a medium sized family. I like her better than any cow I ever tried to milk. She has a splendid bag, and large teats, easy to juice, and she's sensible, gentle and not nervous, as so many Jerseys are. The one we traded for her was a devil on wheels—a Jersey, and wild as a kite. Her teats were small, and she kicked and tossed her head and hooked, and raised hell generally and her calf was worse than she was. If she got through eating before I got through milking she'd turn her head, stare at me in feigned amazement as if she never saw me before and wondered what the hell I was doing there, and then kick out with both hind legs and go careering off around the lot, and sometimes I'd have to lasso her before I could catch her again. She was mean and vicious, and hooked me every chance she got, to say nothing of kicking the milk bucket out of my hand and stamping on my foot. Once I was leading her in at the lot gate and she hooked me in the back, hooked me in the face when I turned, and an instant later hooked me beneath the heart and tore some skin off my ribs. This irritated me, and I gave her a bust on the jaw with my fist that knocked all the fight out of her and nearly broke her jaw. After that she never attempted to hook me again, but pulled all her other tricks, and her infernal calf nearly cost me an eye. Just a few days before it was traded off, along with her, I went into an adjoining lot to catch it and bring back to feed, and it refused to be caught, racing around wildly all over the lot, as big a fool as the old cow, and even meaner. I never could throw a rope worth a hang, and after a few attempts I lost patience, and ran at it and made a sort of flying tackle, aiming to grab it around the neck with my arms. Which I did, but it threw up its head just in time to spike me on its short, sharp horn. It caught me on the brow and instantly my eye was full of blood, but I hung on to the wretched beast, and got the rope on it and dragged it home—dragged is the word, because it always braced its legs and fought back every step of the way. All the time I was feeding the stock blood kept running into my eyes so I could hardly see, and when I got through and went into the house and looked into a glass, I found the horn had struck me just over my left eye, making a deep gash which penetrated to the bone. A fraction of an inch lower and it would have destroyed my eye, past doubt. I put some rub alcohol on it and it healed quickly, leaving only another scar of the many which decorate my features and body. You have no idea what a relief it is to have a cow like Delhi.

I enjoyed very much the story "Out of the Eons". It might as well have carried your name beneath the title, for it was yours, all the way through. I hope you'll write some stories, this summer. You've been absent from Weird Tales too long. Lately I've been trying to break into some new markets specializing on the adventure angle. Top Notch has bought four long stories from me, giving me the cover design on the last issue, and I'm trying to make it regularly.[2] Weird stories offer such a narrow field, and the pay is so slow, that I may be forced to abandon that style of yarn entirely and devote all my efforts elsewhere, though I'd hate to give up fantasy entirely.

Are you doing any travelling this summer? A friend of mine wants me to accompany him to Santa Fe, and I'd like to go, but I don't see how I can. I can't unless I either make some mighty profitable sales soon, or collect at least part of the rather large sum that is owing to me. I do not regard the future of the country with any enthusiasm, especially since the Supreme Court knocked out the NRA.[3] I believe this will have a very bad effect upon business and everything else. It is both amusing and nauseating to listen to the blatting about the Constitution going up from men who for half a Century have trampled on that same Constitution with cleated boots. We are even confronted with the spectacle of Republicans squawking about States' Rights, when always before they had nothing but sneers and abuse for such rights. If Thomas Jefferson could return to America today, I'll bet they'd throw him in jail before he'd talked fifteen minutes.

The weather's getting hot as hell, and I wish you could have some of the ice cream my friend Pink Tyson and I make regularly. He works at the ice-house, and has a three-quart freezer. Sometimes we make ordinary vanilla cream, with maybe bananas and pineapples in it, sometimes we take orange, pineapples, lemons, etc., and freeze them all up together, juice and pulp. Sometimes the manager gets in on it, but sometimes Pink and I clean up the stuff ourselves. Anybody ought to be able to eat a quart and a half of ice cream. That is home-made cream. The kind of stuff they sell at confectionery and drug-stores isn't fit to eat.

With best wishes.

Cordially,
REH

Notes

1. James W. Parker, *Narrative of the Perilous Adventures, Miraculous Escapes and Sufferings of Rev. James W. Parker . . .* (Louisville, KY: Morning Courier Office, 1844). Reprinted as *The Rachel Plummer Narrative: A stirring narrative of adventure, hardship and privation in the early days of Texas, depicting struggles with the Indians and other adventures . . .* ([Palestine, TX]: Rachel Lofton, Susie Hendrix and Jane Kennedy [descendants of James W. Parker], 1926).

2. "Swords of Shahrazar" (October 1934); "The Daughter of Erlik Kahn" (December 1934); "Hawk of the Hills" (June 1935); "Blood of the Gods" (July 1935). The last two stories were both featured on the magazine's cover.

3. On 27 May 1935, the Supreme Court ruled that the act that had created the National Recovery Administration, a New Deal program, was unconstitutional.

[115]

c/o R. H. Barlow
Box 88, De Land, Fla.
July 11, 1935

Dear R E H:—

. . . As for international questions—of course opinions on policies naturally differ. In regard to Anglo-American unity, I am thinking not of local
national units but of a *civilisation* . . . . a thing transcending individual nations
as the Hellenic civilisation transcended Athens, Sparta, Syracuse, or any other
of its compound units. It is not that I value Britain any more than Rhode
Island or Florida or Texas, but that I think all parts of the common cultural
fabric ought to pull together for the sake of common survival. The same is
true of any other cultural fabric—such as the Germanic civilisation represented by Germany and Austria, of the Hispanic world of Old Spain and
Central and South America. United they stand, divided they eventually fall.

Regarding the matter of police procedure—it seems that I still fail to
make myself clear. At least, you cite certain implied comparisons which would
attribute to me an attitude far from that which is really mine. I see that you
used the term "sadism" only metaphorically—but your idea of what I endorse
and approve is certainly much beside the facts. When you speak of 4 or 5
brawny men beating and stamping on a lone woman you speak of something
which did not, so far as I know, figure in the discussion. What I *did* endorse
was simply the necessary measures taken to quell or curb a vicious organised
mob in the interest of public safety and order. This does not involve anything
truly brutal or aggressive—being essentially *defensive* in nature. Your picture of
a savage attack on a defenceless lady does not represent anything in connexion with what I mean. All that I said was that when a mob plants women
amongst its ranks, the resisters of that mob cannot alter their general plan of
campaign—which may or may not include the use of clubs or firearms—
merely because of exceptions to the masculine personnel of the enemy. Any
impartial observer can see that this is an absolutely different thing from any
real "brutality toward women". The whole matter is *impersonal*—a general plan
is devised to keep certain ground clear of certain elements—and the plan is
carried through with a practical team-work which does not and cannot stop
for individual discriminations. The chances are that the mob is 90 or 95%
masculine, anyhow. If it isn't the amazons who allow themselves to be
planted among its ranks know what to expect before they start in. Nobody
tries to take advantage of whatever weakness they may have. Nobody, indeed,
thinks of any individuals. It's all a mathematical routine matter of necessity,
and the actors in it play their parts pretty much as automata—as all disciplined fighters and police have to do in cases of collective action. As I said
before, this sort of necessity has nothing to do with personal standards in
individual cases, and does not mean that the policemen in question are any

more "brutal" toward men or women or children—than anybody else. You'll have to admit that you only hurt any case which you may have, when you imply that I approve of the massacre of women and children (or of men, for that matter)—as you do in connexion with the procedure of Gen. Santa Ana. As I have said dozens of times before, I don't approve of *any* massacres . . . . of any persons of any age or of either sex. What I approve of is simply *the enforcement of order* . . . . with as little damage to anybody as is consistent with the attainment of the given object. To argue, from this attitude on my part, that I approve of the deliberate maltreatment of women and children (or of men), and that I have a contempt for any conqueror who abstains from such maltreatment, is simply to abandon reason and true argument altogether and to take flight into the realm of sheer fantasy. Another definitely false comparison is that implied in your assumption that I belittle acts of daring or sacrifice when the defence of women and children is concerned. Here again there is no relationship between the attitude assumed and any belief of mine. I said that the elaborate forms and ideology of chivalry are artificial growths—which they undoubtedly are. But this did not imply (a) that all acts in defence of the weak are parts of artificial chivalry, or (b) that even the more moderate acts and attitudes of artificial chivalry are without a definite aesthetic and potential social value. On the other hand, I tried to make it clear that acts of courtesy and forbearance in accordance with the traditional code are to be encouraged whenever they do not conflict with the general welfare. That is, a sacrifice in defence of a woman or child is an undeniably beautiful and admirable thing when only the personal fortunes of the sacrificer are at stake. The time when the aesthetic rules break down is *when the sacrifice entails harm to the whole community*. It is noble to die as an individual in defence of one's grandmother . . . . but it not only is not noble but actually criminal to imperil the public safety by leaving a dangerous mob unchecked merely because a few brawny viragoes chance to be in it. To argue that this attitude implies an endorsement of Ben Butler, or some similar needless affronter of women, is simply to disregard the facts.[1] Incidentally, a close examination of the habits of your favourite barbarians in treating the feminine population of conquered towns would not bear out your contention that only civilised men are ungallant. What any orderly policeman has ever done to a fighting communist wench is mild as compared with what the Goths, Gauls, Vikings, and other "noble savages" did to the helpless women of their beaten foes. Chivalry and barbarism don't agree!

I enjoyed tremendously your observations on the differences between East and West Texas—many of which confirmed what I had already thought. The amount of variety within the state is impressive in the highest degree—and suggestive of the region's self-sufficient and almost imperial status. Every division of the U.S. seems to be represented somewhere and in some way.

Your remarks are a virtual treatise, and I wish they could achieve the permanence of print.

The Mexican War question certainly is a peculiar and interesting one; and today I doubt if cautious commentators are quick to formulate any dogmatic opinions on it, one way or the other. It is so much a part of the larger movement or drift whereby the restless Nordic has overspread the earth and crushed the various other races standing in his way, that one finds difficulty in regarding it separately. The same thing always happens, whatever the especial explanation in any one case—or at least, it *has* happened up to the present time. Today—after centuries of expansion—the Nordic seems to have paused and begun to consider a sort of stabilisation . . . a stabilisation involving the abandonment of insecure outposts. Hence the coming relinquishment of the Philippines, and the diminishing protectorate over Cuba, Santo Domingo, Nicaragua, etc. But in 1846 the onward pressure was in full operation. At the time, however, it is certainly doubtful whether many of the individual Texas or California colonists had the idea of wrenching the southwest away from Mexico. In examining the records of the age we find all sorts of differing plans and ideals concerning the region beyond Louisiana—from the Burr dreams of empire downward.[2] Nothing like an unified and deliberate plan can be said to have existed, and the whole problem was mixed up with the struggle to maintain a balance of slave and free territory. From all I have seen, I think you are right in believing that the *typical* American settler in Spanish-Mexican territory meant to abide by the existing government. Thanks enormously, by the way, for your generous quotations from the Texas Declaration of Independence—a document I have never read, and which certainly sheds a vast amount of light on the conditions and difficulties of the period. There is, of course, no doubt—even in the popular mind—of the oppressiveness of the Mexican Government. The only debated question has been the justification of the measures employed in meeting that oppressiveness—and even here there has been no real unanimity of opinion against the revolting Texas in any part of the country. If a Rhode Island paper like the *Woonsocket Patriot* took the anti-revolutionist side, it must be remembered that a Rhode Islander (about whose monument in Providence's North Burial Ground I wrote you some years ago) was among the defenders of the Alamo. Much of the sentiment of the time was, of course, based on sheer misinformation or lack of information—as public sentiment on all questions in all ages invariably is. Today the Mexican War is only a dim legend in the East, about which it is difficult to stir up much intense feeling one way or the other. If any element now harbours a strong pro-Mexican attitude, it is not the descendants of the abolitionists but the foreign radical stratum which finds something reprehensible in any "imperialistic" advance of a strong nation at the expense of a small one.

Your account of James W. Parker—and other bits of history connected with his time and place—is of the keenest interest and vividness, and really ought to go into a book on the southwest, together with other historic reminiscences of yours. If ever you decide to compile such a volume, I'll be glad to lend you the various letters in which you have given material of the kind. I have heard—in a vague way—of the half-white chieftain Quanah; but your letter makes him a much more definite figure. The struggles of Parker and his family surely form an epic—and deserve to be better known than they are. Equally striking is the episode of the boy whose name you do not recall. On mature reflection, I am sure you will realise that the protective heroism of figures like these is *not* belittled by anyone—even by those who recognise the artificial origin of certain extreme attitudes, and who deplore the sacrifice of *public safety and order* (*not* of the *private* security of some *individual*) on behalf of considerations which, *although perfectly valid in relation to private individual ethics,* as many wholly or partly decorative or aesthetic considerations are, cannot be regarded as ultimate cosmic verities *where the safety and integrity of the entire social fabric are concerned.* This distinction ought to be too clear to escape anyone, even when emotion and prejudice play their part. One point in your historical material was wholly new and highly interesting to me—i.e., that the Comanches were themselves invaders in the regions where Americans encountered them. This illustrates one thing which I have always thought in connexion with the oft-repeated censure of the white man's treatment of the Indian. It is true that our ancestors ruthlessly pushed the redskin aside—but after all this is no more than one tribe had always been doing to another. If the English brutally displaced the Iroquois in New York State, so must the Iroquois themselves have displaced the earlier Algonquin tribes when they occupied the region. And so on . . . and so on. . . . Of course, the greater strength and superior weapons of the white man made his case a good deal different—but the general idea is not to be forgotten.

I'm interested by the news of the feline population, and wish I could see some of the furry specimens enumerated. Too bad Mubsy is so self-sacrificing on the food question! In its present well-fed shape, the family must be a delight to see—and I hope the kittens' eyes will soon respond to the boric acid treatment. The way the various mothers pool their kittens is surely picturesque. The stray kitten must be quite a fellow if he can catch milk squirted directly from the cow! Greedy is surely an active young Casanova!

Your cows are likewise an interesting lot—and the touch of Hindoo ancestry adds picturesque atmosphere. Sorry the calf didn't turn out to be a heifer—but better luck may occur next time. That vicious Jersey surely was a termagant, and your fight with her might have been an even more serious matter than it was. Glad you traded her off—I fancy she'll be more useful as beef than as a milk factory!

Glad you liked "Out of the Aeons"—which gives von Junzt's Black Book a bit more publicity. Your recent two-part story was splendidly vivid[3]—in fact, all your recent work has dominated the issues of W T in which it has appeared. No question but that you and Clark Ashton Smith are the twin pillars of the institution. I've written nothing since "The Shadow Out of Time", and am still uncertain about that. Wright's non-receptive attitude does not encourage composition on my part. Glad you're finding new markets for adventure material—though it would be a tragedy indeed if no more of your fantastic tales were to appear!

I was certainly sorry when that supreme court verdict wrecked so much constructive governmental work—and can grimly appreciate the irony inherent in this punctilious legalism on the part of predatory, anti-social interests which have long flouted the constitutional spirit and even letter. It certainly is an age of paradox, but I hope some peaceful way out will be found. Since starting on my trip I haven't kept systematic track of the news, though I see headlines now and then. To my mind, the new tax and industrial programme of the administration looks very good—though I fear it will have a hard time getting past the watchdogs of capital in congress and the courts.

Your description of ice-cream gorges fills me with envy. With the de luxe product to which you are now getting accustomed, you will soon be spoiled for all ordinary frozen refreshments!

As for events in the East—spring was badly delayed in Rhode Island despite a brief preliminary flash in early March. During that flash I had an interesting visitor—Robert Moe, son of an old friend in Milwaukee. This youth graduated from U. of Wis. in 1933 at the age of 20, and is now an electrical engineer with the Gen. Elec. Co., stationed in Bridgeport, Conn. He came to see me in his car, and we explored a number of the quaint colonial seaports down both sides of Narragansett Bay. His second visit—on April 27–8—was still more interesting because of the wider range of exploration. The visitor arrived Saturday morning—the 27th—and we certainly put in a full 2 days. Saturday we visited old Newport—seeing 2 ancient windmills; a flock of sheep with sportive lambkins in the best pastoral tradition; "Whitehall", the 1729–31 home of Dean (later Bishop) Berkeley (author of "Westward the course of Empire takes its way");[4] the Hanging Rocks, where that good cleric composed his well-known "Alciphron; or, the Minute Philosopher"; the lofty cliffs; the strange rock cleft called "Purgatory", where the sea pounds thunderously in; the Overing farmhouse where a small rowboat party of rebels under Col. Wm. Barton captured Genl. Prescott of the regulars in 1777; and the venerable town itself—with 1698 Quaker meeting-house, 1726 Anglican church, 1739 colony-house, 1749 library, 1760 market-house, 1763 Jews' synagogue, and private dwellings as old as 1675. It was a glorious hot day—up to 82° in Providence, though not quite so good in Newport.

Sunday the 28th we went to ancient New Bedford—Nantucket's successor as the world's great whaling centre, whose last lone exemplar of the industry put to sea only 11 or 12 years ago. The marine museum was closed—but
after a tour of the centuried waterfront we set off southward to sample something still better. This was the Round Hills estate of Col. E. H. R. Green (son
of the old female financier and miser Hetty Green) in S. Dartmouth, where the
old whaling barque *Charles W. Morgan* (built 1841) is preserved at a realistic-
looking wharf—but soldily embedded in concrete as a permanent exhibit. We
went all over the vessel—which is tremendously interesting—and snapped
some pictures of it. On the Green estate is also an ancient windmill moved
from Rhode Island. We then explored a region—where southern Mass. ad-
joins southeastern R.I.—which I had never seen before in my life. Splendid
unspoiled countryside with rambling stone walls and idyllic white-steepled
villages of the old New England type. Of the latter the two best specimens—
Adamsville and Little Compton Commons—are both in Rhode Island.
Adamsville contains the world's only known monument to a *hen*—
perpetuating the fame of the Rhode Island Red, a breed developed in that village from East Indian and Chinese gallinaceous forbears. At Little Compton
Commons can be found the home and grave of Elizabeth Alden Pabodie—
daughter of the famed John Alden and Priscilla Mullins of Plymouth, and first
white woman born in New England. This region was once the seat of the Sa-
konnet Indians—whose squaw-sachem Awashonks was persuaded by the
noted old warrior Capt. Benjamin Church not to join King Philip's conspiracy
in 1675. It was settled from Plymouth about 1673, and (like Barrington, Warren, and Bristol) came into Massachusetts in 1691, and into Rhode Island
(when a boundary dispute was settled by George II) in 1747. Capt. Church lies
buried not far from Little Compton Commons. Well—at least we turned
north through Tiverton, where on our left we had some marvellous vistas of
low-lying fields and blue waters. Here we passed the house of the navigator
Capt. Robert Gray, who in 1792 discovered the Columbia River in the far-off
Oregon Country—naming it after his stout Rhode Island barque. Then back
home via Fall River (an ugly mill city across the line in Mass.) and ancient Warren . . . at which latter place we paused at the famous Maxfield's (an ice-cream
establishment which you and Pink Tyson would appreciate—and a rendezvous
of Morton, Cook, Wandrei, and other visitors of mine) for a dinner consisting
entirely of ice cream—a pint and a half each (6 varieties: Moe—chocolate,
coffee, banana, caramel, ginger, pistachio. HPL—chocolate, coffee, banana,
caramel, lemon, strawberry). Finally back to #66—after which I regretfully
guided the guest out of town and took a 4-mile rural and suburban walk before returning home. All in all, quite a session!

On May 3–4–5 I visited my friend Edward H. Cole in the Boston zone,
but cold weather seriously hampered our sightseeing. We covered ancient Marblehead, however—which is attractive under any conceivable set of conditions!

On May 25 I had an interesting visit from young Charles D. Hornig, erstwhile publisher of the *Fantasy Fan* and managing editor of *Wonder Stories*. He is a very pleasant and intelligent youth—reminding one slightly of Donald Wandrei, though with a vaguely quasi-Semitic turn of features. He seemed to appreciate quite keenly the archaic charm of venerable Providence—which is in some respects not unlike his own town of Elizabeth, N.J. I showed him most of the historic high spots, including the hidden churchyard on the ancient hill which I have probably described to you at one time or another. Young Kenneth Sterling (a science-fiction fan who was in Providence from March to June) was also on hand most of the time, making quite a convention of the event. The weather was providentially warm and sunny. I like Hornig very much—and certainly admire the competence which enables him to serve as editor of a full-fledged magazine at the age of 18. He is a very mature, assured sort of person—I'd take him for 22 or 23 at first sight.

Speaking of Providence antiquities—I've lately learned with sorrow that *another* row of ancient buildings in my vicinity is about to feel the vandal's hand. You probably recall my rage at the destruction of the S. Water St. warehouses (1816) in 1929–30. This time the scene of destruction is College St. itself—the doomed row being that huddle of quaint houses and archways reaching from Benefit st. downward to the foot of the hill—on the same (N.) side as the court leading to #66, but beginning 3/4 of a block lower down. Included in the cataclysm are the house of the first president of Brown University (1771), a fine old 1750 specimen, and one of those rare old archways leading under parts of a building to inner courtyards—of which the only perfect specimens in America are those on Providence's ancient hill. (There is a bricked-up specimen in Richmond, and a boarded-up specimen in Philadelphia.) On this site will ascend the new main building of R.I. School of Design. Two palliating and consoling features exist: (a) the preservation, restoration, and incorporation into the new building of the bottom (and only brick) house of the ancient row—the old Franklin Inn, with its quaint inn-yard archway. Thus the survival of *one* of the archways is assured. And (b) the choice of a splendid Providence-Georgian design for the new edifice. The structure's lower units will harmonise with the surviving Franklin Inn, while the upper units will blend in pattern with the residential buildings higher up on the hill. One part will even have a "monitor roof" like #66—

a form especially typical of Providence in the 1790–1820 period. The change is regrettable, yet it is fortunate that the character of the new building will be sthe smae. Obviously, Providence is remaining dominantly true to its traditional Georgian heritage, and avoiding the 'modernistic' epidemic from which even Boston is not quite immune.

Well—as my Charleston bulletin apprised you—the southern trip *did* materialise despite all misgivings. Barlow got home June 3d, and I started on Wednesday the 5th. As I guess I told you, I cut out N.Y. and Washington and made my first stop in ancient Fredericksburg—then straight down to my beloved *Charleston*. The moment I struck the steady heat of the Carolina low country I became stronger and more active—indeed, this southern trip has caused me to feel really *well* and comfortable for the first time in 1935. My sleep actually *rests* me as it never does in the north. Sooner or later I'll have to move down here permanently. Had 2 days in Charleston, then down to De Land via Savannah and Jacksonville. I'm now repeating my visit of 1934 with minor variations. The Johnstons have both moved to the cabin up the road ("Dunover") and Bob's father—Lt. Col. E. D. Barlow, retired—is at home. Bob's elder brother Wayne—a 2nd Lt. from Ft. Sam Houston near San Antonio in your own state—has been here on a furlough and has formed a delightful companion, but recently his leave expired and he left for the west. As for the felidae—Doodlebug (the snow-white patriarch) vanished last autumn, but there are rumours of his being alive and roaming the neighbouring jungle in a wild state. High has seceded from the Barlow fold and joined the Johnstons at Dunover, but is still as friendly as ever. Low has been given away—while Jack, his neck still a trifle stiff from his snake-bite experience of last year, is the dean of the outdoor cats. Henry Clay and Alfred A. Knopf (yellow and gray spotted, respectively) are kittens of Low's, and permanent additions to the extra-mural menage. Within the house are two lordly and pedigreed Persians brought down from Washington by Bob. Of these one—Cyrus—is extremely playful and affectionate, while the other—Darius—is as yet haughty and aloof, though he exhibits subtle signs of mellowing. Cyrus and Darius are yellow in hue, and look precisely alike. They are full brothers.

As for general doings—we read, write letters, classify books, set type in sundry printing projects, explore the country, do revisory work when necessary, and in general follow the programme of last year's visit. Bob has built a cabin across the lake (I helped him), to which—for the sake of seclusion—he transferred his press, desk, and various accessories as soon as it was ready for occupancy. Last week—the colonel's birthday—we all visited Daytona (35 or so miles away on the coast), and the family indulged in sea bathing. Daytona is a rather well-known winter resort. On June 17 we visited a fascinating place—Black Water Creek, a tropical river whose lush scenery suggests the Congo, Amazon, and other exotic streams famed in history and legend. It winds through a steaming jungle of tall, moss-draped cypresses, whose grotesque, twisted roots writhe curiously at the water's edge. Palms lean precariously over the brink, and vines and creepers strew the black, dank earth of the bordering forest aisles. Sinister sunken logs loom up at various points, and in the forest pallid flowers and leprous fungi gleam whitely through a perpetual twilight. It is much like the river at Silver Springs of which I wrote you last year—though I enjoyed it even more because of the more leisurely observing conditions. At Silver Springs I was whizzed ahead in a launch; this time we (Bob, Wayne and I) went along slowly in a rowboat. Each bend of the tortuous stream brought to light some unexpected vista of tropical luxuriance, and we absorbed the spectacle to the full. Snakes and alligators were somewhat in evidence—though none came near our boat. I hope for more trips of this kind, since I am especially sensitive to the beauty of subtropical scenery. Doubtless all this sort of thing is more or less familiar to you through your acquaintance with the rivers, swamps, and bayous of East Texas and Louisiana—but to a northerner it is a fascinating revelation. As for the duration of the present visit—I don't know what it will be. The super-hospitable Barlows won't hear of the setting of a departure date . . . though I surely must break away sooner or later.

. . . . . I remain Yrs most truly
H P L

Notes

1. On 15 May 1862, Maj. Gen. Ben Butler issued General Orders No. 28 to stop the women of New Orleans from harrassing his men, declaring that "when any female shall, by word, gesture, or movement, insult or show contempt for any officer or soldier of the United States, she shall be regarded and held liable to be treated as a woman of the town plying her avocation."
2. Aaron Burr (1756–1836), vice president during Thomas Jefferson's first term (1801–05), planned an invasion of Mexico in order to establish an independent government there. This action, never carried out, led to his trial for treason; he was acquitted.
3. "Beyond the Black River."
4. The line appears in "On the Prospect of Planting Arts and Learning in America" (1752), l. 21, by George Berkeley (1685–1753).

[116]   [nonextant postcards from HPL]

[117]   [TLS]

[c. July 1935][1]

Dear HPL:

Thanks very much for the fine postcard views from your trip. I'm glad you are having such an enjoyable sojourn. Glad, too, that the views I sent from New Mexico proved of interest.

Regarding the question of chivalry, I am sorry if I misunderstood your attitude. When I have used this term it has been simply to indicate the ordinary consideration that the weak (of whatever age or sex) are accorded by the stronger; I was not referring to the fantastic and exaggerated customs and

862   ❋   *A Means to Freedom*

habits of the so-called Age of Chivalry. It is to the unnecessary violation of this principle that I object. You say I use the term "sadism" only metaphorically. I certainly did not. I used it as the only term fit to describe the action of four policemen manhandling a woman whose only offense, even according to their own statement, was that she applied an uncomplimentary term to one of them when he pushed her. You say that in referring to this matter I "speak of something which did not (so far as you knew) figure in the discussion." Then your memory is certainly at fault. This whole discussion was precipitated by my sending you a clipping from a newspaper describing the beating of a woman in a New York police court. (Before you accuse me of taking the word of some radical paper, let me assure you that the clipping was from a definitely capitalistic press.) This clipping I can not produce for the simple reason that, if it has not been destroyed, it is at present in your possession. There is nothing in the description about the Armed Amazons, Venomous Viragoes, and Furious Females you have discussed so vividly. There is no mention of any armed resistance; no mention of any danger to the General Public; even the cops who did the beating only said the woman spoke insultingly to one of them. My contention was that—according to the data supplied by the article which was all either of us had to go by—their action was unnecessary, brutal, sadistic, and degenerate in its nature. You seemed to be trying to defend and justify it, and this, together with your repeated sneers at what you called artificial and decorative chivalry, naturally led me to the assumption that you despised what you seemed to be attacking. You say I'll "have to admit that" I am "hurting any case" I "may have when" I imply that you possess a callous disregard for the ordinary rules of conduct by the strong toward the weak. I don't see how you figure that. When a man seems to attack a certain principle, and sneers at me for defending that principle, I can only conclude that he despises that principle. Of course, it is quite possible for me to misunderstand someone's position. It is evident that in this case I have misunderstood yours. If I have attributed to you a cynical callousness which you do not in reality possess, then I am sorry.

As for your evidently bitter resentment over this matter, I can not see that it is justified, considering the position you have always taken—that I had no right or reason to resent anything you said, because you were motivated solely by a desire to establish Truth. Well, that works as good one way as it does the other. My devotion to truth is as rigid as yours, and there is no more of the personal in my arguments than there is in yours. You say for me to attribute to you a disregard of the common principles of chivalry is "to take flight into the realm of sheer fantasy". Well, for sweep and altitude it doesn't exceed some of your soarings—as the one in which, for instance, you accused me of being "an enemy to humanity"! Your irritation is understandable, but a bit inconsistent. Doubtless I was exasperatingly blunt in attributing to you an attitude I supposed you possessed; but certainly no blunter than you have been in attributing to me attitudes and characteristics you thought I possessed. You have never hesitated to attribute my failure to agree with you on any point to some mental or moral defect on my part. Recalling off-hand the charges you have made against me, I remember that at various times you have accused me of being: Exalter-of-the-Physical-Above-the-Mental; Enemy of Humanity; Foe of Mankind; Apostle of Prejudice; Distorter of Fact; Repudiater of Evolutionary Standards; Over-Emphasizer of Ethics; Sympathizer of Criminals (that one broke all altitude records); Egotist; Poseur; Emotionalist; Defender of Ignorance; Sentimentalist; Romanticist. If I were guilty of all the things of which you've accused me, I not only wouldn't be fit to live; I wouldn't have sense enough to live. But that's all right. I never asked any man to pull his punches in any kind of a contest. If you want to hit hard, you're entitled to. But I naturally supposed you conceded to others the same privileges you assumed for yourself. If my bluntness in attributing to you characteristics I thought you possessed has offended you, I'm sorry; but if you're determined to use brass knuckles in a debate you certainly can't expect your opponent to use feather pillows.

As for your remark about my "contention that only civilized men are ungallant"; that's scarcely accurate. I have never attributed any undue chivalry to the Goths, Huns or any other tribe of barbarians. I am quite aware that the Goths butchered, raped, and plundered without regard for the age or sex of their victims; they did not, however, claim that their raping, butchering and plundering was in defense of art, progress and civilization. Therein they differed from modern "civilized" men. I will not bother to deny the implication in the use of the term "noble savage". You know very well that I have never used that term in reference to any race.

But any discussion about Goths etc., in this connection is beside the point. I have not referred to them in my remarks on chivalry, and I see no reason why they should be lugged in by the ears. It is strange how my defense of them and my criticism of the Romans, in past debates, still rankles. My preference for my Nordic ancestors over your Roman friends is apparently the unforgivable blasphemy, and your evident resentment over this matter enters into practically every debate we have, coloring—and in some cases distorting—your attitude toward every preference I express, and every opinion I offer. Memory of my heresy is mingled in every attack you make on me and my ideas.

Glad you liked my remarks on the various sections of Texas; but I fear they were inadequate and sketchy. As for the Texas revolution, there is no need to let the issue be confused by ambitions of various individuals East of the Mississippi. As far as the relationship between the Texans and Mexico was concerned, the matter was clear-cut; revolution was the only solution, unless the people wished to abandon their homes and all they had worked for and built up, and flee as naked paupers back into the United States—as aliens, for remember they had exchanged their American citizenship for Mexican citizenship. Whatever was the plan or plot of statesmen of the United States, the case of the Texan colonists is clear, open and admits of no argument. They came to Texas at the invitation of the Mexican government who wanted the revenue that would result from the development of the resources of the domain—a development never accomplished by the Mexican settlers of the region—and the Mexican government also desired a strong buffer between the purely Mexican settlements and the Comanches. The inability of both the Spaniards and the Mexicans to successfully oppose the Indian tribes of the north has never been given the recognition it deserves as a factor in the development of the Southwest. First the Lipans and the Apaches, and after them the Kiowas and Comanches repeatedly destroyed the outposts of Latin American civilization and drove back the tide of settlement. The Comanches were justified in their contempt of the Spaniards and Mexicans. The average Comanche warrior was braver, stronger physically, more honorable, quicker-witted, and more intelligent than the average Mexican peon. I have heard Mexicans referred to as savages; they are not even that; they are products of two decadent and rotten civilizations—the degenerate Aztec, and the degenerate Spanish. White people came to Texas, mostly from the Old South and from New England. They formed a rampart against the northern savages, from the Sabine River to San Antonio; a rampart that was never broken. They developed the agricultural potentialities of the region; they complied with all requirements made by the Mexican government. All they ever asked was that that government fulfill its own obligations. This was not done. When Hayden Edwards[2] raised the flag of revolt in Nacogdoches, and declared the Fredonian Republic, the Anglo-Saxon settlers in the other colonies were the first to march against him and drive him into Louisiana. Oppression had not at that time begun, and they knew he was revolting mainly in order to try and elevate his personal fortunes. This the colonists would not stand for; it was only when the outlaw regime of the usurper and adventurer Santa Ana began to apply intolerable oppression to the whole region, that the revolt ensued—and force of arms was used only after every peaceable means had failed. You say that there has been some debate over whether the means ultimately resorted to were justified. They were not only justified, they were inevitable, and presented the only possible solution. Santa Ana had not only violated everything his government had promised, but was marching with a large army to butcher every white man in the State, not because they had attacked him, but because they had tried to persuade him to keep the promises his own government had made voluntarily.

Glad you found my account of the experiences of the Fort Parker colony of some interest. You err, however, in considering James Parker's actions as merely an isolated display of individual ethics, unrelated to the main flow of life. You say that his efforts to save the colony were not only permissible, but admirable because they did not incur any sacrifice of public safety. Great heavens, man, don't you realize that his efforts *were in the interests of public safety?* There was, fundamentally, no real difference between his efforts, and the heroism of a policeman who breaks up a mob. Both risk their own life in the interests of the group. There was much more to James Parker's sacrifices and struggles than merely personal heroism, or "private individual ethics". The whole fabric of frontier life depended on such sacrifices. Just as the peace, safety and security of modern life depends on the readiness of the police to enforce law and order, so the whole frame-work of frontier life depended on the willingness of men like Jim Parker to sacrifice their own ease, and if necessary their lives in the interests of the public safety. In the absence of any organized force to ensure safety (like the modern police) the security of frontier society depended on the courage and decisive actions of its stronger members—like James Parker. This consideration was far wider and deeper than its "relationship to private individual ethics". When James Parker saved the remnants of the colony, he was doing something of far greater significance then merely displaying his own heroism or upholding his own personal ethics. He was playing his part in upholding the foundations and the fabric of the society in which he lived, just as the policeman who helps break up a threatening mob is doing. His heroism was merely another thread in the billions of similar threads that went to make up the warp and the woof of frontier life.

Glad to hear you've had so many interesting visitors. But sorry to learn of the planned destruction of the old houses you spoke of. I can imagine your feelings in the matter.

Yes, my trip to Santa Fe proved satisfying, though less extensive than I had planned. Vinson and I left Cross Plains early the morning of the 19th, June, and followed the Bankhead Highway[3] westward to the Pecos, along the same route we took last summer. As then, we turned north as soon as we crossed the river (at the town of Pecos) and headed in the direction of the town of Carlsbad. Detours owing to highway construction delayed us considerably. They have some damnable roads in New Mexico, once you get off the highways. We didn't stop at Carlsbad, but went on north and spent the night at Roswell, having travelled well over five hundred miles that day. Roswell is a neat, spotlessly modern town, with the usual streams of tourists pouring through continually. The fellow who ran the camp where we spent the night had a Texan accent and said he was from Dallas; but he sounded more like a Grand Prairie man to me. I had a brief conversation with a young fellow from Illinois who was taking a party to the West Coast, by way of Grand Canyon. An outing I envied him. He was a fine, athletic-built blond, with a pleasant manner and cultured voice, but he didn't look particularly rugged. The next morning after breakfast (I drank my wine at a cafe where I saw the most robust waitress I ever saw in my life; her arms were tattooed and bigger and more muscular than mine; I bet she could have licked my athletic blond friend without half trying; she must have been a strong woman in a circus

once) we headed west through the mountains, aiming to hit the El Paso-Santa
Fe highway at San Antonio, about 160 miles west of Roswell. Part of the way
the roads were paved, part of the way they were fair, and part of the way they
were plain hell. That is a hard, bare, sun-scorched country, with narrow
threads of green where streams wander along the canyons.

I'll never forget the long sweep of the road drooping down into Hondo
Valley, looping down and down for I don't know how many hundreds of
feet, with me holding the car in second gear because depending on brakes on
such a road would be ridiculous. The Hondo Valley is like a serpent's track—
long and winding, walled with gigantic bare mountains, with the Hondo River
rippling along its bed, and supplying water for the farmers whose adobe huts
line its banks. Cottonwoods, apple-orchards, alfalfa fields and the like crowd
densely, greedily clutching at every bit of soil the life-giving water can reach.
The verdant green offers a strange contrast to the grim and savage bareness
of the hills that rise on either hand. Semi-tropical luxuriance gives way
abruptly to gaunt nakedness.

We turned off from the Hondo Valley to follow up the Bonito Valley.
And so in the still laziness of a Mexican mid-morning we came to the ancient
village of Lincoln, dreaming amidst its gaunt mountains like the ghost of a
blood-stained past. Of Lincoln Walter Noble Burns, author of "The Saga of
Billy the Kid" has said: "The village went to sleep at the close of the Lincoln
County war and has never awakened again. If a railroad never comes to link it
with the far-away world, it may slumber on for a thousand years. You will
find Lincoln now just as it was when Murphy and McSween and Billy the Kid
knew it. The village is an anachronism; a sort of mummy town . . . . . ."[4]

I can offer no better description. A mummy town. Nowhere have I ever
come face to face with the past more vividly; nowhere has that past become
so realistic, so understandable. It was like stepping out of my own age, into
the fragment of an elder age, that had somehow survived. In Lincoln I felt
the Past, not as dusty, meaningless names, and the outworn repetition of
moldy heroisms, but as a living, breathing reality; it was as if a mythical giant,
thought dead and forgotten, had suddenly reared his awesome head and titan
shoulders above the surrounding mountains and looked at us with living eyes.

Lincoln is a haunted place; it is a dead town; yet it lives with a life that
died fifty years ago.

It stands on a lap of land jutting from the base of the mountains that
form the right wall of the Bonito Valley. To the left the Rio Bonito ripples
along the canyon floor. The ground slopes down from the site of the town, to
the river bed. Down that slope Billy the Kid dropped, with his guns blazing
death, on that red summer night in 1878, when the flames of McSween's
burning house shone crimson on the bodies of its owner and his friends
where they had fallen before the bullet-raked door.

The houses, adobe mostly, straggle on either side of the long, crooked street. Our entrance into the town was peculiarly undramatic. Straggling clumps of trees hid it from our view until we had entered the eastern end of the street. We drove on, slowly, past the reconstructed torreon—the ancient round tower where the early settlers fought off the Apaches—past the old Montana House dance hall—adorned by a sign which stated that "Billy the Kid Cut His Initials On This House"—past the garage which is Lincoln's one reflection of modernity—past the stores where descendants of the Kid's friends and enemies lounged in the growing heat of the day—past the tavern which stands where the McSween house stood—we were both looking for one thing—the old courthouse whence Billy made the most dramatic escape ever made in the Southwest. We rounded a crook in the meandering street and it burst upon us like the impact of a physical blow. There was no mistaking it. We did not—at least I did not—need the sight of the sign upon it to identify it. I had seen its picture—how many times I do not know. I do not know how many times, and in what myriad different ways and occasions I have heard the tale of Billy's escape. It is the most often repeated, the most dramatic of all the tales of Southwestern folk-lore. When you hear a story long enough and often enough, it becomes like a legend. Yet I will not say that the sight of that old house was like meeting a legend face to face; there was nothing fabulous or legendary about the actuality. The realism was too potent, too indisputable to admit any feeling of mythology. If the Kid himself had stepped out of that old house, it would not have surprised me at all.

We explored the exterior, found it locked, and went across the street to the La Paloma saloon which bears a sign that claims existence in the Kid's day. The owner is one Ramon Maes, grandson of Lucio Montoya, "Murphy's sharpshooter" as he told us with pride—a supple, well-built man, tall for a Mexican and broad-shouldered, with a thin-nostrilled Mountain Indian look about his face. The name of Montoya is woven into the Kid's saga. He took part in the three-day fight in which McSween was killed; he lay on the mountain that commanded the Montana House, with Crawford, firing from behind a boulder. Fernando Herrera, firing from the Montana House with a buffalo gun, killed Crawford, and broke Montoya's leg. The range was nine hundred yards, but Herrera was a crack shot. All day Montoya lay in the glare of the sun, with his splintered leg, until, when night fell, his friends dared a sortie to get him. I did not speak of this to his grandson. To him the feud seemed like something that happened yesterday. He was very courteous and eager to point out interesting spots, and answer our questions, but when he spoke of the fighting and the killing, a red flame came into his eyes. The descendants of old enemies live peacefully side by side in the little village; yet I found myself wondering if the old feud were really dead, or if the embers only smoldered, and might be blown to flame by a careless breath. Maes gave us the key to the old courthouse, which once was Murphy's store. It is used as a storeplace for junk now, and there is talk, we were told, of tearing it down to build a community hall. It should be preserved. When it is torn down one of the landmarks of Southwestern history will be gone. We wandered about the old building, entered the room where the Kid was confined—they knew no jail would hold him, so they kept him imprisoned in the courthouse itself. Strange how familiar everything seemed to me, though I had never been within one hundred miles of Lincoln before. Yet it seemed to me that I was going over territory traversed a hundred times before. We tried to re-create the situation that April morning in 1881 when the Kid, tricking his captor, J. Bell, off-guard by a game of monte, snatched his pistol and fought his way to liberty. We followed the route through the rooms and hallway by which Billy marched his prisoner, intending to lock him into the armory. We saw the stair where Bell made his desperate break, and the hole in the wall at the foot where the Kid's bullet had lodged, after tearing its way through Bell's heart. Bell was a Texas man, by the way—Dallas County. We stood at the window from which the Kid watched Bob Ollinger run across the street at the sound of the shot; the same window from which he poured eighteen buckshot into Ollinger's breast from the man's own shotgun. Then we went out onto the balcony from which Billy hurled the fragments of the gun with a curse at the corpse of his victim—and I could close my eyes and imagine that scene, the livid, snarling, flame-eyed figure of the killer, tense with the hate that then broke its bounds of iron control for the first and only time in his whole life— the crumpled corpse sprawled in the dust at the corner of the house, the stiffening fingers spread like claws and digging into the earth with their last convulsion—the men on the porch of the saloon and of the hotel, standing frozen, silent and motionless as statues, like spectators watching a play. Something, too, like men watching a blood-mad tiger and fearful to draw a deep breath lest the dripping fangs and talons strike in their direction. Presently, glancing away along the dusty road, it would not have seemed at all strange had we seen a lithe, pantherish figure on a mustang, in the garb of other days, with fetters still on his ankles and a rifle in each hand, riding westward toward Bacca Canyon—so close-linked in Lincoln seem Yesterday and Today.

From the old courthouse we went to the inn, which stands on the site of the old McSween house. There everything is changed. I could not recreate in my mind the climax of that three-day battle. The only thing that is as it was then is the slope of the land from the edge of the yard down to the river— and on that slope the thickets which sheltered the Kid as he ran are gone. But we learned that the bodies of McSween and most of his companions lie close to where they fell; behind a stable now, unmarked, trampled over by burros and cattle.

From the inn we went back down the street and explored the reconstructed torreon—and encountered my Illinois blond friend who was encountering snags on his trek to the Coast. His car had broken down in the edge of the town, and we gave him all the help we were able to, which consisted in pushing him to the one garage in the town. He was a very pleasant and courteous young man, but seemed nonplused and a bit bewildered at my remarks, which I first attributed to his unfamiliarity with my Texas accent, but presently decided it was my habit of profanity to which he was not accustomed. Hell, it's an unconscious process with me. I've cursed like a sailor ever since I was big enough to talk at all. I asked him if he'd ever heard of the Bloody Lincoln County War, and he said he had not. It looks to me like people—educated people at least—would try to learn something about the countries they intend traversing on their vacations.

I have never felt anywhere the exact sensations Lincoln aroused in me—a sort of horror predominating. If there is a haunted spot on this hemisphere, then Lincoln is haunted. I felt that if I slept the night there, the ghosts of the slain would stalk through my dreams. The town itself seemed like a bleached, grinning skull. There was a feel of skeletons in the earth underfoot. And that, I understand, is no flight of fancy. Every now and then somebody ploughs up a human skull. So many men died in Lincoln. Stand with me a moment on the balcony of the old courthouse. Yonder, to the east, stands the old tower about which, in the past, waves of painted braves washed like a red tide. Their bodies littered the earth like bright-colored leaves when that tide broke. Not once but many times. Yonder in the dusty street men fell when the Horrels rode from Ruidoso one night—Texas men, with a ruthless hate for all Latins impelling them—there, before that squat-built store, Constable Martinez died beneath their bullets, and with him his deputies Gillam and Warner. There, too, fell Bill Horrel. And in that adobe house that was a dance hall then, guns blazed when the Horrels came again, the death of their brother rankling, to stretch four men and a woman dead on the floor. That was before the Kid's time. Come down the years a little. Behind us stands the stair at the foot of which Bell tumbled, with the Kid's bullet through his heart. There at the corner of the house Bob Ollinger fell, with his breast mangled. Yonder, to the east, you can see among the shade trees, the roof of the building which stands where the McSween store stood. A few feet beyond that point Sheriff Brady and his deputy Hindman were struck down by the bullets that rained upon them from the ambush the Kid and his warriors had planned. Brady fell dead there, but when the Kid took his guns from his body, he put another bullet through his head just to make sure. Hindman, shot in the back, lay in the street for half an hour, moaning for water. None dared fetch it to him. It might be construed by the killers as an act of hostility. Peaceable people kept within their doors, clenching their teeth against the agony-edged groans of the dying man. At last Port Stockton, himself a desperado, tending bar at the time, unbuckled his gun-belt and laid his weapons on the bar, filled his sombrero with water and stalked forth, his jaw set stubbornly. The skin must have crawled between his shoulders as he felt the eyes of Billy the Kid on him, opaque, passionless eyes, faintly questioning, weighing his action without emotion, without mercy. Stockton bent and set the brim of his hat to the dying man's lips, while his life hung on the crook of the Kid's trigger finger. But Billy did not fire; Hindman drank and fell back dead. And Stockton went his way unmolested along the trail that led ultimately to his bloody death in Durango. The dusty street stretches still and sleepy in the hot sunshine before us; there is a bird singing in a cottonwood, and a woman calls her child in petulant Spanish. But once that street was a stage for violent and bloody drama. Turn your head now and look at the mountain that rises behind the town. There on the bare, rock-littered slope Crawford and Montoya crouched that hot summer day so long ago. There Crawford died, pitching headlong from the ledge where he crouched, to roll down the long slope like a rag doll. Perhaps he did not die instantly. Men say death came slowly to him, all through the long, hot day as he lay groaning with the agony of a broken back. On the ledge above his comrade Montoya lay with his broken leg. Turn again to the dusty street of Lincoln and look at the inn, which stands where the McSween house stood. Men died in the backyard there—Harvey Morris, Francisco Semora, Vincente Romero, McSween himself, Bob Beckwith. And yonder in the road before the site of the old house George Chapman, the Las Vegas lawyer, was killed by Bill Campbell, one of Murphy's Texan gunmen. No one dared go forth at the sound of the shot; they peered from their windows and saw the body of a man lying in the street, but until daylight came none knew who it was.

Lincoln is a haunted town—yet it is not merely the fact of knowing so many men died there that makes it haunted, to me. I have visited many spots where death was dealt whole-sale: the Alamo, for instance; the battle-field of Goliad; La Bahia, where Fannin's men were massacred; Fort Griffin; Fort McKavett; the hanging-tree in the courthouse yard at Goliad where so many men kicked out their lives. But none of those places ever affected me just as Lincoln did. My conception of them was not tinged with a definite horror as with Lincoln. I think I know why. Burns, in his splendid book that narrates the feud, missed one dominant element entirely; and this is the geographical, or perhaps I should say topographical effect on the inhabitants. I think geography is the reason for the unusually savage and bloodthirsty manner in which the feud was fought out, a savagery that has impressed everyone who has ever made an intelligent study of the feud and the psychology behind it. The valley in which Lincoln lies is isolated from the rest of the world. Vast expanses of desert and mountains separate it from the rest of humanity—deserts too barren to support human life. The people in Lincoln lost touch with the world. Isolated as they were, their own affairs, their relationship with one another, took on an importance and significance out of proportion to their actual meaning. Thrown together too much, jealousies and resentments rankled and grew, feeding upon themselves, until they reached monstrous proportions and culminated in those bloody atrocities which startled even the tough West of that day. Visualize that narrow valley, hidden away among the barren hills, isolated from the world, where its inhabitants inescapably dwelt side by side, hating and being hated, and at last killing and being killed. In such restricted, isolated spots, human passions smolder and burn, feeding on the impulses which give them birth, until they reached a point that can hardly be conceived by dwellers in more fortunate spots. It was with a horror I frankly confess that I visualized the reign of terror that stalked that blood-drenched valley; day and night was a tense waiting, waiting, until the thunder of the sudden guns broke the tension for a moment and men died like flies— and then silence followed, and the tension shut down again. No man who valued his life dared speak; when a shot rang out at night and a human being cried out in agony, no one dared open the door and see who had fallen. I visualized people caught together like rats, fighting in terror and agony and bloodshed; going about their work by day with a shut mouth and an averted eye, momentarily expecting a bullet in the back; and at night lying shuddering behind locked doors, trembling in expectation of the stealthy footstep, the hand on the bolt, the sudden blast of lead through the windows. Feuds in Texas were generally fought out in the open, over wide expanses of country. But the nature of the Bonito Valley determined the nature of the feud— narrow, concentrated, horrible. I have heard of people going mad in isolated places; I believe the Lincoln County War was tinged with madness.

We left Lincoln and went on to Carrizozo, a bewilderingly planless mining town sprawled in the hot, dusty plains between the Sierra Blanca range and the lava beds. We ate dinner in a restaurant that had once been a bank. Vinson thought the crowd was unusually tough looking, but I liked their looks— cattlemen, miners and what-not. They weren't hard looking at all compared to the oil field mobs I've seen. I got a big kick out of watching one old fellow— an old cowman in overalls and a broad-brimmed hat, and an old-timer if there ever was one, with a bristling grey mustache and the keenest, merriest blue eyes I ever saw in a man of his age. He was about the size of a grizzly-bear, his hands were gnarled from years of work with rope and branding iron, and he walked with a limp. But every so often he disappeared into the bar and each time he emerged he was more overflowing with vitality than ever. He must have been seventy at least, but he tucked his stick under his arm and gave a fair imitation of an Apache war-dance while a nickel-music-machine blared away the dismal ballad of John Dillinger. Every time a waitress got outside the counter the old geezer grabbed her and kissed her with a relish that the accumulation of years didn't seem to have diminished any. He was having a hell of a good time, and it did me good just to watch him. After seeing so many men primly tiptoeing through life with their hats in their hands, these days, it's a relief to occasionally see a man who seems to be getting a lusty joy out of life, and who is honest enough not to try to conceal the fact. The old fellow's unrestrained gusto was one of the highlights of the whole journey, to me. We noticed a couple of other fellows too, who seemed to be enjoying themselves—a little, shrivelled up old fellow, and his son, who was no chicken himself; the son had not a tooth in his head, but he was gay and festive. I mention them because we saw them again before we got out of the State.

A few miles beyond Carrizozo we hit the lava beds—a frozen river of black broken rock, three miles wide at the point where we crossed it, and I don't know how long from north to south. A mad, chaotic jumble, black and forbidding, with cactus growing plentifully amidst the chaos, the slender green stems and pink blooms, the color of the ribbons young Mexican girls wear in their hair, contrasting with the blackness of the lava.

We hit the paved highway at San Antonio and drove on, through Socorro, and Albuquerque, and arrived in Santa Fe after nightfall, having driven something over three hundred miles that day.

After the stark and somber realness of Lincoln, I found the artificialities of Santa Fe disappointing, almost irritating. It is a show-place, openly and candidly, subsisting almost entirely on the tourist trade. I wearied of the eternal rushing about, both of tourists trying to see the sights, and of natives trying to grab the tourist dough. I wearied of the crowds of gaping tourists (though I was one myself) who gawked and stared about, seldom with any apparent idea of what it was all about, or any apparent understanding of what they were looking at. I wearied of their outlandish garb—particularly those tourists who wear British style sun-helmets, short-sleeved knit shirts, and knee-length pants; this garb was generally accompanied by a tooth-brush mustache and huge horn-rim glasses. California tourists seemed more guilty of these atrocities than any of the others.

However, we saw the town, and it's worth seeing alright, especially to anyone not familiar with Spanish style architecture. It's much like towns I have visited in old Mexico, with the exception that it is much cleaner and neater. In cleanliness it compares with any town I ever saw. The native population is, of course, predominantly Mexican. Or as they call them out there, Spanish-Americans. You or I would be Anglo-Americans according to their way of putting it. Spanish-American, hell. A Mexican is a Mexican to me, wherever I find him, and I don't consider it necessary for me to hang any prefix on the term "American" when referring to myself.

We went through the art museum which is supposed to be very good, but I shall not pretend to try to pass on it. I know nothing about paintings, and, unless the painting portrays some sort of strenuous action, I care less. Most of the paintings were of New Mexican landscape, and I find the Witt Museum in San Antonio less monotonous, because Texas presents a greater variety of scenery than does New Mexico, and therefore a collection of Texas landscape paintings offers more different scenes. Only one painting stands out in my mind, and I studied that for a long time. It was a large painting of a

half-naked Indian trudging over a desert country, leaning on a staff, and dragging behind him several horses' heads, with portions of the vertebrae still
attached; he was dragging them by means of raw-hide ropes fastened in deep
gashes in the muscles of his back. At first glance I supposed it to portray a
Penitente, but a description was affixed to the painting. It portrayed a scene
the artist had witnessed in Montana, many years before. An old Crow chief
had word that his favorite son had died in Carlisle University; he killed the
boy's horses, cut off their heads, gashed his back and fastened rawhide
thongs into the raw flesh, and dragged those skulls all over the mountains all
day long, to show that neither grief nor physical agony could shake his fortitude. Doubtless it did more to lessen his sorrow than anything he could have
done. I was reminded of Chesterton's lines, about the old Viking:

> "And a man hopes, being foolish,
> Till in white woods apart
> He finds at last the lost bird dead,
> But a man can still hold up his head,
> Though nevermore his heart."[5]

When the world cracks under a man's feet and the sky breaks and falls on his
head, if he can clench his jaws and keep on his feet, and keep his head up, if
for no other reason than the stubborn pride of fighting, then that's something, at least; and if he can't do that, he'd better blow his brains out, like a
gentleman. The title of the picture was "The Stoic."[6]

I found the governor's palace more interesting. It has been made a museum, and contains many relics of early Indian life, of Spanish conquest
times, and of Mexican and American pioneer days. It is an old building, dating back to about 1608. It was occupied for a while by Indians, who drove
the Spaniards out, but were in turn driven out by them. It contains many relics of the Pueblo Indians, but I'll be frank to admit that I've never been able
to work up much interest regarding those people. Neither their peculiar civilization and culture, nor their tragic fate stimulates my imagination very much.
I am much more interested in their barbaric conquerors—the Navajos,
Apaches and Comanches. Nor am I particularly interested in the Spanish era
of the country; my intense interest begins only with the American invasion.

We stayed only one night in Santa Fe. It had been my intention to stay
longer, and then to go on to Taos, thence to Trinidad, Colorado, and then
back to El Paso, touching some point in Arizona, perhaps. But Vinson got in
a swivet to get home, for some reason which he never made entirely clear, but
which seemed so important to him that I didn't press the matter.[7] I did insist
on visiting a cliff-dwelling north of Santa Fe, but we didn't even see that, as it
turned out. The road got more and more hellish as we progressed among the
mountains, the Indians we met were unable, or unwilling to give us any defi-

nite information, and at last in disgust I turned around, in the pueblo of San Ildefonso, and we returned to Santa Fe—and then lit out on the home trail; but not before we encountered our festive Carrizozo friends, father and son, hilariously taking in the town.

It was about the middle of the afternoon when we left Santa Fe, and we only drove to Socorro which lies perhaps a hundred and forty miles south of Santa Fe, where we spent the night. There it was my fullest intention of getting gloriously lit; I've always heard that in those high altitudes liquor is unusually potent. But I reckon it was because I ate a big supper. Anyway, I filled myself right up to the chin with high-powered beer and all it did was to make me drowsy. By the time I realized that I couldn't hold enough beer to make me loop-legged, I was so full that if I had drunk any whiskey or tequila it would have made me sick. So I gave it up in disgust. But while we were tanking who should arrive, with a gust of exuberance and a reek of alcohol, our hilarious friends from Carrizozo. They purchased beer in bottles and sallied forth, their vigor apparently undiminished, and where they went from there I don't know, for we saw them no more, though it wouldn't have surprised me if we had run into them in El Paso.

Next morning we hit the trail through San Antonio, Hot Springs and Las Cruces. North of Hot Springs we turned off to see the Elephant Butte Dam, and it's an impressive sight, but whoever decided the butte looked like an elephant's head must have been full of tequila. If it looked like anything it looked like a monkey's head. I found the dam less interesting than a frisky little redhead who was taking pictures with a pint-sized camera, and who wasn't bashful at all.

North of El Paso we ran into a dust-storm coming up out of old Mexico, but it wasn't so bad. That is to say, I've seen worse. The best-looking town we saw on that run was Las Cruces, where there was the best bar we found on the whole damned trip. Vinson got a bit loop-legged for the first and only time. We hit El Paso in the afternoon having driven only a little over two hundred miles, and Vinson wanted to bat right on through and spend the night somewhere east of the city, but I rebelled. I like El Paso, and I wanted to spend at least one night there. I told him I'd get him home by midnight the next day if my car held together, and he was satisfied with that. We were due to get home two days ahead of our planned schedule anyway. So we spent the night in El Paso, and went to a couple of movies—"The Informer," a damned fine picture, dealing with the Irish revolution of some years back;[8] and another the name of which I can't remember, it was so rotten, but we saw the Baer-Braddock fight pictures at it,[9] and that was even more rotten. I'd drunk nothing but muscatel wine and beer throughout the whole trip, and was in a mood to do some fancy swigging, but Vinson said he didn't feel like it, so I drank only a whiskey sour, a Harry Mitchell Special McGinty[10] and a glass of Burgundy wine, and we went to the shows. I thought after the shows he might feel more festive, but all he wanted to do was hit the hay, which he did, and I sallied forth to a beer garden alone. But I don't like to drink by myself, so I only downed a gin fizz and a bottle of ABC, and came back and went to bed myself. The next day we came home. I went around by Brownwood and left Vinson, then came on home, arriving after about sixteen hours at the wheel., having driven about five hundred and seventy miles during that time.

It was an interesting trip, but next time I go that route, I want to be able to stay longer and cover more territory. I think the continuous grind just about wore Vinson down, though I did all the driving, except a little in the confines of Santa Fe, and a little more in El Paso. He's a good deal bigger than I am—taller and heavier—and only a few months older, but I'm beginning to fear that he doesn't have the stamina and endurance that a man of his age ought to have. Those five-hundred mile a day drives seemed to exhaust him, and leave him no energy for the drinking and sightseeing tours I wanted to relax in after the grind.

Anyway, we were gone five days, drove over 1800 miles—at least I did—and saw plenty of new country. I hope to go back to Santa Fe some day and stay a week or so, and see the country all about it. The town itself is interesting enough in a conventional sort of way, and I may have said, much resembles the towns of Old Mexico, but is cleaner, and more law-abiding. It doesn't have, for instance, or at least we didn't see any of those dives so popular in Mexican border towns, where naked prostitutes of both sexes and various Latin races first dance before the customers, then copulate with each other, and then indulge in various revolting perversions for the entertainment of the crowd, which is generally made up of tourists.

The State seems predominantly Catholic and Mexican. We went into the capitol and I made a point of counting the Mexican names among the legislators. The legislature wasn't in session at the moment, but each man's name was fastened to his desk on a placard. The majority were Mexican. Chavez, Otero, Bacca, Roybal, especially Chavez, are the names which appear most frequently in the population. There seem to be as many Chavez's in New Mexico as there are Gonzaleses in South Texas. I might also add that the State capitol looks about as big as a good-sized Texas county-courthouse. Speaking in general, the Mexican population of New Mexico seems much further advanced, more prosperous and better educated than the Mexican population of Texas and Oklahoma. There are plenty of school-houses, and the Mexicans we saw seemed quicker, more intelligent in general than those of my own State. I'll admit it seemed strange to me to see Mexicans being treated on the same footing as white people. You can certainly tell the difference in the bearing of Mexicans, Indians, negroes and other dark races the instant you cross the Texas line. Texas, whatever its virtues or faults, is a white man's state, and that fact is reflected in the manner of the non-white races. They know their place. Yet I'll admit that the only insolence in the case of negroes I noticed occurred in Texas, some miles east of El Paso. Ahead of us we saw a car with a California license, and ahead of them an auto full of niggers—five or six big, brawny black bucks who might have been coming east to pick cotton. Anyway, the California people wanted past, and the niggers wouldn't pull out to let them past. They went along that way for a half mile, perhaps, the Californian vainly honking his horn, and the niggers laughing at him. At last they did pull over a little, but when he got even with them, before he could pass, they speeded up, and almost ran him off the road. At last he did get past, and by this time I had drawn up right behind them. I was pretty mad already, for one thing because I don't like to see a nigger displaying insolence toward a white man, and another thing, I demand that strangers within the boundaries of the State shall be treated with courtesy, by white or black. I zoomed up behind those coons, honking peremptorily, and they started pulling the same stuff with me as they had with the Californian. I stuck my head out and told them to pull over in a voice that has frequently been compared to the bellowing of a bull, and I wasn't at all choice in my use of words. My request, to put it mildly, was framed in harsh, abusive and profane language. And the black boys pulled over in a hurry. When they saw the Texas license plate on my car, they couldn't get out of our way fast enough. The Californian really should have shot the tires off their car, if he didn't want to do anything more drastic. They knew better.

I haven't done any travelling to speak of since I returned home. Outside of my usual trips to Brownwood and Coleman, I've made only three journeys, and they were very short. Once to De Leon, 45 miles to the east, and over a most damnable road, and back by the way of Comanche and Brownwood. Comanche is the oldest town in this region, and has a varied and violent history. It bore the brunt of Indian attacks in the '60's; they used to camp outside the town and ride up and down the streets at night shooting at the windows while the people fired back at them. The majority of the Rangers who took part in the great Dove Creek fight with the Kickapoos were from Comanche. It was in Comanche that John Wesley Hardin killed Sheriff Webb, for which he was later sentenced—in the same town—to twenty-five years in the pen; and it was in Comanche that Joe Hardin and some of his cousins were lynched. It was a live town fifty years ago. I made a trip to Mineral Wells, which lies about 107 miles east of here, among the Palo Pinto mountains; and a few weeks later another trip east, that time to Weatherford, which lies about thirty miles east of Mineral Wells. Weatherford is the county seat of Parker County, named for the Parker family of old Fort Parker, and in which county I was born. It was in Weatherford, that was danced, so far as I know, the only scalp-dance ever danced by whites in the States. Some Comanches butchered some people in the vicinity, but were caught before they could get back into the Territory. The Rangers brought their scalps back to

Weatherford and strung them up in the square, and the population, male and female, turned out, and danced them in regular Comanche style.

When I was a kid living in Palo Pinto County years ago, I knew a family whose father had been caught by the Comanches, not so terribly many years before. He'd taken a herd of cattle up the trail to a Kansas market and was returning with the money he'd gotten in a trunk. He was riding from Weatherford to his ranch, in a wagon, when the Indians swooped down on him. They'd slipped over the river and struck the settlements before anybody knew they were coming. The man with the rancher got away, as I remember, but he didn't. They shot him full of arrows and scalped him, dumped the trunk on the prairie and burst it open and scattered the contents about, but didn't touch the money. They cut the horses loose though and took them. The rancher's people carried him back to Weatherford, put his hat on his head to hide his scalped condition, and had his picture taken. I saw that picture plenty of times, hanging in their house. It looked lifelike enough, except for the glaze of the eyes.

I mentioned the drouth had been broken up. Now the weather seems going to the other extreme. It's rained until I'm sick of it. The weather is gusty, uncertain and dangerous. The other day it rained over six inches in an hour and a half in a town northwest of here. There hasn't so far been such a cloudburst here, but the weather is cloudy and threatening. It's been very hot and sultry, muggy. I put a thermometer out in the sun one clear day to see how hot it was, but it only registered up to 121, so I don't know how hot it really was. I'm sure it would have gone much further if the thing would have registered any more.

The hottest day of the year came about a couple of weeks ago. It was clear, but stifling, breathless, and along in the middle of the afternoon thunderheads began to roll up and thin whitish-grey clouds started forming. They seemed to form over the town out of the air itself, rather than come up over the horizon. They formed in the east, with broad patches of blue sky between, which gradually became veiled by a sort of light greyish film. I paid very little attention, because it's seldom that any rain or wind to amount to anything comes from the east, especially in the summer. The clouds looked so light I didn't even think it would rain much. But it did start raining, peppering down pretty brisk, and then it began to hail—not big hail stones, but they came pretty fast. I hadn't even bothered to put down the windows or shut the doors, because I thought it wouldn't be anything but a sprinkle. But the rain began to come harder and a light wind sprang up out of the east, and I went to put down the windows in my room, which faces southeast, with windows on both the south and the east sides. And just as I laid hands on a window to lower it, with stunning suddenness the wind rose to a scream, the rain turned into slashing sheets, and the tornado struck! It was the most unexpected thing that ever happened in this town. There wasn't much thunder or lightning, no black, ominous clouds—just a sudden twisting wind that materialized out of nowhere, formed in the east part of the town and whipped savagely across it toward the southwest. Nowhere outside the limits of the town was any damage done.[11]

It didn't blow as hard in the southwestern part of town, where I live, as it did in the eastern part, and it was over quicker. It was just a gust, the single buffet of a giant's fist, and that was all. To me, standing at the open window, it was like a breath-taking slap in the face. The wind, roaring from the northeast, whipped around the house and rushed against the south windows with a terrific impact. It slapped me full in the face and nearly knocked me down. A thick stack of papers and letters on my typewriter table went spiralling to the ceiling and rained to the floor in confusion. I don't remember getting the windows down, but I must have done it in something less than a second. The house was wide open and the wind filled it with a roar. I had a fleeting, momentary sensation of feeling the house expand, as the wind forced the ceiling and walls outward, and I remember yelling: "Shut the doors! This is a storm!" If it had been a real bad one, it would have torn the house apart, for it was wide open. Before I could get out of my room, my mother had shut the outer doors, and the blow had passed before I could get the inner doors closed. I went into the kitchen to close the west windows, but my mother had already closed one and the cook was trying to close the other. She was scared so her hands were shaking and she couldn't get it down, so I closed it for her. No need to ask if my mother was frightened; there's nothing in this universe that can frighten her.

My sensations in that blast were peculiar, and all physical. I didn't have time to get scared. All I was aware of was a sense of bewildering confusion, and a peculiar sort of exhilaration, something like the effect of very strong wine. I attribute that to the electricity in the storm.

It wasn't, after all, a bad storm, though I think the Fort Worth papers gave it a headline. My father read the account in the morning paper—he was in Fort Worth at the time—and immediately phoned to find out what damage had been done. I told him none, having not been to town since the storm, and not aware that any had been done. There was no loss of life, but some property damage. Limbs were twisted off trees—that happened to a mesquite in our cowlot; roofs were damaged in parts of the town, and some windows blown in—blown out rather. The wind got in the houses and forced them outward.

My friend Dock Lee was making for the shelter of a drug store when the storm reached its height. Just as he approached the door the plate glass show-window blew outward, all in one piece,[12] and splintered on his head and the arm he threw up to guard himself with. A piece of the glass stabbed into his side, apparently being checked when it met his ribs. He bled like a stuck hog, but he was lucky it was no worse. It could have disembowelled him if it had hit him just right. A young woman was blown down by the wind, while trying to get to a storm-cellar, and bruised and scratched considerably. Dock's brother Dave, the Tennessean who was thrown through the windshield when I wrecked my car on the flagpole, and the owner of another drugstore, got in Dave's car, I understand, when it started raining and drove to the druggist's house to get a washing off the line before it got soaked. But when they got into the druggist's yard the clothes were already wet, so the druggist told Dave to drive the car into his garage. About that time the wind hit, and the garage started shaking as though it were going to blow away, so they stopped the car and started to wait for the wind to subside, and just then there came a big zinc water cistern weighing several hundred pounds, blown through the air, and it landed on the hood of the car, caving it in and mashing a fender. If it had hit on the top it would have pulverized the men under it; it rolled on over, knocked a dog-house sidewise and the dog set up a yell, and then hit the garage and knocked an end of it loose. Dave and his companion jumped out of the car and headed for the house, and when they hit the concrete stoop, at a high rate of speed, the druggist's legs flew out from under him and he landed on his back with a force that nearly fractured his spine. Dave yanked him to his feet and hauled him into the house, but by that time the storm was over. All that action took place within a few minutes—seconds, rather. It's a bit amusing, were it not so pregnant with serious possibilities, to reflect on human beings scampering madly here and there before the buffeting of a wind gone mad, dodging destruction by blind chance and the skin of their teeth, and winding up with the inglorious climax of a thundering fall on the posterior.

The storm came near making a casualty out of one of the cat-clan. These fool felines don't seem to have sense enough to take refuge properly from the rain, and this time I didn't have time to get them to the barn. After the blow they emerged from the bushes and weeds where they had hidden all pretty much bedraggled, but Beetle, the mangy one, looked like he was about at his last gasp. He staggered a few feet and fell on his belly and lay shaking like he had the ague. I wrapped him up in a warm cloth and put him in the peanut hay so only the tip of his tail was visible and that vibrated like a distress signal for about half an hour. But when he'd dried out and warmed up, he was as good as ever. I had a time with his mange; lubricating oil, with which I once cured a mangy cat, had no effect on him, and having read somewhere that the Arabs treat mangy camels with melted butter, I buttered him thoroughly two or three times a day. He resented this bitterly, though it entailed no physical discomfort on his part; maybe it was just the principle of the thing. The other cats always immediately licked the butter off of him, but either it or something else cured him; though he is still funny looking, because most of the hair came off his legs, shoulders and neck and it hasn't grown back on yet.

If he and his companions were worth their salt, they'd go after the big snake that is apparently hiding somewhere on the place. I've seen his tracks, and he must be a monster to judge from them. I've never seen him; he keeps out of sight in the daytime, and though I've haunted the barns and sheds at night with a flashlight and a machete, I haven't discovered his lair. He's probably a harmless bull snake, but he might be a rattler or a copperhead. If he's a rattler, and I get him, I'll send you the rattles.

Speaking of reptiles, and other crawling menaces, reminds me of an incident that happened a few nights ago. I was awakened out of a sound sleep by the urgent voice of a neighbor on the front porch who called out that there were a couple of thieves in my garage. It was sometime between midnight and one o'clock. This was his story, which I heard after the excitement had quieted down. He said he and his wife had returned home late (they live in a small house west of ours, across a side-street) and were sitting shelling peas before they went to bed, when two men glided up on their back porch and tried the door. He had sold his pistol a few days before, and was unarmed. He blew out the light and he and his wife crouched there in the dark, hoping the lock on the door would hold. It did, and presently the men gave it up, and went to a small store which stands west of his house, and tried the lock on that door. He and his wife watched through the window, it being a fairly bright night, cloudy, but with a moon peeping through the clouds. Presently then, the men abandoned the store, passed through his backyard and began to try to break into my side of our garage, which is behind our house, giving onto the side-street. The doors wouldn't close together and were fastened with a chain. It is possible that a man of small or medium size might have squeezed through. It's been so long since any stealing was done in this neighborhood that I've been careless in guarding against it. Well, this fellow watched from the window, and saw them move out of sight, apparently having gained access into the garage. Then he slipped out his front door and ran across the highway to a house he could get to without being seen by the men in my garage. He thought he could phone us from there, and tell us of the invasion without exposing himself to the sight of the invaders. But the family he went to, a family from Ohio, and who haven't been in Cross Plains long, had no telephone in the house, and far from rallying to help the neighborhood against invading thugs, they discreetly kept out of sight. I think they must have locked the doors and crawled under the beds. At least none of them made any appearance, until late the next day, when the oldest boy came over to ask me if anything was stolen. Anyway, seeing no chance of help there, the man who had first seen the thugs, next ran back across the highway, and came to our front porch, knowing he would probably be seen by the outlaws, but seeing no help for it. Then it was that I woke up and performed the most inexcusably blundering and bone-headed act of my whole career, up to date. All I got was that a couple of thieves were trying to steal my car, and, too near asleep to exercise proper caution, I jumped out of bed, grabbed the first weapon I chanced on, which happened to be a Colt .380 automatic, and went charging out to the garage in plain sight and with no attempt at concealment, not even taking advantage of the fences and trees. If they'd still been lurking in the garage they could have shot me to splinters before I ever saw them. It was a plain boob-trick, which I'll never repeat, and which I wouldn't have pulled then, if I hadn't been half-asleep. There was no need for such blundering tactics; there are plenty of trees and a good big gate I could have come up behind. But if there was ever anybody in my garage, they'd decamped, probably when the man who warned us started yelling on our front porch.

I found nothing stolen, and went back to bed and went to sleep. There were no more disturbances that night. Looking back on the incident, however, I see some elements that seem a bit peculiar, and suggest that perhaps the game isn't yet played out. Please regard as strictly confidential the remarks I am now going to make in regard to the matter. There may have been more to the affair than appeared on the surface. There are three possible solutions to the mystery. The first, and the most likely, is that the man who gave the alarm was telling the truth: that the marauders were outlaws from some other section, wandering through and looking for whatever loot they might pick up. The second possibility is that they were not thieves at all, but the fellow's personal enemies, after his scalp. In that case, he told only part of the truth, and if the men hid in my garage at all, it was not to steal anything, but for the purpose of a refuge or an ambush. The third possibility is that the whole tale was a lie; that the fellow himself is planning some sinister action and invented a story of alien marauders to avert suspicion from himself, when and if his plot and action, whatever it is, has been accomplished. I merely mention this as a possibility; I do not give it as my opinion. I always like to survey all the possibilities of any case where the facts and motives are not entirely clear.

I'm glad you are having such a delightful time in Florida. I enjoyed your descriptions of the rivers and swamps, which seem to be more definitely tropical in their nature than the river-lands of East Texas. I also very much enjoyed your descriptions of places visited in New England before you started on your journey, and appreciate the historical information supplied. And speaking of that—I have recently learned that my branch of the Howard family came originally from Northumberland. What kind of a country is that? About all I know about it is that it lies on the border of Scotland.

Yes, I found "Out of the Eons" fascinating, and tantalizing—tantalizing because it roused my always voracious appetite for more of your stories. I felt greatly complimented that Von Junzt's hellish book should play such a prominent part in it. Have you submitted your "Shadow Out of Time" to Weird Tales?[13] I certainly hope to see it in print soon. In fact, I'd like to see a story of yours in every issue.

By the way, I recently got hold of a book that ought to be read by all writers who strive after realism, and by every man with a drop of Nordic blood in his veins—the "Heimskringla" of Snorre Sturlason.[14] Reading his sagas of the

Norse people, I felt more strongly than ever my instinctive kinship with them, and the kinship between them and frontier people of America. In many ways the Norsemen figuring in his history more resemble the American pioneers of the West more than any other European people I have ever read about. The main difference, as far as I could see, was that the Norsemen were more prone to break their pledged word than were the frontiersmen.

I'm much interested to learn of Klarkashton's carving of dinosaur bone; he is a man of varied talents, indeed.

Hope the weather is less turbulent in the East than it is here, and that your stay in Florida continues to prove as pleasant as it has so far. Thanks again for the pictures. And so, with all best wishes, I remain,

Cordially,
REH.

Notes

1. Dated by RHB "c. J[u]ly 25, 1935."

2. Haden Harrison Edwards (1771–1849), Texas settler and land speculator.

3. The Bankhead Highway, named for Alabama senator John H. Bankhead, extended from Washington, D.C. to San Diego. The segment of the highway REH and Vinson followed was designated US 80 and Texas Highway 1. The route is now followed by Interstate 20. At Pecos, they would have turned northward onto US 285.

4. REH's copy of *The Saga of Billy the Kid* is still in the REH Memorial Collection at Howard Payne University. The quotation is from page 33.

5. G. K. Chesterton (1874–1936), *The Ballad of the White Horse* (New York: John Lane, 1911), p. 42. In Chesterton, the first line reads "being ignorant." There are other slight misquotations.

6. Joseph Henry Sharp (1859–1953), "The Stoic" (1914).

7. In the spring of 1935, Novalyne Price, who had dated REH during most of 1934, had begun dating Truett Vinson. Neither of them, apparently, directly told REH they were dating, but for various reasons seemed to assume he must know. Shortly after his return from New Mexico, REH wrote Novalyne a letter in which he expressed his disappointment that they had kept the fact they were dating a secret from him. It was probably tension over this that was at the root of Vinson's "swivet to get home."

8. *The Informer* (RKO, 1935), directed by John Ford; starring Victor McLaglen, Heather Angel, and Preston Foster. Adapted from the novel by Liam O'Flaherty and dealing with the Irish Civil War (1918–22). Ford and McLaglen won Academy Awards, and the movie earned two other Oscars.

9. James J. Braddock won the heavyweight championship from Max Baer in a unanimous decision, 13 June 1935.

10. For McGinty, see note 106 n. 5. Harry Mitchell was owner of the Harry Mitchell Brewing Company in El Paso, which produced a beer called Special Lager.

11. A tornado struck Cross Plains shortly after 5:00 PM, 12 July 1935, causing several thousands of dollars worth of damage.

12. The large plate glass windows of Sims Drug were blown out during the storm.

13. HPL had not submitted the story to any magazine. In October, Donald Wandrei surreptitiously submitted the story to *Astounding*, which promptly accepted it.

14. Snorri Sturluson (1179–1241), Icelandic poet, historian, and chieftain, author of the *Prose Edda* (a handbook on poetics) and the *Heimskringla*, a history of the Norwegian kings from their legendary descent from the warrior-wizard god Odin down to Magnus Erlingsson (1184). REH's copy of the Everyman's Library edition is in the REH Memorial Collection at Howard Payne University

[118]

c/o Barlow, Box 88,
De Land, Florida
August 7, 1935

Dear Ar-I-Ech:—

. . . . . Now as to our controversies—for once, I am *glad* that a moot question became dragged out beyond the ordinary limits of discussion . . . since the prolongation has brought out details revealing an initial misconception on my part which I am very glad to admit; a misconception which gave rise to many seeming paradoxes in the course of my argument.

I refer to the incident on which our debate about *chivalry* was based. It was my impression that your protest was directed against the rough handling of a turbulent crowd, including women, by the police during the course of some riot around a New York court house. Instead, it appears that the occurrence involved the rough treatment of a lone female prisoner in a court room, merely in retaliation for oral abuse and without any confusion or mob menace. Well—that naturally puts a very different light on the matter! *Of course* such an act was wholly unjustified and indefensible, since no element of military necessity or social expediency was connected with it. Had I realised that *this* was the object of your protest, I would certainly have found no basis for argument—since no partisan of law and order could for a moment condone any needless act of oppression of the weak by the strong. Any incident like this is assumedly rare in the civilised parts of the world—and is probably unheard-of within the boundaries of the British Empire. The cause is, no doubt, sheer *exasperation*—a result of the habitual stubbornness of criminals, who defy the law in every possible way and rely on technicalities to avert the penalties they deserve. Police brutality undoubtedly arises from efforts to overcome the stubborn close-mouthedness of confirmed offenders who are resolved to say nothing and let their lawyers defeat the ends of justice. When the police well know that a thug *did* perpetrate a crime, yet realise that his taciturn denials will probably cause him to escape punishment through the tricks of a shyster, they are strongly tempted to *make him talk somehow*—by physical pressure or otherwise. Hence the habit of treating old offenders roughly. However—I am well aware that their natural cause does not in any way justify the needless and excessive use of rough treatment by the police. The incident you cited—as *now* correctly understood by me—is certainly incapable of defence, and deserves only the severest condemnation. All I can say of it is that such things are uncommon in civilised regions, and are universally condemned by civilised people. Two or three incidents of that sort would certainly precipitate a police shake-up, or municipal investigation of the courts, in any high-grade American city.

Well—all my arguments on the subject will have to be resurveyed and reappraised in the light of this initial mistake. As to the *cause* of my distinctly stupid blunder—it unquestionably proceeded from the fact that I had, at the time, just been reading dozens of radical and communist protests against the sort of thing which I imagined you were protesting against. It has become a sort of stock procedure for bolsheviks to raise a howl every time the police or national guard take necessary steps to protect human life and resources against mob violence and vindictive fury. If the militia use tear-gas or clubs against a milling herd of frenzied destroyers, the bolshevik press will invariably produce headlines reading: COSSACKS POISON PEACEFUL AND INNOCENT WOMEN AND CHILDREN . . . . UNIFORMED ASSASSINS BUTCHER UNARMED WOMEN . . . etc. etc. etc. At the time of your mention of the court incident, headlines and events like these were especially numerous—and I somehow managed to confuse this specific happening with the more common incident of police handling a mixed mob. Considering the crowded nature of my programme and the wide extent of my correspondence, this mistake is perhaps less extraordinary than it might seem on the surface. Anyhow, permit me to extend my heartiest apologies for the blunder, and for the tedious train of unnecessary and misapprehension-based argument which resulted therefrom! Rest assured that I do *not* condone the rough handling of any weak person, male or female, by a strong person or crowd of strong persons— unless (as was *not* so in the cited case) some definite and extreme social necessity (as, for instance, the possession of a bomb or important paper or secret by the criminal) exists. And even in cases of social necessity, rest assured that I do not condone the infliction of any more pain or hardship than is necessary for the given social purpose. All pain-infliction inspired by carelessness, callousness, revengefulness, or perverted emotion (this last, alone, constituting true "sadism") is to be condemned unsparingly and eliminated rigorously whenever found. Which reminds me to clarify the issue regarding "sadism". The fact is, that *sadism* (so-called from the perverted author of "Justine", etc.)[1] is a term applicable *only* to pain-infliction *inspired by perverted eroticism and forming the source of some obscure, quasi-erotic emotional gratification.* Brutality arising from vindictiveness, carelessness, or insensitiveness (and this is the sort figuring in reprehensible police incidents) is *not* genuine *sadism.* It is no less despicable on that account, but it is a wholly different thing based on a wholly different set of motives and instincts. Sadism is confined to an *abnormal* sort of pain-infliction *whose sole purpose is an intrinsic gratification.* There is no *sadism* where vengeance or anger or heedlessness is dominant. The average roughneck, on or off the police force, is a *brute* but *not a sadist.*

Incidentally—don't fancy for a moment that I had anything like "bitter resentment" concerning your interpretation of my attitude—or what seemed to be my attitude—in this matter. My emphatic words were inspired wholly by what *seemed to me* a wild and inexplicable *inconsistency, irrelevance,* and *lack of logic* in that interpretation. I had (in *intent*—though my mistake made it seem otherwise) simply said that the forces of law and order could not afford to imperil the community by refraining from forcible action against lawless mobs when such mobs contain women—and you *appeared* to deduce from that statement (although I now see that you had something else in mind) that I *approved and relished* the massacre of helpless grandmothers and infants by armed forces for no reason at all! I did not feel *resentment,* but was merely nonplussed at what seemed to be an absolute lack of logic. As for what you appear to interpret as accusing or vituperative words on my part—let me repeat that the things I define adversely are *not persons but attitudes.* I may, for example, say that *anyone who believes or wishes a certain thing* is an enemy of mankind or defender of ignorance—but that does not prove that any specific person really believes or wishes that thing in the light of all its implications. If I think, from his own utterances, that anyone in particular believes or wishes such a thing, I may be mistaken. I may fail to comprehend, through lack of a system of reference-associations in common, just what it is that he does believe and wish. Therefore there is nothing personal in anything I may say about a certain sort of attitude or method. I merely say what I think of *the attitude or method itself*—whereas my argumentative opponent of the moment may really diverge very far from the attitude or method toward which—to my mind, and at the moment—he may *seem* to lean. My own position is clear. I am in favour of the development of the human race and the human individual *to the greatest extent of its natural capacity, and in the direction marked out by the ground already covered in the evolution of rational, logical, aesthetic, and imaginative mankind from the instinctive, vegetative, simply-organised amoeba or amphibian or ape.* Anyone *opposed to such development* I regard as an enemy of mankind, apostle of prejudice, defender of ignorance, sentimental romanticist, and all the rest. But *that doesn't necessarily mean any specific individual.* I may be mistaken in interpreting the views of anyone who seems to hold an anti-human, anti-intellectual, and anti-cultural attitude—indeed, I always *feel* in such a case that some mistake has occurred, and that the lack of a common language or set of association-patterns has given rise to mutual misapprehension regarding ultimate meanings. For example—in the case of your contention that civilised men 'claim that raping, butchering and plundering is in defence of art, progress, and civilisation'—I suppose that this statement has a specific meaning, though I can't see where it is applicable. The evils in question, of course, accompany all warfare, and warfare is sometimes waged in the defence of civili-sation—or in the extension of it. But I know of no case where such evils are not deplored and eliminated whenever possible—except among savages and barbarians. While one could hardly advise the abandonment of a war in de-fence of civilisation merely because some of the troops might commit acts of unjustified barbarism against certain of the hostile populations, it would be equally impossible to imagine any truly civilised power as recommending such barbaric acts, or condoning them except as regrettable incidental evils. Cer-tainly, the fruits of civilisation must be preserved at any cost; but the more thoroughly civilised a nation is, the more pains it will take to make that cost as light as possible—light not only to itself, but to mankind as a whole. No-body nowadays seeks to wreak damage and destruction for their own sakes. Now it is impossible that you do not recognise and appreciate these facts—but somewhere between that comprehension and your expressed sentiment as grasped by me a barrier of language or interpretation has arisen. I know there's a mistake somewhere—perhaps in my interpretation of your words—but as yet I can't place my finger on it. All I know is that the acquisitions of human development—knowledge, reason, taste, scholarship, sensitiveness—must be preserved at any cost, and that he who opposes their preservation (whoever he may be—that's not saying that any specific person opposes it) is an enemy of mankind. He is such, because he is contributing toward the de-struction of the only things which make life worth living by a human being with all his natural capacities developed. The world of developed man must stand firm against any atavistical assaults from the underworld of sub-men. So far as the question of Roman versus Goth is concerned—there need be no personal prejudice involved in a pro-Roman attitude. What Rome represented was simply *the massed achievements of mankind*—the fruits of man's struggle against ignorance and crudity. Most of this heritage was not even Roman, and a good deal of it was Nordic (for everything comes from *Greece,* and the glory of Greece began when the Nordic Achaians conquered and re-cast the abo-riginal Minoan-Mediterranean population of Hellas and the Ionian coast)—but it was Rome who perpetuated, guarded, and upheld it. To this day no nation is really civilised which did not come under the influence of that classi-cal heritage which Rome transmitted.

Returning to the American scene—I can clearly appreciate your remarks concerning early Texas, and am sure you are right in believing that the Anglo-Saxon settlers could not have adopted any course other than that which they did adopt. The details you give are tremendously interesting—and it is truly a pity that this chapter of history is not generally known to the nation at large. These events are really of nation-wide significance as milestones in the proc-ess of territorial expansion, yet outside the southwest they remain absolutely unknown save for a few words in school textbooks about the Alamo and Gens. Scott and Taylor and the Battle of Buena Vista and so on. During the present decade there has been a very valuable movement toward the study and popularisation of regional history *in the regions concerned.* The next step is to incorporate the gist of these regional annals into the public scholarship of *the nation at large.* You, I hope, may play some part in such a process—for who is more sympathetically saturated with the very essence of the Southwest (and Texas in particular) than yourself?

As for the heroism of James Parker—certainly it is all the more to be valued because of its social significance. Naturally, heroism and the subordination of individual to group welfare are social necessities in frontier as well as settled regions—in fact, in frontier regions a vast part of all social action has to be expressed as individual heroism. I did not lose sight of this in considering the exploits of Parker, even if I failed to emphasise it. Any stress I may have laid on the purely *individual* element was merely to effect a contrast with actions which, although individually gallant and admirable, are in a larger sense anti-social and therefore to be discouraged. At the moment, I wished merely to say that the acts of Parker were wholly to be admired because they did *not* involve any anti-social waste or disorder.

Well, you've certainly had a magnificent trip, which I envy to the very bottom line! The vanity of landscape must have been immensely impressive, while the historic element was surely precisely in your line. Your description of Lincoln, N. M. is a classic in itself, and I can well imagine the depth and poignancy of the impression behind it. I can feel the sinister antiquity and insidious deadness of the old town as you draw it, and fancy it must be as haunting and fascinating a place as one could find in the whole Southwest. Your photographs of the restored round tower and ancient courthouse help to visualise the scene—and here let me say that I hope something can be done to save the court house from its threatened destruction. It must have been enormously moving to meet the actual descendants of those who fought the battles you have so often studied and chronicled, and I am glad you encountered an heir as intelligent, sympathetic, and well-informed as Señor Maes. Too bad so much is changed at the site of the McSween house. I recall your describing the battle and burning there in one of your letters—a veritably Homeric scene. Incidentally, I share your sentiments about the propriety of knowing the history and traditions of any region one lives in or travels through. If I knew nothing of the background of a region, I couldn't enjoy being there at all. Every time I take a trip I read up as extensively as possible on the places I'm going to see—so that when I get there, each site and object will have some meaning for me. I can't understand a traveller like the Illinoian you encountered—although I see such people daily. It is amusing how little most of the people around here know of Florida history—even after years and decades of continuous residence. If I ever made a southwestern trip, the first thing I'd do would be to get out my file of your letters and go over the magnificent historical epics here and there imbedded in them.

In the present epistle, your description of Lincoln and its brooding isolation, violent history, and residue of sinister atmosphere forms a premier high
spot. I can veritably see the old place festering in its remote valley and simmer-
ing beneath the parching rays of a New Mexican sun. You make it memora-
ble—and increase my wish that I may see the Southwest at first-hand some day.

Carrizzo with its ex-bank restaurant and colourful crowds must form in
some ways the precise antithesis of Lincoln. Santa Fe, I imagine, must be
something of a high spot despite its modern artificiality and air of showmanship. It is a pity when a fine old town becomes self-conscious and exhibition-
istic—laying on extra touches of pseudo-quaintness and attracting crowds of
tourists, vacationists, and artistic pretenders. All too many of the East's ancient towns have suffered from this malady—Rockport, Marblehead, Provincetown, Nantucket, and St. Augustine being typical examples. But if such a
town still preserves its old buildings and street lines in unspoiled condition it
cannot help being fascinating—no matter how badly cluttered up with "stu-
dios" and "gift shoppes" and other intrusive excrescences it may be. One can
always capture something of the old charm by visiting it out of season—or
threading the venerable lanes at odd hours when the tourists and pseudo-
artists aren't about. Santa Fe, I imagine, must be much like this—a sort of
western edition of St. Augustine. Thanks to you and other friends I have acquired quite a few pictures of Santa Fe, and can imagine something of its antiquarian fascination. It is probably more visibly Hispanic than St. Augustine,
though perhaps not so full of houses of the oldest type. I imagine, for instance, that actual 16th century buildings are rare. Sorry you didn't get a
chance to visit some typical cliff-dwellings and pueblos—for such could not
fail to be worth seeing, even though your primary interest is not in the culture
they represent. Well, anyhow, it seems to have been a great trip, all told; and I
can imagine how many vivid permanent impressions you derived from it.
Next time I hope you can include even more historic high spots—though you
surely did work in a goodly quota this time!

Your observations on New Mexico as a whole are extremely interesting—revealing an environment in some respects absolutely unique. I suppose
that nowhere else in the United States is the Spanish-speaking element so
numerous. In Florida a great many of the St. Augustine families linger on—
Sanchez, Ponce, Segui, Usina, etc.—but they are without exception English-
speaking . . . although still Catholic in religion. In the end, the New Mexican
Spanish-speakers will probably be Anglicised—such being the general trend
whenever a foreign region is incorporated into the continuous fabric of an
Anglo-Saxon land. It was so in Florida—and has proved so with the French
in Louisiana. Quebec remains French only because of an artificial resistance
to assimilation not likely to be duplicated elsewhere. Puerto Rico stays Spanish partly from such patriotic resistance and partly because its unsettled territorial status and West Indian insularity hinder the natural. By the way—is

New Mexico *legally* bi-lingual as Quebec is—so that legal notices, official signs, etc. have to be in both English and Spanish (like Quebec's English and French)? I believe I mentioned to you the odd effect of Quebec's dual signs:

NE STATIONNEZ PAZ   ARRÊT DE TRAMWAYS
NO PARKING   CAR STOP

TRAVERSE DU CHEMIN DE FER
RAILWAY CROSSING

—etc. etc. Regarding the Spanish-speaking population of New Mexico—isn't it a fact that the better elements of it are *really* different from the low-grade ¾ Indian peon stock usually known as Mexican? I had an idea that the high-grade population of the Spanish Southwest—N. M.–Arizona–California— was pretty surely European in blood, and that in New Mexico it has survived without much change. That would surely create an element vastly different from the greasy peon stock—a group of solid middle-class Spaniards well-born and well-descended, and just as racially Aryan, though in a Latin way, as we are. Such a population could hardly mix much with the typical Mexicans. As you know—the newly appointed U.S. Senator from N. M. is a *Chavez*. Am I wrong in this impression? I'll admit that I haven't any specific documentary evidence to back it up—but I merely picked up the notion somehow. I may remark that the Spanish of St. Augustine come most emphatically under this head. They are all pure European white—no mixture of any sort having affected them. They are now, of course, freely intermarrying with the Anglo-Americans—have been, indeed, since the advent of U.S. rule in 1819. Florida is as much a white man's state as Texas—with a rigid colour-line against niggers, and with the tribal, swamp-dwelling Seminoles utterly separate—but the ancient Genevors and Garcias and Menendez's of St. Augustine are so proudly and obviously pure white that no one begrudges them a place on the right side of the line. This perfect equality does not, however, hold good for their fellow-Spaniards from Cuba, who are beginning to immigrate into southern Florida. Except in Key West, which was always half-Cuban, the Spaniard from the West Indies occupies about the same place that the omni-present Italian occupies in the north. He uses the white man's compartments in stations, coaches, etc., but is definitely regarded as a foreigner. The Cuban negro and mulatto, of course, is segregated with other blacks. Just now Miami is worried about its growing Cuban colony. It used to be extremely Anglo-Saxon; but as Cuba gets more turbulent and Key West gets more poverty-stricken, more and more Cubans flock to the South Florida metropolis. Tampa has an enormous Cuban quarter (very quaint—I've explored it) called Ybor City. By the way—that incident of the Texas blacks and the California car was certainly of a sort to make white blood boil! You handled the Sons of Ham in just about the right way!

Your later, shorter journeys seem to have contained a good deal of interest. Comanche is surely a repository of stirring memories—and perpetuates a name well-calculated to arouse fear.

Well—judging from all signs, your local drought certainly seems to be over—and how! That storm surely forms a classic of its kind—and I don't wonder that your father telephoned home in anxiety after hearing of it! I don't know when I've seen a more vivid chronicle of pluvial fury than is afforded by your account of the downpour at Cross Plains. The *suddenness* must have made it all the more dramatic. Your friend Lee surely had a strenuous time with his car—though a good deal less strenuous than his brother had a year ago last Christmas! Curious that the cats didn't make for cover. Down here the outdoor felidae immediately seek refuge under the house (which is cellarless and raised because of the low, watery terrain) when one of the big downpours comes. It certainly can rain oceans in Florida—though the present year is predominantly a dry one. This is supposed to be the rainy season—with a shower around noon each day—but actually a majority of the days are uniformly sunny. It was wet enough last year, though—with the St. John's River occasionally flooding its banks. Sorry Beetle suffered so much from the torrent—though he surely received kindly and effective treatment from his mater. I hope, by the way, that the furry contingent will be getting after that unseen serpent before long. He certainly sounds interesting! Down here several snakes have been shot since my advent—all small ones, though large enough to be skinned for bookbinding purposes. By the way—I'm obliged to record two more local feline disappearances . . . I told you that old white Doodlebug vanished last winter. Within the past month both High and Jack (the latter the hero of last year's snake encounter) have followed the snowy patriarch into the realm of obscurity—though natives assure us that all three are probably still alive and flourishing. Reversions of cats to a wild state are common in Florida—dwellers in remote places telling of legions of them seen and heard in the woods at night. The Barlovian felidae are now reduced to four—Henry Clay (yellow) and Alfred A. Knopf (tiger) outdoors, and Cyrus and Darius (yellow Persians) indoors. Up at the Johnston cottage are two more—San Marcos (tiger) and San Sebastian (yellow). Henry, Alfred, Marcos, and Sebastian are all kittens of Low—who has been given to a grocery store in Eustis. The two saints are of the summer '34 crop, whilst Henry and Alfred were born last winter. It is curious that both of Low's litters consisted of 2 male kittens—one yellow and one tiger. She herself is tiger. Back in Providence my little black friend Johnny Perkins is getting to be a formidable fighting man—menacing the peace of the quiet Elders of the Kappa Alpha Tau. He can put old Pres. Randall to flight just by arching his back and hissing—but valiant Mr. Osterberg is less easily daunted. Johnny has a little white-and-black sister now—but she will probably be given away as soon as she is able to leave the maternal bosom. I'll certainly be glad to see Mr. Perkins in my return. My aunt says he comes to call quite frequently—curling up and purring in his favourite chair.

The incident of the Cross Plains marauder is surely exciting enough, and I shall be interested to hear of further developments. The part played by the next-door neighbour is surely odd enough (or at least potentially so), and it would not be surprising if there were more to the matter than appears on the surface. No—I certainly won't spread any reports of the matter!

. . . .

I'm interested to hear that your direct paternal line sprang from Northumberland. That is also the source of my Allgood line—the line of my father's mother. Regarding the nature of the country—it is generally a region of wide moors and rolling hills, diversified in places by more placid rustic scenery (not unlike that of New England), and rising in the N. and W. into the black and rugged Pennine and Cheviot hills—marking the borders of Scotland. Hadrian's wall crosses it—through a wild and hilly countryside—and numerous other remains of Roman occupation from 80 A.D. onward exist. Its principal port and capital is Newcastle-upon-Tyne—once a Roman station, and still containing the ruins of the Pons Aelii, the bridge across the Tyne built by Hadrian. It was first invaded by the Saxons in A.D. 547, and formed the kingdom known as Bernicia. Up to the time of the Norman conquest Northumberland, Durham, and York formed a roughly dual unit—sometimes the rival kingdoms of Bernicia and Devia, and sometimes the single kingdom of Northumbria. From the middle of the 9th century onward, Northumbria was constantly overrun by the Danes—who founded royal dynasties there, and introduced a vast Scandinavian element into the population. I dare say you and I inherit Scandinavian blood from this source. In Durham and York the presence of the Danes is widely attested by the numerous place-names ending in -*by* and -*thorpe* (*Whitby, Althorpe*), though the invasion was less thorough in Northumberland proper—or Bernicia. The Northumbrians resisted William the Conqueror more vigorously than any other inhabitants of Britain, but were finally subdued. The Normans rebuilt the Saxon abbeys, and added many noble edifices of their own. In succeeding years Northumberland was the scene of many wars with the Scots—as the Ballad of Chevy-Chase eloquently attests. As for industries—coal mining has been conducted since Roman times. Lead, silver, and iron have likewise been mined. Fishing and agriculture have always flourished, and sheep-raising is at present a major pursuit. Newcastle is the centre of a busy—and no doubt detestably ugly—manufacturing area. The city itself is noted chiefly for coal-exporting and shipbuilding—indeed, it is probably the greatest shipbuilding centre in the world. The region whence my ancestors spring is not far from Hexham—near Hadrian's Wall. I like to think that the blood of some centurion or legionary—somebody with a name like M. Valerius Subinus, P. Aelius Gallus, or Cn. Julius Martialis—descends to me through some obscure channel—as is by no means theoretically or practically impossible.

My stay in Florida has certainly been delightful in the extreme. The Barlows—with typical super-hospitality—are urging me to stay all winter—but I really could not be away from my own library and files that long. Much as I hate the northern winter, I shall have to be hitting the trail before long. Am so broke that I doubt if I can stay anywhere save St. Augustine and Charleston en route home.

The other day we all had an interesting trip to a scenic spot some 20 m. S.W. of here—Rock Springs, where amidst a picturesque wooded valley a crystal stream issues forth from twin black tunnels in the side of a lofty tree-crowned cliff of hard-packed clay. About 60 ft. inside the larger of these tunnels there is a vast hidden chamber of eternal night—once used by the Indians as a refuge from their foes—beyond which is another aperture leading back to unplumbed and inconceivable abysses of inner earth. The stream at one point widens out into a bathing pool—in which the Barlows disported while I roamed the neighbouring woodlands and enjoyed the spectacle of the cliff and tunnels. The public is not allowed to crawl in to the tunnels and see the hidden cave—although this prohibition is a relatively recent one. I hope to see this spot again very shortly.

July W T mediocre—August looks like nothing extra. Received *Marvel Tales*—ambitious size but rotten contents. Rumours regarding a successor to the F F occur now and then, but no paper of the sort has yet appeared. Meanwhile I'm always on the lookout for your stories—of which I trust I shall see another specimen before long.

Every good wish—
Yrs most cordially—
E'ch-Pi-El

Notes

1. Donatien-Alphonse-François, marquis de Sade (1740–1814), author of *Justine* (1791) and other pornographic works.

[119]　　[ANS][1]

[Postmarked Cassia, Fla.,
12 August 1935]

_____ of the Panhandle! Hope you're finding it up to all expectations. Knowing *all* of one's native state is a sizeable task where Texas is concerned! I'll be interested in hearing of your impressions of the northern territory. Later on I hope you can complete your knowledge by seeing the Big Ben region. ¶ I have not yet seen *every* region of my own microscopic state even now—because of lack of transportation. As you know, I slightly enlarged my knowledge last spring. ¶ Shall be interested in seeing your biography in *Fantasy Magazine*. Rimel shewed me the excellent linoleum block silhouette he had prepared. ¶ Find it hard to break away from Florida, but ought to be on the road in a week or two. It surely has been a great visit! ¶ Judging from your postcard, the Panhandle has some great scenery. Palo Duro Park—with its Devil's Tombstone—would seem to form almost the ultimate word in natural fantasy! ¶ All good wishes—E'ch-Pi-El

Notes

1. Front: A Florida Sunset.

[120]   [ANS][1]

[Postmarked De Land, Fla.,
19 August 1935]

Thanks abundantly for the fresh batch of photographs & cards. Glad to see glimpses of your home & household—& of the various points of interest in the Panhandle. Palo Duro certainly is a great place! You seem to have had a magnificent time, & I hope such events may be frequently repeated. ¶ Am leaving De Land today for St. Augustine, Charleston, & points N. The number & lengths of the stops I shall make will depend on my finances. I'll send you any cards of interesting places which you haven't seen before if I can find any. I fear, though, that I've sent about everything on the market in the places I visit so frequently! ¶ This has certainly been a great visit—from June 9 to Aug. 18. It has quite set me on my feet physically. The Barlows are also leaving—going on a fortnight's visit to Daytona Beach. ¶ All good wishes
—E'ch-Pi-El

Notes

1. Front: A Florida Sunset.

[121]   [ANS][1]

[Postmarked Saint Augustine, Fla.,
20 August 1935]

On the road at last! The Barlows have gone to Daytona for a fortnight, & here I am back amidst the ancient lanes of San Agustin . . . a town that was 42 years old when the first colonist arrived at Jamestown. Here for a week—got a good basement (but above ground) room with bath & kitchenette for only *$3.50,* & am eating on 20¢ per day, with beans as a base. On to Savannah Aug. 26; Charleston the same afternoon. The length of my stay in Charleston depends on my cash. Doubt if I can make any stop at all N. of there. ¶ Well, it has been a great summer! ¶ Presume you're back from the Panhandle trip. I surely appreciated the news you sent!

All good wishes—

H P L

Notes

1. Front: Post Office and Custom House, St. Augustine, Fla.

[122]   [ANS]¹

[Postmarked Charleston, S.C.,
27 August 1935]

Greetings from ancient Charleston! Out of luck with postcards—nothing new, & in general the poorest assortment in years. Like a homecoming to strike Anglo-American colonial architecture—white steeples, fanlighted doorways, railed double flights of steps, &c—after nearly 3 months in a region of Hispanic traditions. But Charleston seems curiously *northern* in contrast to Florida—less moss on the trees, fewer & smaller palmettos, no jungle effects, no rainy season, & so on. Here for 4 days—as long as my cash will take me. Then Richmond & the north—mere 1-day stops. I may possibly find a way to pause in N Y long enough to greet the gang. ¶ Barlow came up from Daytona & paid me a surprise visit while I was in St. Augustine. We viewed the Indian skeletons unearthed last year. ¶ I was so eager to get to Charleston that I cut out Savannah—whizzing through on the 'bus at 5 a.m. ¶ Shall be glad to get home to my books & things, though I dread the cold of the north. ¶ All good wishes—

E'ch-Pi-El

Notes

1. Front: Wentworth Street, showing Grace Episcopal Church, Charleston, S. C.

[123]   [TLS]

Cross Plains, Texas
October 3, 1935

Dear HPL:

Here are some clippings which might interest you. The one about "Uncle Gus" and the one about the generous plutocrat who gave the boy a dime for returning a $39,000 check were on the same page of the same paper, and I was struck by the contrast of human natures, and of the methods of the old-time frontier people with modern go-getting business men.¹ There were plenty of "Uncle Gus's" in the past generations of Texas, though not many were financially as able to exercise their quiet philanthropy as he. But there's damn few "Uncle Gus's" being produced by this highly-advanced age, anywhere.

The other clipping, as you see, is a brief account of the cannon episode of Gonzales, where yesterday the affair was celebrated on its hundredth birthday.

By the way, I listened to Il Duce's speech over the radio yesterday,[2] and its translation; a more sickening and nauseating outspewing of blustering hypocrisy never offended my ears; though I found equally revolting the brainless cheers of the thousands of poor idiots he is leading to the shambles.

Cordially,
REH.

Notes

1. The two stories appeared on the front page of the *Dallas Morning News*, 2 October 1935. "Uncle Gus Wilson, Collin County Pioneer, Nearly Penniless at His Death" related how Wilson had given away more than $750,000 to individuals, schools and churches during his lifetime. "The pioneer, who never married, made it a habit to buy automobiles and farms for anyone who caught his fancy with a kind or industrious act," the paper reported. "Landholders returning from the field might find the deed or mortgage to their property hidden under the dinner plate; a newly-married couple might discover a fully-equipped new car in the garage of their new home. To one boy, he gave $1,000 in stock because he did not look up from his cotton-hoeing job when Wilson passed." The other article, "Return of $39,000 Check Wins Dime Reward for Boy," reported on an incident in St. Louis, in which an 18-year-old messenger found in the street a check for $39,000, endorsed by the payee, and returned it to the man. "He dug down in his pocket and pulled out a nickel," the boy is quoted as saying. "Then he told me he thought it was worth more than that and handed me a dime. I hardly knew what to say."
2. In his speech on 2 October 1935, Fascist dictator Benito Mussolini insisted that Italy was determined to move forward with its conquest of Ethiopia and offered his rationale. Italian troops were at the time massed on the Ethiopian border and had already clashed with Ethiopian troops, though the invasion officially began on 3 October.

[124]   [TMS]

[5 December 1935]

Dear HPL:

A rather belated reply to your interesting letter. Thanks for the postcard views you enclosed. I'm glad that your visit was so enjoyable and hope you'll be able to repeat it soon.[1]

Glancing briefly at our controversy—if what is merely a clash of opposing cultures could be so called—I note your remark to the effect that probably misconceptions arise through what you aptly call a "lack of a common language or set of association patterns." You may remember that in an earlier letter I expressed a doubt that we could ever reach a common plane of understanding, having so few tastes and experiences in common. My life has been almost antipodal, in its associations, to yours. I've had little acquaintance with scholars, artists and literary people, whereas these types obviously have formed the bulk of your companions. Not being familiar with these types, it's easy for me to misunderstand their ideas and opinions. I'm also but little fitted to deal with abstract ideas which do not, apparently, have any connection with everyday reality as I know it. I've never had much time to devote to theories and philosophies. My life has been a daily grapple with vital—perhaps sordid—facts, connected with the very elements of existence. Obviously, when confronted with questions or matters dealing with or lapping over into the realms of metaphysics, philosophies and theories I am guilty of blunders and stupidities amazing to men who have devoted much time to these things. I am almost as unfamiliar with the world of theory and intellectual research as I am with Mars. On the other hand it seems obvious from your own arguments that you've had little if any first-hand contact with the rough sides and the raw edges of existence; if you had, you couldn't possibly have some of the ideas you have, and so many of my views and statements wouldn't seem so inexplicable and outrageous to you. It is inevitable that we should constantly misunderstand each other. Probably it's mostly my fault, through a vague and blundering style of expression on the one hand, and sheer ignorance of the intellectual view point on the other—my ignorance, I mean, of course. I'm sure I have misunderstood you frequently. I find it difficult to believe that some of your views are as arbitrary and intolerant as they look on paper.

You express amazement at my statement that "civilized" men try to justify their looting, butchering and plundering by claiming that these things are done in the interests of art, progress and culture. That this simple statement of fact should cause surprize, amazes me in return. People claiming to possess superior civilization have always veneered their rapaciousness by such claims. You say some wars are waged in defense of civilization. Can you name a recent one? Was it the Mexican War in which a Latin culture was simply replaced, in some regions, by an Anglo-Saxon culture? Was it the Civil War, in which an agricultural oligarchy was crushed by an industrial oligarchy? Was it the Spanish-American War in which our capitalists grabbed an island for its wealth in sugar? Or was it the world war in which the Germans butchered to expand Kultur, and the Allies fought "to make the world safe for democracy"? (And incidentally to protect Wall Street's European investments.) Or is it the present tussle in Africa where the wops are civilizing the benighted Ethiopians with poison gas and dum-dum bullets?

I find it hard to understand your surprize because I say that civilized men always claim the highest motives, even when perpetrating the most infamous atrocities. You wouldn't find my statement of fact any cause for wonder if any of your people had lived in Texas during the reconstruction period when certain benevolent gentlemen were "defending and expanding civilization" by the means of whole-sale thievery and organized murder. I recall one noted carpet-bagger in particular; speaking to a horde of freed slaves, he bellowed: "The white barbarians who enslaved you are doomed! Civilization has come to stay! Follow me into Waco tonight! We will leave not one man, woman or child alive!" (About that time some of the "barbarians" he planned to butcher opened fire from the brush and the stalwart hero didn't stop running until he crossed the Rio Grande.)[2]

You don't have to go that far back. Your friend Mussolini is a striking modern-day example. In that speech of his I heard translated he spoke feelingly of the expansion of civilization. From time to time he has announced: "The sword and civilization go hand in hand!" "Wherever the Italian flag waves it will be as a symbol of civilization!" "Africa must be brought into civilization!" It is not, of course, because of any selfish motive that he has invaded a helpless country, bombing, burning and gassing both combatants and non-combatants by the thousands. Oh, no, according to his own assertions it is all in the interest of art, culture and progress, just as the German war-lords were determined to confer the advantages of Teutonic Kultur on a benighted world, by fire and lead and steel. Civilized nations never, never have any selfish motives for butchering, raping and looting; only horrid barbarians have those. When the Belgians mutilated several thousand Congo niggers that was in the defense of civilization, too. When Germany surged across defenseless Belgium that too was in defense of civilization, as represented by themselves. But the Allies, too, defended civilization. Each side claimed to be the sole defender of civilization in that carnage. You say that "the fruits of civilization must be preserved at all costs." Just who is trying to loot these fruits? The Ethiopians? You say that in preserving these fruits, all civilized people "make that cost as light as possible" to their benighted opponents. Is that why civilized scientists are working overtime to try to invent gasses that will wipe out entire civilian populations, and why war-plans of all modern powers frankly include the destruction of non-combatants? I suppose it was with a view of making things light for their fiendish enemies, that the super-cultured English soldiers of a few generations ago made a practice of cutting off the breasts of Irish women with shears. It must have been a great comfort to the poor, mutilated women to know that their suffering did not result from any brutal motive (such as only barbarians have) but from the highest and loftiest motives on the part of their mutilators—i.e., the preservation of the higher culture. Doubtless, too, it was for the same high principle that Tarleton's British cavalry tortured women and murdered children in the Carolinas[3]—they, too, justified themselves as civilized men battling heroically against the vicious, uncivilized settlers. The same when the ultra-awfully-civilized British and Tories turned the red Indians loose on the homes of the men they were fighting, and heroically paid bounties on the scalps, not only of fighting men, but also of women and children. It is probably in accord to the same principle—that of sparing their enemies as much as possible—that modern war-makers bomb defenseless towns with large civilian populations, mangling and destroying women and children and old men by the thousands.

You say that only barbarians practice whole-sale butcheries and massacres. Did you ever hear of the Mountain Meadow massacre?[4] The men who did that were fresh from the older settled sections and from Europe. You consider the pioneers of Texas as barbarians compared to the Europeans you idealize. But I challenge you to produce one single episode of blood-spilling in early-day Texas that even approached, in whole-sale butchery, such incidents as Walter Raleigh's slaughter of the Italian mercenaries in Ireland;[5] Essex's slaughter of 400 Irish women and children;[6] Clanrickard's butchery of prisoners after Kinsale;[7] the wholesale executions after Monmouth's rebellion;[8] Cromwell's massacres in Ireland;[9] the extermination of the Australian natives by British settlers;[10] Leopold's butcheries of the Congo negroes;[11] the bombing of civilians in the world war; or the present slaughter of women and children by your Fascist friends in Ethiopia. One bomb dropped in a crowded city by a cultured, civilized war-maker kills more women, children and helpless old men than ever were killed altogether in the wars waged by the Texas pioneers throughout nearly a century of constant battling. You say massacres are exclusively limited to barbarians; since you classify my pioneer ancestors and their associates with barbarians, then if you are to prove your point, you should show where they wallowed in slaughter and butchery. But you can't show one incident where they ever made a slaughter of women and children and helpless men. They did not even retaliate with a massacre for Goliad[12] and the other atrocities committed by the Mexicans. They spared Santa Ana's life, and the lives of all Mexicans who laid down their arms. They didn't even massacre Comanches. British soldiers shot Afghan women because they mutilated prisoners and wounded, and Italian soldiers are killing Amhara women for the same reason; but Texans did not war on women, though the Comanche, Lipan and Apache squaws committed mutilations as revolting as any ever conceived. (The soldiers of one certain fort did make a practice of unexpectedly attacking friendly Indian villages, killing the men and children, and chaining the young women in the fort until they died from continual raping, when their bodies were tossed out for the buzzards; but those soldiers were neither pioneers nor Texans; and they justified their actions as "civilized" men always have, by saying their victims were mere savages.) There was never, on the part of the Texas pioneers, even any such whole-sale slaughter as culminated the Pequot War.[13] Not, at least, as far as Indian women and children were concerned. The Western pioneers, as a class, ignorant of the blessings of European civilization, didn't even know that white men were capable of making war on women; they left that to Mexicans and Indians.

You will probably take all this a direct attack on civilization. It isn't intended as such. I'm only replying to your comment that you were surprized that I should say that civilized men justified their thieveries and butcheries by asserting motives of progress.

You don't have to go to war to find this hypocrisy. Every corporation that has ever come into the Southwest bent solely on looting the region's people and resources has waved a banner of "progress and civilization"! A few years ago we, the native element, kicked out the rottenest, most cynical and most corrupt administration that had been inflicted on the State since carpet-bag days. And what a howl went up from the outside interests that supported it and were fed by it in turn! And what was the burden of their squawk? Mainly that we had "turned the clock back"! Dealt a blow to "civilization" from which the State would recover only when "they" got back in power. Newspapers in other states took up the yowl and solemnly announced that Texas had taken a step back into barbarism which was her natural state. Why was all this caterwauling? Because we refused any longer to see our natural resources stolen from under our noses. Because we were tired of seeing corporations located in other sections grab huge monopolies on resources which they sucked dry and departed with bulging money-bags, leaving a devastated land behind them; or else grab resources on the promise of development but which they did not develop, but merely held them to keep them from being developed by somebody else, which might have interfered with the profits of the corporation's activities in some distant section. Just as the Insull interests held the Colorado River and its tributaries, impoverishing thousands of people of their rightful water supply.[14] That the capitalist looters should throw a smoke-screen of claims for progress and civilization and advancement is not surprising; as with professional soldiers, dictators and imperialists, it is their favorite slogan; but it is ironic for disinterested parties to attack us as "opposing the expansion of civilization" when we are merely fighting the interests which, in the Southwest, are the greatest obstacles in the way of that progress and development which civilized people claim to support. I remember a few years ago when I was in South Texas, shortly after I left Austin, a certain bill was introduced which was a plain move on the part of a certain powerful interest to plunder the State's resources wholesale. An honest and patriotic legislator defeated the bill, and exposed the purposes of its backers, and he had scarcely left the capital when he was set on by the hired thugs of that certain powerful interest, and slugged, beaten and kicked almost into insensibility.[15] That's the sort of "expansion of civilization" native Texans have to deal with. Please let me say that I don't accuse all alien interests of motives of plunder and exploitation. To do so would be ridiculous. Probably the mass of them are honest and upright; but there are always wolves among the sheep, and invariably the former proclaim the same aims and motives as the latter. Great care should be taken in distinguishing between them, and one should not be fooled by slogans.

As for the charge of "enemy of humanity," the distinction you draw between attitudes and individuals seems a bit fine to me. I see no difference between telling a man he is an enemy of humanity and telling him that his attitude constitutes an enmity to humanity. You apparently feel that any opinion, ideal, preference, or belief that differs widely from those you hold constitutes an attack on human development and indicates an enmity to humanity, as you have made this charge (phrased in one way or another) not only in connection with my philosophical convictions, political affiliations and sociological theories, but also in regard to my personal preferences and private habits, necessitated, in many cases, by the environment in which I live. If, as it appears, I am to be penalized for merely being born in a region that differs from somebody else's region, I see little use in trying to answer the charge.

You say: "The world of developed men must stand firm against any atavistic assault from the underworld of sub-men." Just who are these ape-men who are intent on destroying all that is good and exalting all that is bad? Don't you think you're going a bit far in classifying ordinary citizens with gangsters, hoodlums, thugs and other criminals? True, we can't all be scientists, scholars or artists; but many of us, indeed, most of us, are as law-abiding as you are.

As for the definition of the term "sadism" I must indeed be ineffectual in my style of expression if I left the impression that I'm so ignorant that I don't know what the term means. At least I've read what Havelock Ellis[16] and other leading psychologists have had to say about it, and have in my possession a very good work on sadism and masochism by a noted German scholar.[17] Incidentally, according to your own definition of it, you erred in applying the term to the bowie-knife duelling of the Southwest, as you once did.

Glad you found the accounts of my trips of some interest. I certainly enjoyed your comments on Florida and adjacent regions. But then I always find your descriptions interesting in the extreme. You are probably right in assuming that the Latin population of New Mexico will eventually be Anglicized.

But it will be a slow process, for migration into the State is comparatively sparse, and probably more than balanced by the drift of Latins from Mexico. To the best of my knowledge New Mexico is legally bi-lingual, though all the highway signs I remember seeing were in English. As for that matter, you could say the same for San Antonio, as far [as] the store signs are concerned. You ask concerning the different classes of Latin New Mexicans. Of course, I wasn't there long enough, and didn't see enough of New Mexican society to make any positive statements about conditions. But the higher class New Mexicans are undoubtedly of a purer and superior stock than the ordinary peons—more Spanish blood and less Indians. But I doubt (though I can't swear to it) if the upper classes in New Mexico are as purely Spanish as those of Florida. It must be remembered that New Mexico was colonized, not directly from Spain, but from Old Mexico, where an intermingling with Aztec strains had already been going on for some years; that for many years New Mexico was an isolated region with little chance of contact with other European colonies; and that the region's native Indians were peaceful and semi-civilized, offering no great barrier to the mixing of their race with the conquerors. I have an idea that the Spaniards of early New Mexico mixed a great deal more with the Indians than did those of Florida. However, there is probably a strong Anglo-Saxon strain in many of the better families, for in the early days of American rule, a good many Americans settled there, first as traders and trappers, later as soldiers and cattlemen, and married Mexican women. By the way, the first European colony in Texas, Ysleta, was settled by people from Santa Fe, fleeing an Indian revolt in 1680.

I think I sent you some pictures of the Panhandle. My parents and I went to Amarillo in the latter part of July. None of us had ever been to that city, and I wanted to see if the high altitude, 4500 feet, might help a persistent cough that had been bothering my mother. Those upland plains are monotonous to look at, but the atmosphere whips fresh blood and new life through the veins; at least it always did with me. We ate our dinner at the little town of Post, a few miles this side of the Cap Rock. Everything looked placid enough, but there was a secret tension evident at times—had been ever since Sheriff Cato shot Stafford, the Federal G-Man, on the street a few months before.[18] Of the merits of the case I have nothing to say. A court acquitted Cato and all those accused of conspiracy with him, and the prosecution was unable to prove its accusations of a gigantic dope-ring, to protect which, it claimed, Cato shot the Federal agent. Most [of] its witnesses were dope-fiends, apparently, and the court refused to accept some of their testimony, I understand. Narcotic agents had been very busy in the State for some time, and some people thought some of them had gone too far. Cato had the reputation of being an honest and courageous officer. So, for that matter, had Stafford. But Stafford was from New York, and I can not but feel that he was not as familiar with the ways and traditions of the section he had to deal with, as he should have been. Without commenting on the merits of the case, I will only say that to me, it seems as if it might have been a mutual misunderstanding—arising from the clash of utterly different cultures. Judging from newspaper accounts, each merely acted in accordance with the normal customs and traditions of his particular environment. It's a pity that people's patterns of thought and action, formed by custom, tradition and conventions, are not more flexible than they are.

We reached Lubbock a few hours later, and from Plainview on it was new territory to all of us. Lubbock, a few months before, was also the scene of the trial of another officer, the sheriff of an adjoining county,[19] who was charged with protecting bootleggers and dealing with liquor himself. He was sentenced to three years, but he must have cleaned up while he was at it; one man alone testified to having paid him fifteen hundred dollars for the privilege of selling liquor fifteen days in his territory. I was particularly interested in the case, because the sheriff on trial was born and raised near Cross Plains, and some of the witnesses against him were former citizens of Callahan County. The case seemed proved against him, but as a law-officer in the Oil Belt, years ago, he proved himself a brave man, and it was said of him that he never took a penny of protection money from a high-jacker.

We got to Amarillo well before sunset, having driven nearly 400 miles since morning. My mother had not regained her strength from her operation, but she stood the trip remarkably well. Amarillo is a town of some 43,000 people, and extremely modern and up-to-date, though somehow it doesn't seem like a typical Texas town. It had a remarkable growth, springing from a small village to about its present size in just a few years. It spreads over an amazing territory, but, like most West Texas towns which have grown up since the beginning of the machine age, it has broad, straight streets, easy to drive on, and is very clean in appearance. It may some day be the biggest city in the State, if the Great Plains are ever developed as they should be. With its close proximity to the "Bread Belt of the Nation" it has great possibilities as an industrial center.

The next morning we drove out to the Canadian River, some twenty-five miles north of Amarillo. It's a treacherous, turbulent river, running through shallow, rugged canyons. In some places dry canyons parallel the main bed, cut out by overflows, or caused by the river changing its course.

Returning to Amarillo we ate breakfast and then started on our homeward journey. At Canyon, eighteen miles south of Amarillo, we turned eastward and drove several miles to the Palo Duro canyon, the eastern-most of the great gorges of the west. A narrow road, a mile long, meandered down into the canyon, which is a thousand feet deep and perhaps eighty miles long, and we drove along the canyon floor for several miles, seeing some of the most vivid and rugged scenery I have ever seen anywhere, even in the Rocky Mountains of New Mexico. A small creek twists along the floor, and the road, which workmen were even then improving, crosses it repeatedly. Near one of those crossings was fought the last Indian fight ever to be fought in Texas— that is, the last formal engagement, if it might be so-called, when scouts and soldiers surprized and captured the Comanches who had taken refuge in the canyon, in 1874.

The Palo Duro is considered by some historians to have been the cradle of the Comanche race. At least it is certain that it was the homeland of the tribe for some centuries. Others consider that the tribe originated and developed somewhere on the plains of the Middle West, and drifted south to the Palo Duro as late as 1700. This is probably erroneous, for it is pretty certain that Coronado found Comanches living in the Palo Duro in 1541. It is possible that the theory of southward drift in 1700 is a confusion with an eastward and southward movement that did occur about that date, but which originated from the Palo Duro, where the Comanches had been living since drifting down from the north centuries before. There was an expansion movement on the part of the Comanches in the latter part of the eighteenth century. Before that time Apaches had occupied western and central Texas, and these were swept southward and westward, with their Lipan kin, before the onslaught of the conquering Comanches, who were soon destroying Spanish outposts along the San Saba, Concho and Llano Rivers, harrying the outskirts of San Antonio, and raiding deep into Mexico itself. Spanish development of the country north of the Rio Grande was checked and hindered, and there is a possibility that the Latins might eventually have been driven south of the Rio Grande entirely, but for the intervention of the Anglo-Saxon colonists. These drove the Comanches implacably northward and westward, shattering their power in battle after battle, until the last remnant of the once proud and merciless nation was cornered and captured in the ancient cradle of their race, and banished permanently to a reservation in the Territory.

There is, I understand, talk of building a road through the canyon, which at present, except for a few miles of passable, but unpaved road, has only horse-trails. This road would connect with the trans-continental highways in the northern part of the State, and would prove one of the most striking scenic drives in the country. I feel sure it will eventually be accomplished.

Returning to Canyon City, the home of the West Texas State Teachers Normal, we wanted to visit the museum, which I understand is the most complete thing of its kind in the State;[20] but it is open only on certain days in the summer, and that wasn't one of the days.

So we came south, following the road we had taken in our northward travels, and reached the town of Sweetwater, in Nolan County, before sunset. It was formerly a clean, likable cattle-town, but now, since it is becoming an industrial center, has attracted some pretty unsavory characters, as well as many decent and honest citizens. While having my car greased (and being just full enough of beer to be talkative) I listened to a tale by one of the mechanics concerning the activities of a mysterious character who had tried to rob his house on more than one occasion, and once had even got into his bedroom, while he slept, and tried to ransack the place. He said he suspected a certain dope-fiend and announced his intention of filling the offender's legs with lead on the next offense. I heartily sympathized with him, but doubted the wisdom of aiming at the fellow's legs.

Returning to the tourist camp where we were staying I got a glimpse of another phase of life when a small girl and her young brother came out of a cabin and wistfully eyed a melon that had just been cut. We shared with them, of course, and this inspired the girl to volunteer unasked information concerning herself and her parents. They were nice looking kids, but poorly dressed, and were, the child volunteered, being taken to California by their mother. She naively prattled away of watching her mother being beaten by their father, and it was rather revolting to hear her matter-of-fact tones relating how their father had, on one occasion, pinned their mother against the wall and beaten her eye nearly out of her head. This tale confirmed the fact that they were not natives of Texas, which of course was evident from their accents any way. They told where they were from, but that doesn't matter.

Next morning we turned south, a hundred miles or so to San Angelo, traversing a rugged and rather barren country I hadn't visited since we lived in that region, more than twenty years ago. We passed through Bronte, where we were living when the Orient railroad came through there, and which I, at least, hadn't seen since we moved away.[21] It was named for the noted author, when founded by a colony of English, in the latter part of the nineteenth century, but they starved out or were absorbed by the hard-bitten native settlers, who shortened the pronunciation to one syllable. We ate breakfast in San Angelo, which is about 105 miles from Cross Plains, and reached home shortly after noon, having driven nearly 1000 miles in about three days.

After returning from Amarillo, I did little travelling for some months. My motoring was limited to a few trips to Weatherford, Mineral Wells, Comanche, etc., sometimes for watermelons. As you possibly know, Weatherford is the most famous water-melon market in Texas, which State is approached only by Georgia in the quantity of melons produced, and approached by none in the quality of the vegetable. Trucks come from all over the Mid-West and the West to buy the melons which are displayed by the thousands in the big square in Weatherford. But it was a poor year for melons. They were not as good as usual, and were higher. For a hundred pound melon they demanded a dollar, or sometimes even more. The best melon I tasted the entire season was a fifteen pound melon I bought for a nickel in Comanche.

About the middle part of October I went to the only football game I've seen this year, and it was a lousy scoreless tie.[22] But I enjoyed it more than I might, because before we got there Pink Tyson, Dave Lee and myself started hitting the bottle, and for the first time in many months I got pretty well soused, well, at least mellow and hilarious. I believe Brownwood is getting more tolerant and easy-going than it once was. They used to be pretty hard on drunks, but nobody had a harsh word for us this time. Of course we didn't raise any hell, and there was a big crowd of merrymakers in town. I did go back into a cafe after my coat which I'd forgotten and upset the stand with a crash when I pulled it off, and damaged its foot. It ordinarily embarrasses me to find myself suddenly the center of attention as happened then, with the cafe crowded with people, but I had too much liquor in me to be daunted. I brandished my wallet and announced blatantly that I would pay for any damage I did, but the management good-naturedly refused. Well, we had a good time at the game sitting on the top-row seats and yelling, anyway. After the game we tried to find my old friend Clyde Smith, partly through friendship and partly because we wanted some more liquor which he could be depended upon to produce, but after looking for some time it suddenly occurred to us that none of us knew where he lived, so we gave it up.[23] You may remember Smith as collaborator with me in "Red Blades of Black Cathay" in *Oriental Stories*. I believe his second marital venture is proving successful; at least, I understand he has grown from 150 pounds to 230 pounds, which would speak well for his health, at least. I well remember the last riot we went on before he got married; he, Tyson, Vinson and I started to go somewhere to a movie, or some other innocent pastime, but we started drinking whiskey, and that called for beer, and along about midnight we found ourselves in a den of iniquity in a county-seat town about fifty miles east of here. The beer was punk and the girls were worse—well, there was one I remember with pleasure, a blond with a figure like—well, no matter.

Anyway, when I got back from the afore-mentioned football game, I found the Prices had arrived from California.[24] I'd decided they wouldn't get to Cross Plains till the next day, which is why I went to the ball-game. They stayed only three days before they left for Mexico City, which disappointed, as I had hoped to entertain them for a week at least. Naturally Ed and I had many long conversations, or you might almost say just one, lasting his entire stay here. He's certainly succeeding in the writing game and I'm mighty glad of it, for he deserves it, both as to literary merit and as to hard work getting where he is.

About the middle of November my mother's health became so poor we took her to the Torbett Sanatorium in Marlin, Texas, where more than a gallon of fluid was drawn off her pleura. She stayed at Marlin two weeks. It is a small town, the county-seat of Falls County, about 200 miles east of here. We drove there in my car, through the picturesque hill-countries of Brown, Mills and Coryell Counties, through the towns of Goldthwaite, Gatesville of bloody memories, and Waco.[25] Near Waco the country changes to the lowland plains of East Texas. Marlin is a few miles east of the Brazos River, in a rich, but, to a hillman, a monotonous prairie country.

When I learned that my mother would have to stay in Marlin for a few weeks, I came back to Cross Plains, to bring my father home, and to get my typewriter. We travelled by another, more northern route, through Bosque, Erath, Eastland and Comanche Counties, following one of the oldest paved highways in the State,[26] which twists through the Bosque mountains in a way that would break a snake's back. Going back to Marlin I followed yet another route, through Mills, Lampasas, and Bell Counties.[27] It was farther that way, but led through a strikingly picturesque country. However, along each route there were stretches of striking scenery, hills painted red with sumac, brown by oak leaves, green by mesquite, and yellow by elm and other trees. Between

Cross Plains and Brownwood, the morning I left, I saw a phenomenon which I venture to say was the first of its kind ever to be seen in Central West Texas, and would have been impossible a few years ago.

It was a clear, cold, frosty morning, the sun not yet up. As I drove out of Cross Plains, but little after dawn, I saw steam rising from a small lake where wild ducks swam by the hundreds. Then, many miles farther on, as I approached the valley of the Jim Ned, I saw what looked like a long bar of cloud stretching for miles along the horizon. Yet everywhere else it was clear. As I approached the Jim Ned, which runs between rugged hills, I saw that it was a heavy, white fog rising from the water, and filling the valley as far as I could see in each direction. This doubtless seems too common a thing to notice, to anyone accustomed to big rivers, but here in West Texas, where the streams are so small and the water so scarce, it constituted an occurence so rare as to be unique, to the best of my knowledge. But the building of the Brownwood dam, ten miles below the spot where I crossed the Jim Ned, has backed water up the creek and made a real river out of it, big enough to send up a cloud of dense mist on such a morning as I have described. As I crossed the bridge I could hardly see the water beneath me, and the sky overhead was revealed only in irregular blue patches; the sun was about to rise and the fog seemed luminous, almost. Not grey and damp and depressing, but purely white, with almost a rosy tinge, through which the sky peeped here and there, with a rare and delicate blue. As I drove out of the valley and looked back, I saw the river hidden by the fog which nowhere rose over a hundred or so feet in height. Far away to the east the long line of fog grew into a gigantic billowy cloud that hung over the lake, invisible from that spot. And the fog had sent out questing fingers that floated up every creek and branch that ran into the river. When I got to Brownwood, which stands in a basin traversed by Pecan Bayou, the town too, was veiled with the mist. It seems a strange thing, somehow, that we should have a body of water in this country so big that it emanates a regular fog.

I stayed a week in Marlin, after my return, and wrote several stories. It's a quiet little town, a noted health resort, and more niggers than you can imagine; two thousand of them, out of a total population of five thousand people. I picked up a few items of history formerly unknown to me, mostly from a good friend of mine who has charge of the electrical department of the sanatorium, and the only man that I, at least, ever met, who would talk freely about the bloody days of Coryell County, following the Civil War.[28] He was born in that county; he witnessed the execution of the only three men ever hanged—legally—in Gatesville.[29] At the age of sixteen he was serving as a sheriff's deputy. Repeated attempts were made on his life, and several times his dogs routed mysterious visitors in the night who had sneaked in the yard to shoot him as he slept. He said he never dared open the barn door in the morning to feed his horse without having a pistol ready in his hand. His readiness to talk about those times contrasted strongly with the attitude of an old ranchman I met in the little town of Copperas Cove, in Coryell County, last spring when my car broke down and we were forced to spend several hours there. He was a fine-looking, intelligent old gentleman but I got little information out of him. He was polite, courteous, as almost all old-timers are, but evidently the fierce happenings of those early, bloody days were burned so vividly on his consciousness that he would not recall them. I think I made a mistake in telling him that my grandfather had owned a sheep-ranch in the adjoining county of Lampasas in those days. I think that roused his suspicions that perhaps I was not the harmless history-hunting author I professed to be. Old men sometimes live in the past, and do not realize that times have so utterly changed. I'm sure that he wasn't one of the men who burned the house on my grandfather's ranch and secretly butchered his sheep; but he might have thought I had come back for revenge on somebody—after nearly fifty years! It's hard for some of these old men to realize that the old feuds smoldered out years ago and will never be relighted. I was beginning to gain his confidence before I left him; he had asked me many questions concerning the number of my relatives, where they lived, where they had formerly lived, etc., and seemed much relieved when I assured him most of them lived in Arkansas, Missouri and Oklahoma. If I could have stayed with him for a few days, slept in his house, eaten with him, ridden over his pastures with him, he would eventually have told me all I wanted to know. Indeed, his invitation for me to spend a few days with him was a hint to that effect. But I wasn't in a position to accept. Caution in speech was ingrained into such men, in their youth; before they'll talk to you about the wild days, you must first win their confidence. And when you have won it, there's no limit to their trust in you.

I met another old-timer, of a somewhat different social class, but equally reticent, in my region of the country a few months later, also a Coryell County man, and was somewhat amused by his wrigglings to avoid giving direct answers to questions of what happened in that county fifty years ago; when I asked him bluntly if a certain family were not all horse-thieves, he almost fell out of the car.

While in Marlin I had many enjoyable conversations with the son of the man who gave me the Coryell County history, a talented young man, with remarkable artistic ability.[30] He is not only a portrait-painter of great ability but has considerable literary talent. He is a great admirer of your work, by the way. I think he could have been a success either as a painter or a writer, but, while attending an art school in California, he became interested in the occult, and now devotes practically all his time to this study. He is sincere in his devotion to it, but I regret his interest in it, since it has caused him to neglect his undoubted talents. I can not have any sympathy for this occult business. However, if that's what he wants to do and enjoys doing, then I'm not one to criticize.

While in East Texas I did a little exploring of various counties, including Falls, Milam, and Robertson. The country differs much from my own region. The altitude is more than a thousand feet lower, for one thing, and the terrain is monotonously flat, or gently rolling. There is more timber, and the trees are much bigger. The air is generally still, so much so that I began to long for the misty uplands before I left. There is much misty, damp, cloudy weather, and it never gets very cold there. Life seems to move more leisurely there, and many people speak with a soft slurring Southern accent, never heard among the natives of the hill-countries. Our accent is West Texan, a dialect that does not copy any other anywhere else.

We were just about to start for Cross Plains one morning, my father having come to Marlin in his own car, with bed-clothes to make a bed in my car for my mother, when it started raining, and rained most of the day. But the next day was clear and we started early, my mother and I in my car and my father following in his car. We came by the road that runs through Gatesville, and over a hundred miles of it was unpaved. However we didn't stick, although it was extremely slippery in places. Once I met a car in one of the worst places imaginable. The ruts were fair enough, but on each side was a stretch of thin, treacherous mud. The ruts held the wheels so for a moment I was afraid I wasn't going to be able to get the car over in time to avoid a collision and I read the same fear in the face of the other driver as he struggled with his wheel. I swung over by sheer strength, though, and when we hit that greasy mud, the car turned crossways of the road three times before I could get it under control and back in the ruts again. I accomplished it by sheer beef and muscle, and was damned glad I possessed at least enough of them to keep the car from wrecking itself. It's such little incidents as that which make me unable to accept the assertion of the "anti-physicallists" that a modern man doesn't need any muscles.

When we got into the hill-country proper, the roads got better, and I drove from Goldthwaite to Cross Plains, 75 miles, in about an hour and fifty minutes, which breaks no records but isn't bad time with a small car and roads not of the best.

I was highly honored to be asked to contribute to "The Challenge From Beyond" yarn, along with you, Miss Moore, Merritt, and Long.[31] I hope my share didn't weaken the strength of the story too much. The rest of you did fine work, as you all always do. Appearing in such a company will probably remain my chief claim to fame. I'm also delighted to note the forthcoming appearance of your stories in *Astounding Stories*.[32] I hope you'll make this market regularly. Street & Smith pays good rates, for these times, and pays promptly. I see no reason why you shouldn't have nine or ten stories a year in that magazine. I've made a few new markets since writing you, but am not making sales as regularly as I wish, or need. However, I hope this slump is due rather to the wrench of changing my style of work rather than an indication of staleness. The last yarn I sold to *Weird Tales*—and it well may be the last fantasy I'll ever write—was a three-part Conan serial which was the bloodiest and most sexy weird story I ever wrote.[33] I have been dissatisfied with my handling of decaying races in stories, for the reason that degeneracy is so prevalent in such races that even in fiction it can not be ignored as a motive and as a fact if the fiction is to have any claim to realism. I have ignored it in all other stories, as one of the taboos, but I did not ignore it in this story. When, or if, you ever read it, I'd like to know how you like my handling of the subject of lesbianism.

In my efforts to make new markets I've been "splashing the field" as Price calls it. One market I tried was *Spicy Adventure*, a sex magazine to which Ed is the star contributor. I sold the first yarn I tried,[34] but doubt if I could make that market regularly, as it requires a deft, jaunty style foreign to my natural style. However, I'll probably try it again. Why don't you give it a whirl? You can use a pen name if you like; I did, and I think most of its contributors do.[35] The maximum length is about 5000 words. That sort of yarn is easy to write, if not to sell. If they reject it, you've only wasted a day or so. If they accept it, you're fifty bucks to the good, and they pay promptly. They like good strong plots, but the sex element is a cinch; any man can write that part of it. Just write up one of your own sex adventures, altered to fit the plot. That's the way I did with the yarn I sold them.

Thanks immensely for the data about Northumberland. While most of the English blood has been washed out of my line by strains of Irish O'Tyrrells, Colliers, McHenrys, Ervins, etc., still I'm glad to know what kind of country the thin British strain represents. I've read the Ballad to which you allude, and maybe some Englishman of my ancestry was at that scrap, but I've got an idea I had more kin on the Scotch side at that fight.

By the way, since you've been so generous in giving me the dope about one of the former homelands of my people, I'm going to impose on your generosity some more and ask you about the country around Currituck Sound in North Carolina.[36] The Ervins were living on a plantation in Currituck Precinct in 1724 and for how many years before that date I don't know. I suppose that precinct was adjacent to the Sound or the town by that name, and I have a vague idea that the country thereabouts is swampy, though of course I've never been there. Do you know what time the Scotch-Irish began to come into North Carolina? I've always understood that it was about 1725, or later. But the Ervins, at that time, had been in North Carolina for a long time, and they came directly from Ireland, and not from Pennsylvania as so many of the later Scotch-Irish settlers came. They must, for some reason, have come with the English settlers who, as I understand it, were the first colonists in North Carolina. Or perhaps the Scotch-Irish drift began earlier than I suppose.

Several months ago I had a dream so vivid and unusual that the next day I wrote it up, just as I dreamed it, and it has recently occurred to me that you might be interested in reading it; please return it at your leisure, though there's no hurry.[37]

Thanks again for the postcard views, and best wishes.

Cordially,
REH

Notes

1. Probably a reference to HPL's visit to New Haven on 8 October (see *SLL* 5.211–12) or his visit to Boston with Samuel Loveman on 16–18 October (*SLL* 5.212).

2. The "noted carpet-bagger" would be "Colonel Leopard" (see p. 168).

3. Col. Banastre Tarleton (1754–1833), British officer during American Revolution.

4. In the summer of 1857, Mormons and their Indian allies killed 140 immigrants bound for California at Mountain Meadows, about 320 miles southwest of Salt Lake. The Mormons had been upset by news that federal troops were advancing on them and provoked by the boasts of some members of the emigrant party that they had aided in kicking Mormons out of Missouri. Jack London fictionalized the episode as one of the past-life episodes recalled by the protagonist of *The Star-Rover* (1915), a book REH owned.

5. The reference is to the defeat and massacre of a papal force at Smerwick in 1580 by English forces under the command of Sir Walter Ralegh (1552–1618) and the Earl of Ormond.

6. Walter Devereux (1541?–1576), first Earl of Essex, stormed Rathlin Island, where rebellious Scots of County Antrim had sent their women and children for safety, and massacred all, in 1575.

7. Probably a reference to Richard Burke (1568?–1635), fourth Earl of Clanrickard, staunch supporter of Queen Elizabeth and commander of cavalry force at Battle of Kinsale (1601) against O'Neill.

8. James Scott (1649–1685), bastard son of Charles II and first Duke of Monmouth, at Charles's death in 1685 returned to England from exile on the Continent and claimed the right to the throne over James II. He was defeated and captured; his supporters were mercilessly punished in what came to be known as the "Bloody Assizes."

9. Oliver Cromwell (1599–1658), leader of the Parliamentary revolt that deposed and executed Charles I in the English Civil War (1642–1649), ruthlessly suppressed rebellions that had sprung up in Ireland in support of the monarchy, 1649–50. His most infamous outrage was the slaughter of more than 2,000 persons at Drogheda.

10. The expansion of white settlements in Australia led to an unofficial policy of exterminating the aboriginal population. In Tasmania, between 1800 and 1830, the aboriginal population decreased from about 4,000 to less than 500; ultimately, the depopulation there was almost total. In Victoria, a population estimated at 10,000 was reduced to 2,000 within 30 years of the colony's founding.

11. Leopold II (1835–1909), king of Belgium (1865–1909), became interested in African colonization in the 1870s. He was granted sovereignty over the Congo by the Berlin Conference (1884–85). He was widely criticized for his harsh treatment of

natives in the region, especially in the years 1903–05.

12. During the Texas Revolution, Col. James W. Fannin, Jr., surrendered his outnumbered force at Goliad on 20 March 1836. On orders of Mexican President, General Santa Ana, the entire force of 390 or more men was executed on 27 March and buried in a common grave.

13. In 1637, the Pequot Indians, under the leadership of their chief, Sassacus, became increasingly warlike and a threat both to the English colonists of Massachussetts and Connecticut and the Dutch at New Amsterdam (later New York). In June of that year, a force of Massachussetts Puritans and their Narragansett and Mohegan allies made a night attack on a fortified Pequot town, burning it and slaughtering its 600 inhabitants. The only other engagement of this "war" was the surrender of a party of Pequots trapped in a swamp: the men were killed, the boys sold to the West Indies, and the women and girls distributed among the colonists as slaves.

14. Samuel Insull, whose Midwest Utilities Company attempted to build a hydroelectric dam on the Colorado River beginning in 1931; work was halted when the Insull holdings went bankrupt in 1932. See REH to HPL, 9 August 1932 (p. 355).

15. Apparently a reference to an attack on state representative Gordon Burns of Huntsville on 24 April 1933, in an Austin hotel lobby, by a lobbyist representing oil interests. Burns had spoken on the floor that afternoon against a bill to create an oil and gas commission to assume oversight responsibilities that had been the province of the Railroad Commission. Burns and others believed that the legislation was an attempt by major oil companies to expand their influence. There were conflicting accounts of the fight: most agreed that Burns was first attacked by Charles Roeser, president of the Texas Oil Conservation Association, but some witnesses insisted that only the two men were involved, while others stated that Burns was attacked and then kicked, while he was on the ground, ten to fifteen men who had been with Roeser. Burns spent several days in a hospital.

16. Henry Havelock Ellis (1859–1939), British physician and psychologist. His pioneering study of human sexuality, *Studies in the Psychology of Sex* (7 vols., 1897–1928), banned in Britain, was published in the U.S., and for many years available only to physicians.

17. A list of books in REH's papers includes "Sadism and Masochism, Eulenberg, New Era Press." This would be Albert Eulenburg, *Algolagnia: The Psychology, Neurology and Physiology of Sadistic Love and Masochism,* translated by Harold Kent (1934).

18. Sheriff W. F. Cato of Post shot Federal narcotics agent Spencer Stafford with a machine gun, 7 February 1935, outside a veterinarian's office where Stafford and another agent were checking narcotics records. Cato and three others were charged with conspiracy to kill Stafford and involvement with a narcotics ring. Cato pleaded self-defense, claiming he did not know Stafford was a federal agent and that Stafford had pointed a gun at him. All the men were acquitted at their trial.

19. Sheriff J. L. (Len) Irvin of Lamb County was charged with protecting bootleggers, selling liquor privileges in the county between 1926 and 1935, and having threatened federal agents. He received a two-year sentence. A Joseph L. Irvin is enumerated in the 1910 U.S. Census living in Justice Precinct 4, Callahan County, Texas, but no data from other census records have been located.

20. The Panhandle-Plains Historical Museum, opened in 1933, still considered one of the finest in the state.

21. The Howards lived in Bronte c. 1909, when REH was three years old. In that year, the first train on the Kansas City, Mexico and Orient Railway came to the town, though the tracks had been completed two years earlier.

22. The Howard Payne College Yellow Jackets played scoreless tie games against Trinity College (4 October) and Austin College (18 October 1935). REH presumably refers to the latter game.

23. Tevis Clyde Smith married Rubye Barkley in September 1934. His marriage and his job with the Walker–Smith wholesale grocery company, which required him to travel a large territory covering West Texas and part of New Mexico, led him to spend less time with his friends. He and REH last saw each other in January 1935.

24. The Prices visited REH while on their way to Mexico City, in mid-October 1935.

25. This route would have followed Texas State Highway 7/US 84 from Brownwood to Waco, and SH 6 to Marlin.

26. Probably what was then Texas SH 67, now State Highway 6. In 1935 SH 6 went north from Waco to Dallas, but southeastward from Waco to near Galveston (as it does today).

27. This route would have followed Texas State Highway 74A (now US 84/183) from Brownwood through Mills County, SH 74/US 190 (now US 183) to Lampasas, SH 53/US 190 (still US 190) to Temple, and SH 139 (now FM 438, FM 935, and SH 7) to Marlin.

28. The friend was Frank Torbett, father of Thurston Torbett, and on the staff of the Torbett Sanatorium, founded and run by his older brother John. The Torbett family had come to Texas from Alabama between 1868 and 1872, and by 1880 were in Coryell County. In the years following the Civil War, Coryell County was open rangeland, crossed by a feeder route of the Chisholm Trail. After the war, there were many un-branded cattle roaming free, and the county authorized the branding of the cattle, after payment of a fee, to raise funds for the support of widows and orphans of Confederate soldiers. Unfortunately, this policy promoted cattle rustling. When local law enforce-ment officers proved incapable of coping with the problem (there were seven sheriffs in a ten-year period), local cattlemen took to dispensing swift justice with shotgun or rope.

29. Two men, Jim Leeper and Ed Powell, were hanged in 1891 for the murder of John T. Mathes in 1889 during an attempted hold-up. It was the only public execution in Gatesville.

30. I.e., Thurston Torbett.

31. Published in *Fantasy Magazine* (September 1935). REH's installment was fourth, following HPL.

32. *At the Mountains of Madness* and "The Shadow out of Time."

33. "Red Nails."

34. "She-Devil" (original title "The Girl on the Hell-Ship"). REH had four other sto-ries in the magazine.

35. REH used the pen-name "Sam Walser" for these stories.

36. In the extreme northeastern corner of the North Carolina coast.

37. This dream account remains unidentified.

[125]   [nonextant letter by HPL]

1936

[11 February 1936]

Dear HPL:

Glad you enjoyed the dream write-up I sent you. Long narrative dreams are fairly common with me, and sometimes my dream personality is in no way connected with my actual personality. I have been a 16th Century Englishman, a prehistoric man, a blue-coated United States cavalryman campaigning against the Sioux in the years following the Civil War, a yellow-haired Italian of the Renaissance, a Norman nobleman of the 11th Century, a weird-eyed flowing-bearded Gothic fighting-man, a bare-footed Irish kern of the 17th Century, an Indian, a Serb in baggy trousers fighting Turks with a curved saber, a prize-fighter, and I've wandered all up and down the 19th Century as a trapper, a westward-bound emigrant, a bar-tender, a hunter, an Indian-fighter, a trail-driver, cowboy—once I was John Wesley Hardin! I remember very well indeed the Roman dream of yours which Long used in his story. As I told you then it was an imaginative and poetic masterpiece.

As for our controversy, and regarding my remarks about philosophy, I was not, as you seem to think, attacking philosophers or depreciating philosophy. I merely said—or I meant to say—that many of your ideas and theories have little connection with everyday life *as I know it*. That was no depreciation of the science of philosophy. I simply meant that many of the standards and theories which guide your life, are unfitted to guide mine. I don't question that they are perfectly valid and vital for you and your environments and traditional way of living. But my way of living necessarily differs from yours. I don't see how you can expect a man born on the bald western prairie and raised on ranches and farms and in border towns and oil belts to have precisely the same beliefs, the same opinions, the same traditions and the same customs as a man born and raised in an East Coast city. Nor is there any real reason for believing that the habits and thought-ways developed by the latter environment have any more cosmic significance than the habits and thought-ways developed by the former. You uphold the one set and condemn the other merely because one is familiar to you and the other isn't. There's nothing really outlandish, barbaric or incongruous about the western scene. It only seems so to you because it's so different from the eastern way of living.

I'm glad you've decided that I'm not an "enemy of humanity" after all. You say you use the term only to designate such people who "would voluntarily destroy the kind of life prevailing in Scandinavia or Britain or pre-war Germany in favour of the kind of life prevailing in Borneo or ancient Gaul or the Djuka country." Well, that must let everybody out for I can't imagine any sane person having such an ambition as this. As for myself, it's true I've of-

915

fered some criticisms against certain phases of the modern system, but who hasn't? You have yourself. And just why have I offered most of these criticisms? At the very beginning of this argument an attack of civilization was farthest from my mind. In a way you yourself forced me into a position of apparent attack on civilization by assuming that every time I disagreed with you about anything, I *was* attacking civilization. In the beginning I had occasion to state a few personal preferences, with no thought at all of precipitating a debate. But I found them, and myself attacked with a vigor that amazed me. I understand now that you were outraged and surprized only because these preferences were so unfamiliar to you, being, as they were, so alien from the conventional preferences of your particular and geographic social group. But I didn't understand that then, and I sought to explain and defend my position. Somewhere in the debate you drew some awful pictures of "barbaric" life—which I did not deny. I have never denied the violence and ferocity of barbarism. But I thought—possibly because of my own stupidity—that you were attributing *all* the violence and injustice in the universe to the barbarians—apparently including the people of the West, past and present. I retorted that cruelties and injustices were committed by civilized people too. You challenged that statement. I produced my evidence. That's all there is to it. When I have narrated various atrocities committed by "civilized" people, I have merely been answering your challenge to prove my statements. I never said that civilized people committed more atrocities than barbarians. I merely said they were not guiltless—and calling themselves civilized, their guilt was less excusable than the same guilt in a barbarian.

Take for instance, the recent discussion concerning the pretenses of "expanding civilization" that nations use in plundering weaker tribes. I commented on the hypocrisy of the announcement a stronger nation makes that its butchering and looting is in the interests of culture and progress. You questioned this—or seemed to question it. I proved what I had said. Now you express surprize that "such claims are ever very widely believed." What's that got to do with it? I said such claims *were* made. I didn't say anybody believed them. If a man shoots at me, he has shot at me, whether he hits me or not.

As for the cases I gave of atrocities committed by civilized people: I can't see that any comparison with the deeds of the Afghans, Abyssinians or Jivaros has any weight with the point I was making. I didn't offer the actions of these people as comparison; I didn't even mention them. I compared the actions of the so-called civilized people with the actions of my pioneer ancestors and their contemporaries. I challenged you to show proofs that the Texas pioneers ever committed any wholesale atrocities to match those I enumerated. You say I "still seem to think that" you "attack the western pioneers" in spite of your repeated expressions of admiration for them. No, I don't think you consciously *attack* them, according to your standards. I realize you have expressed an admiration for them in general. Yet you have consistently attributed to them—and to their modern descendants—a brutality and callousness which you seem to think sets them at a disadvantage with the Europeans. The first accusation of "enmity to civilization" that I remember you making was when I expressed an admiration for the frontier way of life. Throughout this entire discussion you have consistently taken the position that my fondness and admiration for the pioneers was an attack on civilization. You have repeatedly compared the pioneers and their descendants with the people of Europe, to the extreme disadvantage of the former, attributing to them a viciousness and cruelty not found in the European. Perhaps I have been mistaken, but how could I keep from supposing that you class us as barbarians, considering all the phases of your arguments? You even advised me to spend a year in some Eastern city so I could get some idea of how civilized people act. And throughout you have taken the position that the defects in modern Western life resulted from a survival of frontier traditions, and that the Europeans were far superior to Western people in kindness, justice, benevolence, intelligence, ethics, and practically every other way. All right. If we're barbarians we ought to act like barbarians. If they're a superior breed they ought to act like it. I challenged you to show one instance where the people of Texas, past or present, indulged in wholesale torture, looting and butchery, such as has been the actions of Europeans time and again. You say we are more callous, brutal and cruel than they are. I merely ask you to prove it, not by theory, but by fact. Anybody can say: 'It is an accepted fact that pioneers and their descendants are more brutal than civilized people.' Accepted by whom? The civilized people. Before I accept a "fact" it must be proved solidly, by actual happenings, which are the only things my admittedly scanty brain can recognize as proofs. You excuse the atrocities committed by the Belgians and Germans in Africa, the Germans in Belgium, the English in Ireland and America, by saying such things are natural in the stress of war and colonization. All right. Why didn't the pioneers of Texas resort to these acts of butchery then? What were they doing, if not colonizing and fighting? And their fighting-colonizing period lasted more than fifty years. If it is inevitable that white men revert to savagery under such conditions, why didn't they revert? English soldiers and Italian soldiers butchered Afghan and Ethiopian women because of their mutilation of the wounded and captured. But the Texans didn't consider it necessary to make war on the Comanche women, who were equally guilty. Why didn't the Texans go to the extremes you say are natural results of war and colonization? Was it because there weren't so many hysterical neurotics among them? They had a code and they lived up to it. They didn't abandon it with emotional hysteria when they found the going tough. The European has a high-sounding code; but he seems to desert it with remarkable promptness at the least excuse.

I note in the discussion of sadism, you insist on applying it to frontier life in general. In a former letter you said "the average roughneck is not a sadist." But the designation you refuse to apply to a thug, you would apply to a pioneer. You show surprize because I consider your attitude toward the pioneers one of bias. How could I think otherwise, when you seek to classify them on a lower plane than the criminal element of your own region? It is not necessary that I should attempt to refute this charge. It is idle to accuse the frontiersmen of degeneracy, whatever else their faults might have been. That a mob of degenerates could not possibly have accomplished what they *did* accomplish, ought to be evident to the most prejudiced.

Concerning warfare fought to defend civilization, when I asked for an example of such a war, I was not referring to wars waged between rival civilizations. I was referring—or rather, asking for an example of a war fought to preserve civilization itself against the attacks of barbarism. That you had to go back to the Austro-Turkish wars of 1683 proves my contention that no recent wars have had that motive or excuse.

Your defense of the modern habit of bombing defenseless towns and butchering helpless non-combatants is a striking example of the difference between the European viewpoint and the Western-American viewpoint. My people, in all their many wars, never found it necessary to destroy women, old men and children, even when savages were their opponents. You maintain that such butchery is merciful. I'm glad the Yankee soldiers who sacked my grandfather's farm in Mississippi didn't have such ideas of mercy. They stole everything they could get their hands on, but they didn't consider it would be an act of mercy to cut my grandmother's throat and impale my aunts on the fence pickets. Regardless of their looting, they didn't offer the helpless women-folk any harm. European ideals certainly must be invading the country if Americans are advocating and applauding the wholesale destruction of helpless non-combatants.

As for the Italian effort in Africa, it had not been my intention to start a debate about it, knowing as I did your intense admiration for Mussolini and your sympathies for the Fascists. But since the question has come up, lest a misunderstanding arise concerning my views, I'll bluntly say that I do not consider the Ethiopian invasion a sincere colonizing movement on the part of a whole people. I believe it to be a frantic ruse on the part of a crumbling dictator to keep himself in power by diverting the attention and force of the people he has ruled by force and guile. Mussolini's no Caesar; he's a damned rogue, a fact which has been brought more forcibly to my recognition by recently glancing at a book of his career by a newspaper man named Bond[1]—a book which can not be classed as anti-Fascist propaganda, for the author voices his contempt of Communism and Socialism as strongly as Fascism. He says he wants colonies; why hasn't he colonized Eritrea and his other African possessions? If he had to have new land, why didn't he offer to buy it? It would have been cheaper in the long run than grabbing it by war. Some think he should be allowed to grab Abyssinia and "civilize" it. Personally, I'm not in favor of any sort of intervention merely to keep Ethiopia from being gobbled up. I don't blame the English for being perturbed, but I'm not so naive that I think they are altruistic or moved by a principle. Italian occupation of Ethiopia would be a threat to the British empire. But there's no use in America taking a hand either way. But I regard, as extremely dangerous to the peace of the world, any viewpoint or policy that would give the more powerful nations a free hand with the weaker ones. If we justify Italy's grabbing of Ethiopia, how can we condemn Japan's seizing of Manchuria, China, Australia and India? What objection could we offer against Germany's grabbing Austria, Finland, Poland, Scandinavia? Or Russia's grabbing all the weaker countries about her? But you may say, let us consider that the "civilized" countries and regions held by the civilized countries, are sacred and inviolate, and give the plunderers a free hand with the uncivilized regions. All right. What regions are these? Who's to judge? The people who do the looting? These folks always consider their victims as uncivilized. Germany is uncivilized according to the Russian view, and vice versa. If the doors are thrown wide open and the announcement made that any uncivilized region is to be made fair loot for anybody strong enough to grab it, what's to prevent the Germans, for instance, announcing that their Baltic neighbors are guilty of uncivilized ways and customs, and moving in and grabbing their property? The people of Texas, New Mexico, Arizona and California consider themselves more highly civilized than the people of Old Mexico. If the "civilized" races are to be allowed to enrich themselves at will by the conquest of the less advanced (according to the standards of the aggressors) why shouldn't we Western Americans cross the Rio Grande and grab what we want?

I don't know what the attitude toward the Italian move is in other parts of the country, but everybody I've encountered in these parts, and all my Western correspondents who have expressed themselves, hope that Mussolini and his tin soldiers will get the hell kicked out of them. And I think they're in a fair way to do it. I don't think he had any idea what he was getting into. I pity the wops he's leading to the shambles, but in a way they deserve it for letting themselves be driven by such a swine. Probably the affair will be settled eventually by England getting Ethiopia into her empire.[2] That would probably be the best all around. I honestly believe the Ethiopians would be better off under British rule than under their own. But I don't believe they'd be better off under Italian rule. Latins have neither colonizing nor governing capacity. I've seen evidences of their efforts in Mexico. The average Mexican peon is no better off than his ancestors were as Aztec peasants. As for the loudly advertised question of slavery in Ethiopia, why should Italy be so suddenly and piously concerned? Slavery has been practiced continually in her own African possessions, and is still being practiced, in Eritrea and elsewhere.

As for the police, I can't understand why you repeatedly charge me with objecting to the *necessary* routine of keeping the peace, when all I have ever objected to was acts of *unnecessary* and *wanton* brutality; all I ever said was that these acts are more common than you seem to realize, and I say this, not because I'm such a Goddamned fool as to have an actual prejudice against the police, but simply because my studies of the matter, over a period of some six years, have convinced me that it is the truth.

As for supposed lawlessness in Texas, you say, in regard to the pioneers that you "felt sure they would be the last to wish their descendants to struggle against any avoidable obstacle." I'll be frank to say that I don't understand what you're driving at here. I'm not aware that we're struggling against anything, except to keep what's rightfully ours, and to resist vandalistic aggression and exploitation—a resistance, I had thought, from some of your remarks, that you were in sympathy with. I fear, though, that you entertain a misconception of the pioneers if you believe they would want their descendants to meekly submit to oppression, even though the would-be oppressors might happen to lay claims to "superior" culture.

I am glad to see that you have decided that I "do not actually oppose civilization in principle." This is by no means a radical view to arrive at, considering that I have always opposed the very things that the highest code of civilization pretends to oppose, and that my main criticism of "civilized" men has always been directed, not at their expressed code of life, but at their rather consistent failure to live up to that code. In many cases when you apparently thought I was attacking civilization, I was simply pointing out the fact that certain laws and customs necessary and helpful in the East or in Europe, were not only unnecessary, but would be actually harmful or impotent if applied in the West. If you would study the physical conditions that will always differentiate the West from the East, you would see that my viewpoint was not based on a blind hostility to Eastern and European ways, but on a realistic conception of the conditions and needs of the West. I read a good article pertaining to this subject not long ago, written by a university professor, long accepted as an authority. He mentioned the common fallacy of considering the West as merely an underdeveloped extension of the East, and asserted that most of the supposed lawlessness of the West was the fault of, not the law-breakers, but the makers of the laws.[3] Men are *forced* to break laws they can not keep.

I note your remarks on American accents with much interest, and am glad to hear of the research work being done in regard to the subject. Thanks for the items you enclosed in your letter, all proved very interesting. I received "Haunter of the Dark" from Price and sent it on to Rimel as instructed.[4] I consider it a splendid piece of work. As a weird story and a work of art I have no criticisms to offer. I enjoyed reading it immensely and see no reason why it should not be accepted by any magazine dealing in the fantastic.

As for my own fantasy writing, whether or not I do any future work in that field depends a good deal on the editors themselves. I would hate to abandon weird writing entirely, but my financial needs are urgent, immediate and imperious. Slowness of payment in the fantastic field forces me into other lines against my will.[5]

Thank you very much for the data regarding the Currituck district of North Carolina. You confirm my belief that the Ervins came to that region before the main drift of Scotch-Irish migration began. Or rather, you confirm my belief that the Scotch-Irish drift began some years after the Ervins came, for I already knew the approximate date of their arrival. I understand that most of the Scotch-Irish were Lowlanders originally, and the various books on genealogy speak of the Ervins as a border family. But my people have always spoken of their Scotch strain as Highlander, and as late as the early part of the nineteenth century a branch of the family living in the Piedmont, and more Scotch than Irish, spoke Gaelic exclusively among themselves and made themselves understood in English only with difficulty. Somehow, my branch of the Ervins were Highlanders before they became Irish.

Please pardon the shortness of this letter, but I've had to snatch such moments as I could to answer it, and it's possible that it seems disconnected and muddled in spots. I've had little opportunity to do any writing of any kind for the past month. In fact this letter is the longest bit of writing I've done since about the 20th of January. After our return from Marlin we stayed at home for about two weeks, and then my mother's pleura filled again, and we took her to a hospital in San Angelo, 105 miles southwest of Cross Plains. After a few days then we put her in a sanatorium about seventeen miles northwest of San Angelo,[6] where she stayed for six weeks, when her condition got so bad we put her back in the hospital at San Angelo. She remained there twelve days, and then we brought her home, since it seemed they had done all they could for her. Her condition is very bad, and she requires frequent aspirations, which are painful, weakening and dangerous. It is wonderful with what fortitude she endures her afflictions; in every hospital she has been, the doctors and nurses speak of her cheerfulness, her nerve, and her steadiness in the highest terms. But it is only what can be expected in a woman of the old pioneer stock. This has been a bitter winter, and the harshness of the weather has hurt her. First one woman and then another we hired to help wait on her has been taken sick herself, so the job of nursing my mother has been done largely by my father and myself. She is subject to distressing and continual sweats, and naturally has to have constant attention, so I find little, if any, time to write, which is why this letter is brief, and possibly so disconnected. Some times we have to be up all night with her. There seems to be little we or anyone can do to help her, though God knows I'd make any sacrifice, including my own life, if it could purchase her any relief.

This has been the worst winter since 1929, one blizzard after another, combined with dust storms bringing epidemics of sickness, and sleets and snows, but no rain, no real moisture. We are in the grip of a drouth and the outlook is grim. If it does not rain this country will be racked and torn by storms and tornadoes in the spring. The growing grain has already wilted and withered, and in a few more months stock-water will be getting low. The destruction of the farm-planning and crop-control legislation will hurt the farmers and ranchers bitterly in this country.[7] They will endure it; they have always endured hardships, since the first white settler walked into the State behind his ox cart, to change his moccasins for boots, his coonskin cap for a sombrero, and his axe for a lariat. But this year will bring much for all to endure.

Personally, the cold weather hasn't bothered me much, I mean in so far as my physical comfort has been concerned. During most of the worst cold weather I spent most of the time either at San Angelo or on the road going or coming, and I became so toughened to the cold that I seldom bothered even to put on an overcoat, unless the weather was close to zero, and never found it necessary to put on underwear in the most bitter weather.

San Angelo is a likable town of about 25,000 people, on the bank of the South Concho, amongst vast, rolling prairies.[8] It is [the] biggest mohair market on this continent, and much more Western in air and viewpoint than the hill-towns in this vicinity, as well as more cosmopolitan. This phrase, used in connection with such a small town, may seem incongruous. But it must be remembered that a town of 20,000, 30,000, or 40,000 in the West is much more important in the pattern of things than an Eastern town of the same size. San Angelo is the largest town between Fort Worth and El Paso, and draws from an enormous trade territory extending for hundreds of miles in every direction, including vast, rich areas of farming land and cattle country. The streets are broad and straight, everything modern and up to date, the attitude of the people friendly and good natured, typically Western. Technically and mechanically West Texas is more highly developed than East Texas (of course excepting the cities of East Texas, such as Houston, San Antonio, Dallas, etc.) and it seems to me that general standards of education are higher—higher than in this Central hill-country, too, I believe. The contrast of costumes on San Angelo streets are interesting: suits and dresses such as you would see on the streets of San Antonio or New Orleans contrasted with ten-gallon hats and spurred boots. San Angelo is, by the way, famous for its hat-shops and boot-shops. People living in San Antonio, Saint Louis, Santa Fe and other distant points often have their boots made there. I got just the sort of a hat I had been looking for, and unable to find, for some time. It's a fast stepping town, and comparatively wide-open. As in any typically West Texas town there is plenty of drinking, fighting and love-making going on all the time. I believe you would find much of interest in the museum in the administrative building of old Fort Concho, established, as I remember, in 1868 and abandoned as a post in 1889. A public school now stands in the middle of the parade-square, but many of the old buildings are still standing, some of the officers' houses now being used as residences.

With best wishes.

Cordially,
REH

Notes

1. John Bond, *Mussolini, the Wild Man of Europe* (1929).

2. The Italian army captured Addis Ababa and proclaimed Ethiopia a vassal of the Italian crown in May 1936.

3. Probably Walter Prescott Webb, who wrote in "The Mysteries of the Great Plains in American Life" (chapter XI of his *The Great Plains*, 1931), "The blame for a great deal of Western lawlessness rests more with the lawmaker than with the lawbreaker." REH quotes extensively from Webb's book in his letter of 13 May 1936 (see pp. 948ff.).

4. HPL was circulating the story in manuscript among his colleagues, including E. Hoffmann Price and Duane W. Rimel.

5. *WT* had been months behind in its payments to REH, at least since the beginning of 1935 and probably much longer. At the time of his death in June 1936, the magazine owed him more than $1350.

6. The Texas State Sanitorium, at Carlsbad, Texas.

7. The Agricultural Adjustment Act, a New Deal program that had been very good for the farmers but had cut into the profits of processors, distributors, and bankers, was struck down by the U.S. Supreme Court on 6 January 1936. The court held that the Constitution did not give Congress the power to regulate agriculture.

8. A note on the original typescript of the letter reads: "San Angelo is 90 mi., airline, from Cross Plains. Howard knew the entire region. Yer maps show San Angelo as at confluence of North Concho and Middle Concho Rivers. Perhaps R.E.H. uses an old, 'unofficial' designation. And I've known maps to be wrong! E. Hoffmann Price May 11, 1945." Fort Concho was established at the confluence of the North and South Concho rivers; the town which became San Angelo grew up across the North Concho from the fort.

[127]

66 College St.,
Providence, R.I.,
May 7, 1936.

Dear R E H:—

. . . . . As for the good old controversy—I surely didn't expect the inhabitants of widely differentiated regions to have identical tastes and customs, and am sorry I conveyed such an idea. When I said that *philosophy* has a connexion with *all* phases of *every* kind of every-day life, I did not use the general term to signify any limited *part* of philosophy which may have been under discussion (I don't recall details) and which may not have been applicable to all regions and types of culture. I meant simply that the broad, inclusive subject of philosophy as a whole does indeed cover the whole range of human entity and activity—seeking to explain and correlate whatever it finds, and looking for any general values which may underlie the various manifestations of different groups. That such values exist, can hardly be seriously disputed. No difference in regional standards can conceal the fact that Patagonians and Esquimaux live on an absolutely (so far as terrestrial organic life is concerned) lower plane than Englishmen and Frenchmen—that they have left the greater part of their possibilities undeveloped, and therefore live closer to the amoebal plane than do races who have trained their innate capacities and filled and sensitised their cerebral-aesthetic apparatus.

As for the term "enemy of humanity" as I used it—I think there is always present in society a small minority to whom that term can be applied in the given sense. While not all of this minority would care to lower the prevailing life-level to the wholly savage state, it is undeniable that they would like to see it pulled down to an intolerable degree of mediocrity. This actual hostility to the best human achievements is found in many proletarian groups and peasantries, and was markedly manifest in the earlier stages of both French and Russian revolutions. It also exists in the theories of many 'back-to-nature' cults which stem from Lord Monboddo and Rousseau—and is of course strong among a good many of the backward races themselves, who hate the white man and all his works. My mistake regarding your own attitude—as I originally made it—arose from my impression that you invariably exulted in the destruction of developed human groups by undeveloped groups, and ignored the achievements and advantages of development through dislike of that inevitable loss of a few primitive advantages which forms the price of net growth. Such a misunderstanding is hardly to be wondered at in view of the wide area covered by the debate, and the scanty time in which I had to analyse statements and formulate replies.

Something of a similar misunderstanding seems to envelope your impression of my statements about the southwest. I have always emphasised my regrettable ignorance of the region, and have never attempted to form judgments from such fragmentary and second-hand information as I have. Whenever I have given opinions, these have had to do *only with certain acts and attitudes*—irrespective of region. I have no present knowledge of the extent to which those acts and attitudes are really typical of any given place. The fact is, until the beginning of the present argument I had no idea that the southwest differed at all radically from the east in its major basic folkways. It was my belief that violence had vanished 30 or 40 years ago, and that the legend of persons going about armed in the 20th century was an invention of the dime novelists and cinema producers. So you can see that I had no prejudice to start with. Even now I don't believe that things are as violent as the pulps and films assume, or that law-abiding, non-encroaching persons are forced to wear armour and artillery on the public streets. Nor did I claim that the southwest's *past* was any more barbaric than the conditions of colonisation compelled it to be. I thought I emphasised this point. My argument was that any region ought to be glad to get through its period of perilous colonisation—with the attendant disadvantages—and reach a condition of orderly stability in which the inhabitants can attain a better-rounded development. And I am sure that a great part of the southwest *has* reached such a condition and duly appreciates it.

I believe I can now see where your idea of my unjust attitude arose—although I later disavowed the initial mistake which gave rise to the misconception. At a time when I believed the southwest not *essentially* different from the rest of the country (of course, *every* local area has its *minor* individualities), you pointed out certain grave evils connected with corrupt law enforcement—evils involving the frequent unjust arrest and physical mistreatment of innocent persons. These seemed very strange to me, because no parallels exist in regions which I know. Naturally I sought an *explanation* of such a difference from familiar conditions; and at that early stage of the debate it seemed natural to ask whether some peculiarity of the local tradition might not be responsible for the phenomenon—a phenomenon involving lack of respect for the inviolability of the human person. It was only a theory and a query—sustained at the moment by a parallel discussion in which the late survival of primitive conditions had been mentioned. In the course of time that theory was proved wrong—it being shown by you that the given acts of lawlessness and violence were perpetrated by large *non-southwestern* corporations, and that even the personal agents were to a great extent alien to the southwest. (This matter, by the way, influenced considerably the slow leftward swing of my social and political attitude since 1931.) However, I suppose my original advancing of the local-tradition theory conveyed the impression that I was attacking the southwest—an impression which lasted long after I had abandoned the theory which gave it rise. As it really was, the only evils I had in mind were those which you had brought up. So you may see that I *never* assumed a priori that the descendants of pioneers must necessarily be more callous and lawless than others. Any impression to that effect which my language may have conveyed must be a sheer mistake. Surely you will realise the obviousness of this on reflecting that at first I did not believe in *any* extensive southwestern lawlessness or violence (as distinguished from the criminality common to *all* communities and kept in control by police power) after about 1900. Without doubt, hasty phraseology has caused extensive misunderstandings on both sides.

Regarding the special point brought up in your latest letter—the statement that the American settlers in the southwest exercised a greater kindness and fairness and consideration toward the native inhabitants (Indians, Spaniards, and mixtures of the two) than is usually exercised by the white invaders of a conquered region—I don't recall that we ever discussed it before. It is certainly keenly interesting, and would form excellent material for sociological study. It does not, however, prove that civilised races are more cruel than uncivilised ones. Rather does it prove the reverse, since the advancing south-westerners *were* the vanguard of a civilised race. I doubt whether the non-civilised Indians exercised a reciprocal considerateness toward the settlers! Actually, I believe a broad survey of world history will convince you that such isolated cases of kindness and chivalry on the part of advancing conquerors can hardly be held typical of mankind, either barbaric or civilised. They are the exceptions—and while they *do* occur every now and then because of strongly operating individual influences and local group traditions (the settlement of Rhode Island by Roger Williams, that of Pennsylvania by William Penn, that of Georgia by Genl. Oglethorpe, and (except for the Iroquois wars) that of Canada by the French, are reasonable examples), they have never been typical of mankind as a whole. All barbaric nations are brutal beyond description, and few civilised groups can prevent themselves from reverting to this condition under the stress of certain particular conditions. War is an universal brutaliser; and once a group is committed to a policy of wholesale killing, it tends to maker fewer and fewer distinctions between the types it shall kill and the types it shall spare. So far as I can see, modern warfare is not only *not more* ruthless in intention than ancient or savage warfare, but is in certain instances *less so*. I am certainly no defender of brutality, and wish most ardently that some way existed to limit the violence with which international disputes are settled, or national ambitions gratified. When I *seem* to excuse atrocities I am really not doing so at all—but am merely criticising the justice of singling out *one nation's* conduct when *all nations as a whole* have done exactly the same thing under parallel conditions. Exceptions to the general rule are *so rare, and so purely local,* that I cannot see how they may justly be set up as criteria. The pioneers of the southwest, or the English under Williams in Rhode Island, or the Georgia settlers under Oglethorpe, did not indeed follow the course of the Celts in neolithic Britain, or the Germans in Gaul, or the Italians in Abyssinia, or the Abyssinians in other parts of Abyssinia than their own, etc. etc. etc. But can whole nations be expected to share the special ethical attitudes which from their very nature are peculiar to small, compact groups under the strong influence of local traditions? Obviously—since the basic instincts of the human animal are against it—they cannot. The *bulk* of every racial and national group on earth has always acted just about the same, and always will, under the given conditions. The growth of civilisation lessens the frequency of such outbursts, but can scarcely abolish them altogether. The only way to lessen international brutality is to let *all* weak groups be absorbed by the strong ones which covet them, and to teach the surviving strong ones that the status quo can be disturbed only at a frightful cost which affects the victor as well as the vanquished. Now and then terrible and brutal wars *will* break out despite every precaution. Indeed, one or two more may end the present phase of western civilisation. But an increased use of reason can conceivably reduce immensely the number of *occasions for war;* so that the net amount of brutality will be decreased, and the chances for civilisation's survival strengthened. The worst provocative force is that of commercial greed, and I believe this will lessen as the internal government of the nations grows more and more socialistic—as it inevitably must. In future centuries the government and economic structure of nations will probably be such that their inhabitants will have *much less to gain* from any extension of territory, or any capture of a foreign market or trade route, than they have at present. A fully capitalistic America under the rule of big-business puppets like Hoover or Landon or Knox would provoke a war with Japan to keep the Chinese market open, whereas a reasonably socialistic and self-sufficient America would fight Japan only *defensively*—to resist some Japanese attempt to seize territory inhabited by Anglo-Saxons.[1] If Italy had evolved a stage or two along the road of social development she would not have been so eager to conquer Abyssinia—but we cannot hurry the process of sociology beyond certain limits. The same uncontrollable forces which in some cases lead ultimately to a sound equilibrium also produce trying intermediate stages, awkward temporary compromises, and now and then utter national collapses. We have had to go through our capitalistic and land-grabbing stages, and so must Italy. No one of the great nations averages much worse than any other—for where one is backward in one way, it is likely to be ahead in another way. Just now the most repellent and exasperating of the great powers are Soviet Russia and Nazi Germany—and yet each of these grotesquely situated nations embodies many *isolated* points of superiority which the others (though superior in other respects) would do well to copy.

Regarding *degrees of brutality in war*—this is a subject involving very complex psychological processes, and certain utterly different sets of emotional distinctions. There are the differences in feeling in different culture-groups regarding the limitation of warfare in actual or potential combatants, the differences of attitude determined by the racial and cultural status of the enemy (an average white would sanction deeds against Indians or Negroes or Arabs or Mongolians—or even whites of a despised or sharply differentiated group—which he would not sanction against whites of his own kind), and the differences determined by the *mode of combat.* This latter point is subtle but potent. As war grows more mechanical and impersonal—interposing elaborate barriers and distances between attacker and attacked—certain natural scruples of humanity seem to lessen. Thus a general who would not think of stabbing a non-combatant himself, and who would hesitate long before ordering his men to stab non-combatants, might conceivably consent to a bombing campaign in which thousands of non-combatants would perish. The *scale* and *remoteness* and *impersonality* of a wholesale bomb or gas attack tends—emotionally—to break down the natural scruples of the civilised human being regarding the inviolability of the human person, and the aesthetic repugnance to the blotting out of the defenceless. One who would never slay a non-combatant whom he could see, or whose name he knew, or whom he could directly envisage as a helpless human being, might very conceivably sign an order for the gassing of a whole city—an action on so vast a scale that the idea of individual deaths becomes lost in the almost abstract concept of *clearing up a mathematical area*. Not that this makes death any easier for the victims—but it certainly involves a genuine distinction in the emotional attitude of the attacker from the attitude of a conqueror who *personally* rides down a civilian crowd and bathes his sword in the blood of the innocent. It is part of the whole shift of emotional values produced by the machine age—the increasing trend toward the collective and impersonal viewing of mankind. All this is something we can't stop. What we must try to stop as far as possible is the *initial precipitation* of major wars. As to the term *sadism*—I forget just how I used it, but I'm sure I didn't apply it to anything other than an attitude which finds positive *pleasure* in the infliction of violence; i.e., violence *for its own sake* as distinguished from advantages obtained *through* violence. I couldn't have said that 'all pioneers were sadists'—for no such absurd idea crossed my mind. I might have said that a regime of violence *tends to bring out sadistic qualities in those who might not otherwise exhibit or develop them* (and the anecdotes of all warfare, both frontier and international, seem to contain enough instances of wanton butchery and disregard of the inviolability of the human body to sustain such an assumption), but I don't see how I could have said more than that. I certainly *do* think that it takes a lower grade of coarseness to slay or mutilate a human being with one's own hands, except in self-defence or in organised battle, than to plan for the annihilation (with as little pain as possible) of persons in certain areas for some purpose which one honestly believes to be of vast and transcendent importance. Probably I express this so clumsily that it seems like poor ethics—but there's a very definite idea behind it. What I mean is that the greatest justification of any killing or injury of a human being is *worthiness of object*. The less a death-dealer thinks of the joy of personal vengeance or victory or blood-lust, and the more he thinks of some vast ideal outside himself (such as the furtherance of a racial, moral, or national cause) which makes the infliction of death on certain persons a stern and regrettable necessity, the higher he stands in what we may regard as an universal ethical scale. At least it seems so to me. I realise that this kind of idealistic impersonality is not the same as the other sort of impersonality—arising from scale, distance, and mechanical media, and distinctly inferior in ethical status—which I mentioned previously. This lower or mechanical impersonality (whose basis is really *lack of imagination*) has dangerous possibilities in its temptations toward the irresponsible infliction of widespread death—though even so it involves less coarseness and callousness than does personal killing. Even the more idealistic sort of death-dealing impersonality has its perils—when fanaticism overcomes judgment, and the killer mistakes a purely personal conviction for a truly necessary cause. No—we can't justly endorse any sort of killing except in defence of oneself, or of some racial or national fabric representing one's larger self. When we fail to become actively indignant at some example of aggressive warfare it is not that we approve the action, but that we recognise in it the operation of an universal tendency which all groups practice equally at the present stage of civilisation as during past stages. What checks our acutest sympathy for the weaker party is our sadly certain knowledge that he would behave exactly like his oppressor if he had the chance. Thus in the case of a war which does not involve our own country—and in which no prejudice of ours is involved—we tend quite logically to dismiss the ethical side and judge it solely by *its result as related to the welfare of western civilisation in general.* Altogether, many of the most ethically indefensible wars—like the snatching of the two Americas from the Indians—have been of the greatest value to the white race and its culture; giving it ampler room for development and expansion, increasing its natural resources, and providing a setting for the growth of new and beneficial cultural variants. Who would truly wish North America restored to its aboriginal tribes, or Australia to its blackfellows, or South Africa to its negroes? Many technically "unjust" wars are waged against races so low or degraded or mutually murderous that the conquered people are actually benefited in the end by the change. The sodden Hindoos, warring corruptly against one another and with their masses in a state of the most incredible degradation, have been much better off under British rule than they would have been if left to stew in their own rottenness. Nor have the Abyssinians suffered any more in their conquest by Italy than they formerly suffered through constant tribal warfare, habitual cruelty and treachery, and omnipresent filth and loathsome disease. The statesman or diplomat who really wishes to help the human race will pay less attention to colonial wars against backward peoples than to the paramount problem of averting wars among civilised nations. Certainly, all wars of conquest ought to be *discouraged* as far as possible—but is it worthwhile to embroil the great powers (and lead millions to the slaughter for a cause which scarcely concerns them) for the sake of preventing a minor act of aggression which would not in itself sacrifice nearly as many lives or work even an eighth or sixteenth as much harm to civilisation? It seems to me that each different international crisis will have to be considered separately by each of the great powers. When a power is not originally involved, its future course ought to be determined by the probable effect of various possible outcomes upon itself, or upon the type of civilisation it represents. Only when it sees itself menaced—or when it sees peril for the larger cultural unit to which it belongs—is it really justified in entering a war which it could keep out of. Some conquests—such as that of the far eastern mainland by Japan—are not essentially illogical. We have no business trying to keep Japan out of China or Mongolia or Soviet Russia, for our culture suffers no direct blow thereby. But resistance to the death *is* justified when Japan turns against *us* and threatens Australia or California or Hawaii or New Zealand. In Europe the smaller states have constantly changed hands in the past and will probably do so in the future. Any change which involves an interference with a developed race's folkways and language and cultural integrity is cruelly deplorable—but in each threatened case it is up to each neutral power to decide whether armed intervention is really justified in the interest of general civilisation. However—in practice, most nations do instinctively draw a line betwixt the civilised and the definitely non-civilised. Russia never extirpated the native culture of Finland, Poland, and the Baltic states as she did that of the barbarous Mongol tribes which she met in her long march across Siberia, nor did Spain try to Hispanicise the Netherlands when she controlled them. There are of course exceptions like Alsace-Lorraine under German rule—but most of these exceptions are on a very small scale involving *parts* of nations rather than whole ones. Sometimes a nation forms a sort of borderline case—Mexico being an example. *As a whole,* Mexico has enough of an established Hispanic civilisation to win it a place in the instinctively favoured category, but this is not true of *all its parts.* When at various times the U.S. took sections of its southern neighbour, these sections were among the least settled and civilised—hence the gradual Americanisation. But if we were to conquer the *entire country* in some future war, it seems certain that the intensively developed central area containing the capital would be granted a cultural autonomy like that enjoyed by Puerto Rico. The same distinctions existed in the ancient world. Very deep-seated cultures were seldom displaced by conquest—that of Egypt, for example, persisting (save for the Alexandrian region) under Persian, Grecian, and Roman rule. Rome also never disturbed Greek culture in any conquered region which possessed it. A barbaric province would soon be Latinised—but a Greek region remained Greek. Thus you may see that the establishment of tacit distinctions between the civilised and the barbaric isn't quite as ambiguous a matter as you assume. There *is* a certain vague agreement on the subject among the dominant culture-groups of the world. Certainly, a profound and well-defined national civilisation is a vast aid to group-survival. It forms something which most conquerors respect. But even so, the best guarantee of a continuous cultural welfare is the military strength to defend one's own soil against any possible aggressor.

I'm not against any sensible effort or diplomatic policy aimed at checking wars—in fact, I'm wholeheartedly *for* such. The only things I oppose are ill-considered and futile policies (like that of the League of Nations, which attempts *too much*)[2] virtually foredoomed to failure and likely to *cause* more wars than they can prevent. Also, I'm in favour of all possible efforts to diminish the barbarousness of warfare. I merely point out that no very wide success in this latter line can logically be expected, and that one can't well condemn in any *single* power what *all* generally practice. The *real* advances in the humane conduct of war will probably pertain less to *methods of attack* than to *the aftermath of attack*. There will never be any lessening of the purpose and spirit of attack—*to gain a given objective at any cost*—but there will probably be an increase of conscientiousness and skill in caring for the surviving victims . . . . medical attention, hospital service, treatment of prisoners, etc. However, there will probably also be a greater willingness to choose, out of several attacking methods of presumably equal effectiveness, that which is least painful and barbarous. If two gasses are equally lethal, that causing death most painlessly will be chosen.

The only things I can see to do about war are these:

1) To increase socialisation within nations as far as possible, thus tending to remove commercial incentives to war.

2) To reform public education in such a way as to encourage logical thinking and emphasise the suicidal disastrousness of warfare for both victor and vanquished, and for civilisation as a whole. Also, to lay greater stress on humanity and decency, and on the gravity of their violation. This can be done only in a socialised civilisation where the principle of *competition* is condemned. The ideas of *war and defence* should be made absolutely synonymous.

3) To remove the power of declaring war from small arbitrary groups, and to advocate ceaselessly a realistic, enlightened diplomacy which shall have the preservation of peace as its paramount object—a diplomacy divorced as far as possible from prejudice and caprice, willing to sacrifice lesser ends for greater, and ready to overlook trivial provocations in the quest for logical and workable permanent adjustments.

4) To encourage international cultural ties in order to remove deep-seated misconceptions and prejudices. Not to interfere with the native culture of each nation, but to supplement this culture with an intelligent *comprehension and appreciation* of other cultures. This course would differ equally from the fanatical and narrow nationalism of the Nazis, and from the colourless and diffusive internationalism of the decadent "intelligentsia" of the 1920's.

These palliatives will not end all wars—for nothing can do that. But they can conceivably avert dozens of wars which would otherwise break out and exact their tragic toll. All we can logically strive for is *to cut the number of wars down to a minimum*.

Now as to Abyssinia and Italy—while I would rather see the region under British control, I cannot mourn very deeply at the present outcome . . . unless, of course, it forms the starting-point of an Italian policy which threatens the peace of Europe. The natives themselves are infinitely the gainers—for they have never done anything in the past but kill one another off and fester in filth and disease. Sanitation and decency will be introduced, and the health and morals of the country will increase enormously—even though an Anglo-Saxon rule would have been still better. As for Italian motives in the conquest—I see no real difference between these and the motives behind any colonial expansion. The theory that the war was a dramatic gesture to save Fascist prestige is a popular one with many liberals, but I can't see any basis for it. Anyone who knows Italians realises how solidly and enthusiastically they are behind the present regime. The dissenters are noisy, but very few. Providence's Italians (21.2% of the city's population) are virtually all red-hot Fascists, as the reports of their meetings and placards in their shop-windows attest. Mussolini needed no boost among his own people. The truth is that Italian colonisation in East Africa is an ambition half a century old, which has never flagged for a moment. The government may or may not have decided to stage this present conquest just when it did for the benefit of Italian prestige abroad. In *any* case the move would have come sooner or later. Italy began colonising around Assab and Massawa in 1886, and in 1889—when old Menelik came to the Abyssinian throne—claimed a protectorate over Abyssinia. In that year also the colony of Eritrea was formally organised. There was a slight backing down in 1892, but in 1896 the claim was again asserted— ending with the famous military disaster at Adowa. That closed matters for the time being, for Italy was very weak at the time, but the acquisition of Abyssinia was always part of the Italian foreign policy. Somaliland had an Italian settlement from 1889 onward, and in 1926 Great Britain ceded a small area of British East Africa to add to it. Expansion in this region never left the Italian mind. Italy was one of the guarantors of Abyssinia's independence in 1906, but these external gestures mean little. She might have been content with a protectorate if all had gone well in that quarter. In 1928 she gave Abyssinia a free port at Assab, and in 1930 was cordially represented at the coronation of Ras Tafari—the more recent Haile Selassie, King of Kings and Conquering Lion of Judah. But if she couldn't have a protectorate she meant to have a colony. The Abyssinians continued to be troublesome (for their emperor could not even begin to control his savage vassals), and by a couple of years ago the present denouement became inevitable. It was only a question of *when* it would occur. Now it *has* occurred—and the pious sanctionists may twiddle their thumbs! I think the Italians can make good use of Abyssinia with equal benefit to themselves and the natives. Eritrea is not suitable for extensive white colonisation—agriculturally or climatically (though it *has* 4565 Italian residents)—but the highlands of Abyssinia proper are very suitable indeed, and with proper roads and other improvements will probably form a splendid outlet for Italian enterprise. Then, too, no one knows the mineral resources of this hitherto wasted land. As for the *necessity* of the new colony to Italy—this is of course something at which only a profound economist could guess. With an increasingly socialised regime, colonial exploitation might not be necessary; but under full capitalism it is. Italy could not have bought the region, and no other suitable region was for sale. In any case, the settled policy of 50 years would scarcely have been eradicated from the national consciousness. Ethically the seizure was of course wrong. But why didn't the solemn and virtuous League apply its "sanctions" to Japan's seizure of Manchuria in 1931? There is no strong member of the League which has not done exactly what Italy has just done—and the best thing to do now about "sanctions" is to forget them. The time to take a stand against Italy is when she makes some move really hostile to the general peace of the world. As for American sentiment regarding the recent conflict—I think it *averages* neutral. Idealists are sympathetic with the defeated savages, and some fear the growing power of Italy; but so far as I can see the bulk of the population in various parts of the country tend toward complete indifference. Providence— with nearly a quarter of its population Italian (though this Italian element is concentrated in its own region)—tends more or less to feel on the Italian side. The intelligentsia are pro-Abyssinian (or rather pro-League), and the old Yankee stock naturally tend to be; but nothing of this gets into the press. With Italians forming a good percentage of subscribers and advertisers—and increasingly prominent in local politics—even the old mill-owning oligarchy which controls the *Journal* and *Bulletin* tend to go slow. The war was generally featured from the Italian angle, and a "victory" meant an Italian advance. The mixed lower classes of the city (influenced both by the sentiment of the vast Italian element and by the irrational proletarian hatred of Great Britain) were definitely pro-Italian. It was amusing to contrast the response of New York (Jewish-communist, and fiercely anti-Fascist) and Providence cinema audiences to news reels of the war. The New Yorkers hissed the Italians and cheered the niggers, but the Providentians wildly applauded the Italians. I fancy that the Latin cast of our proletariat (Portugese and French-Canadian in addition to Italian) gives a natural bias toward sympathy with any Latin power. One may add that the old American stock was by no means unanimous in its anti-Italian attitude. Providence has especially strong cultural ties with the best elements of Italian life—a condition long antedating the coming of the immigrants, and perhaps arising from the intermarriage of some of our ancient families with the Italian nobility. Our great clock tower on the Brown campus (a stone's throw from #66), our fountain in front of the station, various statues in public places, and other local landmarks are the gift of Count Paolo Bagnotti and other Italians connected with local families. Our artists have always studied in Italy, and the leader of them (Col. H. Anthony Dyer) is a Fascist enthusiast who often addresses the local Italians in their native tongue. Only the other night he presided at a great victory meeting on Federal Hill. The John Hay Library of Brown University, next door to 66 College st., is a marble palazzo in the Italian Renaissance style, and bears on its facade a bronze bust of Dante. Nor is Providence without its Roman arch (a memorial gate for World War veterans on the Brown Campus) and Roman column (Victory monument down town) to remind the world that this city is built on seven hills in the *precise* latitude (41° 50′ N.) of Rome. It is curious how this earlier stream of Italian cultural sympathy—centreing in the old Anglo-Saxon residents of birth and education—coalesces with the new influence supplied by Italian immigrants! Well—the African affair is over now, and the feelings on each side will soon evaporate so far as America is concerned. I only hope that no messy aftermath will be precipitated in Europe in an effort to save the face of the poor old League!

By the way—about Latins as colonisers, I don't think one can generalise too freely. Different Latin nations differ, and some of the historic failures were due to causes no longer existing. Between the 16th century Spaniard and the system he bequeathed to the new World and the 20th century Fascist Italian there is an enormous gulf. The modern Italian knows the folly of the plundering policy pursued by Old Spain, and has the benefit of the most recent sociological research in matters of colonial administration. Not that he could do as well as England—for the Englishman, like the classic Roman, has a natural special genius for empire—but that he would not necessarily repeat the mistakes of other Mediterraneans. That nations can learn the art of imperial administration after a bad start is shown by France—who made a mess of her colonies in the New World, but who has since become a very competent coloniser on a modest scale in North Africa, Indo-China, and elsewhere.

About my remark that the pioneers of Texas 'would be the last to wish their descendants to struggle against any avoidable obstacle'—I don't see how it could seem obscure, or how it could be interpreted as expressing a belief that the pioneers would wish their heirs to submit to oppression. What I meant—and what I thought I explained in the context—was simply this: that I do not believe the pioneers would wish to prevent the growth of those facilities and legal safeguards which save their descendants from the ceaseless and exacting struggle against nature and lawless enemies and the hardships of isolation which they had to endure. My remark was a reply to the wish of some that the pioneer age could return—or rather, of regret that it has passed. I was trying to point out that the vanished frontier period was really no Golden Age even though it demanded great characters to live through it. You cannot call a period ideal when its conditions of life were so hard that only the very strongest could survive. The pioneers had to be great in order to exist at all when it required exhausting toil, unending vigilance, prodigious strength and courage, and constant warlike exertion in order to secure the necessities of life and save themselves from being slaughtered—*but are those requirements desirable?* It seems to me illogical to assume that they are. They were necessarily evils of their time, and the pioneers deserve endless honour for having overcome them—but how can we regard them as other than evils? War demands and develops great men—but do we call it an ideal state? People wage war in order to enjoy the fruits of the peace which that war will secure. In the same way, the pioneers embarked on a perilous and difficult mode of life in order that they—or their descendants—might enjoy the improved conditions which would follow the completion of that struggle. It is incredible to assume that they intrinsically *preferred,* and wished their descendants to endure, a strained and gruelling programme which involved famine, violence, and exhausting struggle, and which prevented the victims from enjoying any of the fruits of a secure and orderly existence. Common sanity impels us to believe that these heroic trail-makers *realised* the hardships they so bravely faced—that they did not consider devastating toil, ceaseless battle, maddening isolation, and primitive facilities an ideal way of life. They had a larger vision which caused them to conceive of an expanded empire and a wider domain for their children, and to that vision they sacrificed their individual lives. But they did not, I am sure, picture their own terrible struggle as *an end in itself* or a proper set of conditions *to keep alive after it could be remedied.* They expected to establish—and did, I am sure, establish—a new seat of orderly life in which their descendants might be free to develop all sides of their lives in proper proportion. The hardships and necessary lawlessness of the frontier were *means to an end* . . . . obstacles to be overcome *in order to build a new region of settled civilisation* where people might keep alive without constant warfare, and where the primitive hardships of the wilderness might be sufficiently smoothed down to permit people to enjoy the fruits of life instead of ceaselessly fighting for existence itself. What would they think if they heard their descendants *envying* them all the obstacles and hardships and lawlessness which they so painfully endured because such things *had* to be endured? It is really doing the pioneers an injustice—robbing them of credit for bravely facing a hard and unpleasant and self-denying way of life—to assume that their painful ordeal was a delightful or desirable condition which ought to be prolonged or revived. What is *desirable* in hunger and thirst, lack of materials, absence of protection, constantly recurrent fighting, and all the rest of the old frontier conditions? These things surely bred great characters—but so does war! Well—*that* is what I meant when I said that the pioneers would not wish their descendants to struggle against avoidable obstacles. In 1860 and 1870 and 1880 and 1890 hunger, thirst, lack of materials, isolation, absence of police regulation, constant lawlessness, etc. etc. etc. were *unavoidable obstacles.* They were there, and had to be overcome because they could not be swept away at once . . . . and we honour the pioneers for having swept them away. But today they are *avoidable obstacles.* They do not need to be there, and to a great extent are *not* there. People can live without spending all their energy in merely *keeping alive,* and can thus reap the *benefits of being alive,* hitherto denied. (That is, to the imperfect extent common to the bulk of the civilised world) Would it now be sensible to *wish the old obstacles back* . . . . obstacles which today are *avoidable and unnecessary?* Would it indeed duplicate the bravery of the pioneer, who *struggled from necessity,* to re-erect the now-avoidable obstacles which hampered him and wore him out, and indulge in a revived struggle against them purely for *sport?* This is what I meant when I said that the founders of the southwest would scarcely wish their children to suffer *needlessly* the hardships which they themselves bravely suffered *through necessity*. THE WHOLE SECRET OF GREATNESS IN THE PIONEERS IS THAT THEY VALIANTLY BATTLED AMIDST A SET OF HARSH CONDITIONS UNSUITED TO HUMAN HAPPINESS AND PERMANENT WELFARE. The way to honour them is to appreciate the fabric of law and order and security *which they built through their own sacrificial endurance of lawlessness and hardship and insecurity*. Don't wish the lawlessness and hardship and insecurity back! I really can't see how this remark of mine could have been taken as a guess that the pioneers would wish their descendants to succumb to oppression! Naturally, the very *reverse* is true. The evil conditions now existing through the pressure of unscrupulous corporations and otherwise—are *today's unavoidable obstacles* (corresponding to the famines and Indian raids and outlaws and lack of protection of the past) which must be met just as bravely as the older unavoidable obstacles were met when they existed. Therefore the pioneers would urge their sons *to face and fight the new troubles, but without wishing the old troubles back*. The *ultimate goal* cannot well be other than a law-abiding and orderly state, in which each citizen will have a natural place, a just return for his services, a decent amount of leisure, proper facilities for education and the development of personality, and reasonable guarantees of physical safety in times of peace in exchange for law-abiding and non-encroaching conduct. Let me add that I feel sure that this *is* the goal of the southwest, as well as of all civilised countries.

Switching to genealogy—there is no question but that Scotch-Irish individuals and families frequently entered the American colonies long before the great 18th century migration. It is interesting to know that one of the Ervin branches spoke Gaelic—and as late as the 1800 period. A genealogical expert might turn up additional facts regarding your line—especially one who specialised in the families of North Carolina. I never realised what a complex science—enough to engross a scholar's whole life—genealogy is, until a friend of mine took it up in a serious way. The amount that an expert can uncover from slender clues seems well-nigh incredible to a layman. Different researchers specialise in certain regions—or even certain families—but the general methods are more or less the same, so that a little close surveying soon fits an expert for any new field. In recent years the subject has markedly gained in prominence in the United States.

. . . .

Yrs most cordially and sincerely,
H P L

Notes

1. Alf Landon (1887–1987), governor of Kansas (1932–36) and Republican candidate for president in 1936. Frank Knox (1874–1944), Republican politician who ran for

the Republican nomination for president in 1936, but lost to Landon. He later became secretary of the navy under Franklin D. Roosevelt (1940–44).

2. HPL had criticized the League of Nations upon its very formation in 1919, in the essay "In the Editor's Study: The League."

[128]   [TLS]

Cross Plains, Texas,
May 13, 1936.

Dear HPL:

I am indeed sorry to hear that you and your Aunt have been ill,[1] and I sincerely trust that this finds you both entirely recovered. Yes, I read about the floods you had in New England. We were having dust storms about that time. It has been a hellish winter and a damnable spring.

Returning to our controversy, I certainly have no reason to dispute your assertion that the subject of philosophy covers all human activities. Why should I deny it? But this fact doesn't prove that some custom or activity typical of the East Coast of America is necessarily of more cosmic importance than some custom or activity typical of the Western part of the country. Stating the indisputable fact that philosophical standards exist doesn't prove that the folk ways and traditions of Rhode Island, Pennsylvania or Virginia are more universally "right" than the traditions and folk ways of Texas, Arizona or Kansas.

As for my challenge to you to produce evidence to prove that the Texas pioneers ever committed any wanton atrocities to equal the hysterical outbursts of butchery and torture that have been characteristic of European history—I thought I explained my purpose. I thought it was your belief—and that you had asserted or intimated—that the pioneers were more brutal and callous than the civilized Europeans you so ardently admire. I pointed out the numerous reasons I had for believing this, whether rightly or wrongly. I told you that I was sorry if I had misunderstood your attitude, and I repeat it. Aside from that I can't see how you can read into my challenge an attempt to prove that barbarians were less brutal than civilized people. Of course the Indians and Mexicans practised the most horrible cruelties on the people. I made that clear in pointing out that the Texans had all the reasons for ferocious retaliations that you've given in excusing the bloody acts committed by civilized Europeans. The Texans did retaliate in open battle; but not by the butchery and torture of helpless non-combatants. You have ignored the point I was making, the question I asked which is this: *If your super-civilized Europeans are so much superior in humaneness, mental-balance, and justice, than people following a pioneer life, then why have they always committed cruelties and revolting butcheries that a Texas pioneer would have scorned to commit?* I started out to prove that the civilized Europeans you were always citing as paragons of behavior have been guilty of more detestable treachery, violence, wanton brutality, sadism and cowardice than the Southwestern pioneers ever dreamed of. And I have proved it, which you must admit, unless you can produce the evidence I challenged you to produce. That is the main issue with me, and not to be side-tracked by an argument that what the pioneers did is not important in a "larger" sense. That's got nothing to do with it. The question is: whether the pioneers were more, or less, brutal than your cultured Europeans.

I note with interest your comments on civilized warfare, and am again impressed by what seems to me the incongruity of your viewpoint—the fact that you, who expressed so much resentful horror at the idea of fights and feuds in the southwest, open battles between equally matched opponents, should now complacently regard and defend the wholesale butchery of help-less men, women and children. Apparently, according to the intellectual viewpoint, it is not *what* is done that matters, but *who* does it. Thus for a bar-barous Western American to shoot down his man in an open broil, that's horrifying brutality and a relic of barbarism. But for a sacred European to bomb a crowded city and murder thousands of helpless people, that's quite logical and commendable. You say a man who sits in a safe place a thousand miles away from the scene of battle and *orders* the destruction of several thou-sand people he never saw, is of vastly higher type than the man who in the heat of blood splits a few skulls with his own saber. In other words, the man who hires his murders done, is of a higher type than the man who at least has guts enough to go do them himself. You and I differ there, and evidently our regional cultures differ. We of the Southwest never had any respect for any kind of a murderer, but we despise a man who hires his killings done more than we do the man who goes out and does them himself. I would not will-ingly commit violence on anybody. But if it was necessary I could kill a man with a gun, a knife, a club or my bare hands; but I could not, under any cir-cumstances, cause the destruction of innocent people a thousand miles away, people I'd never seen and who'd never done me harm. And I don't believe such destruction ever was or ever will be necessary, and that such slaughter is simply sadistic and degenerate. I realize that you consider this blasphemous, as you don't consider it possible for a modern European to have any unwor-thy motives. But I don't see any difference between the Huns swarming into a city and slicing the people down with swords, and an English, German or Italian aviator flying over a city and dropping bombs that will rip the brains out of children, disembowel old men and dismember women.

I am interested in your remarks about the impersonal way with which it is now the fad to view the human race; quite true. That is the true scientific viewpoint, according to some, and quite wipes away the blood and bits of guts and hair. The butchery of a city becomes: "the cleaning up of a given area" and so ceases to be bloody murder, and becomes a beautiful mathe-matical problem to be worked out by placid scientists and scholarly intellectuals at a safe distance, who would never, never think of getting their hands in the blood and foecal matter. Once when I was a kid, another boy came to me with the proposition that I help him raid a chicken roost. I told him, profanely, that I wasn't in the habit of stealing. He replied that we wouldn't call it stealing; we'd call it "swiping"! For years I thought hard of him, but now I see I did him an injustice. He was simply the forerunner of our modern intelligentsia, one of the first to syrup one's conscience by calling an ugly thing a pretty name. I told him then that chicken stealing was stealing by whatever name it was called. I say now that murder is murder, by whatever highsounding name it is called.

As for the necessity of this butchery—wars were won in the past without killing the non-combatants. Once civilized people condemned the wanton slaughter as a relic of barbarism. It is only this rotting civilization which defends and applauds the gutting of people unable to bear arms.

Your conception of international policy seems to be that the strong should join hands to plunder the weak. Yet you say that the citizens of the nations should be educated in justice, decency, fairness, etc. I don't think such teachings would have much effect on the average individual who saw them repudiated every day by his government, in its dealings with weaker nations. You are hardly correct in saying that I regard as ambiguous the distinction between civilized races and barbaric races. Not at all. The generally accepted idea is precisely like yours. Those who are strong enough to loot the others are the "civilized" and the conquered are the barbarians.

As for the Italo-Ethiopian question, I doubt if it's entirely settled. Success, even in such a sordid matter as this, will undoubtedly go to Mussolini's head. He already suffers from illusions of grandeur. He sees himself as Caesar already. Whipping a bunch of niggers armed with muzzle-loading trade muskets (and he'd never have whipped them even if they hadn't got to fighting among themselves) is quite enough to allow him to strut and pose as a conqueror. The English were fools not to jump him and wipe him out as soon as he started to "expand". They'll have to fight him sooner or later, and the longer they wait the harder he'll be to lick. But when the British at last get enough of his blatant arrogance and stupidity and greed, they'll give him the damnedest licking a Wop has got since the days of Alaric. As for American sentiment, every western paper I've ever read has reflected strong anti-Mussolini sentiments, especially the Texas papers, which are not forced to lick the boots of a lot of foreigners and can say what the editors think. I realize that Mussolini has a number of rump-kissers in America—Arthur Brisbane being the foremost and most blatant[2]—but Fascism will have a hell of a time ever getting hold of the Great Plains States. I see no reason to think that Italian colonization will turn Ethiopia into a Utopia. As for Latin colonization in general, what's so admirable about France's various plundering of African and Asiatic countries? She maintains herself in North Africa, at least, by putting down one series of revolts after another, which would certainly not seem to indicate that the natives are particularly enraptured with French rule. You ought to read Hector France's "Musk, Hashish and Blood" and some of Seabrook's travel books if you want to get a realistic view of French colonial policy.[3]

Returning to the question of the pioneers: you say the pioneer age was no Golden Age. When did I ever say it was? True, I once said that I wish I could have lived on the Texas frontier. I repeat that wish. But what do you find in that statement that leads you to believe that I consider the pioneer epoch as "an ideal"? You prefer to live in New England. But you'd be surprised and resentful if I accused you of considering New England as an ideal region without flaw, or the 20th century as a Golden Age. Why then should you conclude that my wish to have lived in early Texas reflects a belief that it was perfect? I simply say that in spite of its unquestioned drawbacks and hardships, the time and place suited my particular temperament better than any other. I think I understand why you have so often sneered at what you call my idealization of a Golden Age. For a long time it puzzled me that you should assume so much ignorance, on my part, of a region in which I was born and raised, and in whose history I have been steeped since early childhood. All my life pioneers and their sons and daughters have formed the bulk of the people with whom I have associated. I myself, in my childhood, experienced the tag-end of the last wave of colonization. There is no reason under God's sun why I should have a romantic or idealized conception of the frontier. And yet you have repeatedly attributed to me a viewpoint that could be held only by some half-baked youngster living in a big city ten thousand miles away from the West. As I say, this puzzled me for a long time. But I think I understand it. You feel that an Eastern or European city environment is the only one a man of reasonable intelligence could possibly prefer. Therefore, when a man of at least average mentality as I hope I am, expresses a desire for an environment so alien to the Eastern urban one, you come to the conclusion that it is the result of an erroneous conception on his part. If he prefers something that differs from the Eastern thing, then he *must* be romanticizing and idealizing. All of which, if you'll pardon me, for I mean no offense, is the bunk. The trouble with your point of view is that the frontier is so alien to everything you personally like and desire that you don't see anything good at all about it. To you it seems merely a ghastly, hideous welter of blood, violence and misery with no compensating features whatever. But I see another side of it, which I find impossible to explain to anyone who is personally unfamiliar with pioneer and semi-pioneer life. Why abuse me because I'm close enough to that region and era to see the good as well as the bad of it?

This whole discussion was precipitated when I innocently remarked that I wished I had lived in Texas a hundred or so years ago. And so I do. You disputed that statement, which seemed to me about as logical as disputing my statement that I liked fried liver and onions. Foolishly I started out to show you why I so desired, which was as sensible as it would have been for me to try to show why I like beefsteak. Then to my amazement I learned that my preference reflected a large and elaborate repudiation of all evolutionary and biological standards. The more I tried to explain the logic and reason of my preference, the more I floundered and the more biting onslaughts I provoked. You seemed to feel—and [in] fact seem still to feel—that my preference for frontier life is criminal in its nature. You seem to believe that I love the frontier *because* of its blood-shed and occasional lawlessness, instead of *in spite* of those things. You love New England, but you hate cold weather, don't you? Well, isn't it possible for another man to love a region enough to put up with its admitted drawbacks? I love Texas so much that I wish I'd had a hand in building the present greatness of the State, and it's the height of absurdity to claim that this feeling of mine reflects a hatred of human development. The civilization of the frontier (and it *was* a distinct civilization of its own) was a damn sight more highly developed than you realize. My defense of the frontier has not been a defense of ignorance and brutality; I have simply tried to show you that these things were not as abysmal as you believe. I have tried to get you to look at the frontier from Western standards, instead of New England standards, which are not always applicable.

Nor have I ever said anything to justify your belief that I wish to destroy the cities, shoot the cattle, turn the farms back to the buffalo range and revert to pioneer ways. I realize the frontier epoch is over. I merely say that I wish I had lived then, instead of now. That wish is not nearly so outrageously uncommon as you believe, nor is it any evidence of a twisted viewpoint or a repudiation of human standards. As far as I'm personally concerned, it would suit me all right if conditions West of the Mississippi were just like they were in 1845, but I don't expect the bulk of humanity to concur—though a good many of them would if they knew the truth of frontier life, and compared it with the present scramble for existence. Frontier life had its drawbacks, its occasional dangers, but I've known plenty of old men and women who lived through its wildest days and were never in any more jeopardy of life and limb than the modern who dares a highway in his automobile. There was no breadline on the frontier, nor necessity for one; there was no dole; there was no unemployment. There were no strikes, or anti-Fascist, anti-Communist or anti-this-or-that riots. There were no neuroses or psychological phobias. People were healthy and hearty and wholesome. Their life was by no means the awful round of horrors and hardships conjured up by writers who view that life from afar off and are shocked by things they could never endure because they never had to endure them. People enjoyed their simple pleasures a damn sight more than any modern enjoys anything he does. Even now many of the survivors of that epoch, at greatly advanced ages, show much more zest for living, enthusiasm and ability to enjoy life than any of their descendants, or their descendants' contemporaries. What I'm trying to make clear is that pioneer life was not altogether the shuddersome hell of horrors you seem to think it was. It just looks that way to you because it was so different from your own.

You say "what would they think if they heard their descendants *envying* them" their sort of life? I'll tell you what they'd think. Most of them would think their descendants were showing a God damned sight more sense than they ever gave us credit for having. How do I know? Because I *have* expressed that envying desire to many and many an old-timer and heard him, or her, loudly concur. Please remember that to me pioneers are not people who have been dead and gone five hundred years and never lived around here anyhow, but associates, neighbors, friends, in some cases enemies. I wish you could see the scorn with which many highly intelligent old frontiersmen regard the aims and struggles of our modern existence. You say it's incredible to suppose that the pioneers enjoyed their existence, or liked frontier life. Let's see just how much basis that statement has in reality. First I'll quote Billy Dixon, a pioneer of pioneers, hero of the bloody Buffalo Wallow fight, one of the heroes of Adobe Walls, winner of the Congressional Medal for bravery, scout for General Miles, buffalo hunter, ranchman and frontiersman. Billy said: "I fear that the conquest of savagery in the Southwest was due more to love of adventure than to any wish that cities should arise in the desert, or that the highways of civilization should take the place of the trails of the Indian and the buffalo. *In fact, many of us believed and hoped that the wilderness would remain forever.* Life there was to our liking. Its freedom, its dangers, its tax upon strength and courage, gave a zest to living, especially to young men, unapproached by anything to be found in civilized communities."[4] What do you think about that?

His wife, a cultured, talented Virginia lady who came west after she was grown and married him, and who now is a widely known writer and an authority on Western history, remarked in one of her books: "The heart swells with emotion at remembrance of the wild, free life along those old trails, and knowledge that they have vanished forever brings a feeling of deep regret. Railroads, to be sure, meet modern needs, and have changed the wilderness into garden, but, nevertheless, beyond and above all these demands of a higher civilization, with its commerce and its feverish haste, remains the thought that something worth while has been lost, at least to those who found joy in braving dangers and in overcoming the obstacles of primitive conditions. What a living, moving, thrilling panorama stretched along the old trails! How vast the wealth that rolled past!"[5]

Again Billy Dixon said, on one occasion: "I . . . . found living in town worse than it could have been in jail. I decided to go still further west." If pioneers hated their lot, why did so many "go further west" when they found the country settling up around them? I have no patience with civilization's neurotic conception of the frontiersmen as blind, dumb, ignorant peasants shrieking in misery and hating their condition.

Hardships? Sure, but they didn't matter to people like them, though I don't doubt a few of the things they laughed at would make a gibbering neuropath out of the average modern. When Billy Dixon's wife first came west she taught school in a log cabin on the Canadian. Of this he said: "There were no desks or modern fixtures. A barrel of drinking water was hauled once a week. There were large cracks between the logs and when the weather got cold the teacher and pupils chinked and daubed the walls to keep out the cold. These were little things, however, to a young woman in love with the West and her surroundings, *and later on my wife often remarked that this was one of the happiest years of her life.*"

Again, in his old age, Dixon said: "I am often questioned about my experiences on the frontier, as if the life had been filled with unbearable hardships, to be shunned and forgotten. *Gladly would I live it all over again*, such is my cast of mind and my hunger for the freedom of the big wide places. I would run the risks and endure all the hardships that were naturally ours just for the contentment and freedom to be found in such an outdoor life."

Again he said, remembering old times: "Drinking the pure fresh air of the Plains, we rolled from our blankets every morning, clear-headed and ready for any enterprises. Just to feel one's self living in that country was a joy. We heard nothing and cared nothing about politics; it made little difference to us who was president of the United States; we worked hard, had enough money for our common needs, and were happy, *happier perhaps than we ever were in later years.*"

That was when he and his friends were hunting buffaloes in the forbidden Indian country, in constant peril of their lives, and when they should have been most miserable and gloomy, according to your conception of the time and region.

Let's see what Josiah Gregg, the Santa Fe trader, and author of "Commerce of the Prairies," a book every American ought to read, had to say about the awfulness of pioneer life. He wrote, in New York, 1844:

"I have striven in vain to reconcile myself to the even tenor of civilized life in the United States; and have sought in its amusements and its society a substitute for those high excitements which have attached me so strongly to Prairie life. Yet I am almost ashamed to confess that scarcely a day passes without my experiencing a pang of regret that I am not now roving at large upon those western plains. Nor do I find my taste peculiar; for I have hardly known a man, who has ever become familiar with the kind of life which I have led for so many years, that has not relinquished it with regret.

"There is more than one way of explaining this apparent incongruity. In the first place—the wild, unsettled and independent life of the Prairie trader, makes perfect freedom of nearly every kind of social dependence an absolute necessity of his being. He is in daily, nay hourly exposure of his life and property, and in the habit of relying upon his own arm and his own gun both for protection and support. Is he wronged? No court or jury is called to adjudicate upon his disputes or his abuses, save his own conscience; and no powers are invoked to redress them, save those with which the God of Nature has endowed them. He knows no government—no laws, save those of his own creation and adoption. He lives in no society which he must look up to or propitiate. The exchange of this untrammelled condition—this sovereign independence, for a life in civilization, where both his physical and moral freedom are invaded at every turn, by the complicated machinery of social institutions, is certainly likely to commend itself to but few,—not even to all those who have been educated to find their enjoyments in the arts and elegancies peculiar to civilized society;—as is evinced by the frequent instances of men of letters, refinement and of wealth, voluntarily abandoning society for a life upon the Prairies, or in the still more savage mountain wilds.

"A 'tour on the prairies' is certainly a *dangerous* experiment for him who would live a quiet contented life at home among his friends and relatives; not so dangerous to life or health, as prejudicial to his domestic habits. Those who have lived pent up in our large cities, know but little of the broad, unembarrassed freedom of the Great Western Prairies. Viewing them from a snug fireside, they seem crowded with dangers, and with labors and with sufferings; but once upon them, and these appear to vanish—they are soon forgotten.

"It will hardly be a matter of surprize then, when I add, that this passion for Prairie life, how paradoxical soever it may seem, will be very apt to lead me upon the Plains again, to spread my bed with the mustang and the buffalo, under the broad canopy of heaven,—there to seek to maintain undisturbed my confidence in men, by fraternizing with the little prairie dogs and wild colts, and the still wilder Indians—the *unconquered Sabaeans of the Great American Desert.*'[6]

The underlinings in Gregg are his own. You will probably assert that one can not generalize from the few excerpts I've quoted, but it ought to be obvious that I can't quote all the things that uphold my assertions. I've merely selected a few of the most characteristic, to show you that pioneer life was not so awful as you think, and that it was not altogether abhorrent to the men and women who lived it. You will probably say that this doesn't mean anything in a wider sense, however, because these men were not "developed" (though how even an intellectual could call a scholar like Josiah Gregg undeveloped is more than I can guess) and that their preferences would never be shared by a developed man—meaning a European or Eastern city dweller. It seems to me that a weakness in your argument is your evident belief that there is only one line of development to be considered or preferred—and that is the line naturally followed by a man of scholarly tastes living in a big city either in Europe or on the Atlantic sea-board. If a man isn't developed along this line, I think you don't consider him developed at all, regardless of how finely he may be adapted to the existence of some other section of the continent.

Your weakness in regard to arguments concerning the West is a tendency to look on the West as merely and undeveloped extension of the East. You seem to believe that the West differs from the East only in its flaws and faults, and that when we become properly civilized, West and East will be indistinguishable. Like many people, you ignore the *physical* conditions that set the West apart from the East. You feel that anything that differs from the European-Eastern pattern is wrong and ought to be abolished. You believe that if anything is done a certain way on the Atlantic sea-board, it ought to be done that way in Texas, North Dakota and Kansas. If that's the case, if anything typically Eastern is right, and anything typically Western is wrong, why is it that thousands of people who come west to settle quickly adopt western ways and soon become indistinguishable from the native masses? Why do they find it necessary to abandon so many of their habits, customs and even ways of thinking in order to cope with the *natural* conditions of the West? I can't find that these people consider that the change is one of retrogression. I have yet to find a new-made Westerner who feels that he has slipped back into barbarism because he has adopted the ways of his chosen region. And I can tell you another thing: after an Easterner has lived in the West a little while you ordinarily couldn't drag him back to his old home with a team of oxen. This town contains oodles of people who came from the East, and they're here to stay, or if they move it will be south or west. If Western ways are based on fallacious thinking, what explains this? Your belief that Western pioneer ways are all wrong, and that certain ways and standards of thinking (the European-Atlantic Seaboard pattern, to be exact) are based on cosmic truths which are not altered by different physical facts, reminds me strongly of one colony of immigrants which didn't change its ways.

They came from Massachusetts some years ago and settled in one of the primitive regions of Southwestern Texas. They, too, considered that all their preferences, customs, habits, and ways of doing things were based on unalterable cosmic truths which had no relation to physical environments. And they refused to make any effort to adapt themselves to their changed environment. They were wealthy people, accomplished, likable. The native Texans liked them and tried to help them, but they couldn't be helped because they refused to see that ways suited to one region were not suitable to another. They refused to see that because they believed that everything they did, according to inherited customs, was in accordance with some cosmic law or truth. If they skinned a cat a certain way in their native region, then it was blasphemy against the laws of God and man to skin one any other way, even when the cat was a Mexican polecat. They had any number of intellectual arguments to prove that their way of doing things was the "superior" way, and therefore should work. The only argument against that was the fact that it didn't work. What happened? A ten-year old prairie child could have predicted the answer. They all went broke, lost their investments, lost their lands and returned in miserable defeat to their own region—while all around them people from the same part of the country were thriving and growing rich, merely because they recognized physical conditions, and were not obsessed with the belief that the standards and ways of their native regions were unalterable cosmic laws. These people, please remember, had no human adversaries to struggle against. No human being opposed them in any way; what licked them was the same physical conditions that will always lick the man who tries to apply Eastern standards to Western life. The poor devils' idea was this: that the superior man adheres to a certain rigid pattern, each phase of which, whether it be voting a political ticket, judging an art gallery or currying a mule, is based on recognition of evolutionary standards and cosmic law. To do anything differently would be to repudiate evolutionary standards and cosmic law. Anybody who did anything or thought anything different from themselves, was a repudiator and a barbarian. (Not that they agreed entirely among themselves, but "that's different"!) Their standards, habits and ways of living and thinking were simply the result of adapting themselves to a certain, special region over a long period of time, and were largely unfit for a different region. But they didn't think so. Their whole viewpoint was, after all, based on a conviction of their own absolute superiority over the people West of the Alleghenies. And they couldn't prove their theory.

Let us see what Professor Walter Prescott Webb says, in his great book, "The Great Plains,"[7] about the idea that the West is only an undeveloped extension of Eastern America. But first let us quote, as he does, John Wesley Powell: "The physical conditions which exist in that land, and which inexorably control the operations of men, are such that the industries of the West are necessarily unlike those of the East, and their institutions must be adapted to their industrial wants. It is thus that a new phase of Aryan civilization is being developed in the western half of America." Why should it be concluded that that new phase should be inferior to the older phase, on the Eastern seaboard and the Central forests? Wissler, in "Man and Culture," says: "It appears that topography, fauna and flora form an environment-complex, and as such go far to determine the areas of cultural diffusion and though we once said that culture mocks at the bounds set up by politics, we may now add that it approaches geographical boundaries with its hat in its hand."[8] One of these boundaries is the 98th meridian. It was so in Indian times and it is so now. Webb says: "The historical truth that becomes apparent in the end is that the Great Plains have bent and molded Anglo-American life, have destroyed traditions, and have influenced institutions in a most singular manner.

"The Great Plains offered such a contrast to the region east of the ninety-eighth meridian, the region with which American civilization had been familiar until about 1840, as to bring about a marked change in the ways of pioneering and living. For two centuries American pioneers had been working out a technique for the utilization of the humid regions east of the Mississippi River. They had found solutions for their problems and were conquering the frontier at a steadily accelerating rate. Then in the early nineteenth century they crossed the Mississippi and came out on the Great Plains, an environment with which they had no experience. The result was a complete though temporary breakdown of the machinery and ways of pioneering. They began to make adjustments.

"As one contrasts the civilization of the Great Plains with that of the eastern timberland, one sees what may be called an institutional *fault* (comparable to a geological fault) running from middle Texas to Illinois or Dakota, roughly following the ninety-eighth meridian. At this fault the ways of life and of living were changed. Practically every institution that was carried across it was either broken and remade or else greatly altered.

"An effort to understand the historical influence of the Great Plains on American civilization would be futile without a clear comprehension of the physical forces that have worked and continue to work in that region. These forces, historically speaking, are constant and eternal; therefore they make a permanent factor in the interpretation of history—one that must be understood. If the Great Plains forced man to make radical changes, sweeping innovations in his ways of living, the cause lies almost wholly in the physical aspects of the land."

But I fancy I have quoted enough to show the reasons why the West will always be different from the East, and that certain ways of thinking and living must change when men come West. I have been somewhat bothered in the past by your evident belief that my ambitions, aspirations and beliefs were merely the screwy twists of a callow and misinformed individual—that nobody else in the world had any of the ideas and ways I have—whereas I can lay little claim to even a screwy individuality, and in most ways merely follow the traditional pattern of my region. There are as many men in the West like me as there are in the East like you—more, because not many people can equal your intellectual accomplishments, whereas there are about six million people in Texas alone who are smarter than I am.

Another thing—your insistence that my love of the frontier and my preference for ways which even now are considered semi-barbaric in the civilized regions, are "romantic." There's no basis for that belief. It's no more romantic for me to love 19th Century Texas than it is for you to love 19th Century New England. If either of us declared a devotion to some region we'd never seen, that would be romanticism. But why should it be vital and reasonable for you to wish you'd lived in New England a hundred years ago, and "romantic" and absurd for me to wish I'd lived in Texas a hundred years ago? Webb brings such a point up in his book.

"To *whom* did the West and the Westerner appear spectacular and romantic? Who made the judgments? Who set the standards? The West appeared romantic to those who were not of it—to the Easterner, who saw the outward aspects of a strange life without understanding its meaning and deeper significance. The East set the standards, wrote the books, and made the laws. What it did not comprehend was strange, romantic, spectacular. The Easterner did not ride horses as did the Westerner. He did not wear a six-shooter, because the law prohibited it and because law made it unnecessary. He did not herd cattle or wear boots or red handkerchiefs or spurs. He could not see that a normal person could do such things."

When I first read that I immediately understood what I had not been able to understand before—your attitude toward my preferences and aspirations, which were perfectly reasonable and natural. The people in the civilized regions evidently have set down this rule: "What we like and do is normal and reasonable; anything that differs from our pattern is outlandish, spectacular and romantic, and he is a sentimentalist and a romanticist who desires anything that does not fall within the circle of our daily experiences." I reckon my preference for the ways of my own region, though perfectly natural, seem as outrageous to you as the six-shooters, wild horses and spurs did to "civilized" people not many years ago. But it's just like Webb says: "If we could dispel this haze of romance we could view Western life as it was in reality—logical, perfectly in accord ultimately with the laws laid down by the inscrutable Plains."

I didn't intend to inflict all this stuff on you, but when I get started on my favorite theme I hardly know when to stop; I'll quote just one more thing from Webb: "The salient truth, the essential truth, is that the West cannot be understood as a mere extension of things Eastern." That's what I've said all along, and after all, ignorant backwoodsman though I admittedly am, still I have been far east enough to be able to contrast East with West and draw inevitable conclusions.

One of your main objections to pioneer life seems to be the fact that there wasn't a policeman on every block. But before the industrial upheaval brought in a swarm of aliens, I have lived for years in communities in which there wasn't an officer of the law within forty miles, and human life and property was a damn sight safer than it is in any city, west or east. Nobody ever locked a door, nobody was ever ravished, mobbed or murdered. We didn't have a jail and we never needed one. And incidentally the people of those communities were all pioneers and the sons and daughters and grandsons and grand-daughters of pioneers. They knew how to live together in peace without the necessity of policemen on their neck all the time. How do you explain that?

As for modern Texas, it is true that we fight more among ourselves, to-day, probably more than is common in most states. But that's no reason for a stranger to feel that his life would be in danger in the state. You don't have to take my word for it. Ask our mutual friend Ed Price if he ever had to fight for his life while he was in Texas. It seems hard for an outlander to under-stand Southwestern psychology, from a distance; a man who kills another in a feud is not necessarily a murderer. He may be a fine, upright citizen. Not many years ago we had a State Adjutant-general who had killed two men in street-fights. But that didn't mean that he made a practise of shooting down inoffensive strangers. In this State we always consider the method of killing. We hate and despise and generally electrocute a cold-blooded murderer who kills a weaker person or by unfair advantage. But we don't despise and ostra-cise a man who kills another in fair, open, even fight where the odds are equal. And we recognize—even the courts to some extent recognize—the right of a man to take certain matters into his own hands, without recourse to law. There are some wrongs too deep to be righted in court—at least that's the way we look at it, and we have as much right to follow our traditions as the people of other regions have to follow theirs.

As for whether a peaceable stranger would be safe in Texas—thousands of tourists pass through here every year. Have you ever heard of any atrocities committed on any of them? A few months ago I had an opportunity to get the viewpoint of a man from your part of the country. I picked up a hitch-hiker in the edge of San Angelo and carried him about seventeen miles along the Big Spring road. I don't make a practise of picking up hitch-hikers, be-cause there are too many criminals among them, who don't hesitate to knock you in the head and take your car—aliens, most of them, from other States, but a few natives gone wrong. But when I saw this fellow, I thought he was a school-boy of the town, and picked him up before I realized my mistake—which I did as soon as he got in the car, for I saw he was much older than I'd thought. As soon as he opened his mouth I knew by his accent he was no Texan. He was better dressed and seemed more intelligent than the general run of hitch-hikers, but I wasn't disposed to take any chances, so as soon as we were out of the town I drew a pistol and stuck it under my left knee where I could reach it conveniently, at the same time telling him not to be alarmed, that that was merely a precaution that I always took when riding with a stranger. (If I could have got the gun in place without him seeing it, I'd have preferred it, but I couldn't.) He laughed and said it didn't frighten him, and presently began talking at a great rate. He said he was from Michigan, and told me his name, which was of old English origin, and he seemed well edu-cated, a college degree at least, I should judge. He spoke casually of his wan-derings and apparently he'd been in most regions of the United States. He spoke rather bitterly of the treatment accorded hitch-hiking strangers in the old Southern States, such as Virginia, Georgia, Tennessee and the like and said he wouldn't go back there, even on a pleasure trip. Then he said: "This is my first visit in Texas, and I'm pleasantly surprized. I've always been well treated in Oklahoma, New Mexico, Arizona and the other western states, but I've been warned repeatedly against Texas. Numbers of fellows have told me it is the toughest State in the Union, and if I came down here I'd get my head shot off. That's the bunk. I've been treated better here than any place I ever went to. I'm heading for California by way of El Paso. I met my first Texan in Little Rock. He was an old fellow who was driving to Dallas, and he wanted somebody to drive his car for him. I volunteered, and he looked me over, and then he pulled out a gun as long as my arm, and said. 'Do you see this?' I said: 'There's no use holding me up; I haven't got any money. 'Hold you up, hell!' he said. 'I'm just showin' you this so you won't try any monkey business with me!' I drove him to Dallas and we got along fine. He took me home with him and gave me a big dinner. That night I stayed in the YMCA and I didn't know how the boys there would take to me because I'm from the North."

I interrupted him here to say: "You needn't have had any fear about that. We have no sectional prejudices in Texas. We don't give a damn where a man comes from. It's what he is, personally, that counts."

"That's what I found out," he answered. "The boys made me feel at home, and when they went out to have some fun, they insisted on me going along. I had a fine time, and the next day I caught rides to Waco, then the next on here. Everybody I've met has treated me fine. I haven't found it a hard State."

"No honest man will," I told him. "It's a hard State on grafters, criminals, gyppers, and crooks. That's all. If you're on the level you'll be well treated wherever you go or stay."

"I've found it so," said he. "The men who warned me against the State were just such men as you've mentioned. They came here with the idea that they were so smart they could gyp the natives out of their teeth. They found the Texans were smart as they were, and a good deal too tough for them. So they got out, or were kicked out, and now carry a grudge against the State. But I like it. I've got a brother in El Paso. I feel kind of like a Texan already. I don't know whether I'll go on to California or not. If I can get a job in El Paso, I'm going to settle there and become a Texan in reality."

There was no reason for him to spill all this to me if he didn't mean it. He had no cause to flatter me about my state, nor did I start him on his remarks. I said nothing much at all to him at first, because like most hillmen I am taciturn with strangers, regardless of how garrulous I may be with friends. He began the conversation and carried it on of his own accord, and I can only conclude that he was sincere in what he said.

The past few months have been rather hard on us all, especially my mother. I have certainly been disillusioned regarding specialists and hospitals. Most of the specialists we've had dealings with—with one notable exception, a splendid little fellow in San Angelo—have proved to be blatant jackasses, incompetent theorists. And some of them have not only State-wide but nation-wide reputations. We put my mother in a sanatorium, expecting that she would get better treatment than we were able to give her. I went there in January and found that they were not only neglecting her, but that such treatment as she was getting was so little suited to her case that even a layman like myself could see it. She would not have lived much longer in their hands. They, like so many moderns, thought only of their blasted routine—my father and I knocked their God-damned routine into a cocked hat, and they ran around like a bunch of neurotic old women holding up their hands in helpless bewilderment. He saved my mother's life when they were helpless, and we put her in a hospital where at least she'd get good care. But though they were good, honest, willing people, they couldn't understand her case and we brought her home. Then in the latter part of February, in desperation, we took her to a sanitarium in East Texas, where in times past we have got good service. But the head of the place left for Detroit just after we got there, leaving his conceited jackass of a son in charge, who was fresh from study in Baltimore or Boston, or some place,[9] and full of his own importance, and authority, and the usual theories—theories—theories—my God, I've had my belly-full of theories in the past few months. To show his authority he neglected my mother—or tried to—trying to refuse to do things for her even I knew she needed. But before we got through with him he was damned glad to do everything my father suggested—suggested hell, ordered. Because my father quickly saw that the little louse was just as full of damfool theories and just as devoid of practical sense as most of the other wonderful specialists we'd encountered. (The greatest jackass of them all was a fellow from California; one of the most sincere and best-natured was a man from Maine, but he too was full of theories he couldn't prove and like most of them, inclined to regard a human being as a guinea pig for experiments; no man's going to experiment with any of my folks while I can stand on my feet and hold up my hands.) To get back to the youthful prodigy, he was amazed at the situation he encountered, I think. That part of Texas is much like some of the old Southern States—an aristocratic caste of a few wealthy families and hordes of negroes and poor whites who have to submit to any kind of treatment. I think we were the first hill-people this young rat had ever met, and the experience certainly subdued his arrogance, as far as we were concerned. Meeting somebody he couldn't bully seemed to be a new and rather terrifying experience to him. Anyway, after he learned his lesson he did the best he could, but that wasn't much. Following my father's orders, he did improve her condition enough for us to bring her home. That trip, over two hundred miles over rough roads mostly, was an experience the very memory of which makes me wince. How my mother in her weakened condition stood it, I don't know. Seeing we could expect nothing from specialists or hospitals, we brought her home, in the early part of March, and we've been here ever since. We got goats and for weeks she lived mainly on their milk. She seemed to be improving a little when she had an attack of acute pleurisy on her right side, which until then hadn't been affected. My father handled that, and she was definitely on the mend, although the sweats never ceased, when in the early part of April we had the worst dust storm I ever saw in my life, and she developed pneumonia. There seemed no hope for her, yet she managed to live through the attack. Cold weather hung on, and it still isn't as warm as it usually is this time of the year. But comparatively warm weather has brought about a lessening of her sweats and she is much more comfortable than she was; also breath sounds in the affected lung seem to indicate that there is little if any fluid there. I don't know whether she'll live or not—she is very weak and weighs only 109 pounds—150 pounds is her normal weight—and very few kinds of food agree with her; but if she does live, she will owe her life to my father's efforts and his experience gained by nearly forty years of frontier practise. Again and again he saved her when the experts and specialists were helpless. Just an old country doctor, but he has that qualification so many of our smart modern scientists lack—ordinary common sense; the experts themselves have had to admit that.

She started sweating in January and it's just the last few days that there has been any appreciable lessening of it. Many a night she had to be changed six or seven times, and that many times a day—sometimes more. Woman after woman we hired, and they quit, either worn out by their work, or unwilling to do it, though my father and I did most of it. Sometimes when we could get a couple of good women we'd get a short breathing spell. Again there were times when we couldn't get anybody, and I not only took care of my mother, while my father handled his wide practice, but did all the housework, washing, and cooking. I've gone for nearly a week at a time without even taking off my shoes, just snatching a nap as I could between times. Things are better now, but anything can happen, and I'm not optimistic. But whatever happens we have such satisfaction that there is in knowing that we've fought the best fight that was in us all the way, without asking quarter from anything or anybody, and doing the best we knew how.

Naturally I haven't been able to do much writing the past few months, but I have managed to sell a few more bubby-twisters to Spicy Adventures, keep the Breckinridge Elkins series going, sell Thrilling Mysteries another blood-curdler, and make new markets in Cowboy Stories and Complete Stories. To say nothing of writing several yarns that haven't clicked yet. I've also taken a short run into Central East Texas (to talk to the surgeon who operated [on] my mother last spring) and one into South Texas (to buy some

German wine for my mother from Ludwig Borauer who makes the best in the world); I've learned to mix a dozen or so new drinks, have renewed an old love affair and broken it off again, developed a new set of exercises with sledge-hammers, read several new books, made some more enemies, learned how to take care of milch goats, so altogether the year that brings me into middle age has so far been a rather stormy one. Anyway my health is splendid, my muscles are harder than they've been in years and my literary prospects look good—though of course anything can happen.

Yes, I certainly did like "Haunter of the Dark." And I got a big kick out of your sonnet in the current issue of the Phantagraph,[10] which is the first copy of that publication I'd seen. A nice looking little magazine, and one which I hope will have a better future than many of such ventures. I believe of all the various clans of readers, the weird and scientific-fiction fans are the most loyal and active. Glad to hear that "Innsmouth" is coming out in book form. Glad, too, that the illustrations for your magnificent "Mountains of Madness" are so suitable, though no illustrations could do justice to the story itself.

I find it more and more difficult to write anything but western yarns. I have definitely abandoned the detective field, where I never had any success anyway, and which represents a type of story I actively detest. I can scarcely endure to read one, much less write one. Attempts to make a living by writing historical fiction proved a flop, though a certain editor is considering a series of piratical yarns, if I can remodel the first to suit his tastes. But I am not expecting much from it. I have become so wrapped up in western themes that I have not, as yet, written a follow-up yarn for the last Oriental adventure novelet bought by Street & Smith, though Kline's been urging me to get one in circulation. I will write some more, doubtless, but even my interest in things Oriental is waning in comparison to my interest in the drama of early America. The new editor of Argosy[11] has asked me to create a new western character on the order of Breckinridge Elkins, and I've made one in the person of Pike Bearfield of Wolf Mountain, Texas. I don't know how he'll come out. If I can get a series running in Argosy, keep the Elkins series running in Action Stories, now a monthly, and the Buckner J. Grimes yarns in Cowboy Stories, I'll feel justified in devoting practically all my time to the writing of western stories. I have always felt that if I ever accomplished anything worthwhile in the literary field, it would be with stories dealing of the central and western frontier.

Hoping this finds you and your Aunt fully recovered, I am,

Most cordially yours,

REH

Notes

1. HPL's aunt, Annie E. P. Gamwell, was suffering from breast cancer and had to undergo a mastectomy (although HPL told his colleagues that she was suffering from

"grippe"). HPL himself claimed to be suffering from "grippe"—in reality the cancer of the intestine that would prove fatal in 1937.

2. Arthur Brisbane (letter 75, n. 1) followed William Randolph Hearst's orders in supporting Mussolini and, for a time, Hitler as part of Hearst's anti-Communist crusade. He and Hearst visited Italy in 1936.

3. France's book was in REH's library at the time of his death; William Seabrook was the author of several travel books, notably *Adventures in Arabia* (1927), *The Magic Island* (1929), and *Jungle Ways* (1931).

4. This and following quotes are from *Life and Adventures of "Billy" Dixon, of Adobe Walls, Texas Panhandle,* Compiled by Frederick S. Barde (Guthrie, OK: Printed by the Co-operative Publishing Co., 1914), a copy of which was in REH's library.

5. This quotation is also from *Life and Adventures of "Billy" Dixon;* the 1927 reprint of the book by P. L. Turner Company bears Mrs. Olive K[ing] Dixon's name as author: most of the book was dictated to her by her husband (1850–1913).

6. REH's copy of Josiah Gregg, *A Reprint Edition of Commerce of the Prairies: The Journal of a Santa Fe Trader* (Dallas: The Southwest Press, 1933), is in the REH Memorial Collection at Howard Payne University. The material quoted here is from pp. 319–20 of this edition.

7. Walter Prescott Webb (1888–1963), *The Great Plains* (Boston: Ginn & Co., 1931). REH's copy of the book was donated to the REH Memorial Collection but is no longer in the library's holdings.

8. REH appears to be quoting this passage from p. 3 of *The Great Plains.*

9. Dr. John W. Torbett, Jr., studied medicine at Baylor Medical College in Dallas, and then interned at King's County Hospital in New York, and spent another year after completing his internship as a house physician there, before returning to Marlin to join the staff at the sanatorium founded and operated by his father.

10. "Night-Gaunts," sonnet XX of *Fungi from Yuggoth.*

11. In early 1936, John F. Byrne, to whom REH had sold stories for *Fight Stories* and *Action Stories,* was named editor of *Argosy.*

[129]   [nonextant letter by HPL][1]

[c. late May 1936]

Notes

1. See HPL to Donald Wandrei, 24 June 1936: "It is probable that Two-Gun never read my last letter to him—a 32-page affair mailed about a week before the bad news reached me" (*Mysteries of Time and Spirit,* p. 379). REH died on 11 June.

Addendum

[35a]   [AN, on envelope]

[postmarked 15 October 1931]

[P.S.] Here are some views of the extremely quaint region W. Paul Cook & I have just been visiting.

[64a]   [AN, from calendar pad][1]

[n.d., but c. 15 September 1932]

Wandrei & I have read these tales with keen interest & appreciation. Best wishes for their ultimate publication! Dwyer seems to have enjoyed them greatly, too. The climax of "The God in the Bowl" is splendidly vivid!
—HPL

Notes

1. REH had clipped this note to his manuscript "The God in the Bowl."

The following are quotations from Lovecraft's letters to Howard, made by Howard in letters to others. The original letters are non-extant.

[40a/41a]   [REH to Tevis Clyde Smith, September 1930, *CL* 2.69]
"Speaking of Derleth, Lovecraft says: 'His work in *W.T.* does not represent him at all, being merely pot-boiling hack material; but his really serious products (on the order of Marcel Proust) display qualities amounting almost to genius.'"

[40a]   [REH to Tevis Clyde Smith, September 1930, *CL* 2.71–72]
"I got a letter from Lovecraft wherein he tells me, much to my chagrin, that Cthulhu, R'lyeh, Yuggoth, Yog-Sothoth, and so on are figments of his own imagination. He says: 'The reason for its echoes in Dr. de Castro's work is that the latter gentleman is a revision-client of mine—into whose tales I have stuck these glancing references for sheer fun. If any other clients of mine get work placed in W.T., you will perhaps find a still wider spread of the cult of Azathoth, Cthulhu, and the Great Old Ones. The *Necronomicon* of the mad Arab Abdul Alhazred is likewise something which must yet be written in order to possess objective reality. Abdul is a favorite dream-character of mine—indeed, that is what I used to call myself when I was five years old and a

transported devotee of Andrew Lang's version of the *Arabian Nights*. A few years ago I prepared a mock-erudite synopsis of Abdul's life, and of the post-humous vicissitudes and translations of his hideous and unmentionable work *Al Azif* (called—some blighting Greek word—by the Byzantine (something) Theodoras Philetas, who translated it into late Greek in A.D. 900!)—a synopsis which I shall follow in future references to the dark and accursed thing. Long has alluded to the Necronomicon in some things of his—in fact, I think it is rather good fun to have this artificial mythology given an air of versimilitude (?) by aside citation. Clark Ashton Smith is (something) another mock anthology, revolving around the black, furry toad-god Tsathoggua, whose name had variant forms amongst the Atlanteans, Lemurians, and Hyperboreans who worshipped him after he emerged from inner Earth (whither he came from Outer Space, with Saturn as a stepping stone). I am using Tsathoggua in several tales of my own and of revision-clients'—although Wright rejected the Smith tale in which he originally appeared. It would be amusing to identify your Kathulos with my Cthulhu—indeed, I may so adopt him in some future black allusion. Incidentally, Long and I often debate about the real folklore basis of Machen's nightmare witch cults (referring here, I guess to 'The Red Hand' and so on). I think they are Machen's own inventions, for I never heard of them elsewhere; but Long cannot get over the idea that they have an actual source in European myth. Can you give us any light on this? We haven't the temerity to ask Machen himself.'"

[50a]   [REH to Tevis Clyde Smith, Sep 1930, *CL* 2.71-72]
"Lovecraft wrote me [. . .] 'You are certainly a genuine poet in every sense of the word'. And further on in the letter he said, 'Your poem [i.e., "Echoes From an Iron Harp"]—as I said at the beginning of this letter—is powerful and splendid.' 'I don't know anyone today who reproduces the ancient Aryan emotions as powerfully, vividly, and sincerely as you do. This mood is almost obsolete in Europe and the Eastern U.S.; and if it is to have continued literary expression, such will probably come from the Southwest.'"

Robert E Howard sometimes wrote drafts of letters to Lovecraft, before he executed and mailed a final letter. Such drafts are included in Robert E. Howard, *The Collected Letters of Robert E. Howard: Index and Addenda.*

Appendix

With a Set of Rattlesnake Rattles

Here is the emblem of a lethal form of life for which I have no love, but a definite admiration. The wearer of this emblem is inflexibly individualistic. He mingles not with the herd, nor bows before the thrones of the mighty. Between him and the lords of the earth lies an everlasting feud that shall not be quenched until the last man lies dying and the Conqueror sways in shimmering coils above him.

Lapped in sombre mystery he goes his subtle way, touched by neither pity nor mercy. Realizations of ultimate certitudes are his, when the worm rises and the vulture sinks and the flesh shreds back to the earth that bore it. Other beings may make for Life, but he is consecrated to Death. Promise of ultimate dissolution shimmers in his visible being, and the cold soulless certainty of destruction is in his sibilances. The buzzards mark his path by the pregnant waving of the tall grasses, and the blind worms that gnaw in the dark are glad because of him. The foot of a king can not tread on him with impunity, nor the ignorant hand of innocence bruise him unscathed. The emperor who sits enthroned in gold and purple, with his diadem in the thunderclouds and his sandals on the groaning backs of the nations, let him dare to walk where the rank grass quivers without a wind, and the lethal scent of decay is heavy in the air. Let him dare—and try if his pomp and glory and his lines of steel and gold will awe the coiling death or check the dart of the wedge-shaped head.

For when he sings in the dark it is the voice of Death crackling between fleshless jaw-bones. He reveres not, nor fears, nor sinks his crest for any scruple. He strikes, and the strongest man is carrion for flapping things and crawling things. He is a Lord of the Dark Places, and wise are they whose feet disturb not his meditations.

The Beast from the Abyss

Having spent most of my life in oil boom towns, I am not unfamiliar with the sight of torn and mangled humanity. Oftener than I like to remember I have seen men suffering, bleeding and dying from machinery accidents, knife stabs, gunshot wounds, and other mishaps. Yet I believe the most sickening spectacle of all was that of a crippled cat limping along a sidewalk, and dragging behind it a broken leg which hung to the stump only by the skin. On that splintered stump the animal was essaying to walk, occasionally emitting a low moaning cry that only slightly resembled the ordinary vocal expressions of a feline.

There is something particularly harrowing about the sight of an animal in pain; a desperate despair, undiluted by hope or reason, that makes it, in a way, a more awful and tragic sight than that of an injured human. In the agony cry of a cat all the blind abysmal anguish of the black cosmic pits seems concentrated. It is a scream from the jungle, the death howl of a Past unspeakably distant, forgotten and denied by humanity, yet which still lies like a sleeping shadow at the back of the subconsciousness, to be awakened into shuddering memory by a pain-edged yell from a bestial mouth.

Not only in agony and death is the cat a reminder of that brutish Past. In his anger cries and his love cries, his gliding course through the grass, the hunger that burns shamelessly from his slitted eyes, in all his movements and actions is advertised his kinship with the wild, his tamelessness, and his contempt for man.

Inferior to the dog the cat is, nevertheless, more like human beings than is the former. For he is vain yet servile, greedy yet fastidious, lazy, lustful and selfish. That last characteristic is, indeed, the dominant feline trait. He is monumentally selfish. In his self love he is brazen, candid and unashamed.

Giving nothing in return, he demands everything—and demands it in a rasping, hungry, whining squall that seems to tremble with self-pity, and accuse the world at large of perfidy and broken contract. His eyes are suspicious and avaricious, the eyes of a miser. His manner is at once arrogant and debased. He arches his back and rubs himself against humanity's leg, dirging a doleful plea, while his eyes glare threats and his claws slide convulsively in and out of their padded sheaths.

He is inordinate in his demands, and he gives no thanks for bounty. His only religion is an unfaltering belief in the divine rights of cats. The dog exists only for man, man exists only for cats. The introverted feline conceives himself to be ever the center of the universe. In his narrow skull there is no room for the finer feelings.

Pull a drowning kitten out of the gutter and provide him with a soft cushion to sleep upon, and cream as often as he desires. Shelter, pamper and coddle him all his useless and self-centered life. What will he give you in return? He will allow you to stroke his fur; he will bestow upon you a condescending purr, after the manner of one conferring a great favor. There evidences of his gratitude end. Your house may burn over your head, thugs may break in, rape your wife, knock Uncle Theobald in the head, and string you up by your thumbs to make you reveal the whereabouts of your hoarded wealth. The average dog would die in the defense even of Uncle Theobald. But your fat and pampered feline will look on without interest; he will make no exertions in your behalf, and after the fray, will, likely as not, make a hearty meal off your unprotected corpse.

I have heard of but one cat who ever paid for his salt, and that was through no virtue of his own, but rather the ingenuity of his owner. A good many years ago there was a wanderer who traversed the state of Arkansas in a buggy, accompanied by a large fat cat of nondescript ancestry. This wayfarer toiled not, neither did he spin, and he was a lank, harried-looking individual who wore the aspect of starvation, even when he was full of food.

His method of acquiring meals without work was simple and artistic. Leaving his horse and buggy concealed behind a convenient thicket, he would approach a farmhouse tottering slightly, as if from long fast, carrying the cat under his arm. A knock on the door having summoned the housewife with her stare of suspicion, he would not resort to any such crude and obvious tactics as asking for a hand-out. No; hat in hand, and humbly, he would beg for a pinch of salt.

"Lan's sake," would be the almost invariable reply. "What do you want salt for?"

"M'am," the genius would reply tremulously, "I'm so terrible hungry I'm a-goin' to eat this here cat."

Practically in every case the good woman was so shocked that she dragged the feebly protesting wayfarer into the house and filled his belly—and the cat's—with the best of her larder.

I am not a victim of the peculiar cat-phobia which afflicts some people, neither am I one of those whose fondness for the animals is as inexplicable and tyrannical in its way as the above mentioned repulsion. I can take cats or leave them alone.

In my childhood I was ordinarily surrounded by cats. Occasionally they were given to me; more often they simply drifted in and settled. Sometimes they drifted out just as mysteriously. I am speaking of ordinary cats, country cats, alley cats, cats without pedigree or pride of ancestry. Mongrel animals, like mongrel people, are by far the most interesting as a study.

In my part of the country, high-priced, pure-blooded felines were unknown until a comparatively recent date. Such terms as Persians, Angoras, Maltese, Manx, and the like, meant little or nothing. A cat was a cat, and classified only according to its ability to catch mice. Of late I notice a distinct modification in the blood-stream of the common American alley-cat; thoroughbred strains are mingling with the common soil, producing cats of remarkable hue and shape. Whether it will improve the democratic mongrel population or not, is a question only time can answer.

For myself, give me an alley cat every time. I remember with what intense feelings of disgust I viewed the first thoroughbred cat I ever saw—a cumbersome ball of grey fur, with the wide blank stare of utter stupidity. A dog came barking wildly across the yard, the pampered aristocrat goggled dumbly, then lumbered across the porch and attempted to climb a post. An alley cat would have shot up that shaft like a streak of grey lightning, to turn at a vantage point and spit down evil vituperation on its enemy's head. This blundering inbred monster tumbled ignominiously from the column and sprawled—*on its back*—in front of the dog, who was so astounded by the phenomenon that it evidently concluded that its prey was not a cat after all, and hastily took itself off. It was not the first time that a battle was won by awkward stupidity.

I once lived on a farm infested by rats beyond description. They broke up setting hens, devoured eggs and small chickens, and gnawed holes in the floor of the house. The building was old, the floors rotten. The rats played havoc with them. I nailed strips of tin over the holes they gnawed, and in the night I could hear their teeth grating on the tin, and their squeals of rage. Traps proved ineffectual. Rats are wise, not so easily snared as mice. The natural alternative was cats—eleven of them, to be exact. Thereafter the old farm was a battle-ground. The big grey wharf rats, as we called them, are no mean foes for a cat. More than once I have seen one of them defeat a full-grown feline in pitched battle. The ferocity of the cornered rat is proverbial, and unlike many such proverbs, borne out by actuality. On several occasions my cousin and I hastened to the aid of our feline allies with bricks and baseball bats.

The most valiant of all the crew was a grey cat of medium size called, through some obscure process, Fessler. Despite the fact that he was once ignominiously routed by a giant rat in a Homeric battle that should have formed the base for a whole cycle of rodent hero-sagas, he was a cat among cats. In him, fantastic as it may seem, I sometimes seemed to detect a fleeting shadow of an emotion that was almost affection.

He had poise and dignity; most cats have these qualities. He had courage—for which, despite legends to the contrary, the feline race in general is not noted. He was a mouser of note. He was intelligent—the most intelligent cat I have ever known. In the end, when all the cats but one died in one of those unexplainable plagues that strikes communities of felines, he dragged himself back to the house to die. Stricken, he had retired to the barn, and there he fought out his losing battle alone; but with death on him, he tottered from his retreat, staggered painfully through the night, and sank down beneath my window, where his body was found the next morning. It was as if, in his last extremity, he sought the human aid that mere instinct could not have prompted him to seek.

Most of the other cats died in solitary refuges of their own. One, a black kitten, recovered, but was so thin and weak it could not stand. My cousin shot a rabbit, cut it up, and fed the cat the raw meat. Unable to stand, it crouched above the warm flesh, ate enough to have burst a well cat, then, turning on its side, smiled as plainly as any human ever smiles, and sank into death like one falling asleep. It has been my misfortune to see many animals die, but I never saw a more peaceful, contented death than that. My cousin and I interred it beside its brothers and sisters who had perished in the plague, firing over it a military salute. May my own death be as easy as that cat's!

I said one cat lived. For all I know, she may be living yet, populating the mesquite-grown hills with her progeny. For she was a veritable phoenix of a cat, defying death, and rising from the ruins of catdom unharmed, and generally with a fresh litter of squalling young.

She was large of body, variegated of color—a somewhat confusing mixture of white, yellow and black. Her face was dusky, so she was named Blackface. She had a sister, a smaller cat, who seemed borne down by the woes of the world. Her face was the comically tragic mask of a weary clown. She died in the Big Plague.

But Blackface did not die. Just before the cats began to fall, she vanished, and I supposed that she had been stricken and dragged herself away to die in the bushes. But I was mistaken. After the last of her companions had been gathered to their ancestors, after the polluted gathering places had been cleaned by time and the elements, Blackface came home. With her came a brood of long-legged kittens. She remained at the farm until the youngsters were ready to wean, then once more she disappeared. When she returned, a few weeks later, she returned alone.

I had begun to accumulate cats again, and as long as I lived on the farm, I enjoyed periods of cat-inflation, separated by times during which the mysterious plague returned and wiped them out. But the plague never got Blackface. Each time, just before the slaughter began, she vanished mysteriously, nor did she return until the last cat had died, and the danger of contamination had passed. That happened too many times to be dismissed as coincidence. Somehow, that she-cat knew, and avoided the doom that struck down her companions.

She was taciturn, cryptic, laden with mysterious wisdom older than Egypt. She did not raise her kittens about her. I think that she had learned there was danger in thickly populated centers. Always, when they were able to fend for themselves, she led them into the woods and lost them. And however impossible it may be for a human being to "lose" a cat, none of them ever came back to the farm from which Blackface led them. But the countryside began to be infested with "wild" cats. Her sons and daughters dwelt in the mesquite flats, in the chapparal, and among the cactus beds. Some few of them took up at farmhouses and became mousers of fame; but most of them remained untamed, hunters and slayers, devourers of birds and rodents and young rabbits, and, I suspect, of chickens.

Blackface was cloaked in mystery. She came in the night, and in the night she went. She bore her kittens in the deep woods, brought them back to civilization for a space that they might be sheltered while in their helpless infancy—and that her own work might be less arduous—and back to the woods she took them when the time was ripe.

As the years passed, her returns to civilization became less and less frequent. At last she did not even bring her brood, but supported them in the wilderness. The primitive called her, and the call was stronger than the urge to slothful ease. She was silent, primordial, drawn to the wild. She came no more to the dwellings of man, but I had glimpses of her at dawn or twilight, flashing like a streak of black-barred gold through the tall grass, or gliding phantom-like through the mesquites. The fire in her elemental eyes was undimmed, the muscles rippling under her fur unsoftened by age. That was nearly twenty years ago. It would not surprize me to learn that she still lives among the cactus-grown valleys and the mesquite-clad hills. Some things are too elemental to die.

Just now I am uncertain as to the number of cats I possess. I could not prove my ownership of a single cat, but several have come and taken up their abode in the feed shed and beside the back step, allowed me to feed them, and at times bestowed on me the favor of a purr. So as long as no one claims them, I suppose I can look on them as my property.

I am uncertain as to their numbers, because there has been an addition to the community, and I do not know how many. I hear them squalling among the hay bales, but I have not had an opportunity to count them. I know only that they are the offspring of a stocky, lazy grey cat, whose democratic mongrel blood is diluted with some sort of thoroughbred stock.

At one time there were five. One was a black and white cats whose visits were furtive and soon ceased. One was a grey and white female, undersized, as so many good mousers are, and like a good killer, possessed of a peculiarly thin whining voice. Because of her preference to the sheds and feed stalls, she bore the casual name of Barn-cat. Another was a magnificent image of primitive savagery—a giant yellow cat, plainly a half-breed, mongrel mixed with some stock that might have been Persian. So he was referred to as "the Persian."

I have found that the average yellow cat is deficient in courage. The Persian was an exception. He was the biggest, most powerful, mixed-breed I ever saw, and the fiercest. He was always ravenous, and his powerful jaws crushed chicken bones in a startling manner. He ate, indeed, more like a dog than a cat. He was not indolent or fastidious. He was a lusty soldier of fortune, without morals or scruples, but possessed of an enviable vitality.

He was enamored of Barn-cat, and no woman could have acted the coquette with greater perfection. She treated him like a dog. He wooed her in his most ingratiating manner, to be rewarded by spitting abuse and scratches. A lion in his dealings with members of his own sex, he was a lamb with Barn-cat.

Let him approach her in the most respectable manner, and she was transformed into a spitting, clawing fury. Then when he retired discouraged, she invariably followed him, picking at him, teasing him, and giving him no peace of mind. Yet if he took hope and attempted any advances on the ground of her actions, she instantly assumed the part of an insulted virgin and greeted him with bared teeth and claws.

Her treatment of him was in strong contrast with her attitude toward Hoot, a big white and black spotted cat whose coloring made him look as if he were wearing the nose guard of a football helmet. Hoot was too lazy to woo Barn-cat, and she tolerated him, or rather ignored him entirely. He could push her off his chosen napping-spot, step on her ear on his way to the feed pan, or even appropriate choice morsels from her personal meal, and she showed no resentment, whereas if the Persian attempted any of these things, she was ready to rend him. On the other hand, her contempt for Hoot was apparent, and she never accorded him either the resentment or the teasing she accorded the Persian.

Their romance was not so very different from some human romances, and like all romances, came to its end. The Persian was a fighter. So much of his time was spent recovering from wounds, that he was always gaunt, and there were always several partly healed scars on his head and body. Finally he limped in with fresh wounds and a broken leg. He lay around for a short time, refusing assistance, and then disappeared. I think that, following his instincts, he dragged himself away somewhere to die.

Barn-cat's career was short. Soon after her lover met his end, she appeared one morning with her tail almost chewed off close to her body. Doubtless she had internal wounds. She was the only one of the crew worth her salt as a mouser, and while she normally avoided the big grey rats, I believe they were at last responsible for her doom. At any rate, she too vanished with her wounds and did not return.

The grey cat and her kittens remain, with Hoot, who still sleeps in the sun, too lazy even to keep himself clean. He is the only cat I ever saw which allowed its fur to remain dusty. After a sandstorm he is a disreputable sight for days. Perhaps he catches mice at night, but he shows no enthusiasm for anything but loafing during the day.

The life of a cat is not numbered by nine. Usually it is short, violent and tragic. He suffers, and makes others suffer if he can. He is primitive, bestially selfish. He is, in short, a creature of terrible and awful potentialities, a crystalization of primordial self-love, a materialization of the blackness and squalor of the abyss. He is a green-eyed, steel-thewed, fur-clad block of darkness hewed from the Pits which know not light, nor sympathy, nor dreams, nor hope, nor beauty, nor anything except hunger and the satiating of hunger. But he has dwelt with man since the beginning, and when the last man lies down and dies, a cat will watch his throes, and likelier than not, will gorge its abysmal hunger on his cooling flesh.

Dr. I. M. Howard: Letters to H. P. Lovecraft

[1] [TLS]

Cross Plains, Texas
June 29, 1936

Mr. H.P. Lovecraft
66 College Street
Providence, R.I.

My Dear Mr. Lovecraft:

It is barely possible through some other source that you may have heard of the death of Robert E. Howard, my son. If not, I will say that after three weeks of vigilent watching at his mothers bedside, on the morning of June 11, 1936, at eight O'clock he slipped out of the house, entered his car which was standing in front of the garage, raised the windows and fired a shot through his brain. The cook standing at the window at the back part of the house, saw him go get in his car. She thought he was fixing to drive to town as he usually did, when she heard the muffeled sound of the gun, she saw him fall over the sterring wheel. She ran in the house and called the physician who was in the house. The doctor was taking a cup of coffee in the dinning room and I was talking with him. We rushed to the car and found him. We at first that it was a death shot but bullet had passed through the brain. He shot himself just above the temple. It came out on the opposite side, just above and behind the left ear. He lived eight hours and never regained consciousness.

I was watching Robert as this was premeditated and I knew it but I did not think that he would kill himself before his mother went. His mother was in coma and had been for many hours when this occured. There were two trained nurses in the house and doctors there all the time. He did not ask a doctor nither did he ask me, but he asked a nurse if she thought his mother would ever regain consciousness enough to know him and the nurse told him she feared not. This was un-known to me. Had I known, I might have prevented this, because I know now that he fully had made up his mind not to see his mother die.

Last March a year ago, again when his mother was very low in the Kings Daughters Hospital in Temple, Texas, Dr. McCelvey expressed a fear that she would not recover, he began to talk to me about his business, and I at once understood what it meant. I began to talk to him, trying to dissuade him from souch a course, but his mother began to improve. And immediately she began to improve, he became cheerful and no more was said. Again this year in February, while his mother was very sick and not expected to live but a few days, at that time she was in the Shannon Hospital in San Angelo, Texas. San

Angelo is something like one hundred miles from here. He was driving back and forth daily from San Angelo to home. One evening he told me I would find his business, what little there was to it, all carefully written up and in a large envelope in his desk. Again I begged him not to do it but he possitively did not intend to live after his mother was gone.

As the months grew on, his mother showed some improvement. He accepted her condition as one of permnant improvement and one that would continue. I knew well that it would not but I kept it from him. Two weeks before she died, she began to decling rapidly. I saw the awful worry that came over him. I was following him and watching him closely but did not think he would do anything until his mother was gone.

In that I was mistaken, because he never intended to see his mother die. The night before his death, he assumed an almost cheerful attitude, seemed very much interested about me, as if he intended to take the lead and take care of me. He came to me in the night, put his arm around me and said, buck up, you are equal to it, you will go through it all right. He completely disarmed me of the intention of his death, but I well knew what to expect afterwards. He died without ever showing the least return of consciousness at four O'clock, June 11, 1936. His mother lingered thirty-one hours, never regaining consciousness.

I buried them both in the Greenleaf Cemetary at Brownwood, Texas. I selected caskets exactly alike. He had purchased a burial lot a week before this happened. It was in the ristricted portion of the cemetary. The purchase carried with it a perpetual up-keep.

When he bought the lot, he went to the Sexton and wanted to know if it was a bonified contract and if it would be taken care of. He said to the Sexton "I want to know if the lot will be kept in order. My father and I will go away and never come again.["] Mr. Bass, the Sexton, was under the impression that he contemplated something in which we would all go, but he did not expect to kill me, but knew the shock would would kill me. He was careful to keep nurses and doctors around me, but no doubt thought I would die from shock, and which I think the last few lines he ever typed would indicate. These lines were found on a strip of paper in his bill folder in his hip pocket after he shot himself. The lines follow:

> All fled—all done, so lift me on the pyre—
> The Feast is over and the lamps expire.[1]

I do not know whether these words were a quotation or orriginal, but they were typed no doubt shortly before his death.

I do not know what was in his mind. I have tried to interept this as being the last of all the family, The Feast as the thirty years of love of the family life in our home. Robert loved me with a love that was beautiful, He loved my companship above that of any one else and every time opportunity afforded he spent his time with me if prefference to any one else, but being a country doctor and practicing medicine in a country comparatively thinly settled, away from home most of the time, but when I was permitted to be at home, our hours were spent pleasantly on discussion of men, women, animals, out-door life, adventure, history of long lived frontiersmen, and such like, He was a great reader. It made me so happy to set and listen. He acquirred a knowledge by reading, of history that I never knew. Lest I worry you with this I will close, but will say in conclusion Mr. Lovecraft, that Robert was a great admirer of you. I have often heard him say that you were the best Weird writter in the world and he keenly enjoyed corresponding with you. Often expressed hope that you might visit in our home some day, so that he, his mother and I might see and know you personally. Robert greatly admired all Weird writters, often heard him speak of each separately and express the highest admiration of all. He said they were a bunch of great men and he admired all of them very much.

The Howard Payne College of Brownwood has asked for letters from correspondents. If it is agreeable with you I will furnish them with some of your correspondence to him as he has some in his files and they are interested in letters.

His books were given to the Howard Payne College and will be known as the Robert E. Howard Memorial Collection. It is so arranged that it is possible to add to it as friends see fit. If you have a book that you would like to add to it with an autograph it will be greatly appreciated.

Yours very truly,

Dr. I. M. Howard.

I am mailing you a bundle of papers that contains the full of it all.

Notes

1. A paraphrase of the final lines of various stanzas of Viola Garvin's "The House of Cæsar," in *Songs of Adventure*, ed. Robert Frothingham (Houghton Mifflin, 1926), pp. 154–55: "All dim, all pale—so lift me on the pyre— / The Feast is over and the lamps expire!" (ll. 33–34; note that l. 5 begins "All done, all fled,").

[2] [TLS]

Cross Plains, Texas,
August 14, 1936

Mr. H. P. Lovecraft
66 College St.,
Providence, Rhode Island.

My dear Mr. Lovecraft:

In as much as you will be one of the parties who will write Robert's Obituary I am sending you a poem. This poem has never been submitted to any one. I sent Mr. Wright a copy and one to Mr. Price. I am undecided whether this poem will ever be published or not. I will say to you as I said to Mr. Wright if the poem in any way detracts from Robert's reputation as a writer I would not under any consideration want it to be published. Robert was a stalwart character, both physically, mentally, and spiritually, therefore, if I thought people who read this poem would think he was weak in any respect or a weakling I would not for ten thousand worlds like this have it published, and too I don't know just what effect it would have on same person or persons who might be inclined or had been tempted in their life to take the course that he took. For these reasons I am keeping this poem, and I am asking Robert's friends that they keep it from the public gaze.

After consulting with Robert's friends if they think there might not be any untoward results in any way from the publishing of same I would then give my consent for it to be published. I want you to read and ponder over it and your opinion will be appreciated by me.

I hope that you are well and going on in a good way.

Sincerely
Dr. I. M. Howard.

P. S. I appreciated your last letter very much, more than words can express.

[P.]P.S. I am mailing you a copy of an essay written by Robert at the age or 17 when he finished highschool. The newspaper in which it was published was old, had become faded and rotten and in order to preserve this essay it became necessary to reprint it so I had a number of sheets printed and am sending you one.

[3] [TLS]

Cross Plains, Texas,
October 30, 1936.

Mr. H. P. Lovecraft,
66 College Street,
Providence, Rhode Island.

Dear Mr. Lovecraft:

I am sending to you today, by mail, under separate cover, Robert's photograph. Robert was a great admirer of you and I have carefully filed all of your letters, that I found among his papers (and there are many of them, both post cards and letters). I prize them very highly.

I wish to thank you for your contributions to the Library. It seems that Robert carefully preserved all of your Letters and also the letters he received from Mr. Price, as well as every comunication from Mr. Farnsworth Wright. I don't think he ever lost a scrap of paper of his private correspondence. He kept them all in a huge steel trunk.

I hope this photograph reaches you in good condition.

Very truly yours,
Doctor I. M. Howard

IMH/zs

[4] [ANS]

[Postmarked Cross Plains, Tex.,
Nov. 22, 1936.]
Cross Plains, Texas

Nov. 21·1936. Mr. H. P. Lovecraft—I am sending you today under seprate cover the centenial edition of The Coleman Democratic Voice it contains a write up of old Camp Colerado or Colorado Post it was written several years ago by Robert the envelope also contains an answer to Mr. Wrights letter of enquiry—relative to Roberts litterary degrees of cours Robert had no degrees as his letter to Mr Wright Robert like myself did not underestimate the value of education without education we both tried to carry on as best we could

Yours sincerely
Doctor I M Howard

Glossary of Frequently Mentioned Names

Ackerman, Forrest J. (1916–2008), young science fiction fan, agent, and editor and sporadic correspondent with HPL. He, HPL, RHB, and others engaged in a bitter feud over the merits of Clark Ashton Smith's work in the "Boiling Point" column of the *Fantasy Fan* (1933–34).

Baldwin, F[ranklin] Lee (1913–1987), weird fiction fan who came into epistolary contact with HPL in 1933. He wrote an early biography, "H. P. Lovecraft: A Biographical Sketch" (*Fantasy Magazine*, April 1935).

Barlow, R[obert] H[ayward] (1918–1951), author and collector. As a teenager he corresponded with HPL and acted as his host during two long visits to Florida in the summers of 1934 and 1935. In the 1930s he wrote several works of weird and fantasy fiction, some in collaboration with HPL. HPL appointed him his literary executor. He assisted August Derleth and Donald Wandrei in preparing the early HPL volumes for Arkham House. In the 1940s he went to Mexico and became a distinguished anthropologist. He died by suicide.

Bates, Harry (1900–1981), editor of *Strange Tales* and *Astounding Stories*. HPL repeatedly submitted stories to him, but all were rejected because they did not contain a sufficiency of "action."

Bierce, Ambrose (1842–1914?), American author and journalist. His collections of horror and Civil War tales, *Tales of Soldiers and Civilians* (1891; later titled *In the Midst of Life*) and *Can Such Things Be?* (1893) are landmarks. He was also the author of *The Devil's Dictionary* (1906 [as *The Cynic's Word Book*]) and enormous quantities of journalism, chiefly for the Hearst papers.

Bishop, Zealia Brown (Reed) (1897–1968), HPL's revision client. HPL ghostwrote "The Curse of Yig" (1928), "The Mound" (1929–30), and "Medusa's Coil" (1930) for her based on her slim plot synopses.

Blackwood, Algernon (1869–1951), leading British writer of weird fiction who gained celebrity with *John Silence—Physician Extraordinary* (1908), *Incredible Adventures* (1914), and other volumes. HPL considered his novella "The Willows" (1907) the greatest weird tale in literature.

Cave, Hugh B[arnett] (1910–2004), prolific author of stories for the pulp magazines. He lived near HPL in Pawtucket, R.I. They corresponded briefly but never met.

Clark, Lillian D[elora] (1847–1932), HPL's elder aunt, with whom he lived at 10 Barnes Street (1926–32).

Cole, Edward H[arold] (1892–1966), longtime amateur associate of HPL, living in the Boston area.

Cook, W. Paul (1881–1948), publisher of the *Monadnock Monthly*, the *Vagrant*, and other amateur journals. In 1927 he issued the *Recluse*, containing HPL's "Supernatural Horror in Literature."

Crawford, William L[evy] (1911–1984), editor of *Marvel Tales* and *Unusual Stories* and publisher of the Visionary Press, which issued HPL's *The Shadow over Innsmouth* (1936).

de Castro, Adolphe (1859–1959), formerly Gustav Adolphe Danziger, author, co-translator with Ambrose Bierce of Richard Voss's *The Monk and the Hangman's Daughter,* and correspondent of HPL. HPL revised his stories "The Last Test" and "The Electric Executioner."

de la Mare, Walter (1873–1956), distinguished British poet and author of such volumes of weird tales as *The Riddle and Other Tales* (1923) and *The Connoisseur and Other Stories* (1926).

Derleth, August W[illiam] (1909–1971), author of weird tales and also a long series of regional and historical works set in his native Wisconsin. After HPL's death, he and Donald Wandrei founded the publishing firm of Arkham House to preserve HPL's work in book form.

Dunsany, Lord (Edward John Moreton Drax Plunkett) (1878–1957), Irish writer of fantasy tales whose work notably influenced HPL after HPL read it in 1919.

Dwyer, Bernard Austin (1897–1943), weird fiction fan living in West Shokan, NY, and correspondent of HPL.

Farnese, Harold S. (1885–1945), composer who set some of HPL's poems to music. He corresponded sporadically with HPL from 1932 to 1937.

Gamwell, Annie E[mmeline] P[hillips] (1866–1941), HPL's younger aunt, living with him at 66 College Street (1933–37).

Hamilton, Edmond (1904–1977), prolific author of weird and science fiction tales for the pulp magazines. HPL admired his story "The Monster-God of Mamurth" (*WT*, Aug. 1926).

Hornig, Charles D[erwin] (1916–1999), youthful editor of the *Fantasy Fan* (1933–35) and later associate editor of *Wonder Stories*.

Houdini, Harry (pseudonym of Ehrich Weiss, 1874–1926), magician and debunker of spiritualism. HPL ghostwrote "Under the Pyramids" (published in *WT* as "Imprisoned with the Pharaohs") for him. Later, Houdini commissioned HPL and C. M. Eddy, Jr., to work on a treatise entitled *The Cancer of Superstition,* but died before it could be completed.

Howard, Dr. Isaac Mordecai (1871–1944), father of REH.

James, M[ontague] R[hodes] (1862–1936), pioneering British writer of ghost stories whose work was much admired by HPL.

Kirk, George [Willard] (1898–1962), member of the Kalem Club. He published *Twenty-one Letters of Ambrose Bierce* (1922) and ran the Chelsea Bookshop in New York.

Kline, Otis Adelbert (1891–1946), successful pulp author who in the 1930s turned his attention increasingly to acting as an agent for other writers. He began representing REH in the spring of 1933, and after REH's death he continued to represent his work on behalf of REH's father.

Lee, Dave (1903–1976), born in Tennessee, close friend of REH. He is the "Tennesseean" referred to in letters of January 1934 and July 1935.

Lee, Dock (1908–1986), brother of Dave Lee, friend of REH.

Lenniger, August (1906–1989), agent for E. Hoffmann Price and others.

Long, Frank Belknap (1901–1994), poet, prolific writer of fantasy, horror, and science fiction tales for the pulps, and one of HPL's closest friends and correspondents. He wrote the memoir *Howard Phillips Lovecraft: Dreamer on the Nightside* (1975).

Loveman, Samuel (1887–1976), poet and longtime friend of HPL as well as of Ambrose Bierce, Hart Crane, and George Sterling. Author of *The Hermaphrodite* (1926) and other works.

Lumley, William (1880–1960), eccentric late associate of HPL for whom HPL ghostwrote "The Diary of Alonzo Typer" (1935).

Machen, Arthur (1863–1947), Welsh author of weird fiction much admired by HPL.

Mashburn, W[allace] Kirk[patrick] (1900–1968), a fan of weird fiction, author of several stories in *Weird Tales* and other pulp magazines. REH and Mashburn corresponded, but apparently none of the letters survive.

Mencken, H[enry] L[ouis] (1880–1956), prolific journalist and cultural critic whose essay "The Sahara of the Bozart" (in *Prejudices: Second Series* [1920]) offended REH by its condemnation of the barrenness of Southern culture.

Merritt, A[braham] (1884–1943), popular writer of weird and adventure stories for the pulps, and longtime editor of the *American Weekly* (the magazine supplement to the Hearst papers). He and HPL first met in New York in 1934 and sporadically thereafter.

Morton, James F[erdinand] (1870–1941), amateur journalist, author of many tracts on race prejudice, free thought, and taxation, and longtime friend of HPL.

Munn, H[arold] Warner (1903–1981), prolific contributor to the pulp magazines and sporadic correspondent of HPL, living near W. Paul Cook in Athol, MA.

Musser, Ben[jamin] F[rancis] (1889–1951), poet, editor of *JAPM: The Poetry Weekly* and *Contemporary Verse*, in each of which he published a poem by REH. Author of *Dipped in Aloes* [1929?], *The Passion Called Poetry* [1930?], and *Queen of Arts: Twenty Papers Treating of Poets and Poetry, Together with Four Addresses to Third Order of St. Francis* (1937). He and REH met at the home of Lexie Dean Robertson in Rising Star, Texas, in October 1929.

Owen, Frank (1893-1968), author of Oriental fantasies for *Weird Tales*, *Oriental Stories*, and other magazines.

Price, E[dgar] Hoffmann (1898–1988), prolific pulp writer of weird and adventure tales. HPL met him in New Orleans in 1932 and corresponded extensively with him thereafter. In 1934 he traveled to Texas to meet REH.

Quinn, Seabury (1889–1969), prolific author of weird and detective tales to the pulps, notably a series of tales involving the psychic detective Jules de Grandin. He edited *Casket and Sunnyside* and other trade publications for morticians.

Shea, J[oseph] Vernon (1912–1981), young weird fiction fan from Pittsburgh who began corresponding with HPL in 1931.

Smith, Clark Ashton (1893–1961), prolific California poet and writer of fantasy tales. He received a "fan" letter from HPL in 1922 and continued to correspond with him until HPL's death.

Smith, Tevis Clyde, Jr. (1908–1984), one of REH's best friends. He and REH met when REH attended Brownwood High School to complete his final year of schooling (1922–23), and they remained close friends for over ten years. They wrote hundreds of letters to each other filled with poetry, parodies, and philosophic musings, and collaborated on several stories, one of which, "Red Blades of Black Cathay," was published in *Oriental Stories* (February–March 1931).

Sterling, Kenneth (1920–1995), science fiction fan and late associate of HPL.

Swanson, Carl, a fan from North Dakota who wrote to several authors of weird and science fiction asking for contributions to a magazine he planned to publish, to be called *The Galaxy*. It was never realized.

Talman, Wilfred B[lanch] (1904–1986), late member of the Kalem Club. He and HPL collaborated on the story "Two Black Bottles" (1926).

Tully, Jim (1886–1947), author of acclaimed novels such as *Beggars of Life* (1924) and *Shanty Irish* (1928). The child of extremely poor Irish immigrants, Tully was sent to an orphanage at age seven, when his mother died. When he was fourteen, Tully ran away and began a life as hobo, circus hand, and laborer, and tried professional boxing for a time before he began writing. His first poem appeared in a newspaper in 1911, and his first novel in 1922. He was one of REH's favorite writers.

Tyson, Lindsey ("Pink") (1907–1994), REH's best friend in Cross Plains. Also the son of a doctor, he shared with REH an enjoyment of the outdoors and sports such as boxing and football, but he had no particular literary interests.

Vinson, Truett (1905–1981), one of REH's best friends, along with Tevis Clyde Smith, to whom he introduced REH in 1922 when all three were attending Brownwood High School.

Wandrei, Donald (1908–1987), poet and fiction writer who began corresponding with HPL in 1926. He visited HPL in Providence in 1927 and 1932 and saw him frequently when HPL visited New York in the 1930s. With August Derleth, he founded Arkham House to preserve HPL's work in book form.

Wandrei, Howard (1909–1956), brother of Donald Wandrei and superlative fantasy artist. He also wrote horror and mystery tales for the pulp magazines.

Whitehead, Henry S[t. Clair] (1882–1932), Episcopal clergyman and accomplished author of weird and adventure tales for the pulp magazines, many of them set in the Caribbean.

Wright, Farnsworth (1888–1940), editor of *Weird Tales* (1924–40).

Bibliography

A. Works by Robert E. Howard

i. Books

Always Comes Evening. Ed. Glenn Lord. Sauk City, WI: Arkham House, 1957.

The Best of Robert E. Howard: Volume 1, Crimson Shadows. Ed. Rusty Burke. New York: Del Rey Books, 2007.

The Best of Robert E. Howard: Volume 2, Grim Lands. Ed. Rusty Burke. New York: Del Rey Books, 2007.

The Black Stranger and Other American Tales. Ed. Steven Tompkins. Lincoln: University of Nebraska Press, 2005.

The Bloody Crown of Conan. Ed. Patrice Louinet. New York: Del Rey Books, 2004.

Boxing Stories. Ed. Chris Gruber. Lincoln: University of Nebraska Press, 2005.

Bran Mak Morn: The Last King. Ed. Rusty Burke. New York: Del Rey Books, 2005.

The Collected Letters of Robert E. Howard. Ed. Rob Roehm. Plano, TX: The Robert E. Howard Foundation Press, 2007–08. 3 vols.

The Collected Letters of Robert E. Howard: Index and Addenda. Ed. Bobby Derie. [Plano, TX]: Robert E. Howard Foundation Press, [2015].

The Coming of Conan the Cimmerian. Ed. Patrice Louinet. New York: Del Rey Books, 2003.

The Complete Action Stories. Holicong, PA: Wildside Press, 2003.

The Conquering Sword of Conan. Ed. Patrice Louinet. New York: Del Rey Books, 2005.

The End of the Trail: Western Stories. Ed. Rusty Burke. Lincoln: University of Nebraska Press, 2005.

The Horror Stories of Robert E. Howard. Ed. Rusty Burke. New York: Del Rey Books, 2008.

Kull: Exile of Atlantis. Ed. Patrice Louinet. New York: Del Rey Books, 2006.

Lord of Samarcand and Other Adventure Tales of the Old Orient. Ed. Rusty Burke. Lincoln: University of Nebraska Press, 2005.

Post Oaks and Sand Roughs. Hampton Falls, NH: Donald M. Grant, 1990.

The Riot at Bucksnort and Other Western Tales. Ed. David Gentzel. Lincoln: University of Nebraska Press, 2005.

The Savage Tales of Solomon Kane. Ed. Rusty Burke. New York: Del Rey Books, 2004.

Selected Letters 1923–1936. Edited by Glenn Lord, with Rusty Burke, S. T. Joshi, and Steve Behrends. West Warwick, RI: Necronomicon Press, 1989–91. 2 vols.

Waterfront Fists and Others. Holicong, PA: Wildside Press, 2003.

ii. Stories

"Alleys of Darkness." *Magic Carpet Magazine* 4, No. 1 (January 1934): 29–38. In *WF*.

"Alleys of Peril." *Fight Stories* 3, No. 8 (January 1931): 42–52. In *WF*.

"Beyond the Black River." *WT* 25, No. 5 (May 1935): 591–608; 25, No. 6 (June 1935): 734–54. In *CSC, BO1*.

"Bill Smalley and the Power of the Human Eye." *The Dark Man*, No. 2 (July 1991): 25–30.

"Black Canaan." *WT* 27, No. 6 (June 1936): 662–84. In *HS*.

"Black Colossus." *WT* 21, No. 6 (June 1933): 675–99. In *CCC*.

"The Black Stone." *WT* 18, No. 4 (November 1931): 500–11. In Christine Campbell Thomson, ed. *Grim Death* [*Not at Night* series.] London: Selwyn & Blount, 1932. In *BO1, HS*.

"The Blood of Belshazzar." *Oriental Stories*, Fall 1931. In *LS*.

"Boot-Hill Payoff" (with Robert Enders Allen [Chandler Whipple]). *Western Aces* 3, No. 4 (October 1935): 53–85. In *ET* (under original title, "The Last Ride").

"The Cairn on the Headland." *Strange Tales* 3, No. 1 (January 1933): 122–135. In *HS*.

"The Challenge from Beyond" (with C. L. Moore, A. Merritt, H. P. Lovecraft, and Frank Belknap Long). *Fantasy Magazine* 5, no. 4 (September 1935): 221–29.

"The Children of the Night." *WT* 17, No. 3 (April–May 1931): 353–63. In *BMM, HS*.

"College Socks." *Sport Story Magazine* 32, No. 6 (September 25, 1931): 37–49.

"Crowd-Horror." *Argosy All-Story Weekly* 205, No. 2 (July 20, 1929): 249–261. In *BS*.

"The Dark Man." *WT* 18, No. 5 (December 1931): 586–600, 714–18, 720. In *BMM, BO1*.

"The Devil in Iron." *WT* 24, No. 2 (August 1934): 146–66. In *CCC*.

"The Dream Snake." *WT* 11, No. 2 (February 1928): 257–61. In *HS*.

"The Footfalls Within." *WT* 18, No. 2 (September 1931): 150–59, 285–86. In *STSK*.

"The Frost-Giant's Daughter." In *Rogues in the House*. West Kingston, RI: Donald M. Grant, 1976, pp. 71–91. In *CCC*.

"The Garden of Fear." *Marvel Tales* 1, No. 2 (July–August 1934): 11–29. In *Gardens of Fear*. Holicong, PA: Wildside Press, 2006.

"A Gent from Bear Creek." *Action Stories* 12, No. 10 (October 1934): 48–57. In *CA*.

"The God in the Bowl." In *The Tower of the Elephant*. West Kingston, RI: Donald M. Grant, 1975, pp. 55–94. In *CCC*.

"The Gods of Bal-Sagoth." *WT* 18, No. 3 (October 1931): 302–19, 421–31. In *BSA*.

"The Grisly Horror." (Original title: "Moon of Zambebwei.") *WT* 25, No. 2 (February 1934): 169–88. In *Beyond the Black River*. Holicong, PA: Wildside Press, 2007.

"The Hand of Obeah." *Crypt of Cthulhu* 2, No. 8 (Whole No. 16) (Michaelmas 1983): 13–34.

"The Hills of the Dead." *WT* 16, No. 2 (August 1930): 162–73, 284–87. In *STSK*.

"The Hoofed Thing." *Weirdbook* No. 3 (1970): 3–11 (as "Usurp the Night"). In *HS*.

"The Horror from the Mound." *WT* 19, No. 5 (May 1932): 655–66. In *BSA, HS*.

"The Hour of the Dragon." *WT* 26, No. 6 (December 1935): 658–84; 27, No. 1 (January 1936): 72–105; 27, No. 2 (February 1936): 188–210; 27, No. 3 (March 1936): 323–44; 27, No. 4 (April 1936): 450–71. In *BCC*.

"The House of Arabu." In Donald A. Wollheim, ed. *Avon Fantasy Reader No. 18*. New York: Avon, 1952, pp. 3–20 (as "The Witch from Hell's Kitchen"). In *HS*.

"The Hyena." *WT* 11, No. 3 (March 1928): 405–13. In *Shadow Kingdoms*. Holicong, PA: Wildside Press, 2004.

"In the Forest of Villefère." *WT* 6, No. 2 (August 1925): 185–87. In *HS*.

"Kings of the Night." *WT* 16, No. 5 (November 1930): 609–30. In *BMM, KEA, BO1*.

"Lord of Samarcand." *Oriental Stories* 2, No. 2 (Spring 1932): 210–233. In *LS, BO2*.

"The Lost Race." *WT* 9, No. 1 (January 1927): 74–82. In *BMM*.

"Marchers of Valhalla." In *Marchers of Valhalla*. West Kingston, RI: Donald M. Grant, 1972, pp. 11–78. In *BSA*.

"The Moon of Skulls." *WT* 15, No. 6 (June 1930): 736–51, 857–61; 16, No. 1 (July 1930): 107–20. In *STSK*.

"Old Garfield's Heart." *WT* 22, No. 6 (December 1933): 724–30. In *BSA, BO2, HS*.

"The People of the Black Circle." *WT* 24, No. 3 (September 1934): 274–95; 24, No. 4 (October 1934): 488–504; 24, No. 5 (November 1934): 619–36. In *BCC, BO1*.

"People of the Dark." *Strange Tales* 2, No. 2 (June 1932): 92–105. In *HS*.

"The Phoenix on the Sword." *WT* 20, No. 6 (December 1932): 769–84. In *CCC*.

"Pigeons from Hell." *WT* 31, No. 5 (May 1938): 534–53. In *BSA, BO2, HS*.

"The Pool of the Black One." *WT* 22, No. 4 (October 1933): 447–66. In *CCC*.

"Queen of the Black Coast." *WT* 23, No. 5 (May 1934): 530–49. In *CCC*.

"Red Blades of Black Cathay" (with Tevis Clyde Smith, Jr.). *Oriental Stories* 1, No. 3 (February–March 1931): 294–313, 432. In *LS*.

"Red Nails." *WT* 28, No. 1 (July 1936): 16–35; 28, No. 2 (August–September 1936): 205–21; 28, No. 3 (October 1936): 334–53. In *CSC, BO2.*

"Red Shadows." *WT* 12, No. 2 (August 1928): 149–64, 282–84. In *STSK, BO1.*

"The Scarlet Citadel." *WT* 21, No. 1 (January 1933): 51–77. In *CCC.*

"Sea Curse." *WT* 11, No. 5 (May 1928): 617–21. In *HS.*

"The Shadow of the Vulture." *Magic Carpet Magazine* 4, No. 1 (January 1934): 39–65. In *LS.*

"Shadows in the Moonlight." *WT* 23, No. 4 (April 1934): 466–87. In *CCC* (under original title, "Iron Shadows in the Moon").

"She-Devil." *Spicy-Adventure Stories* 4, No. 1 (April 1936): 56–67, 110–12.

"Skull-Face." *WT* 14, No. 4 (October 1929): 450–72, 572–74; 14, No. 5 (November 1929): 659–73; 14, No. 6 (December 1929): 809–25. In *The Moon of Skulls.* Holicong, PA: Wildside Press, 2006.

"The Sowers of the Thunder." *Oriental Stories* 2, No. 1 (Winter 1932): 80–106. In *LS.*

"Spear and Fang." *WT* 6, No. 1 (July 1925): 111–15. In *Shadow Kingdoms.* Holicong, PA: Wildside Press, 2004.

"Talons in the Dark." *Strange Detective Stories* 5, No. 1 (December 1933): 48–59 (as "Black Talons"). In *Graveyard Rats and Others.* Holicong, PA: Wildside Press, 2003.

"Taveral Manor." *Howard Reader* No. 8 (August 2003): 9–17.

"The Thing on the Roof." *WT* 19, No. 2 (February 1932): 213–19. In *HS.*

"The Tower of the Elephant." *WT* 21, No. 3 (March 1933): 306–22. In *CCC, BO2.*

"Usurp the Night." See "The Hoofed Thing."

"The Valley of the Lost." *Startling Mystery Stories* 1, No. 4 (Spring 1967): 28–49 (as "The Secret of Lost Valley"). In *BSA, HS.*

"The Voice of El-Lil." *Oriental Stories* 1, No. 1 (October–November 1930): 112–27. In *LS.*

"Vultures of Wahpeton." *Smashing Novels Magazine* 1, No. 4 (December 1936): 40–79 (as "Vultures of Whapeton"). In *ET.*

"Wings in the Night." *WT* 20, No. 1 (July 1932): 33–52. In *STSK, BO2.*

"Wolfshead." *WT* 7, No. 4 (April 1926): 437–48, 570–72, 574–75. In *HS.*

"Wolves Beyond the Border." In *The Conan Chronicles. Volume 2: The Hour of the Dragon.* London: Millenium, [2001], pp. 273–294. In *CSC.*

"Worms of the Earth." *WT* 20, No. 5 (November 1932): 604–24. In *BMM, BO1, HS.*

iii. Essays

"The Beast from the Abyss." *Howard Collector* 3, No. 3 (Whole No. 15) (Autumn 1971): 5–15. In *The Howard Collector.* New York: Ace Books, 1979.

"The Ghost of Camp Colorado." *Texaco Star* 18, No. 4 (April 1931): 13–15. In *ET*.

The Hyborian Age. Los Angeles: LANY Cooperative Publications, 1938. In *CCC*.

"Kelly the Conjure Man." *Howard Collector* 1, No. 5 (Summer 1964): 15–20. In *HS*.

iv. Poems

"Arkham." *WT* 20, No. 2 (August 1932): 217.

"Autumn." *WT* 21, No. 4 (April 1933): 422.

"Cimmeria." *Howard Collector* 2, No. 1 (Whole No. 7) (Winter 1965): 17–18. In *CCC*, *BO2*.

"The Grim Land." In *The Grim Land and Others*. Lamoni, IA: Stygian Isle Press, 1976, p. [14].

"The Man in the Myth." Apparently lost.

"Red Thunder." *JAPM: The Poetry Weekly* 3, No. 12 (16 September 1929).

"Rueben's Brethren." *Junto* (appearance not seen). *Howard Collector* 2, No. 5 (Whole No. 11) (Spring 1969): 16.

"Saul Falls on His Sword." Apparently lost.

B. Works by H. P. Lovecraft

i. Books

The Ancient Track: Complete Poetical Works. Ed. S. T. Joshi. San Francisco: Night Shade, 2001.

At the Mountains of Madness and Other Novels. Ed. S. T. Joshi. Sauk City, WI: Arkham House, 1985.

Collected Essays. Ed. S. T. Joshi. New York: Hippocampus Press, 2004–06. 5 vols.

Dagon and Other Macabre Tales. Ed. S. T. Joshi. Sauk City, WI: Arkham House, 1986.

The Dunwich Horror and Others. Ed. S. T. Joshi. Sauk City, WI: Arkham House, 1984.

Miscellaneous Writings. Ed. S. T. Joshi. Sauk City, WI: Arkham House, 1995.

Mysteries of Time and Spirit: The Letters of H. P. Lovecraft and Donald Wandrei. Ed. S. T. Joshi and David E. Schultz. San Francisco: Night Shade Books, 2002.

O Fortunate Floridian: H. P. Lovecraft's Letters to R. H. Barlow. Ed. S. T. Joshi and David E. Schultz. Tampa: University of Tampa Press, 2007.

Selected Letters. Ed. August Derleth, Donald Wandrei, and James Turner. Sauk City, WI: Arkham House, 1965–76. 5 vols.

The Shadow over Innsmouth. Everett, PA: Visionary Publishing Co., 1936.

ii. Stories

At the Mountains of Madness. Astounding Stories 16, No. 6 (February 1936): 8–32; 17, No. 1 (March 1936): 125–55; 17, No. 2 (April 1936): 132–50. In *MM*.

"The Beast in the Cave." *Vagrant* No. 7 (June 1918): 113–20. In *D*.

"The Call of Cthulhu." *WT* 11, No. 2 (February 1928): 159–78, 287. In *DH*.

"The Challenge from Beyond" (with C. L. Moore, A. Merritt, Robert E. Howard, and Frank Belknap Long). See A.ii. above.

"The Colour out of Space." *Amazing Stories* 2, No. 6 (September 1927): 557–67. In *DH*.

"The Curse of Yig" (revised for Zealia Bishop). *WT* 14, No. 5 (November 1929): 625–36. In *HM*.

"Dagon." *Vagrant* No. 11 (November 1919): 23–29. *WT* 2, No. 3 (October 1923): 23–25. *WT* 27, no. 1 (January 1936): 118–23. In *D*.

"The Dreams in the Witch House." *WT* 22, No. 1 (July 1933): 86–111. In *MM*.

"The Dunwich Horror." *WT* 13, No. 4 (April 1929): 481–508. In *DH*.

"The Electric Executioner" (revised for Adolphe de Castro). *WT* 16, No. 2 (August 1930): 223–36. In *HM*.

"Facts concerning the Late Arthur Jermyn and His Family." *Wolverine* No. 9 (March 1921): 3–11; No. 10 (June 1921): 6–11. *WT* 3, No. 4 (April 1924): 15–18 (as "The White Ape"). *WT* 25, No. 5 (May 1935): 642–48 (as "Arthur Jermyn"). In *D*.

"The Festival." *WT* 5, No. 1 (January 1925): 169–74. *WT* 22, No. 4 (October 1933): 519–20, 522–28. In *D*.

"The Haunter of the Dark." *WT* 28, No. 5 (December 1936): 538–53. In *DH*.

"He." *WT* 8, No. 3 (September 1926): 373–80. In *D*.

"Herbert West—Reanimator." *Home Brew* 1, No. 1 (February 1922): 19–25; 1, No. 2 (March 1922): 45–50; 1, No. 3 (April 1922): 21–26; 1, No. 4 (May 1922): 53–58; 1, No. 5 (June 1922): 45–50; 1, No. 6 (July 1922): 57–62 (as "Grewsome Tales"). In *D*.

"The Horror at Red Hook." *WT* 9, No. 1 (January 1927): 59–73. In *D*.

"The Horror in the Museum" (revised for Hazel Heald). *WT* 22, No. 1 (July 1933): 49–68. In *HM*.

"In the Vault." *Tryout* 10, No. 6 (November 1925): [3–17]. *WT* 19, No. 4 (April 1932): 459–65. In *DH*.

"The Lurking Fear." *Home Brew* 2, No. 6 (January 1923): 4–10; 3, No. 1 (February 1923): 18–23; 3, No. 2 (March 1923): 31–37, 44, 48; 3, No. 3 (April 1923): 35–42. *WT* 11, No. 6 (June 1928): 791–804. In *D*.

"Medusa's Coil" (revised for Zealia Bishop). *WT* 33, No. 1 (January 1939): 26–53. In *HM*.

"The Moon-Bog." *WT* 7, No. 6 (June 1926): 805–10. In *D*.

"The Music of Erich Zann." *National Amateur* 44, No. 5 (March 1922): 38–40. *WT* 5, No. 5 (May 1925): 219–24. In Dashiell Hammett, ed. *Creeps by*

Night: Chills and Thrills. New York: John Day Co., 1931, pp. 347–63. *Evening Standard* (London) No. 33,754 (24 October 1932): 20–21. *WT* 24, No. 5 (November 1934): 644–48, 655–56. In *DH.*

"Out of the Aeons" (revised for Hazel Heald). *WT* 25, No. 4 (April 1935): 478–96. In *HM.*

"The Outsider." *WT* 7, No. 4 (April 1926): 449–53. *WT* 17, No. 4 (June–July 1931): 566–71. In *DH.*

"Pickman's Model." *WT* 10, No. 4 (October 1927): 505–14. *WT* 28, No. 4 (December 1936): 495–505. In *DH.*

"The Picture in the House." *National Amateur* 41, No. 6 (July 1919): 246–49. *WT* 3, No. 1 (January 1924): 40–42. *WT* 29, No. 3 (March 1937): 370–73. In *DH.*

"Polaris." *Philosopher* 1, No. 1 (December 1920): 3–5. *National Amateur* 48, No. 5 (May 1926): 48–49. *FF* 1, No. 6 (February 1934): 83–85. In *D.*

"The Rats in the Walls." *WT* 3, No. 3 (March 1924): 25–31. *WT* 15, No. 6 (June 1930): 841–53. In *DH.*

"The Shadow out of Time." *Astounding Stories* 17, No. 4 (June 1936): 110–54. New York: Hippocampus Press, 2000 (corrected text).

"The Shadow over Innsmouth." Everett, PA: Visionary Publishing Co., 1936. In *DH.*

"The Silver Key." *WT* 13, No. 1 (January 1929): 41–49, 144. In *MM.*

"The Strange High House in the Mist." *WT* 18, No. 3 (October 1931): 394–400. In *D.*

"The Temple." *WT* 6, No. 3 (September 1925): 329–36, 429–31. *WT* 27, No. 2 (February 1936): 239–44, 246–49. In *D.*

"The Terrible Old Man." *Tryout* 7, No. 4 (July 1921): [10–14]. *WT* 8, No. 2 (August 1926): 191–92. In *DH.*

"The Thing on the Doorstep." *WT* 29, No. 1 (January 1937): 52–70. In *DH.*

"Through the Gates of the Silver Key" (with E. Hoffmann Price). *WT* 24, No. 1 (July 1934): 60–85. In *MM.*

"The Tomb." *Vagrant* No. 14 (March 1922): 50–64. *WT* 7, No. 1 (January 1926): 117–23. In *D.*

"The Unnamable." *WT* 6, No. 1 (July 1925): 78–82. In *D.*

"The Very Old Folk." *Scient-Snaps* 3, No. 3 (Summer 1940): 4–8. In *MW.*

"The Whisperer in Darkness." *WT* 18, No. 1 (August 1931): 32–73. In *DH.*

"The White Ship." *United Amateur* 19, No. 2 (November 1919): 30–33. *WT* 9, No. 3 (March 1927): 386–89. In *D.*

iii. Essays

"An Account of a Trip to the Fairbanks House . . ." In *CE* 4.

"Cats and Dogs." *Leaves* No. 1 (Summer 1937): 25–34. In *CE* 5.

Commonplace Book. In *CE* 5.

"A Descent to Avernus." *Bacon's Essays* 2, No. 2 (Summer 1929): 8. In *CE* 4.

Further Criticism of Poetry. [Louisville, KY: Press of George G. Fetter, 1932.] In
  CE 2.
"Homes and Shrines of Poe." *Californian* 2, No. 3 (Winter 1934): 8–10. In *CE* 4.
"Idealism and Materialism—A Reflection." *National Amateur* 41, No. 6 (July
  1919 [i.e., Spring 1921]): 278–81. In *CE* 5.
"In the Editor's Study: The League." *Conservative* 5, No. 1 (July 1919): 9–10.
  In *CE* 5.
"Observations on Several Parts of America." In *CE* 4.
"Some Dutch Footprints in New England." *De Halve Maen* 9, No. 1 (18 Oc-
  tober 1933): 2, 4. In *CE* 4.
"Some Notes on Interplanetary Fiction." *Californian* 3, No. 3 (Winter 1935):
  39–42. In *CE* 2.
"Supernatural Horror in Literature." *Recluse* No. 1 (1927): 23–59. Rev. ed. in
  Fantasy Fan (October 1933–February 1935). Rev. ed. in *The Outsider and
  Others*. Sauk City, WI: Arkham House, 1939. In *CE* 2.

iv. Poems (all in *AT*)

"The East India Brick Row." *Providence Journal* 102, No. 7 (8 January 1930): 13.
Fungi from Yuggoth.
    I. "The Book." *Fantasy Fan* 2, No. 2 (Oct. 1934): 24.
    IV. "Recognition." *Driftwind* 11, No. 5 (December 1936): 180.
    VI. "The Lamp." *Driftwind* 5, No. 5 (March 1931): 16.
    IX. "The Courtyard." *WT* 16, No. 3 (September 1930): 322.
    XIV. "Star-Winds." *WT* 16, No. 3 (September 1930): 322.
    XVI. "The Window." *Driftwind* 5 (April 1931 [Special issue]): 15.
    XIX. "The Bells." *WT* 16, No. 6 (December 1930): 798.
    XX. "Night-Gaunts." *Providence Journal* 102, No. 73 (26 March 1930): 15.
    Phantagraph 4, No. 3 ([June] 1936): 8.
    XXIII. "Mirage." *WT* 17, No. 2 (February–March 1931): 175.
    XXVII. "The Elder Pharos." *WT* 17, No. 2 (February–March 1931): 175.
    XXX. "Background." *Providence Journal* 102, No. 91 (16 April 1930): 13.
    Galleon 1, No. 4 (June 1935): 8.
    XXXI. "The Dweller." *Providence Journal* 102, No. 110 (7 May 1930): 15.
    Phantagraph 4, No. 2 (November–December 1935): [3].
    XXXII. "Alienation." *WT* 17, No. 3 (April–May 1931): 374.

C. Works by Others

Alden, Abner (1758?–1820). *The Reader: Containing the Art of Delivery, Articulation,
  Accent, Pronunciation,* [etc]. 1802. 3rd ed. Boston: Printed by J. T. Buck-
  ingham for Thomas & Andrews, 1808. [*LL* 16]
The Arabian Nights Entertainments. Selected and Edited by Andrew Lang. New
  York: Longmans, Green, 1898. [*LL* 38]

Benoît, Pierre (1886–1962). *Atlantida*. Trans. Mary C. Tongue and Mary Ross. New York: Duffield, 1920.

Bierce, Ambrose (1842–1914?). "The Middle Toe of the Right Foot." *San Francisco Examiner* (17 August 1890). In *Tales of Soldiers and Civilians*. San Francisco: E. L. G. Steele, 1891. Later in *Can Such Things Be?* 1910. New York: Boni & Liveright (Modern Library), 1918. [*LL* 87]

Blackwood, Algernon (1869–1951). "The Willows." In *The Listener and Other Stories*. London: Eveleigh Nash, 1907.

Bond, John. *Mussolini, the Wild Man of Europe*. Washington, DC: Independent Publishing Co., 1929.

Briffault, Robert (1876–1948). *Breakdown: The Collapse of Traditional Civilization*. New York: Brentano, 1932.

Burns, Walter Noble. *The Saga of Billy the Kid*. Garden City, NY: Doubleday, Page & Co., 1926.

Burton, Warren (1800–1866). *The District School as It Was*. By One Who Went to It. Edited by Clifton Johnson. Boston: Lee & Shepard, 1897. [*LL* 140]

Conrad, Joseph (1857–1924). *Lord Jim*. Edinburgh: William Blackwood, 1900.

de Castro, Adolphe (1859–1959). *Portrait of Ambrose Bierce*. Preface by [Frank] Belknap Long. New York: Century Co., 1929.

Derleth, August (1909–1971). "Five Alone." *Pagany* 3, No. 3 (Summer 1932): 14–44. In *Place of Hawks*. New York: Loring & Mussey, 1935. [*LL* 235]

———. "Nella." *Pagany* 3, No. 1 (Winter 1932): 134–39.

———. "Old Ladies." *Midland* 19, No. 1 (January–February 1932): 5–9. Rewritten as "Take Arms!" and included in *Evening in Spring*. New York: Scribner, 1941.

Eddison, E. R. (1882–1945). *The Worm Ouroboros: A Romance*. New York: Albert & Charles Boni, 1926. [*LL* 291]

France, Hector. *Musk, Hashish and Blood*. London, 1900.

Gray, Zane (1872–1939). *The Border Legion*. New York: Grosset & Dunlap, 1916.

Gregg, Josiah 1806–1850). *Commerce of the Prairies; or, The Journal of a Santa Fé Trader*. New York: H. G. Langley, 1844.

Grimm, Jacob Ludwig Karl (1785–1863), and W. K. Grimm (1786–1859). *Fairy Tales*. 1812–15. [*LL* 379]

Gummere, Francis B. (1855–1919). *A Handbook of Poetics, for Students of English Verse*. Boston: Ginn & Co., 1885.

Joyce, Patrick Weston (1827–1914). *The Story of Ancient Irish Civilisation*. London: Longmans, Green, 1907.

Leonard, William Ellery (1876–1944). *The Locomotive God*. New York: Century Co., 1927.

London, Jack (1876–1916). *Martin Eden*. New York: Macmillan, 1908.

Long, Frank Belknap (1901–1994). *The Horror from the Hills. Weird Tales* (January & February–March 1931). Sauk City, WI: Arkham House, 1963.

————. *A Man from Genoa and Other Poems*. Athol, MA: W. Paul Cook, 1926.

Macaulay, Thomas Babington (1800–1859). *Lays of Ancient Rome*. 1842. New York: Bay View Publishing Co., n.d. [*LL* 560]

Machen, Arthur (1863–1947). "The Great God Pan." In *The Great God Pan and The Inmost Light*. London: John Lane, 1894.

————. "Novel of the Black Seal." In *The Three Impostors* (q.v.).

————. "Novel of the White Powder." In *The Three Impostors* (q.v.).

————. "The Red Hand." *Chapman's Magazine* (December 1895). In *The House of Souls*. London: Grant Richards, 1906 (not in American edition [New York: Alfred A. Knopf, 1922 (*LL* 573)]). In *The Three Impostors* (q.v.).

————. "The Shining Pyramid." *Unknown World* (15 May–15 June 1895). In *The Shining Pyramid*. London: Martin Secker, 1925. [*LL* 576]

————. *The Three Impostors*. London: John Lane; Boston: Roberts Bros., 1895. [*LL* 578]

————. "The White People." *Horlick's Magazine* (January 1904). In *The House of Souls* (q.v.).

Matthews, Brander (1852–1929). *A Study of Versification*. Boston: Houghton Mifflin, 1911.

Maturin, Charles Robert (1782–1824). *Melmoth the Wanderer*. 1820. London: Richard Bentley & Son, 1892. 3 vols. [*LL* 599]

Merritt, A. (1884–1943). "The Moon-Pool." *All-Story Weekly* (22 June 1918). [*LL* 17]

————. "The People of the Pit." *All-Story Weekly* (5 January 1918).

————. *The Ship of Ishtar*. *Argosy* (2–30 July 1927). New York: Boni & Liveright, 1928.

Murray, Margaret A. *The Witch-Cult in Western Europe*. Oxford: Clarendon Press, 1921.

O'Neill, Eugene (1888–1953). *The Hairy Ape*. In *The Hairy Ape and Other Plays*. London: Jonathan Cape, 1923.

O'Reilly, Edward (d. 1829). *Sanas Gaoidhilge-Sagsbhearla: An Irish-English Dictionary*. 1817. Rev. by John O'Donovan (1809–1861). Dublin: J. Duffy, 1864.

Randall, John Herman, Jr. (1899–1980). *Our Changing Civilization: How Science and the Machine Are Reconstructing Modern Life*. New York: Frederick A. Stokes Co., 1929.

Smith, Clark Ashton (1893–1961). *The Double Shadow and Other Fantasies*.

————. *Ebony and Crystal: Poems in Verse and Prose*. [Auburn, CA: The Auburn Journal, 1922.] [*LL* 811]

————. "The Third Episode of Vathek." *Leaves* No. 1 (Summer 1937): 1–23 (CAS portion on pp. 17–23).

Smith, G. Elliot (1871–1937). *Human History*. New York: W. W Norton & Co., 1929.

Smith, Tevis Clyde. *Frontier's Generation: The Pioneer History of Brown County with Sidelights on the Surrounding Territory.* Brownwood, TX: The Author, 1931.

Wandrei, Donald (1908–1987). *Dark Odyssey.* With Five Illustrations by Howard Wandrei. St. Paul, MN: Webb Publishing Co., [1931]. [*LL* 917]

———. *Ecstasy and Other Poems.* Athol, MA: Recluse Press, 1928. [*LL* 918]

Webb, Walter Prescott (1888–1963). *The Great Plains.* New York: Grosset & Dunlap, 1931.

Weigall, Arthur (1880–1934). *Wanderings in Roman Britain.* London: T. Butterworth, [1926]. [*LL* 933]

Wells, H[erbert] G[eorge] (1866–1946). *The Time Machine.* London: William Heinemann, 1895.

White, Edward Lucas (1866–1934). *Andivius Hedulio: Adventures of a Roman Nobleman in the Days of the Empire.* New York: E. P. Dutton, 1923. [*LL* 942]

———. *The Unwilling Vestal: A Tale of Rome under the Caesars.* New York: E. P. Dutton, 1918.

Williams, Henry Smith (1863–1943), ed. *The Historians' History of the World.* New York: Outlook Co., 1904–05. 25 vols. Vol. 21: *Scotland, Ireland, England Since 1792.*

Wissler, Clark (1870–1947). *Man and Culture.* New York: Thomas Y. Crowell Co., 1923.

Wright, S. Fowler (1874–1965). *The World Below.* New York: Longmans, Green, 1930. [*LL* 974]

Zimmer, Heinrich (1851–1910). *Keltische Studien.* Berlin: Weidmann, 1881–84. 2 vols.

Works about Robert E. Howard

Burke, Rusty. *Robert E. Howard's Bookshelf.* https://web.archive.org/web/20111009115328/http://www.rehupa.com/bookshelf.htm

Cerasini, Marc A., and Charles Hoffman. *Robert E. Howard.* Mercer Island, WA: Starmont House, 1987.

de Camp, L. Sprague; de Camp, Catherine Crook; and Griffin, Jane Whittington. *Dark Valley Destiny: The Life of Robert E. Howard.* New York: Bluejay Books, 1983.

Ellis, Novalyne Price. *One Who Walked Alone: Robert E. Howard, The Final Years.* West Kingston, RI: Donald M. Grant, 1986.

Finn, Mark. *Blood & Thunder: The Life & Art of Robert E. Howard.* Austin, TX: MonkeyBrain Books, 2006.

Herron, Don, ed. *The Barbaric Triumph: A Critical Anthology on the Writings of Robert E. Howard.* Holicong, PA: Wildside Press, 2004.

———, ed. *The Dark Barbarian: The Writings of Robert E. Howard: A Critical Anthology.* Westport, CT: Greenwood Press, 1984.

Lord, Glenn, ed. *The Last Celt: A Bio-Bibliography of Robert Ervin Howard.* West Kingston, RI: Donald M. Grant, 1976.

Lovecraft, H. P. "In Memoriam: Robert Ervin Howard." *Fantasy Magazine* No. 38 (September 1936): 29–31. In *MW*.

McHaney, Dennis. *Robert E. Howard: World's Greatest Pulpster.* Memphis, TN: Dennis McHaney, 2005.

Szumskyj, Benjamin, ed. *Two-Gun Bob: A Centennial Study of Robert E. Howard.* New York: Hippocampus Press, 2006.

Van Hise, James. *The Fantastic Worlds of Robert E. Howard.* Yucca Valley, CA: James Van Hise, 1997.

Works about H. P. Lovecraft

Burleson, Donald R. *H. P. Lovecraft: A Critical Study.* Westport, CT: Greenwood Press, 1983.

Cannon, Peter, ed. *Lovecraft Remembered.* Sauk City, WI: Arkham House, 1998.

Connors, Scott, ed. *A Century Less a Dream: Selected Criticism of H. P. Lovecraft.* Holicong, PA: Wildside Press, 2002.

Joshi, S. T. *H. P. Lovecraft: A Life.* West Warwick, RI: Necronomicon Press, 1996.

———. *Lovecraft's Library: A Catalogue.* Rev. ed. New York: Hippocampus Press, 2002.

———, ed. *H. P. Lovecraft: Four Decades of Criticism.* Athens: Ohio University Press, 1980.

———, and David E. Schultz. *An H. P. Lovecraft Encyclopedia.* Westport, CT: Greenwood Press, 2001. New York: Hippocampus Press, 2005.

Index

AE (George William Russell) 710, 761
Abdul Alhazred 955
"Account of a Trip to the Fairbanks House, An" (Lovecraft) 145n1
Ackerman, Forrest J 719
Action Stories 788
Adair, John George 705
Adams, S. W. 613n4
Adamson, Carl 455n13
Addison, Joseph 143
Addron College 685
Admirable Crichton, The (Barrie) 641
Adventure 180n23, 202, 213, 231n3, 538–39, 555, 603, 609
Aella, King 756, 777
Aemilianus, Scipio 564
Africa 83–84, 100–101, 125–26, 140–41, 159
Agricola, Cn. Julius 142
Agricultural Adjustment Act 923n7
Alamo 52, 81, 220, 844–45, 855
Alaric 939
Alciphron; or, The Minute Philosopher (Berkeley) 64n, 629, 857
Alden, John 858
Alexander the Great 280, 286, 306, 328, 332
Alexander I (King of Yugoslavia) 818
Alhazred, Abdul 37, 40, 55, 265, 288
All Story Weekly 144
"Alleys of Darkness" (Howard) 687
"Alleys of Peril" (Howard) 132n15, 145
Allgood, William 480
Allison, Clay 551
Allred, James V. 456n22, 822n14
Almagest (Ptolemy) 54
Amarillo, TX 902
Amazing Stories 145
American Author 375, 395
American Civil Liberties Union 476, 576
American Fiction Guild 302, 313, 453
American Legion 372, 407
Ancient Metaphysics (Monboddo) 575
Anderson, Sherwood 510, 532
Andivius Hedulio (White) 656

Anglican church 57, 58
Anne (Queen of England) 762
Antigone (Sophocles) 641
Arabian Nights 40, 55, 101, 265, 580, 955
Arabs 54–55
Archer, Denis 614n12
Argosy 131, 159, 168, 953
Ariovistus 360
"Arkham" (Howard) 238, 246
Arkham House 12
Arminius 142, 143, 360, 573
Armstrong, John 457n19
"Arthur Jermyn" (Lovecraft). *See* "Facts concerning the Late Arthur Jermyn and His Family"
Aryans 18, 19, 22, 25, 27, 33, 35, 42, 43, 47, 54, 70, 74, 83, 103, 117, 120, 125, 134, 140, 152, 159, 162, 169–70, 175, 278, 286, 360, 367, 462, 531, 565, 566, 569, 627, 655, 889
Asbury, Herbert 399n19
Asia 281
Assyrians 33, 43, 53, 82, 99–100, 301–2, 317
Astounding Stories 288, 293, 727, 802, 908
At the Mountains of Madness (Lovecraft) 166, 183, 217, 231, 358n16, 912n31, 953
Atala (Chateaubriand) 304
Atlanteans 956
Attila 83
Aurelius, Marcus (Emperor of Rome) 234, 361
Austin, Stephen F. 103, 844
"Autumn" (Howard) 553
"Avatar" (Gautier) 482
Awashonks 858
Axtell, Governor 155
Aylward, Samkin 353
Azathoth 955
Azif, Al (Alhazred) 40, 956

Babylonians 169, 185, 241
Baer, Max 788n6, 874

Melmoth the Wanderer (Maturin) 202, 526

Mencken, H. L. 510, 532, 550, 621

Mendoza, Daniel 197

Meredith, George 485

Merritt, A. 131, 144–45, 159, 727, 908

"Metzengerstein" (Poe) 761

Mexico and Mexicans 51, 78, 94, 98, 176, 201–2, 221, 227–28, 235, 246, 256, 260–61, 275, 346, 651, 842–45, 855, 864, 875, 900–901

Michelangelo 10, 650, 684–85, 713–14, 760, 771

"Middle Toe of the Right Foot, The" (Bierce) 480

Middleton, John 154

Midland 429

Miller, Jim ("Killer") 303n7, 456n13

Miller, Warren Hastings 291

Millet, Jean-François 672

Millikan, Robert A. 752

Milman, H. H. 746

Milton, John 485

Miniter, Edith 80n18

"Mirage" (Lovecraft) 374

Moe, Robert 857

Moley, Raymond 821

Monboddo, James Burnett, Lord 528, 544, 575, 664, 924

Mongoloids 27, 32, 70, 95, 100, 125, 171, 530–31

Monmouth, John Scott, Duke of 898

Montoya, Lucio 155, 867

Montreal, Canada 426–27

"Moon-Bog, The" (Lovecraft) 23n9

"Moon of Skulls, The" (Howard) 24, 32

"Moon of Zimbabwei, The" (Howard). *See* "Grisly Horror, The"

"Moon Pool, The" (Merritt) 144–45, 727

Mooney, Tom 820–21

Moore, C. L. 762n3, 908

Moore, Thomas 214n7

Morgan, Earl 180n24

Morgan, John Hunt 549

Morgan, J. Pierpont 639, 714

Mormons 910n4

Morris, Harvey 124, 870

Morris, Thomas 76

Morrissey, Tom 392, 440

Morse, Charles W. 417

"Morte Amoreuse, La" (Gautier) 484

Morton, James Ferdinand, Jr. 429n1, 532, 619, 628–29, 790, 802, 858

"Mound, The" (Lovecraft-Bishop) 41n5

Mountain Meadow massacre 898

"Mrs. Lorriquer" (Whitehead) 462

Mullins, Priscilla 858

Mundy, Talbot 101, 510

Munn, H. Warner 47, 290, 292

Murietta, Joaquin 646

Murray, Bill 317–18

Murray, Margaret A. 31n5, 38, 72, 73, 655

Murrell, John A. 157, 158, 167–68, 422, 431

"Music of Erich Zann, The" (Lovecraft) 159, 214, 229, 486, 533, 631n6

Musk, Hashish and Blood (France) 940

Muslims 82, 356

Musser, Benjamin Francis 97, 552

Mussolini, Benito 11, 212, 501, 676, 792, 819, 895, 897, 918, 919, 939

NRA (National Recovery Administration) 671, 759, 852

"Nameless City, The" (Lovecraft) 189n4, 267n4

Nameless Cults (Juntz) 279, 357, 612, 762

Natchez, MS 304–5, 423

Nathan, George Jean 510

National Amateur Press Association 463

Naumkeag Indians 658

Nazism 676–77, 709, 752, 758, 809, 927, 931

Necronomicon (Alhazred) 37, 40, 56, 279, 287, 288, 308, 357, 955, 956

"Nella" (Derleth) 401n2, 429

Nennius 20

Nero (Emperor of Rome) 234, 361

New Bedford, MA 619, 858

New Braunfels, Texas 51, 79, 82

New Orleans, La. 122, 150, 166, 167, 255, 263, 269, 305–6, 312–13, 314, 315, 337, 381, 423–24, 430, 436, 442, 444, 463–64, 465, 479, 508, 525, 544

CPSIA information can be obtained
at www.ICGtesting.com
Printed in the USA
BVHW040929020720
582457BV00009B/123